SCOTT, FORESMAN

Discover SCIENCE

Teacher's Annotated Edition Authors

Robert G. Guy
Classroom Teacher
Big Lake Elementary School
Sedro-Wooley, Washington

Dr. Robert J. Miller
Professor of Science Education
Eastern Kentucky University
Richmond, Kentucky

Mary Jane Roscoe
Teacher and Team Coordinator
Fairwood Alternative Elementary School of Individually Guided Education
Columbus, Ohio

Anita Snell
Elementary Coordinator for Early Childhood Education
Spring Branch Independent School District
Houston, Texas

Sheri L. Thomas
Classroom Teacher
McLouth Unified School District #342
McLouth, Kansas

Pupil's Edition Authors

Dr. Michael R. Cohen
Professor of Science and Environmental Education
School of Education
Indiana University
Indianapolis, Indiana

Dr. Timothy M. Cooney
Chairperson K-12 Science Program
Malcolm Price Laboratory School
University of Northern Iowa
Cedar Falls, Iowa

Cheryl M. Hawthorne
Science Curriculum Specialist
Mathematics, Engineering, Science Achievement Program (MESA)
Stanford University
Stanford, California

Dr. Alan J. McCormack
Professor of Science Education
San Diego State University
San Diego, California

Dr. Jay M. Pasachoff
Director, Hopkins Observatory
Williams College
Williamstown, Massachusetts

Dr. Naomi Pasachoff
Research Associate
Williams College
Williamstown, Massachusetts

Karin L. Rhines
Science/Educational Consultant
Valhalla, New York

Dr. Irwin L. Slesnick
Professor of Biology
Western Washington University
Bellingham, Washington

Scott Foresman and Company
Editorial Offices: Glenview, Illinois

Regional Offices: Sunnyvale, California • Tucker, Georgia • Glenview, Illinois • Oakland, New Jersey • Dallas, Texas

Cooperative Learning Consultant
Dr. Robert E. Slavin
Director, Elementary School Program
Center for Research on Elementary and Middle Schools
Johns Hopkins University
Baltimore, Maryland

Gifted Education Consultants
Hilda P. Hobson
Teacher of the Gifted
W.B. Wicker School
Sanford, North Carolina

Christine Kuehn
Assistant Professor of Education
University of South Carolina
Columbia, South Carolina

Nancy Linkel York
Teacher of the Gifted
W.B. Wicker School
Sanford, North Carolina

Special Education Consultants
Susan E. Affleck
Classroom Teacher
Salt Creek Elementary School
Elk Grove Village, Illinois

Dr. Dale R. Jordan
Director
Jordan Diagnostic Center
Oklahoma City, Oklahoma

Dr. Shirley T. King
Learning Disabilities Teacher
Helfrich Park Middle School
Evansville, Indiana

Jeannie Rae McCoun
Learning Disabilities Teacher
Mary M. McClelland Elementary School
Indianapolis, Indiana

Thinking Skills Consultant
Dr. Joseph P. Riley II
Professor of Science Education
University of Georgia
Athens, Georgia

Reading Consultants
Patricia T. Hinske
Reading Specialist
Cardinal Stritch College
Milwaukee, Wisconsin

Dr. Robert A. Pavlik
Professor and Chairperson of Reading/Language Arts Department
Cardinal Stritch College

Dr. Alfredo Schifini
Reading Consultant
Downey, California

Consultants

Special Content Consultant
Dr. Abraham S. Flexor
Science Education Consultant
Boulder, Colorado

Health Consultant
Dr. Julius B. Richmond
John D. MacArthur Professor of Health Policy
Director, Division of Health Policy Research and Education
Harvard University
Advisor on Child Health Policy
Children's Hospital of Boston
Boston, Massachusetts

Safety Consultant
Dr. Jack A. Gerlovich
Science Education Safety Consultant/Author
Des Moines, Iowa

Process Skills Consultant
Dr. Alfred Devito
Professor Emeritus Science Education
Purdue University
West Lafayette, Indiana

Activity Consultants
Edward Al Pankow
Teacher
Petaluma City Schools
Petaluma, California

Valerie Pankow
Teacher and Writer
Petaluma City Schools
Petaluma, California

Science and Technology Consultant
Dr. David E. Newton
Adjunct Professor—Science and Social Issues
University of San Francisco
College of Professional Studies
San Francisco, California

ISBN: 0-673-42071-X

78910GBC9796959493929190

Reviewers and Content Specialists

Dr. Ramona J. Anshutz
Science Specialist
Kansas State Department of Education
Topeka, Kansas
Teresa M. Auldridge
Science Education Consultant
Amelia, Virginia
Annette M. Barzal
Classroom Teacher
Willetts Middle School
Brunswick, Ohio
James Haggard Brannon
Classroom Teacher
Ames Community Schools
Ames, Iowa
Priscilla L. Callison
Science Teacher
Topeka Adventure Center
Topeka, Kansas
Rochelle F. Cohen
Education Coordinator
Indianapolis Head Start
Indianapolis, Indiana
Linda Lewis Cundiff
Classroom Teacher
R. F. Bayless Elementary School
Lubbock, Texas
Dr. Patricia Dahl
Classroom Teacher
Bloomington Oak Grove Intermediate School
Bloomington, Minnesota
Audrey J. Dick
Supervisor, Elementary Education
Cincinnati Public Schools
Cincinnati, Ohio
Nancy B. Drabik
Reading Specialist
George Washington School
Wyckoff, New Jersey
Bennie Y. Fleming
Science Supervisor
Providence School District
Providence, Rhode Island
Mike Graf
Classroom Teacher
Branch Elementary School
Arroyo Grande, California
Thelma Robinson Graham
Classroom Teacher
Pearl Spann Elementary School
Jackson, Mississippi
Dr. Claude A. Hanson
Science Supervisor
Boise Public Schools
Boise, Idaho
Dr. Jean D. Harlan
Psychologist, Early Childhood Consultant
Lighthouse Counseling Associates
Racine, Wisconsin
Dr. Rebecca P. Harlin
Assistant Professor of Reading
State University of New York—Geneseo
Geneseo, New York
Richard L. Ingraham
Professor of Biology
San José State University
San José, California
Ron Jones
Science Coordinator
Salem Keizer Public Schools
Salem, Oregon
Sara A. Jones
Classroom teacher
Burroughs-Molette Elementary School
Brunswick, Georgia
Dr. Judy LaCavera
Director of Curriculum and Instruction
Learning Alternatives
Vienna, Ohio
Jack Laubisch
K-12 Science, Health, and Outdoor Education Coordinator
West Clermont Local School District
Amelia, Ohio
Douglas M. McPhee
Classroom Teacher/Consultant
Del Mar Hills Elementary School
Del Mar, California
Larry Miller
Classroom Teacher
Caldwell Elementary School
Caldwell, Kansas
Sam Murr
Teacher—Elementary Gifted Science
Academic Center for Enrichment—Mid Del Schools
Midwest City—Del City, Oklahoma
Janet Nakai
Classroom Teacher
Community Consolidated School District #65
Evanston, Illinois
Patricia Osborne
Classroom teacher
Valley Heights Elementary School
Waterville, Kansas
Elisa Pinzón-Umaña
Classroom teacher
Coronado Academy
Albuquerque, New Mexico
Dr. Jeanne Phillips
Director of Curriculum and Instruction
Meridian Municipal School District
Meridian, Mississippi
Maria Guadalupe Ramos
Classroom Teacher
Metz Elementary School
Austin, Texas
Elissa Richards
Math/Science Teacher Leader
Granite School District
Salt Lake City, Utah
Sister Mary Christelle Sawicki, C. S. S. F.
Science Curriculum Coordinator
Department of Catholic Education Diocese of Buffalo
Buffalo, New York
Ray E. Smalley
Classroom Teacher/Science Specialist
Cleveland School of Science
Cleveland, Ohio
Norman Sperling
Chabot Observatory
Oakland, California
Lisa D. Torres
Science Coordinator
Lebanon School District
Lebanon, New Hampshire
Alice C. Webb
Early Childhood Resource Teacher
Primary Education Office
Rockledge, Florida

CONTENTS

Discover SCIENCE ...for a lifetime

Complete science content coverage . . . PLUS opportunities to develop the skills needed to

- understand how science works
- learn new concepts
- solve problems
- and make decisions in today's technological society.

Scott, Foresman

Discover SCIENCE

Scott, Foresman

Discover SCIENCE

Series Scope and Sequence

Content in *Discover SCIENCE* is organized into four major units and several content strands. Each unit and strand is developed continuously throughout the program.

		Kindergarten	Grade 1	Grade 2
Life Science	**Plants**	Chapter 4 Seeds and Plants	Chapter 4 Learning About Plants	Chapter 1 How Plants Are Different
	Animals	Chapter 5 Animals (growth, habitats)	Chapter 5 Learning About Animals (differences, pets)	Chapter 2 How Animals Are Different
	Ecology	Chapter 3 Living and Nonliving (characteristics and uses of)	Chapter 3 Living and Nonliving (needs of living things)	Chapter 3 Life on Earth Long Ago
Physical Science	**Matter**	Chapter 6 Comparing and Grouping Matter	Chapter 6 Grouping Things (solids, liquids, gases)	Chapter 4 Matter Around You (grouping, changing)
	Energy	Chapter 7 Heat and Cold Chapter 8 Sound Chapter 9 Movement	Chapter 7 Light, Sound, and Heat Chapter 8 Moving and Working	Chapter 5 Heat, Light, and Sound Chapter 6 Machines and Electricity
Earth Science	**Earth**	Chapter 12 Seasons Chapter 13 Helping our World (conservation)	Chapter 9 The Earth (landforms, water, air)	Chapter 7 Water and Air
	Weather	Chapter 11 Weather (air, wind, temperature)	Chapter 10 Weather (kinds, changes)	Chapter 8 Changes in Weather
	Space	Chapter 10 Earth and Sky	Chapter 11 The Sky (sun, moon, stars)	Chapter 9 The Sun and Other Stars
Human Body		Chapter 1 Your Senses Chapter 2 Growing and Changing (body parts, teeth, eating, exercising)	Chapter 1 Your Senses (learning, using senses) Chapter 2 Growing and Changing	Chapter 10 How Your Body Works Chapter 11 Keeping Healthy

A detailed scope and sequence for grade 1 is found on page T9. Detailed scope and sequences for K-6 are on pages T245-T251.

Grade 3	Grade 4	Grade 5	Grade 6
Chapter 1 Plant Growth	Chapter 1 Flowering Plants	Chapter 2 Plant Processes	Chapter 4 Plant Response
Chapter 2 How Animals Grow and Change	Chapter 2 Animal Behavior	Chapter 3 Invertebrates and Vertebrates	Chapter 1 Cells and Heredity
Chapter 3 Living Things Need Each Other Chapter 4 How People Affect Plants and Animals	Chapter 3 Food Chains and Food Webs Chapter 4 Animal and Plant Adaptations	Chapter 1 Classifying Living Things Chapter 4 Populations and Communities	Chapter 2 The Fossil Record Chapter 3 Change Through Time Chapter 5 Ecosystems and Biomes
Chapter 5 Properties of Matter	Chapter 5 Measuring Matter (length, volume, mass, density)	Chapter 5 Investigating Matter (properties, composition) Chapter 6 Heat and Matter	Chapter 6 Structure of Matter Chapter 7 Changes in Matter
Chapter 6 Work and Machines Chapter 7 Forms of Energy Chapter 8 Sound	Chapter 6 Work and Energy Chapter 7 Electricity and Magnetism Chapter 8 Light and Sound	Chapter 7 Changing Forms of Energy Chapter 8 Energy Resources	Chapter 8 Electrical Energy Chapter 9 Investigating Light and Sound
Chapter 9 Rocks and Soil Chapter 10 Changes in the Earth	Chapter 10 Changes in Landforms Chapter 11 Oceans	Chapter 9 Earth's Changing Crust Chapter 10 Protecting the Environment	Chapter 11 Earth's Moving Plates Chapter 12 Resources and Conservation
Chapter 11 Clouds and Storms	Chapter 9 Measuring Weather Conditions	Chapter 11 Climate	Chapter 10 Forecasting Weather
Chapter 12 The Sun, Moon, and Planets	Chapter 12 Movement in the Solar System	Chapter 12 Mapping the Stars	Chapter 13 Exploring Space
Chapter 13 The Body's Support Chapter 14 Your Body's Health Needs	Chapter 13 Digestion and Circulation Chapter 14 Your Brain and Your Sense Organs	Chapter 13 Body Support, Movement, and Growth Chapter 14 Respiration and Excretion	Chapter 14 The Body's Control Systems Chapter 15 Growing Up Healthy

Science Discovery Center
Science Discovery Center Book

Teacher's Annotated Edition

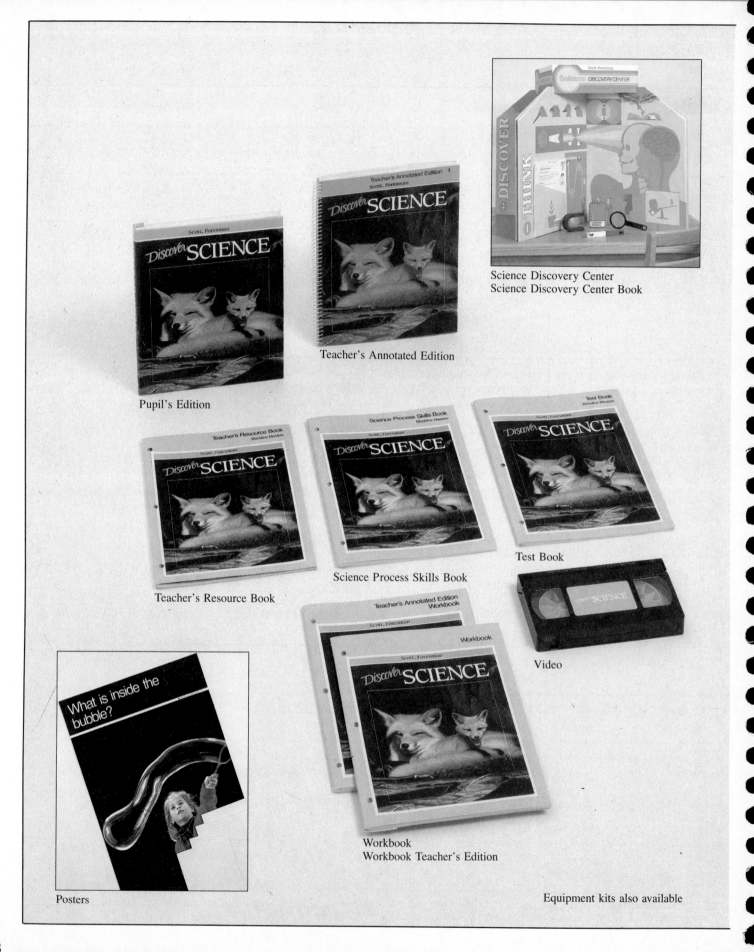

Pupil's Edition

Teacher's Resource Book

Science Process Skills Book

Test Book

Video

Workbook
Workbook Teacher's Edition

Posters

Equipment kits also available

GRADE 1 SCOPE AND SEQUENCE

Life Science

Plants

Chapter 4 Learning About Plants

*Lesson 1 How plants are alike and different
*Lesson 2 How plants grow
*Lesson 3 What plants need to grow
*Lesson 4 Why people need plants

Animals

Chapter 5 Learning About Animals

Lesson 1 Ways animals are different
*Lesson 2 How animals grow
*Lesson 3 Why people need animals
*Lesson 4 How to care for a pet

Ecology

Chapter 3 Living and Nonliving

*Lesson 1 What a living thing is
*Lesson 2 What living things need
*Lesson 3 What nonliving things are like

Physical Science

Matter

Chapter 6 Grouping Things

*Lesson 1 Ways to group things
*Lesson 2 Matter takes up space
*Lesson 3 What solids and liquids are like
*Lesson 4 What gases are like

Energy

Chapter 7 Light, Sound, and Heat

*Lesson 1 How light can change
*Lesson 2 How sound can change
Lesson 3 What can be learned about heat

Chapter 8 Moving and Working

Lesson 1 Ways objects move
Lesson 2 What can move objects (magnets)
*Lesson 3 Work machines can do

Earth Science

Earth

Chapter 9 The Earth

*Lesson 1 Mountains, valleys, soil, rocks, and resources
*Lesson 2 Location of water on earth
*Lesson 3 How air is useful
*Lesson 4 How people use land and water

Weather

Chapter 10 Weather

Lesson 1 Different kinds of weather
*Lesson 2 How weather can change in seasons
*Lesson 3 How weather is important to people

Space

Chapter 11 The Sky

*Lesson 1 What is seen in the sky
Lesson 2 What the sun is like
*Lesson 3 What the moon is like
*Lesson 4 What the stars are like

Human Body

Chapter 1 Your Senses

Lesson 1 Learning
*Lesson 2 Using the senses

Chapter 2 Growing and Changing

*Lesson 1 How people change
*Lesson 2 What helps people grow

Note: If time does not permit you to cover all of the material in this book, it is recommended that the lessons with an asterisk be presented as a core program. This core program represents a balanced treatment of topics throughout the series.

Highly organized

One of the most important features of Scott, Foresman's *Discover SCIENCE* centers on its highly organized lesson structure. The sample on these pages illustrates the close relationship between the lesson titles, content, illustrations, and review. This tight structure improves student comprehension.

The authors of *Discover SCIENCE* encourage you to check for this benefit in any science series you review.

Lesson 4 How Can You Care for a Pet? **1**

People keep some animals as **pets.**
People take care of pets.
2 Pets need food and water.
They need a place to live.
How does this boy care for his pet?

96

Tight lesson structure improves science comprehension

1 → Question-title sets a purpose for reading . . .

2 → clearly indicates the nature of the content . . .

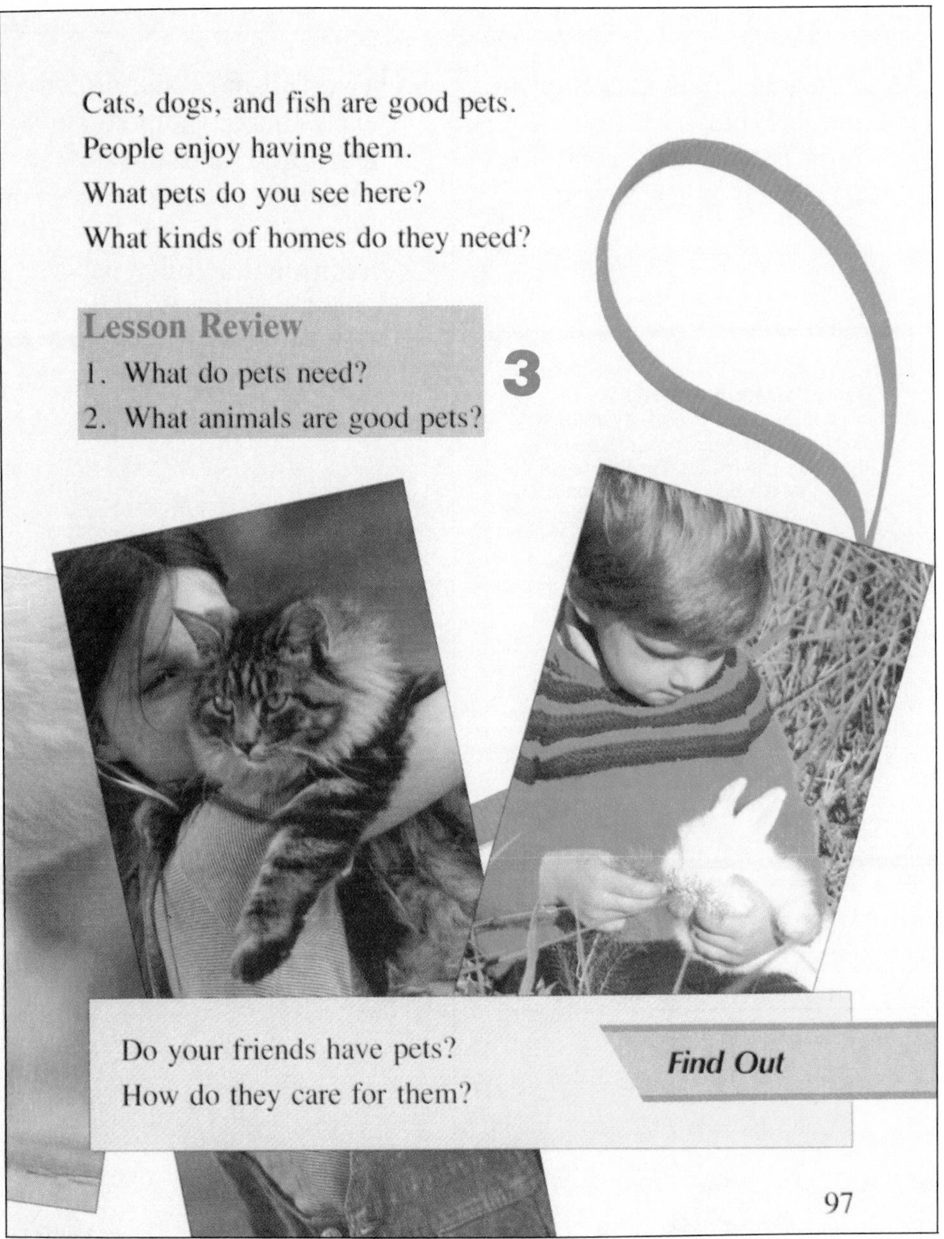

Cats, dogs, and fish are good pets.
People enjoy having them.
What pets do you see here?
What kinds of homes do they need?
Lesson Review
1. What do pets need?
2. What animals are good pets?
3
Do your friends have pets?
How do they care for them?
Find Out
97

3

and relates to the more specific lesson review questions.

Accurate and up to date

A highly qualified authorship and review team incorporated the most recent scientific data available. References to new technology, new information, and recent global events help prepare you and your students for science in the 1990s.

Relevant

Most examples and illustrations are presented in the context of the students' experience. Research shows that students are better able to learn new concepts when they are permitted to draw on their own background experience.

A flexible activity program allows teachers to customize hands-on experience to their needs.

An easy-to-do *DISCOVER* or *TRY THIS* activity begins each chapter and provides a common experience that students can later draw on to assimilate new lesson concepts.

Introducing the Chapter

Matter can be described in many different ways. You might describe some matter by its color or its length. In the activity below, you will learn another way matter can be described. In this chapter, you will learn about the tiny bits that make up matter. You also will learn different ways you can measure matter.

DISCOVER!

Describing Air

One way you can describe air is that it takes up space. You can show that air takes up space by pouring air from one plastic cup to another.

Fill a large plastic container with enough water so that you can hold a cup completely underwater. Hold one plastic cup under the water to fill it with water. Carefully turn the cup upside-down underwater so that the water stays in the cup.

Hold the second cup upside-down above the water. Keeping the cup upside-down, slowly push it into the water until it is under the water. What is inside the cup?

Move the cups next to each other. Now raise the cup filled with water slightly higher than the cup filled with air. Now pour the air from one cup to the other.

Talk About It

1. What happened to the water in the cup when you poured air into it?
2. What can you tell about air from what you observed?

117

A teacher demonstration in the Teacher's Edition provides an active way to introduce every lesson.

Demonstration Activity ♦
Place a few drops of dilute hydrochloric acid on a seashell or piece of limestone. The reaction will cause a fizzing. Tell students that the bubbles form as carbon dioxide is released from the carbonate minerals in the rock or shell. *CAUTION:* Have students wear cover goggles and stay a safe distance away during this demonstration.

Two full-page activities in each chapter help students learn how to follow scientific procedure and interpret data. An additional activity per chapter in the *Workbook* reinforces the use of these skills.

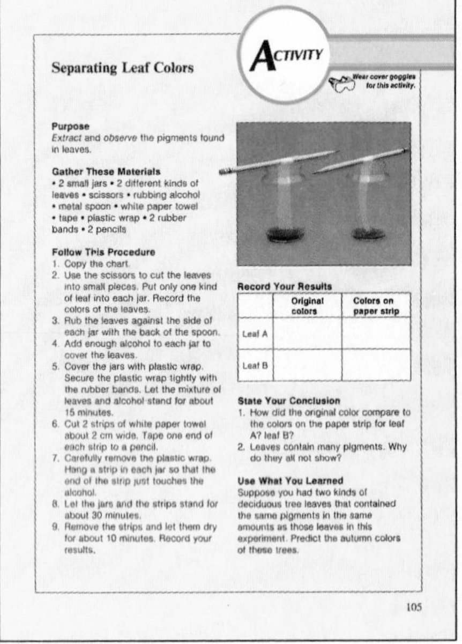

Separating Leaf Colors

ACTIVITY

Wear cover goggles for this activity.

Purpose
Extract and *observe* the pigments found in leaves.

Gather These Materials
• 2 small jars • 2 different kinds of leaves • scissors • rubbing alcohol • metal spoon • white paper towel • tape • plastic wrap • 2 rubber bands • 2 pencils

Follow This Procedure
1. Copy the chart.
2. Use the scissors to cut the leaves into small pieces. Put only one kind of leaf into each jar. Record the colors of the leaves.
3. Rub the leaves against the side of each jar with the back of the spoon.
4. Add enough alcohol to each jar to cover the leaves.
5. Cover the jars with plastic wrap. Secure the plastic wrap tightly with the rubber bands. Let the mixture of leaves and alcohol stand for about 15 minutes.
6. Cut 2 strips of white paper towel about 2 cm wide. Tape one end of each strip to a pencil.
7. Carefully remove the plastic wrap. Hang a strip in each jar so that the end of the strip just touches the alcohol.
8. Let the jars and the strips stand for about 30 minutes.
9. Remove the strips and let them dry for about 10 minutes. Record your results.

Record Your Results

	Original colors	Colors on paper strip
Leaf A		
Leaf B		

State Your Conclusion
1. How did the original color compare to the colors on the paper strip for leaf A? leaf B?
2. Leaves contain many pigments. Why do they all not show?

Use What You Learned
Suppose you had two kinds of deciduous tree leaves that contained the same pigments in the same amounts as those leaves in this experiment. Predict the autumn colors of these trees.

105

A separate *Science Process Skills Book* instructs and assesses whether students understand the basic process skills they use in doing activities. This booklet also teaches the manipulative skills students need to use basic science equipment.

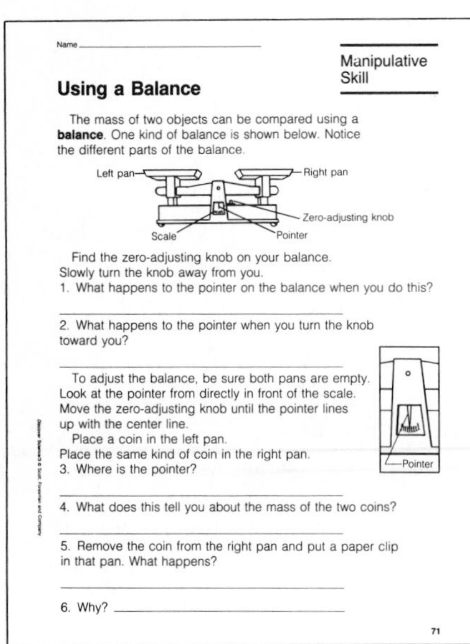

Name ____________

Manipulative Skill

Using a Balance

The mass of two objects can be compared using a **balance**. One kind of balance is shown below. Notice the different parts of the balance.

Find the zero-adjusting knob on your balance. Slowly turn the knob away from you.

1. What happens to the pointer on the balance when you do this?
2. What happens to the pointer when you turn the knob toward you?

To adjust the balance, be sure both pans are empty. Look at the pointer from directly in front of the scale. Move the zero-adjusting knob until the pointer lines up with the center line.

Place a coin in the left pan. Place the same kind of coin in the right pan.

3. Where is the pointer?
4. What does this tell you about the mass of the two coins?
5. Remove the coin from the right pan and put a paper clip in that pan. What happens?
6. Why? ____________

71

Open-ended enrichment experiments found in the *Resource Book* help students recognize variables and controls and design their own procedures.

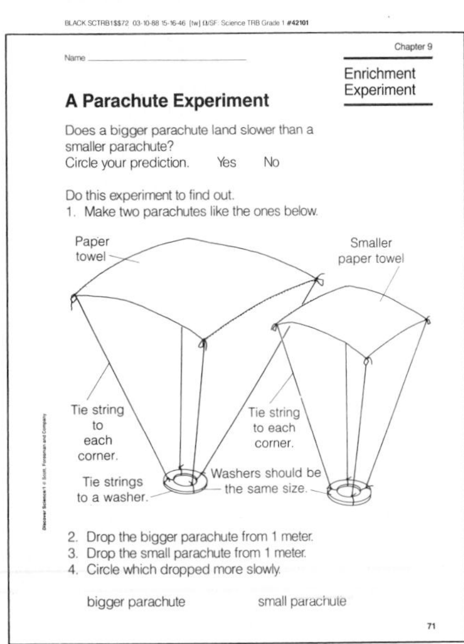

Name ____________

Chapter 9

Enrichment Experiment

A Parachute Experiment

Does a bigger parachute land slower than a smaller parachute?
Circle your prediction. Yes No

Do this experiment to find out.

1. Make two parachutes like the ones below.

2. Drop the bigger parachute from 1 meter.
3. Drop the small parachute from 1 meter.
4. Circle which dropped more slowly.

bigger parachute small parachute

71

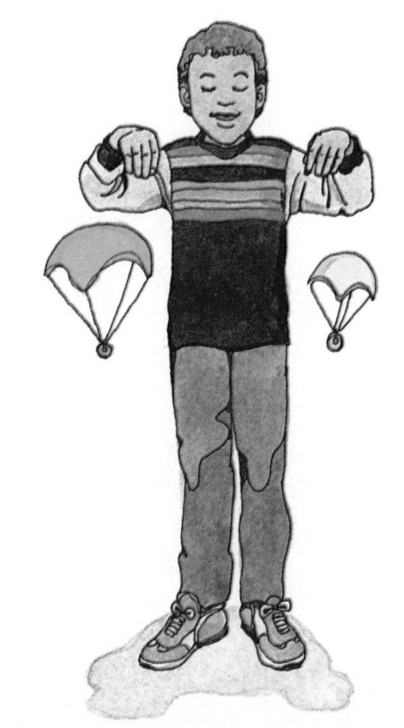

Fun activities at the Science Discovery Center provide independent opportunity for enrichment of each chapter's content.

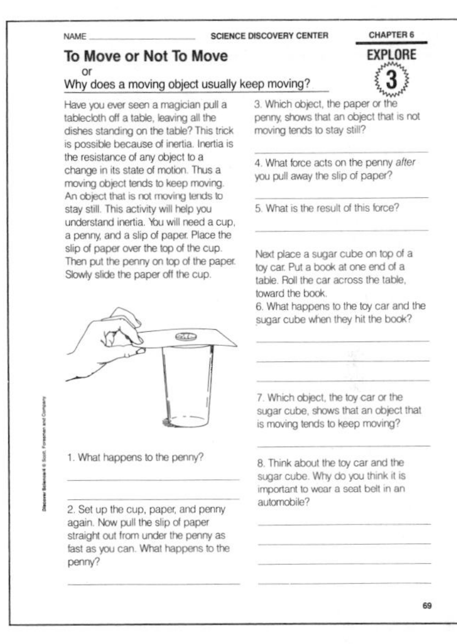

NAME ____________ SCIENCE DISCOVERY CENTER CHAPTER 6

EXPLORE 3

To Move or Not To Move
or
Why does a moving object usually keep moving?

Have you ever seen a magician pull a tablecloth off a table, leaving all the dishes standing on the table? This trick is possible because of inertia. Inertia is the resistance of any object to a change in its state of motion. Thus a moving object tends to keep moving. An object that is not moving tends to stay still. This activity will help you understand inertia. You will need a cup, a penny, and a slip of paper. Place the slip of paper over the top of the cup. Then put the penny on top of the paper. Slowly slide the paper off the cup.

1. What happens to the penny?
2. Set up the cup, paper, and penny again. Now pull the slip of paper straight out from under the penny as fast as you can. What happens to the penny?
3. Which object, the paper or the penny, shows that an object that is not moving tends to stay still?
4. What force acts on the penny *after* you pull away the slip of paper?
5. What is the result of this force?

Next place a sugar cube on top of a toy car. Put a book at one end of a table. Roll the car across the table, toward the book.

6. What happens to the toy car and the sugar cube when they hit the book?
7. Which object, the toy car or the sugar cube, shows that an object that is moving tends to keep moving?
8. Think about the toy car and the sugar cube. Why do you think it is important to wear a seat belt in an automobile?

69

Each chapter ends with a skills feature that teaches students to collect, organize, and interpret data to solve problems.

Skills for Solving Problems

Using a Machine

What work can a machine do?

1. Use the objects in the picture.
   Keep them the same way you see here.
   They make up a machine.
2. Keep the pencil far from the book.
   Push down on the ruler.
   Move the pencil closer to the book.
   Push down on the ruler again.
   Notice how the book moves each time.

158

3. Use your own paper.
Copy what you see here.
Circle how the book moved.

first time	second time
easy	easy
hard	hard

4. What did the machine lift?

159

Other features designed to develop thinking skills

Pupil's Edition

- *TRY THIS* (grades 1 and 2) and *DISCOVER* (grades 3-6) activities at the beginning of each chapter
- In-text questions
- Challenge! question in each lesson review
- *Find Out* (grades 1 and 2) and *Find Out On Your Own* (grades 3-6) at the end of each lesson
- Two formal activities per chapter
- What Do You Think? questions in the *Science and Technology* or *Science and People* feature in each chapter
- Interpretation and application questions in the chapter and unit reviews
- A *Science and Society* feature at the end of each unit (grades 3-6)

Teacher's Edition

- Suggested questions, discussion topics, and activities for every page
- Highlighting of skills used in all Pupil's Edition and Teacher's Edition material

Ancillary Components

- *Science Process Skills Book* for each grade
- Enrichment experiment sheets in the *Resource Book*
- Science Skills and Science Activity sheets in the *Workbook*

Numerous special features relate science to the students' real world.

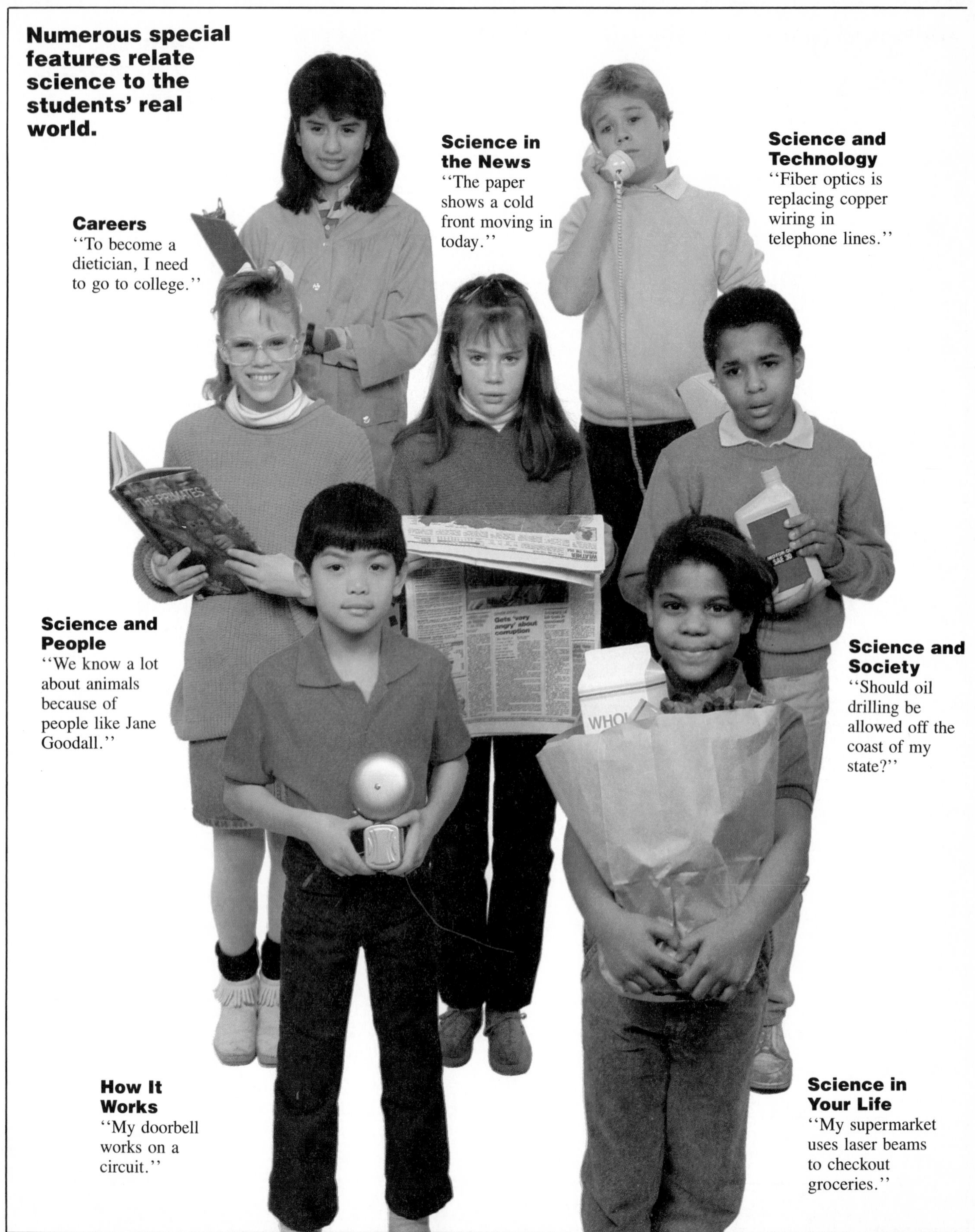

Careers
"To become a dietician, I need to go to college."

Science in the News
"The paper shows a cold front moving in today."

Science and Technology
"Fiber optics is replacing copper wiring in telephone lines."

Science and People
"We know a lot about animals because of people like Jane Goodall."

Science and Society
"Should oil drilling be allowed off the coast of my state?"

How It Works
"My doorbell works on a circuit."

Science in Your Life
"My supermarket uses laser beams to checkout groceries."

Check students' progress at every level for continuous feedback.

✓	**Lesson Review**	■ Provides frequent assessment ■ Correlates with lesson goals
✓	**Independent Study Guide**	■ Additional questions for review
✓	**Chapter Review**	■ Students recall, interpret, and apply information
✓	**Chapter Test**	■ Two forms for grades 3-6 ■ Keyed to lesson objectives
✓	**Unit Review**	■ Integrates chapter concepts ■ Includes essay questions for application
✓	**Unit Test**	■ Includes picture interpretation questions ■ Keyed to lesson objectives

A clearly defined two-part format lets you more easily plan your day.

- A 3-step **TEACHING PLAN** makes the lesson easy to teach.
  1. **Motivate**
     Demonstration and follow-up discussion to begin each lesson effectively
  2. **Teach**
     Time-saving tips to reinforce and extend the content
     Includes questions to ask students–with answers
     Includes possible misconceptions–information to help you correct commonly misunderstood science ideas
  3. **Assess**
     Answers to lesson review questions and *Find Out On Your Own* activities
- A **Teaching Options** section provides added flexibility for your planning.

Background information, extra activities, projects, discussion topics, and strategies found under these headings:
Science Background
Science Anecdote
Reading Strategies
Cooperative Learning
Reinforcement
Enrichment
Special Education
Science and (other subject)
Game Suggestion
Reteaching Suggestion

TEACHING PLAN

LESSON 4
pages 96–97

Lesson Objectives
- *List* kinds of pets.
- *Describe* the care pets need.

Lesson Vocabulary
pets

1 MOTIVATE

Demonstration Activity ♦
Ask students to bring photographs or drawings of their pets to school. (Students who do not have pets could bring pictures of animals they would like to have as pets.) Allow time for students to tell about their pets or the pets they would like to have.

Discussion
Have the students who own pets discuss some of the things they do for their pets or *describe* the care that their pets need. Have the other students tell what kind of care they think the pet they have chosen would need.

[1] Boy provides food, water, shelter, and identification on dog's collar.

Lesson 4 How Can You Care for a Pet?

People keep some animals as **pets.**
People take care of pets.
Pets need food and water.
They need a place to live.
How does this boy care for his pet?[1]

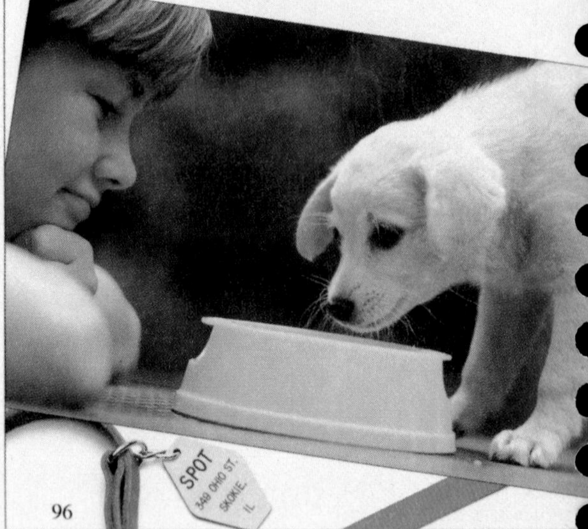

96

Teaching Options

SCIENCE BACKGROUND

Pets are animals that can become accustomed to life with humans. Generally, a pet is also expected to become tame, or manageable. When an animal is domesticated, it begins to rely on its owner for most of its care. Attempts to domesticate such animals as lions, alligators, and monkeys are usually unsuccessful because of the animals' genetic patterns of behavior. Attempts to domesticate such animals have often proved to be hazardous to the animals and their owners. Even domestic animals can be dangerous at times. Care should be taken around animals that are sick, hurt, hungry, or excitable.

Reinforcement

Encourage students with learning disabilities to relate their experiences with pets. Include them in an activity in which you write the names of several types of animals on the chalkboard and ask the students to determine which of the animals would make good pets and which would not. Have them tell what type of home each pet might need.

96 Unit 2 Chapter 5 Lesson 4

♦ *Suitable as a language development activity*

[1] dog, cat, rabbit
[2] Answers should indicate a safe, appropriate shelter.

Cats, dogs, and fish are good pets.
People enjoy having them.
What pets do you see here?[1]
What kinds of homes do they need?[2]

Lesson Review

1. What do pets need?
2. What animals are good pets?

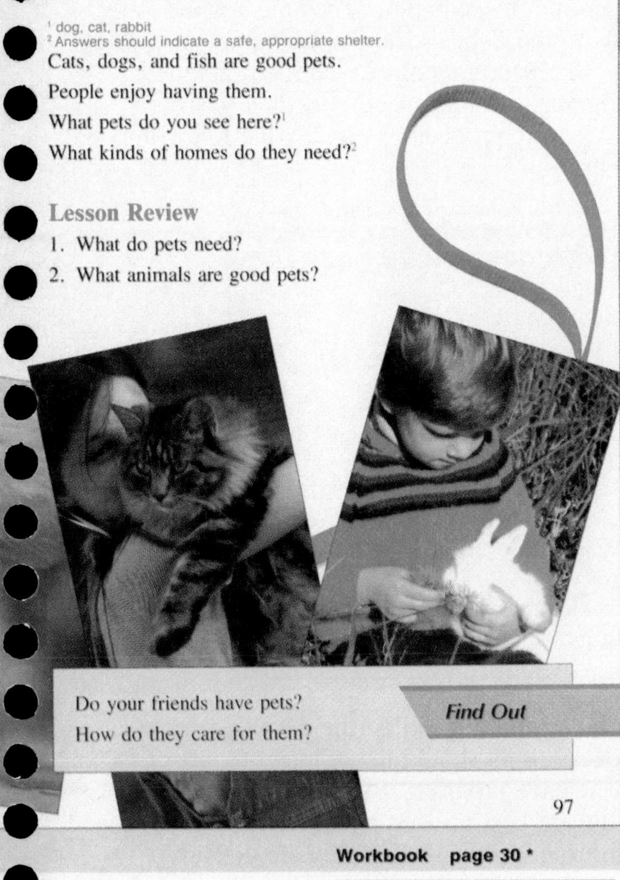

Find Out

Do your friends have pets?
How do they care for them?

97

2 TEACH

Teaching Tips

- Have students read page 96. Have students tell what they like about dogs.
- Ask students to read page 97. Have student *identify* the animals in the picture and tell why they make good pets. Question: **What types of animals would not make good pets?** (Students should *name* animals that are not tame.)
- **Possible Misconception:** Be aware that children sometimes think pets have the same needs as people do.

3 ASSESS

Lesson Review

1. Pets need food, water, and a place to live.
2. Answers should include cats, dogs, and fish.

Challenge! Question: **What is one animal that you think should stay in the wild and not become a pet? Tell why.** (Answers will vary, but should include animals who would be hard to take care of and animals that might be dangerous to humans.) **Thinking Skill:** *Inferring*

Find Out

Students could make a list of the different kinds of pets owned by their friends, and the ways the pets are cared for. **Thinking Skill:** *Restating or explaining ideas*

Workbook page 30 *

Animals Wordsearch

Reteaching Suggestion ♦

Remind students that pets need food, water, and a place to live. Make arrangements to keep a pet, such as a fish or hamster, at school. Allow the students to help you plan what the animal will eat, what type of home it will need, and who will be responsible for its care each day (on a rotating schedule). *CAUTION:* Investigate any allergies your students may have before planning to house a classroom pet. Make certain that any water spilled on the floor is wiped up immediately. Direct students to wash their hands after handling the animal.

*Answers to masters on pages 84E–84F

Other features designed for convenient and successful teaching:

- Two-page insert before each unit includes a Planning Guide and resources (books, community resources, audio visuals, and software).
- Four-page insert before each chapter includes a Planning Guide, a list of preteaching suggestions, and bulletin board ideas.
- Reduced copies of resource masters appear on the pages where they are best used and before each chapter with answers.
- Clearly defined objectives for each lesson and activity aid in planning.
- Safety tips for all activities let you teach with greater confidence.
- Activity Results photographs, where appropriate, help you anticipate outcomes.
- Thinking skills are highlighted wherever they appear in the margin notes so that you can more easily plan to meet specific goals.

Developing Thinking Skills

A major goal of an elementary science program should be the development of thinking skills that will serve students in becoming better problem solvers and intelligent decision makers. Thinking skills include skills people use to collect, understand, interpret, apply, and evaluate information and ideas. The thinking skills emphasized in *Discover SCIENCE* are listed in the chart on page T21. Their classification is based on Bloom's Taxonomy of Educational Objectives, which forms a continuum from basic skills used in information gathering to higher order skills used in synthesizing and evaluating information.

Both basic and higher order thinking skills can be and should be introduced at all elementary grade levels. Cognitive research into the nature of thinking indicates that the activities commonly associated with higher order thinking are not necessarily limited to advanced levels of development. For example, young children engage in complex problem-solving behaviors when they decode a word in reading or imagine beyond the information contained in a story. These same skills can be called upon in science to encourage students to go beyond the data—to provide inferences, make predictions, and analyze information.

Such skills can be successfully employed if the students have a concrete experience or solid knowledge base from which to start. For example, from the common observation that wet pavement dries, students can make inferences about where the water goes. They can make predictions about how long large and small puddles will take to dry.

Teachers can encourage the development of all levels of thinking skills by:

- allowing students to draw upon their familiar, concrete experiences to extend their knowledge
- involving students in learning activities that include hands-on experiences
- developing a science knowledge base of specific facts and organizing principles
- providing extended practice in the use of thinking skills and
- challenging students with questions and problems that require the use of various thinking skills to solve.

Discover SCIENCE incorporates all these points. Program features that develop thinking skills are listed and described on page T21.

Developing Science Process Skills

Thinking skills most closely related to scientific inquiry are identified as science process skills. These are the tools of scientific investigation. They are applied daily by scientists in the field and in the laboratory as part of a procedure that is commonly called the scientific method. Although no one specific method is strictly followed, scientific procedures employ the following process skills.

Science Process Skills
- Observing
- Communicating
- Measuring
- Classifying
- Making and using models
- Recognizing space or time relationships
- Collecting and interpreting data
- Inferring
- Predicting
- Identifying and controlling variables
- Experimenting
- Formulating questions and hypotheses
- Making operational definitions

As with other thinking skills, the development of science process skills should be an integral part of an elementary science program. By their very nature, process skills are best utilized when students are engaged in hands-on experiences—when they are actively involved in scientific investigation. The authors and editors of *Discover SCIENCE* have recognized this maxim. The development of process skills in *Discover SCIENCE* by "doing science" is shown on page T21.

Elementary students bring to class the most basic and important ingredient for scientific inquiry—curiosity about the natural world. With it, students will develop, to a degree, certain thinking and process skills on their own. A program that incorporates thinking and process skills will direct and amplify that development, allowing students to fulfill their potentials as problem solvers and decision makers.

Joseph P. Riley II
University of Georgia

Skills Development in *Discover SCIENCE*

Pupil's Edition

- *TRY THIS* (grades 1-2) and *DISCOVER* (grades 3-6) activities begin each chapter with a focus on process skills development.
- Two additional activities per chapter focus on process skills as students apply newly acquired knowledge to hands-on experiences.
- In-text questions focus students' thinking while reading.
- General text weaves thinking skills throughout by explaining not only what we know but how we came to know it.
- Lesson review questions, including a *Challenge!* question (grades 3-6), extend students' thinking.
- *FIND OUT* (grades 1-2) and *FIND OUT ON YOUR OWN* (grades 3-6) at the end of each lesson emphasize information gathering and communicating skills.
- A *Science and Technology* or *Science and People* feature in each chapter includes *What Do You Think?* questions to stimulate an exchange of ideas in discussions.
- *Skills for Solving Problems,* a special two-page feature in every chapter, focuses on the skills of *making decisions/identifying and solving problems* and *interpreting charts, maps, and graphs.*
- Chapter review and unit review questions require the use of a continuum of thinking skills.
- A *Science and Society* feature at the end of each unit (grades 3-6) encourages critical thinking by focusing on evaluative and decision making skills.

Teacher's Edition

- Suggested questions, discussion topics, and activities in the sidenotes reinforce and extend thinking and process skills.
- Skills used in all Pupil's Edition and Teacher's Edition material are highlighted in heavy italics in the sidenotes.

Ancillary Components

- A *Science Process Skills Book* for each grade contains worksheets that can be used to teach and then assess student mastery of science process skills. In addition, other worksheets teach students the manipulative skills they will need to use basic science equipment.
- *Enrichment Experiment Sheets* in the *Resource Book* focus on process skills associated with experimenting.
- *Science Skills* sheets in the *Workbook* concentrate on higher order thinking skills.
- *Science Activity* sheets in the *Workbook* focus on process skills.

Thinking Skills Developed in *Discover SCIENCE*

1. Gathering and Recalling Information

- Collecting Information/Data
  - Measuring
  - Observing
- Recalling Facts
- Communicating
  - Naming
  - Listing
  - Describing
  - Recording

2. Understanding and Interpreting Information/Data

- Recognizing the Main Idea and Supporting Details
- Recognizing and Using Space or Time Relationships
- Sequencing (Time, Steps in a Process, Following Directions, Place)
- Recognizing Cause and Effect
- Classifying
- Organizing Information
  - Recognizing Patterns and Relationships
  - Comparing (Identifying Similarities)
  - Contrasting (Identifying Differences)
  - Summarizing
- Restating or Explaining Ideas
- Interpreting Charts, Maps, and Graphs
- Comprehending Meaning
- Visualizing
- Making Physical Models
- Identifying Variables
- Interpreting Data

3. Applying, Analyzing, Synthesizing, and Evaluating

- Making Generalizations
- Making Inferences/Inferring
- Making Analogies
- Drawing Conclusions
- Formulating Questions and Hypotheses
- Identifying and Suggesting Alternatives
- Controlling Variables
- Predicting
- Judging and Evaluating
  - Distinguishing Fact from Opinion, Bias, and Propaganda
  - Ranking Ideas and Information According to Criteria
  - Reconciling Inconsistent Criteria
  - Recognizing Relevant Information and Data
  - Recognizing Factual and Logical Inconsistencies
- Making Decisions/Identifying and Solving Problems
- Applying Information to New Situations
- Experimenting
- Making Operational Definitions

High-Potential Students

Perhaps more so than other students, high-potential students benefit from the opportunity to make individual study choices and to structure an activity in a manner that is personally challenging and interesting. Therefore, the *Preteaching Suggestions* page in the front of each chapter in the Teacher's Edition includes an experiment or other project specifically designed for high-potential students. Although direction is provided, individual style and creativity are very much encouraged.

Many other items throughout the Pupil's Edition and Teacher's Edition of *Discover SCIENCE* provide individuals the opportunities to investigate science concepts beyond the basic material presented in the chapters. Such items include science fair projects in the *Preteaching Suggestions,* a variety of extensions in the *Teaching Options* throughout the Teacher's Edition, and questions at the end of each lesson and chapter in the Pupil's Edition that stimulate higher-level thinking skills.

Mainstreamed Students

Discover SCIENCE offers teachers extensive opportunity to make the study of science more rewarding and relevant to mainstreamed students—those who have emotional handicaps; orthopedic, visual, or hearing impairments; learning disabilities; or are mentally retarded. A suggestion for helping students with learning disabilities is included in the *Teaching Options* for each lesson under the heading *Special Education*. These ideas incorporate alternative learning modes.

The *Preteaching Suggestions* in front of each chapter in the Teacher's Edition include specific ideas to help students with handicaps or impairments experience the fullness of learning. These ideas are chapter-specific, but the following general guidelines can be applied throughout your teaching.

Emotionally Handicapped

- Define class rules clearly and be consistent in their enforcement.
- Provide a highly structured environment for activities.
- Encourage interaction in discussions and activities.
- Provide responsibilities such as helping to clean the room or care for a classroom plant or pet.
- Reinforce appropriate behaviors.

Orthopedically Handicapped

- Consult with the school nurse or student's physical therapist to identify the student's limitations.
- Adapt the physical environment of the classroom accordingly.
- Regarding field trips and outdoor activities: choose environments and activities that accommodate the capabilities of all the students.

Visually Impaired

- Use white chalk on a black chalkboard.
- Say out loud what you are writing on the board.
- Seat the student as close to the front as necessary.
- Stress the use of touching and hearing.
- Investigate the use of special learning aids such as sheets of magnifying plastic for reading materials.

Hearing Impaired

- Seat the student near the front of the room.
- Speak clearly.
- Use visual aids whenever possible.

Mentally Retarded

- Provide concrete examples of explanations.
- Use repetition and reinforcing activities.
- Provide hands-on experiences.
- Reinforce appropriate behaviors.

Keep in mind that many mainstreamed students do not expect nor accept any special attention from teachers. Get to know your mainstreamed students. If they especially fear being singled out, avoid highlighting them in class. Special needs may be taken care of outside of class time.

Christine Kuehn
University of South Carolina

In cooperative learning, students work in four- to five-member learning teams to help one another master academic knowledge and skills. Research on cooperative learning has found that if students work on teams that are rewarded based on the learning of all team members, they learn more than do students in traditional classroom settings. By engaging in cooperative learning in the elementary classroom, students become aware of and understand the advantages of such cooperative strategies for future learning endeavors.

To use cooperative learning in *Discover SCIENCE,* first assign students to four-member learning teams. If the class does not divide evenly by four, a few five-member teams may be assigned. Each team should have one relatively high achiever, one low achiever, and two or three average achievers, and should be mixed in sex and ethnicity. Let students choose team names and sit together during science periods. You might change team assignments every four to six weeks.

Two principal cooperative learning formats that can be used in *Discover SCIENCE* are *STAD* (Student Teams–Achievement Divisions) and *Jigsaw*. A brief description of STAD appears on the Chapter Review in the *Teaching Options*. Only the STAD format is recommended for use in Books 1 and 2, but a full description of both STAD and Jigsaw follows for your information and discretionary use.

STAD

In *STAD* students study together to help one another prepare for individual tests. At the end of each chapter, give students about one class period to work in their learning teams to master the material presented in the Chapter Review. After the teams have had enough time to complete the Chapter Review and study the material, give students individual tests covering the chapter content. Teams that average 90% or more on the test may earn attractive Superteam certificates; those that average 80-89% may earn smaller Greatteam certificates. These criteria and rewards may be adjusted to your preferences and circumstances. A reminder of the use of *STAD* is given in the *Teaching Options* on the first page of each Chapter Review.

Jigsaw

In *Jigsaw* each team member becomes an "expert" on a unique topic for a chapter. Four topics are suggested in the *Teaching Options* at the beginning of each chapter in Books 3–6. Assign topics at random. If a team has five members, two may share a topic.

All students should read the entire chapter, but they should especially be looking for information on their own topics. At the end of the chapter, students from different teams who had the same topic meet in "expert groups" to discuss their topics. You may wish to circulate among the groups to guide their discussion and to see that they are focusing on the right information.

After twenty to thirty minutes, have students return to their teams and take turns presenting what they have learned to their teammates. Teams may earn certificates or other rewards based on average team scores, as described for *STAD*.

You may wish to combine *Jigsaw* and *STAD* by allowing students to study the Chapter Review after they have finished reporting to the team on their topics.

Robert E. Slavin
Center for Research on Elementary
and Middle Schools
Johns Hopkins University

Although students who are native speakers of English may experience some difficulty with new science terminology and concepts, students who do not speak English natively are particularly at risk. Limited English proficient (LEP) students do not have the English language skills of listening comprehension, speaking, reading, and writing necessary to sufficiently engage in instruction in English. While some students appear to handle English reasonably well in everyday situations, and are academically quite capable and motivated, they lack the language skills to reason, hypothesize, make predictions, and form and defend logical arguments in English.

Recent advances in language acquisition theory have facilitated an understanding of the process involved in expanding native-language development and in second-language acquisition. For both native- and second-language speakers of English, language is acquired through meaningful communication—by engaging in a genuine exchange of information in a variety of low-anxiety settings. In classrooms this communication involves surrounding learners with language they can understand and devising tasks to use newly acquired language.

Language Development Activities

Discover SCIENCE has integrated language development activities designed to build academic language proficiency and to enhance science instruction for all students. These activities are denoted by a ♦ in the Teacher's Edition for each chapter and include the following:

- *TRY THIS* (on the second page of each chapter in the Pupil's Edition)
- *Demonstration Activity* (on the first page of each lesson)
- *Game Suggestion* (at least one per chapter)
- *Reteaching Suggestion* (on the last page of each lesson).
- *Cooperative Learning* (on the first page of each Chapter Review)

These activities strengthen language ability not only for students who are learning English as a second language, but also for those who speak English fluently, yet have language and literacy needs that inhibit access to science comprehension.

The cooperative learning activities in *Discover SCIENCE* give students the opportunity to accelerate their academic achievements by putting science concepts in their own words. Through a process of group interaction, students engage in directed, meaningful communication. Such interactions are particularly appropriate for LEP students. They provide a low-anxiety setting in which students with more advanced English language skills may help their peers who are newer to the language. Cooperative learning is discussed more fully in the monograph on page T23.

The other activities listed above are suitable for developing language because they involve the use of contextual clues and capitalize on prior knowledge. Simply put, contextual clues may be anything that helps the learner follow what is being said. The demonstration of new science concepts, the use of real objects, and games all assist in getting the main points of a lesson across to students who do not possess fully developed language skills in English.

Success in learning new science information depends heavily on the learner's prior knowledge of the world. The *TRY THIS* activities particularly utilize and focus students' prior knowledge to increase comprehension of new material. Although a classroom may form a myriad of languages and cultures, common experiences with natural phenomena provide a background from which all students can draw.

Useful Teaching Techniques

Language development activities can be used successfully with all students. However, teachers of students who are at low levels of linguistic competence in English are encouraged to use a slower but natural speech rate, shorter sentences, and ample repetitions. Visual aids, audio-visual assistance, and the use of gestures and mime will also serve to make English more comprehensible to LEP students. These techniques, the language development activities, and an interesting, comprehensible text promote a fuller participation in challenging science instruction for all students.

Alfredo Schifini, Ph.D.
Reading Consultant

Discover SCIENCE is written for students of varying reading abilities. The Pupil's Edition applies recent research in the writing style and design of its reading comprehension aids. The Teacher's Edition also applies recent research in the suggestions for guiding students' reading comprehension. *Discover SCIENCE* incorporates reading as a teaching-learning tool in science:

- to build and refine students' knowledge background.
- to help students make connections in their reading.
- to challenge students to think critically.

Reading Comprehension Aids

Monitoring Readability

The authors and editors assessed each lesson using either the Dale-Chall or the Spache Readability Formula. The vocabulary and sentence lengths are appropriate for your students working either independently or under your guidance. The use of reading formulae, however, is only one factor in achieving maximum reading comprehension. *Discover SCIENCE* employs the following additional aids toward achieving that goal.

Clarifying Organization

Each chapter is divided into short lessons. Each lesson has a question-title and contains only those main ideas and supporting details that pertain to the question-title.

Motivating Purposeful Reading

Each chapter opens with an advanced organizer—a paragraph and an accompanying photograph designed to help students activate and connect their background knowledge with new information in the chapter.

The second page of each chapter contains an action-oriented feature entitled *TRY THIS*. This feature invites students to become involved in scientific problem-solving *before* reading new information.

The *Science and People* and *Careers* features motivate students' reading by focusing on the imagination, courage, hard work, frustration, and excitement involved in scientific endeavors. The features of *Science in Your Life, Find Out,* and *How It Works* help students connect the concepts and processes of science with their lives.

Correlating Illustrations to Text

The text contains phrases, statements, or questions that direct students to the purpose, features, or importance of the illustrations. Our goal is to have students use the illustrations to reinforce and expand their understanding of the content. Scientific illustrations are not merely decorative, but an integral part of the content. The tight correlation between text and illustration helps the reader get the most out of both of these elements.

Developing Vocabulary

New science words appear in boldface type when they are first used in the text. These words are defined in context. The *Glossary* provides definitions of all vocabulary terms.

Using an Engaging Writing Style

A distinguishing feature of *Discover SCIENCE* is the degree to which an active, engaging writing style has been incorporated into the program.

- The regular use of the active voice yields more forceful passages and helps students clarify cause-effect relationships. The passive voice is used judiciously for variety or emphasis.
- In-text questions help students activate their backgrounds, summarize, interact with the illustrations, and predict outcomes while reading.
- A judicious use of *you* appears throughout the text to promote students' identification with the information and processes of science.

Assessing and Evaluating

Each lesson contains *Lesson Review* questions to help students verify their initial comprehension of the lesson's concepts. The *Chapter Review* contains a variety of formats to assess, reinforce, and expand student's comprehension and understanding of the material.

Robert A. Pavlik
Professor and Chairperson
Reading/Language Arts Department
Cardinal Stritch College
Milwaukee, Wisconsin

MATERIALS LIST FOR ACTIVITIES AND TRY THIS

Quantities are based on a class size of 30 students.

Item	Quantity
Apple, chopped	10 g
Apple, wedges or slices	30
* Aquarium stones, light brown	3 bags
Baby picture, one of each student	30
* Baking pans, metal	15
* Baking soda	1 box
* Balloons	15
Banana, chopped	10 g
* Blindfolds	15
* Bolts, assorted metal	300
Books	30
* Bottles, clear	15
* Boxes, small	15
* Cardboard (1 meter square)	9 sheets
Cinnamon, ground	10 g
Clay, modeling	15 sticks
Coffee, ground	10 g
* Cologne	10 mL
* Cotton balls	4
• Construction paper	
assorted (3 cm square)	15 pieces
assorted	45 sheets
black	60 sheets
white (10 cm square)	30 pieces
white	30 sheets
Crayons	30 boxes
* Dowel rods	15
• Drawing paper	300 sheets
* Flashlights	15
* Flour	1 small bag
* Funnels, small	15
* Globes	5
• Glue, white	30 bottles
Jars, baby-food size with lids	15
Lamps, varying light intensities	3
Leaves, assorted	600
Lemon, wedges or slices	30
* Lemon juice	10 mL
* Lids for plastic foam cups	10
* Magnets, bar	30
* Mealworms	45
Milk	10 mL
* Mirrors, small hand-type	15
* Mung beans	400 grams
* Nuts, assorted metal	300
Oatmeal	1 box
Objects, assorted, to feel, to listen to, to smell	60
* Objects that float	60
Objects that sink	60
Onion, chopped	10 g
Orange, wedges or slices	30
Paper clips	30
* Paper plates	30
Paper punches	30
• Paper towels	1 roll
Peanuts, in-the-shell	30
Pencils	30
* Pepper, ground	15 g
Plastic foam cups	10
Roasting pans, large	10
* Rocks, assorted	300
Rocks, small	15
• Scissors	30
* Screws, assorted metal	300
Slide projectors	3
Soap, hand	3 bars
* Spools, wooden	15
* Spoons, stainless steel	30
* Sticks, flat wooden	90
* String	60 meters
• Tape, masking	1 roll
• Tape, transparent	1 roll
* Tissue paper, white	3 large sheets
* Toothpicks, wooden or plastic	1 box
Trays, plastic	30
* Vinegar, white	1 bottle
* Washers, assorted metal	300
Water	
Whipping cream	1 liter

*Items included in Scott, Foresman *Discover Science* Master Lab Kit
•Items included in Convenience Kit
Quantities in the kits may vary from quantities listed here.

TEACHING SAFETY IN THE CLASSROOM

Activities throughout *Discover SCIENCE* reinforce and extend science concepts using materials and procedures that are inherently safe. *Discover SCIENCE* teaches that safe procedure is part of sound scientific inquiry. Students who use this program learn not only how to safely investigate the topics at hand; they also develop safety habits that will serve them well in future scientific endeavors.

How does *Discover SCIENCE* accomplish this task? First and foremost, by performing the activities in the text, students learn that simple, safe materials can be used extensively to investigate science concepts. Second, safety reminders regarding procedure are given in the Pupil's Edition wherever appropriate. These include *CAUTION* statements and a cover goggle symbol and statement on appropriate pages. Third, the Teacher's Edition includes safety tips for the various student activities and teacher demonstrations that appear throughout the program. Following is a list of the most general of these tips for the elementary science classroom. If followed from the start, these guidelines should be easily assimilated into classroom procedures by teachers and students alike.

- The proper use of cover goggles that meet American National Standards Institute (ANSI z87.1, 1979) standards should be demonstrated to students. Cover goggles should be worn whenever the potential for eye injury exists; for example, when heating any substance, when using any chemicals including "ordinary" substances such as vinegar, and when using glassware. Even relatively safe items such as rubber bands and balloons can cause eye injury and warrant the use of goggles.

- To prevent student interference with each other and to assist the safe exit of students from the room in case of an emergency, teachers should try to assure that rooms are not overcrowded, that students understand exit procedures, and that aisles are kept uncluttered.

- Teachers should periodically conduct simulations with students for dealing with foreseeable emergencies. Examples might include exiting the room due to an emergency, coping with a fire, aiding someone who has been splashed by a chemical, and helping a fall victim.

- Prior to using any equipment or chemicals, teachers should be certain they understand the proper function and hazards associated with the use of those items. This information should be communicated to the students.

- Unless you know the outcome is safe, you should never mix substances "just to see what happens." No hazardous substances are used in *Discover SCIENCE*. However, the *combining* of certain substances might pose safety problems. For example, mixing ammonia with bleach produces particularly dangerous fumes. Notes about the dangers of mixing chemicals are included on the appropriate pages throughout the program.

- All equipment should be properly stored. The more dangerous items should be kept under lock and key.

- Whenever possible, plastic items should replace glass. If glass containers are essential, temperature- and break-resistant glassware should be selected.

- To prevent slipping and falls, any liquids spilled on tile or hardwood floors should be wiped up immediately.

- If the teacher cannot satisfy himself or herself that all foreseeable dangers have been reduced to an acceptable level, the activity should be altered or eliminated.

Teachers should be aware of all applicable federal, state, and local regulations and relevant guidelines from professional organizations which apply to the activities being performed. Examples would include Occupational Safety and Health Administration (OSHA) standards for workplace safety; state laws relating to cover goggles; local fire department requirements regarding the use of open flame, fire extinguishers, and fire blankets; and National Science Teachers Association (NSTA) suggestions regarding overcrowding. Refer to the following materials for other information about classroom safety.

Dr. Jack A. Gerlovich
Science Education Safety Consultant/Author
Des Moines, Iowa

Downs, G. et al. *Science Safety for Elementary School Teachers,* 1983. Iowa State University Press, Ames, Iowa 50010.

Gerlovich, J., Gerard, T., and Downs, G. *School Science Safety: Elementary,* 1984. Flinn Scientific Co., P.O. Box 219, Batavia, IL 60510.

Scott, Foresman

Discover SCIENCE

Authors

Dr. Michael R. Cohen
Professor of Science and Environmental Education
School of Education
Indiana University
Indianapolis, Indiana

Dr. Timothy M. Cooney
Chairperson K-12 Science Program
Malcolm Price Laboratory School
University of Northern Iowa
Cedar Falls, Iowa

Cheryl M. Hawthorne
Science Curriculum Specialist
Mathematics, Engineering, Science Achievement Program (MESA)
Stanford University
Stanford, California

Dr. Alan J. McCormack
Professor of Science Education
San Diego State University
San Diego, California

Dr. Jay M. Pasachoff
Director, Hopkins Observatory
Williams College
Williamstown, Massachusetts

Dr. Naomi Pasachoff
Research Associate
Williams College
Williamstown, Massachusetts

Karin L. Rhines
Science/Educational Consultant
Valhalla, New York

Dr. Irwin L. Slesnick
Professor of Biology
Western Washington University
Bellingham, Washington

Scott, Foresman and Company
Editorial Offices: Glenview, Illinois

Regional Offices: Sunnyvale, California • Tucker, Georgia •
Glenview, Illinois • Oakland, New Jersey • Dallas, Texas

Consultants

Special Content Consultant

Dr. Abraham S. Flexer
Science Education Consultant
Boulder, Colorado

Health Consultant

Dr. Julius B. Richmond
John D. MacArthur Professor of Health Policy
Director, Division of Health Policy Research and Education
Harvard University
Advisor on Child Health Policy
Children's Hospital of Boston
Boston, Massachusetts

Safety Consultant

Dr. Jack A. Gerlovich
Science Education Safety Consultant/Author
Des Moines, Iowa

Process Skills Consultant

Dr. Alfred DeVito
Professor Emeritus Science Education
Purdue University
West Lafayette, Indiana

Activity Consultants

Edward Al Pankow
Teacher
Petaluma City Schools
Petaluma, California

Valerie Pankow
Teacher and Writer
Petaluma City Schools
Petaluma, California

Science and Technology Consultant

Dr. David E. Newton
Adjunct Professor—Science and Social Issues
University of San Francisco
College of Professional Studies
San Francisco, California

Cooperative Learning Consultant

Dr. Robert E. Slavin
Director, Elementary School Program
Center for Research on Elementary and Middle Schools
Johns Hopkins University
Baltimore, Maryland

Gifted Education Consultants

Hilda P. Hobson
Teacher of the Gifted
W.B. Wicker School
Sanford, North Carolina

Christine Kuehn
Assistant Professor of Education
University of South Carolina
Columbia, South Carolina

Nancy Linkel York
Teacher of the Gifted
W.B. Wicker School
Sanford, North Carolina

Special Education Consultants

Susan E. Affleck
Classroom Teacher
Salt Creek Elementary School
Elk Grove Village, Illinois

Dr. Dale R. Jordan
Director
Jordan Diagnostic Center
Oklahoma City, Oklahoma

Dr. Shirley T. King
Learning Disabilities Teacher
Helfrich Park Middle School
Evansville, Indiana

Jeannie Rae McCoun
Learning Disabilities Teacher
Mary M. McClelland Elementary School
Indianapolis, Indiana

Thinking Skills Consultant

Dr. Joseph P. Riley II
Professor of Science Education
University of Georgia
Athens, Georgia

Reading Consultants

Patricia T. Hinske
Reading Specialist
Cardinal Stritch College
Milwaukee, Wisconsin

Dr. Robert A. Pavlik
Professor and Chairperson of Reading/Language Arts Department
Cardinal Stritch College

Dr. Alfredo Schifini
Reading Consultant
Downey, California

Cover painting commissioned by Scott, Foresman
Artist: Alex Gnidziejko

ISBN: 0-673-42061-2

2345678910RRW979695949392919089

Reviewers and Content Specialists

Dr. Ramona J. Anshutz
Science Specialist
Kansas State Department of Education
Topeka, Kansas

Teresa M. Auldridge
Science Education Consultant
Amelia, Virginia

Annette M. Barzal
Classroom Teacher
Willetts Middle School
Brunswick, Ohio

James Haggard Brannon
Classroom Teacher
Ames Community Schools
Ames, Iowa

Priscilla L. Callison
Science Teacher
Topeka Adventure Center
Topeka, Kansas

Rochelle F. Cohen
Education Coordinator
Indianapolis Head Start
Indianapolis, Indiana

Linda Lewis Cundiff
Classroom Teacher
R. F. Bayless Elementary School
Lubbock, Texas

Dr. Patricia Dahl
Classroom Teacher
Bloomington Oak Grove Intermediate School
Bloomington, Minnesota

Audrey J. Dick
Supervisor, Elementary Education
Cincinnati Public Schools
Cincinnati, Ohio

Nancy B. Drabik
Reading Specialist
George Washington School
Wyckoff, New Jersey

Bennie Y. Fleming
Science Supervisor
Providence School District
Providence, Rhode Island

Mike Graf
Classroom Teacher
Branch Elementary School
Arroyo Grande, California

Thelma Robinson Graham
Classroom Teacher
Pearl Spann Elementary School
Jackson, Mississippi

Robert G. Guy
Classroom Teacher
Big Lake Elementary School
Sedro-Woolley, Washington

Dr. Claude A. Hanson
Science Supervisor
Boise Public Schools
Boise, Idaho

Dr. Jean D. Harlan
Psychologist, Early Childhood Consultant
Lighthouse Counseling Associates
Racine, Wisconsin

Dr. Rebecca P. Harlin
Assistant Professor of Reading
State University of New York—Geneseo
Geneseo, New York

Richard L. Ingraham
Professor of Biology
San José State University
San José, California

Ron Jones
Science Coordinator
Salem Keizer Public Schools
Salem, Oregon

Sara A. Jones
Classroom Teacher
Burroughs-Molette Elementary School
Brunswick, Georgia

Dr. Judy LaCavera
Director of Curriculum and Instruction
Learning Alternatives
Vienna, Ohio

Jack Laubisch
K-12 Science, Health, and Outdoor Education Coordinator
West Clermont Local School District
Amelia, Ohio

Douglas M. McPhee
Classroom Teacher/Consultant
Del Mar Hills Elementary School
Del Mar, California

Larry Miller
Classroom Teacher
Caldwell Elementary School
Caldwell, Kansas

Dr. Robert J. Miller
Professor of Science Education
Eastern Kentucky University
Richmond, Kentucky

Sam Murr
Teacher—Elementary Gifted Science
Academic Center for Enrichment—Mid Del Schools
Midwest City—Del City, Oklahoma

Janet Nakai
Classroom Teacher
Community Consolidated School District #65
Evanston, Illinois

Patricia Osborne
Classroom Teacher
Valley Heights Elementary School
Waterville, Kansas

Elisa Pinzón-Umaña
Classroom Teacher
Coronado Academy
Albuquerque, New Mexico

Dr. Jeanne Phillips
Director of Curriculum and Instruction
Meridian Municipal School District
Meridian, Mississippi

Maria Guadalupe Ramos
Classroom Teacher
Metz Elementary School
Austin, Texas

Elissa Richards
Math/Science Teacher Leader
Granite School District
Salt Lake City, Utah

Mary Jane Roscoe
Teacher and Team Coordinator
Fairwood Alternative Elementary School of Individually Guided Education
Columbus, Ohio

Sister Mary Christelle Sawicki, C. S. S. F.
Science Curriculum Coordinator
Department of Catholic Education Diocese of Buffalo
Buffalo, New York

Ray E. Smalley
Classroom Teacher/Science Specialist
Cleveland School of Science
Cleveland, Ohio

Anita Snell
Elementary Coordinator for Early Childhood Education
Spring Branch Independent School District
Houston, Texas

Norman Sperling
Chabot Observatory
Oakland, California

Sheri L. Thomas
Classroom Teacher
McLouth Unified School District #342
McLouth, Kansas

Lisa D. Torres
Science Coordinator
Lebanon School District
Lebanon, New Hampshire

Alice C. Webb
Early Childhood Resource Teacher
Primary Education Office
Rockledge, Florida

iii

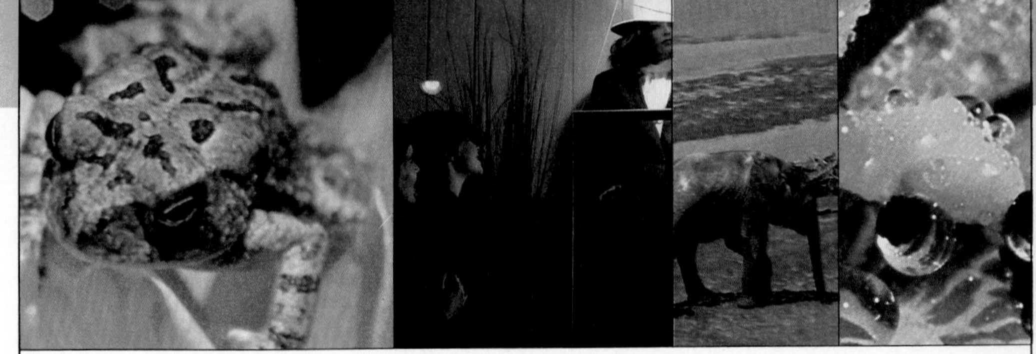

ix

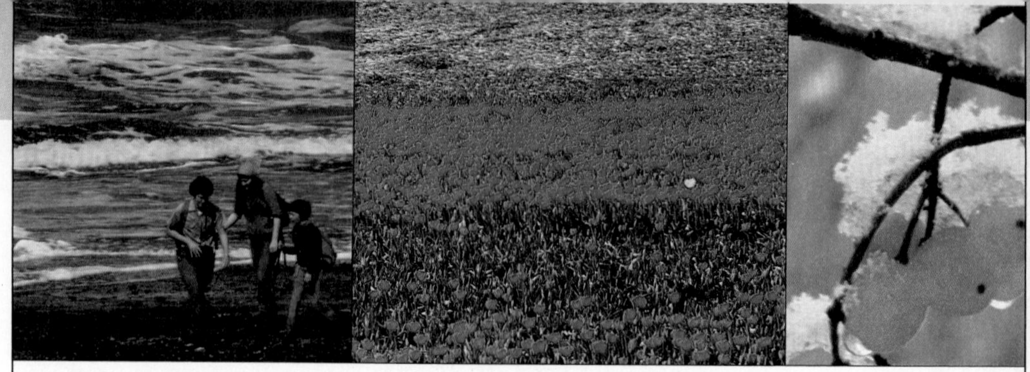

xi

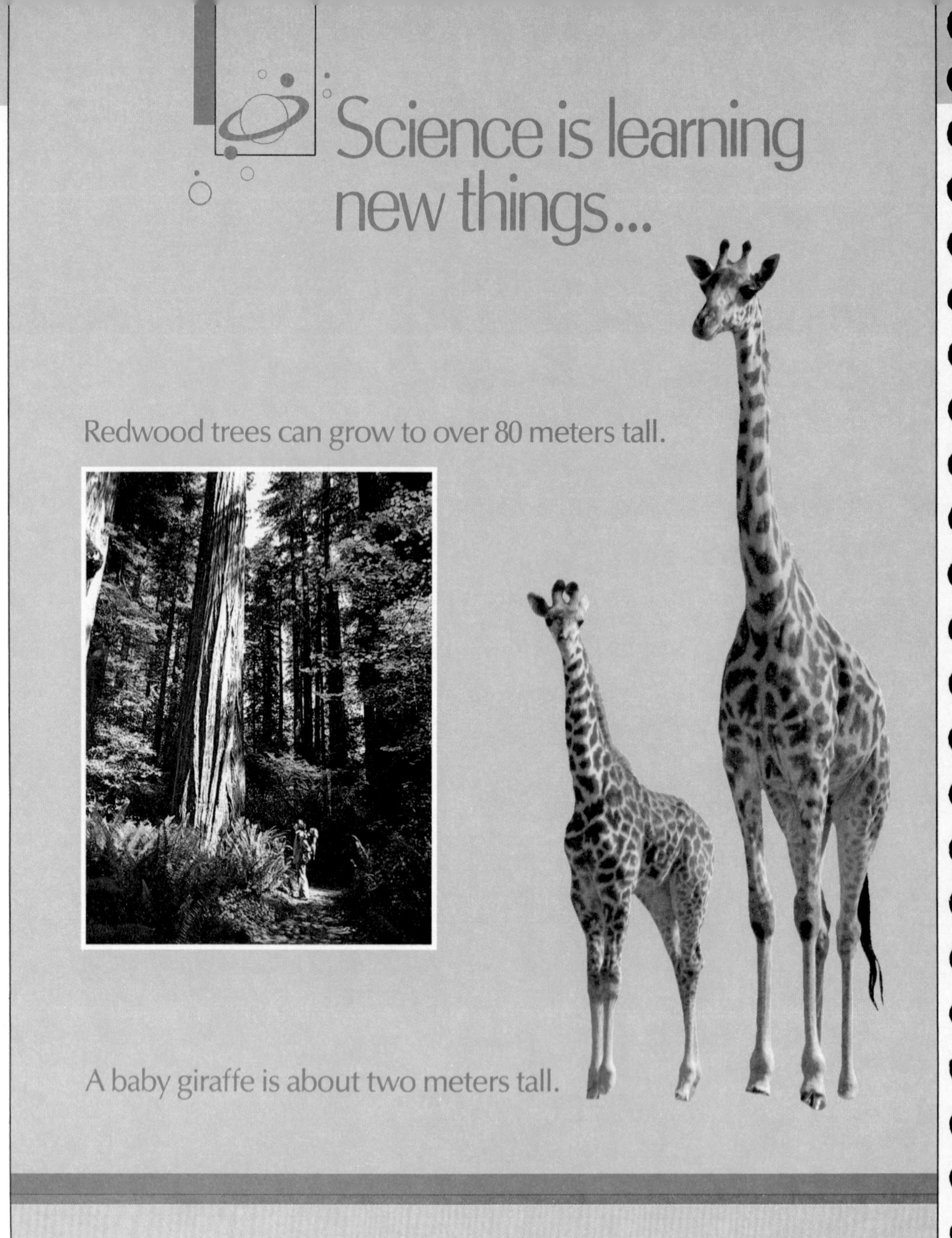
Science is learning
new things...
Redwood trees can grow to over 80 meters tall.
A baby giraffe is about two meters tall.

...and solving problems.

1. Asking questions

"What should I wear to school?"

2. Collecting information

"It looks like it is going to rain."

3. Finding an answer

"I am ready in case it rains."

Science is inventing new things...

The first bicycle was invented around 1816.

It had no pedals.
You pushed it with your feet.

Bicycles with pedals were invented around 1839.

Today there are many kinds of bicycles.
Some bicycles are built for speed.
Some bicycles can go about 100 kilometers per hour.

Most bicycles are just for fun.

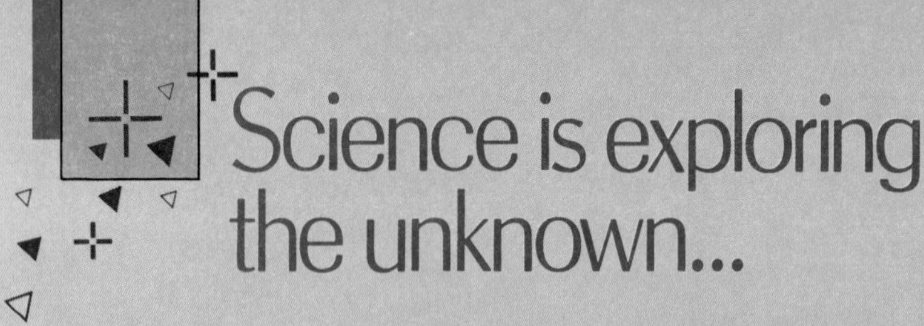

Science is exploring the unknown...

Many different animals live in the oceans.

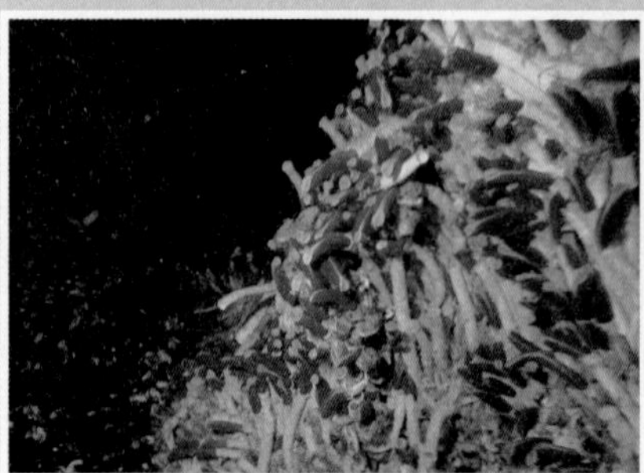

These animals look like plants.
They are called tubeworms.
Tubeworms were first seen in 1977.
They live very deep in the ocean.

Special machines take pictures of tubeworms.

This fish looks like a horse.
It is called a sea horse.

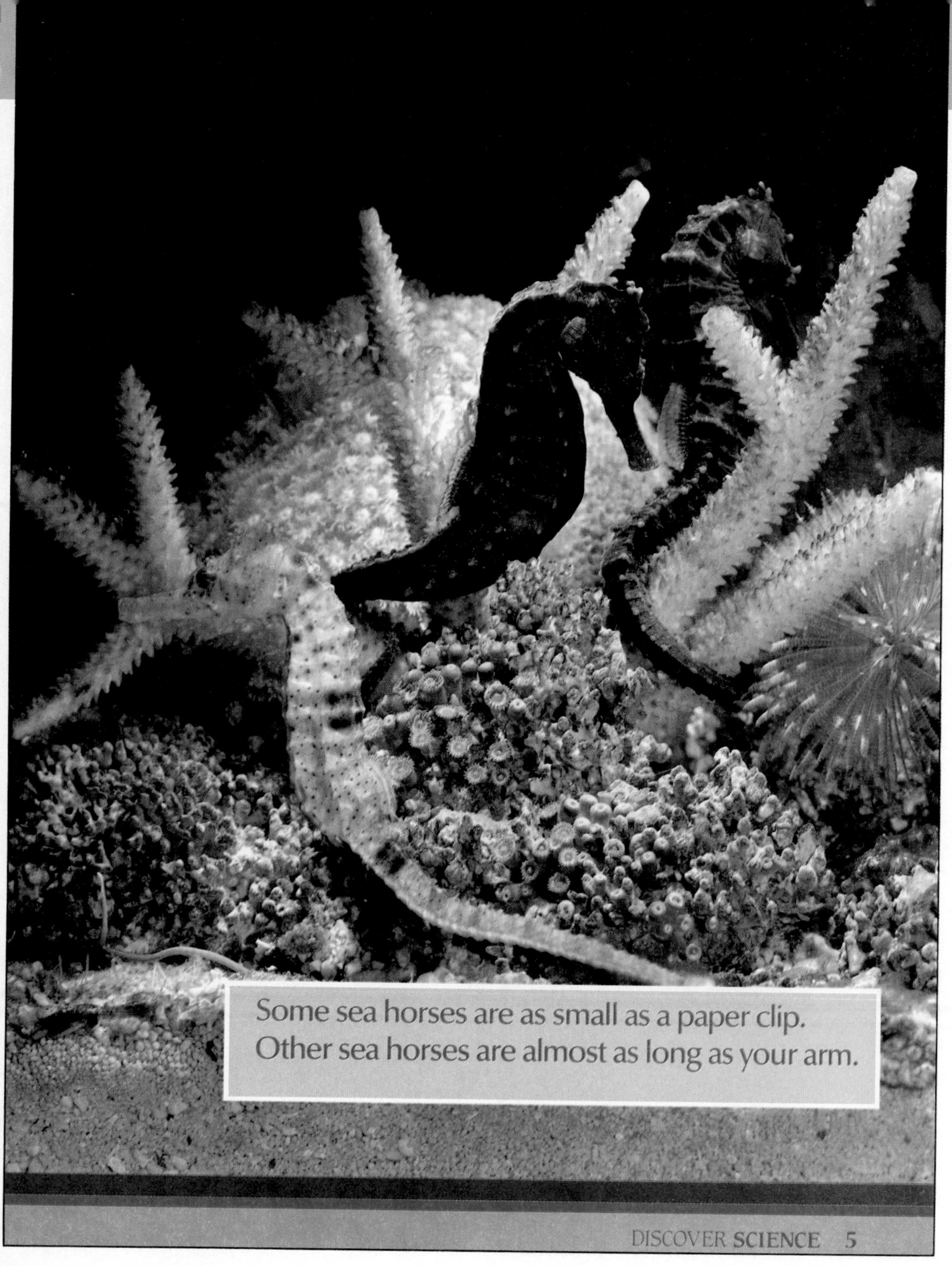
Some sea horses are as small as a paper clip. Other sea horses are almost as long as your arm.

Planning Guide

Unit Components			Pages
Unit Overview			6–7
Chapter 1 Your Senses	**Lesson 1** How Can You Learn?	**Lesson 2** How Do You Use Your Senses?	8–23
Chapter 2 Growing and Changing	**Lesson 1** How Do People Change?	**Lesson 2** What Can Help You Grow?	24–39
Careers	dentists and helpers		40
How It Works	Stethoscope		41
Unit Review			42
Unit Projects			43

Science Process Skills Book
The Science Process Skills Book contains worksheets that can be used to teach and then assess student mastery of the basic science process skills. In addition, other worksheets in this book teach students the manipulative skills they will need to use basic science equipment. Assign these worksheets whenever you think it fits in your curriculum.

Science Resources for the Unit

Resource Books

Elting, Mary. *The Macmillan Book of the Human Body*. Macmillan, 1986. Examines each major body system, focusing on the organs, the purpose of the system, and how it works.

Iveson-Iveson, Joan. *Your Health*. Bookwright Press, 1985. Explains the importance of cleanliness, exercise, and sleep in staying healthy.

Kitzinger, Sheila. *Being Born*. Grosset and Dunlap, 1986. Offers an accurate account of the nine-month process from conception through pregnancy to birth.

Martin, Paul D. *Messengers to the Brain: Our Fantastic Five Senses*. National Geographic Society, 1984. The workings of the sense organs are described. How the brain and nerves receive and process messages is explained.

Peavy, Linda. *Food, Nutrition and You*. Scribner's 1982. Explains the nutritional needs of the body, nutritional components of foods, and the processes by which the body utilizes nourishment.

Rourke, Arlene C. *Diet and Exercise*. Rourke, 1987. Presents basic facts about healthful eating and discusses weight loss, exercise, and dieting disorders.

Community Resources

Invite the school nurse or a local health service worker to talk to the students about vision and hearing screening. Help the students understand the importance of detecting hearing and vision impairments, especially in children who are learning to read and write.

Audio-Visual Resources

Animal Behavior: Fall. International Film Bureau. Film or video, 11 minutes. Shows the physical changes that occur in animals as cold weather approaches.

Bambi Discovers the Five Senses. Walt Disney Educational Media. Filmstrip series or video, 49 minutes. Bambi explores the senses.

The Five Senses. Jam Handy. Filmstrip. A series of five filmstrips.

Getting the Message. National. 3/4-inch video, 15 minutes. Experiments that explore the senses.

Health: Ear Care. AIMS. Film or video, 11 minutes. "Mr." Sun gives a number of important reminders on eye care.

Health: Your Senses and Their Care. AIMS. Film loop.

The Senses. National Geographic. Wonders of Learning Kit (30 booklets, teacher's guide and activity sheets, cassette). Students learn how the sense organs send messages to the brain.

The Senses. Sigma. Film, 10 minutes. Shows how senses help animals know their world.

Senses at Work. McGraw-Hill. Film loop. From the series *Learning Experiences*.

You—And Your Five Senses. Walt Disney. Film or video, 8 minutes each.

Your Ears. Britannica. Film, 6 minutes. The function of the ear is explained, and good health habits are stressed.

Your Eyes. Britannica. Film, 7 minutes. Children in this film demonstrate ways in which we depend on our eyes.

Computer Software

The Eyes Have It (The Five Senses.) Marshware. Apple IIe+, IIe, IIc, 48 K. Students study the basic structure and functions of the eye; then conduct experiments with light rays and corrective lenses.

Smell and Tell (The Five Senses). Marshware. Apple IIe+, IIe, IIc, 48 K. Presents the concepts of how taste and smell work together.

"SEE, JUNIOR? THAT'S WHAT HAPPENS WHEN YOU DON'T EAT YOUR CARROTS."

INTRODUCING UNIT 1

Unit Overview

This unit is designed to stimulate students' awareness of human beings as integrated, dynamic organisms. Students will learn that parts of their bodies have special functions, and that the body parts work together to help a person grow and keep healthy.

About the Photograph

This picture is a thermogram of a hand. It is a record of the heat that the hand radiates. Different tissues, such as bones, blood vessels, muscles, and skin, radiate different amounts of heat. Special equipment translates the varying amounts of heat radiation into a picture. Disorders such as tumors and infections usually generate heat, and are visible on a thermogram.

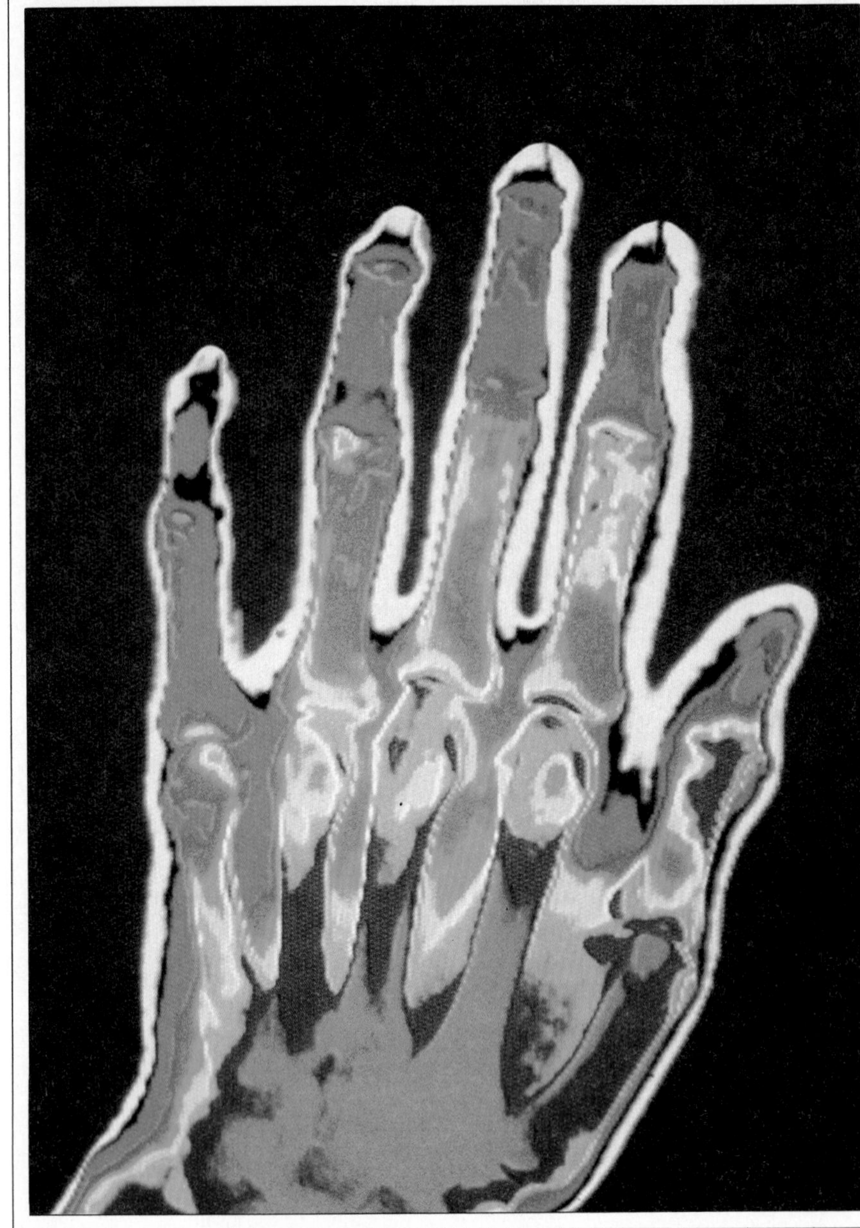

6

Teaching Options

Chapter 1 Preview

Your Senses

In this chapter, students will identify the five senses and name the part of the body associated with each sense. Students will become aware of how their senses help them learn about the world around them. Students also will discover that the information gathered by the senses can help people keep safe.

Chapter 2 Preview

Growing and Changing

This chapter focuses on how children grow and change as they mature. Students will learn that they grow in size and shape, lose their baby teeth, acquire permanent teeth, learn new skills, and learn how to get along better with others as they grow.

[1]hand

Unit 1

Human Body

Look at this special picture.
It shows a part of your body.
What part does the picture show?[1]
Point to the bones in the picture.

Tell how you use this body part.
Then draw a picture of your own hand.

Teaching Tips

- Before students open their books, have them examine their hands. Questions: **What is on the outside of your hands?** (Students might mention skin, fingernails.) **How do you know what is outside?** (Students should say that they can see the outside.)
- Questions: **What is inside your hands?** (Students might mention bones, muscles, blood.) **How do you know what is inside?** (Students might say that they can feel their bones, they have seen pictures or X rays of hands, they have cut their hands and have seen blood.)
- Direct students to the picture on page 6. Question: **Did a baby's hand make this picture?** (No, it is too large to be a baby's hand.)
- If possible, display pictures of hands of persons of various ages—baby, young child, and adult. Questions: **Will your hands change as you grow? Will other parts of your body change as you grow?** Explain that students will be reading about some ways that their bodies will change as they grow.

Teaching Plan

Chapter Components	Skills	Materials
Chapter Opener/*TRY THIS*: Learning About Things pp. 8-9	***TRY THIS*** p. 9 **Science Process Skill** *Observing*	***TRY THIS*** p. 9 (groups of 2) 15 blindfolds, 60 assorted objects to feel, listen, and smell
Lesson 1: How Can You Learn? pp. 10-12	**Thinking Skills** Challenge!: *Inferring* Find Out: *Making generalizations*	**Demonstration** p. 10 apple juice, tinted pitcher, paper cups
Activity: Learning By Smelling p. 13	**Science Process Skills** *Observing, Inferring*	(group of 30) 10 plastic-foam cups and lids, 4 cotton balls, 10mL milk, 10mL lemon juice, 10mL cologne, 10mL white vinegar, 15g ground pepper, 15g chopped onion, 15g chopped banana, 15g ground cinnamon, 15g ground coffee, 15g chopped apple, 30 sheets drawing paper, 30 boxes crayons, 30 pencils
Lesson 2: How Can You Learn? pp. 14-17	**Thinking Skills** Challenge!: *Identifying and suggesting alternatives* Find Out: *Organizing information*	**Demonstration** p. 14 an unusual fruit or vegetable, knife
Activity: Using All Your Senses p. 18	**Science Process Skills** *Observing, Collecting and interpreting data, Communicating*	(individual) 30 peanuts in the shell
Science in Your Life: An Alarm to Help Smell Smoke p. 19	**Thinking Skill** *Drawing conclusions*	
Skills For Solving Problems: Using a Pictograph pp. 20-21	**Problem Solving Skills** *Making decisions/Identifying and solving problems, Interpreting charts, maps, and graphs*	(individual) 20 small squares of construction paper
Chapter Review pp. 22-23	**Thinking Skills** *Restating or explaining ideas, Recognizing cause and effect*	

Teaching Options

Strategies	Extensions		Resource Masters
			Family Letter: *Resource Book* p. 3 Vocabulary Preview: *Workbook* pp. 1-2
	Reinforcement p. 10 Science and Language Arts p. 11 Special Education p. 11	Enrichment p. 11 Reteaching Suggestion p. 12	Science Skills: *Workbook* p. 3
	Enrichment Activity p. 13		
	Reinforcement pp. 14, 16 Special Education p. 15 Enrichment p. 16	Game Suggestion p. 17 Reteaching Suggestion p. 17	Science Activity: *Workbook* p. 4 Science and Math: *Workbook* p. 5 Vocabulary Puzzle: *Workbook* p. 6
	Enrichment Activity p. 18		
			Enrichment Activity: *Resource Book* p. 7
Cooperative Learning p. 22 (Also see p. T23)			Chapter Test: *Test Book* p. 9

Preteaching Suggestions

For Advance Preparation

TRY THIS, page 9
You may wish to cut up food items such as fruit, vegetables, and cheese for this activity.

Demonstration, page 10
Bring a tinted pitcher and apple juice to class.

Activity, page 13
Prepare 5 or 6 smelling cups for each group. Use substances with identifiable odors, such as perfume, onions, vinegar, spices, and banana. Put one substance in each cup, replace lid, and punch small holes in the lid. For liquids, put a ball of liquid-soaked cotton in the cup. Label cups A–E or F.

Demonstration, page 14
Bring an unusual fruit or vegetable to class.

Activity, page 18
Provide one unsalted peanut in the shell for each student.

For Vocabulary Review

Use the following sentences with your students to review the meanings of the underlined words.

1. Your science book has information about the senses.
2. The dog barked outside, but the cat was safe inside.
3. Thunder is sometimes a warning of a storm coming.
4. A fire alarm goes off if there is a fire in the building.
5. A sign showing children crossing a street is a kind of pictograph.

For High-Potential Students

Ask students to survey friends and relatives to find out how people prefer to learn. The survey might include the following three options:

1. listening to someone explain something (hearing)
2. reading about something (seeing)
3. using hands to work with objects (touching)

Have students make charts or bar graphs to share the results of their surveys.

For Mainstreamed Students

For visually impaired students and hearing-impaired students, make popcorn in a domed popcorn popper to emphasize the smell and taste of popcorn. Specific instructions follow. Be sure to keep popper and electrical cords a safe distance from students.

Hearing Impaired
As the popcorn begins to cook in the oil, wiggle your fingers and make a loud hissing sound with your mouth to demonstrate the sound oil makes as it is heated. As the popcorn begins to pop, use larger gestures and more dramatic facial expressions to demonstrate the sound of corn popping.

Visually Impaired
Have visually impaired students put their hands into a container of uncooked popcorn to feel the kernels. Then have each student put a drop of oil on one finger, to feel the slippery quality of it. Cook the popcorn, and let it cool. Have students feel the texture of the cooked popcorn.

For Science Fair Projects

Encourage interested students to do one of the following projects:

1. Classify a variety of objects according to their texture, and make a display showing the results.
2. Observe solid, brightly colored objects by using eyeglasses made of red, green, or yellow cellophane. Then describe how each pair of glasses affects visual perception.
3. Taste different flavors or brands of sugarless gum to determine which flavor or brand keeps its taste the longest. Make a chart ranking the gums in order, from those that keep their flavor for a long time to those that lose their flavor quickly.

Classroom Resources

Bulletin Board
Ask students to draw pictures of things that they smell, taste, feel, see, and hear.

THE FIVE SENSES

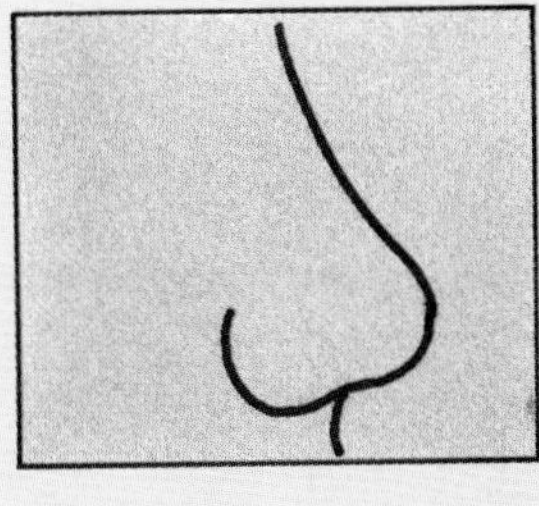
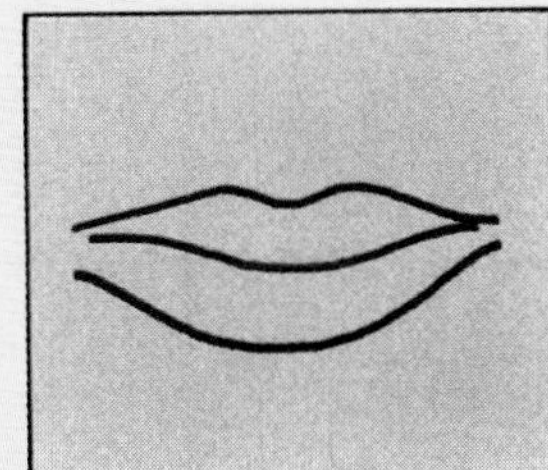
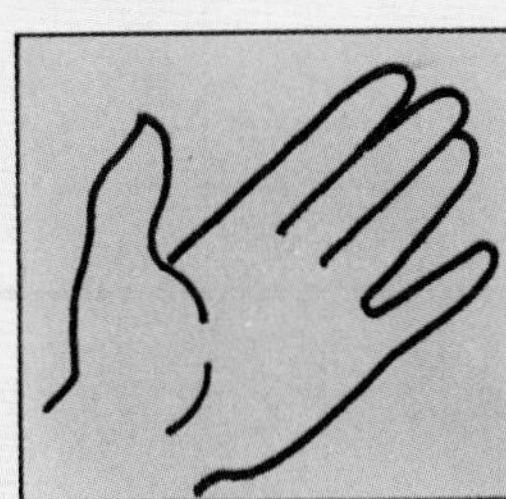
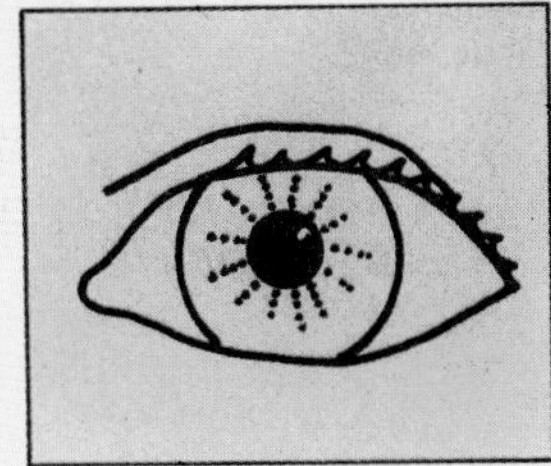
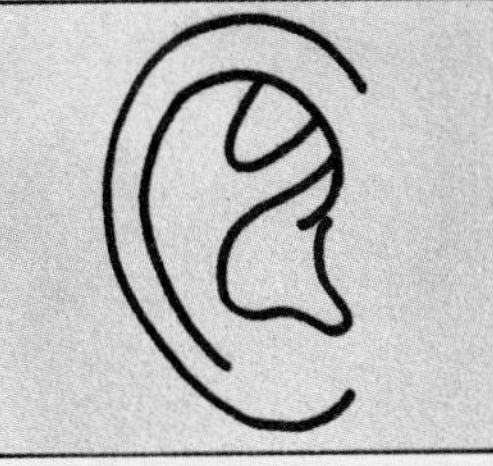

Chapter 1 Poster

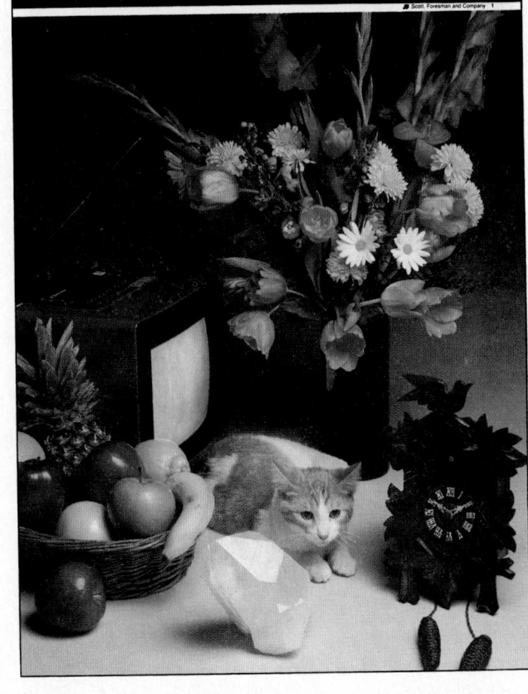
What senses would you use?

Science Discovery Center
Use pages from Chapter 1 in the *Science Discovery Center Book*. Place these worksheets in the appropriate pockets in the Science Discovery Center.

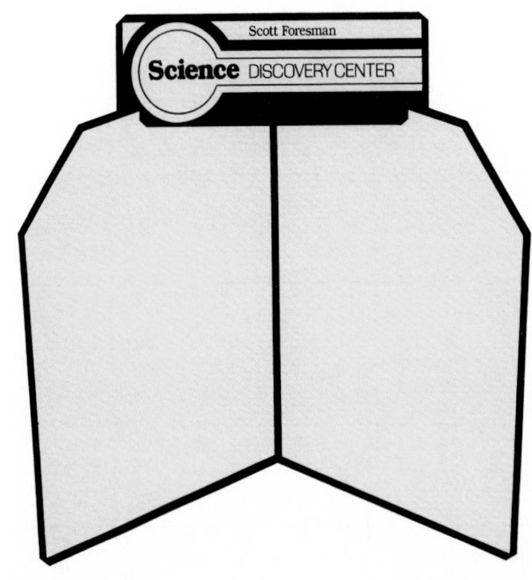
Scott Foresman
Science DISCOVERY CENTER

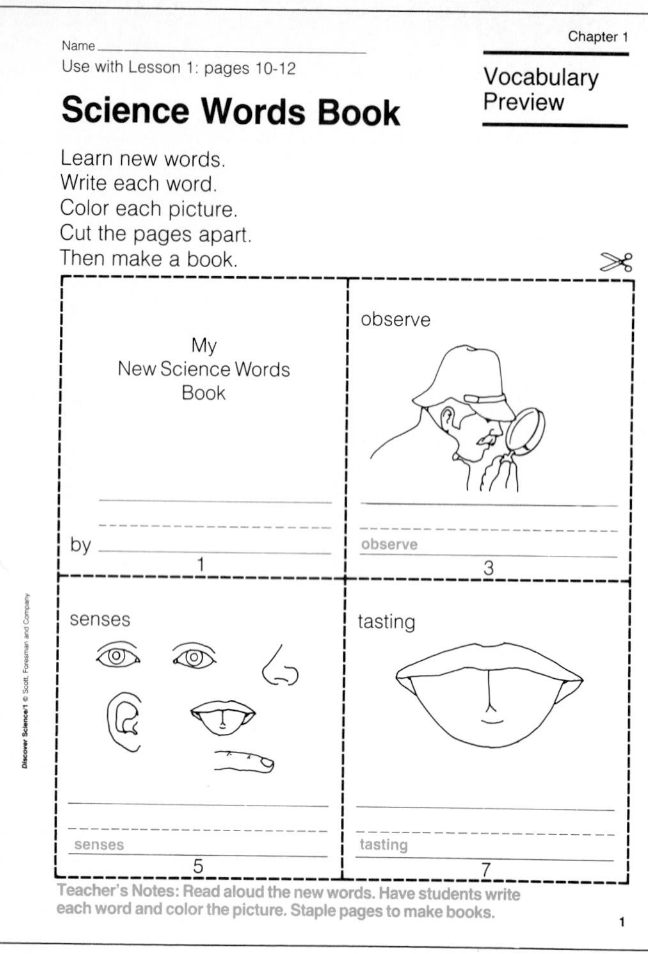

Name ______________________

Use with Lesson 1: pages 10-12

Chapter 1

Vocabulary Preview

Science Words Book

Learn new words.
Write each word.
Color each picture.
Cut the pages apart.
Then make a book.

Teacher's Notes: Read aloud the new words. Have students write each word and color the picture. Staple pages to make books.

1

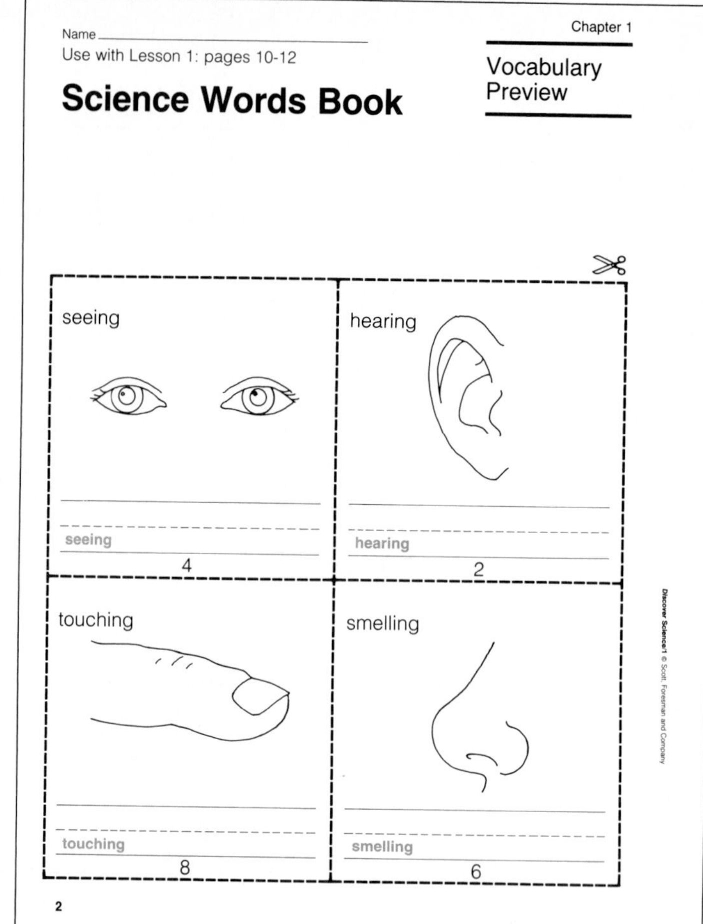

Name ______________________

Use with Lesson 1: pages 10-12

Chapter 1

Vocabulary Preview

Science Words Book

2

Name ______________________

Use with Lesson 1: pages 10-12

Chapter 1

Science Skills

Using Your Senses

Think about the things in each picture.
How could you learn about each thing?
What senses would you use?
Put an X under the sense or senses.

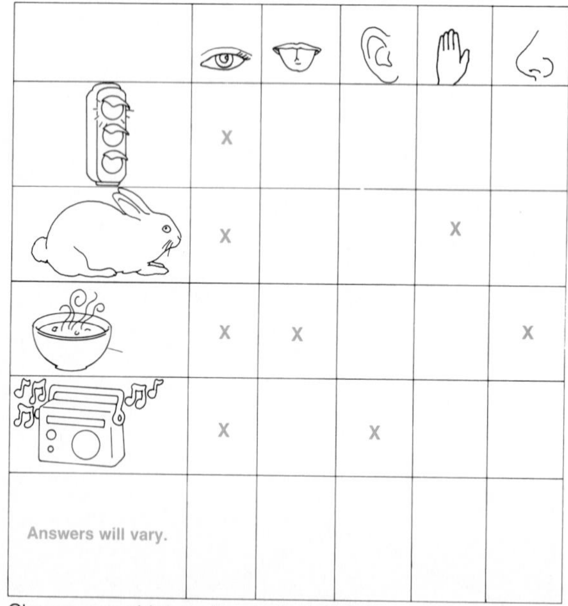

	(eye)	(tongue)	(ear)	(hand)	(nose)
(traffic light)	X				
(rabbit)	X			X	
(soup)	X	X			X
(radio)	X		X		
Answers will vary.					

Choose something to draw in the last box.

Teacher's Notes: Ask students to choose an object to draw in the final left-hand box. Accept all reasonable answers for senses used.

3

Name ______________________

Use with Lesson 2: pages 14-17

Chapter 1

Science Activity

What Can You Hear?

You can make many sounds.
You can make sounds with paper.
You can make sounds with a pencil.
You can make sounds with your hands.
You can make sounds with other things.

Sit back to back with a friend.
Make sounds for your friend to hear.
Ask your friend to tell what makes the sounds.

Have your friend draw what makes the sounds.

1	2	3
Answers will vary. Students will draw pictures of what they perceive through the sense of hearing, such as a pencil tapping, money dropping, an eraser bouncing.		

Teacher's Notes: Encourage inventiveness in choosing sound-making devices.

4

Name ____________

Use with Lesson 2: pages 14-17

Chapter 1

Science and Mathematics

Looking for Shapes

Look for the shapes.
Trace each □ with red.
Trace each △ with blue.
Trace each ○ with green.

4 red squares traced; 2 windows, 1 house, 1 jack-in-the-box.
2 blue triangles: 1 sail, 1 roof.
5 green circles: 2 balls, 3 balloons.

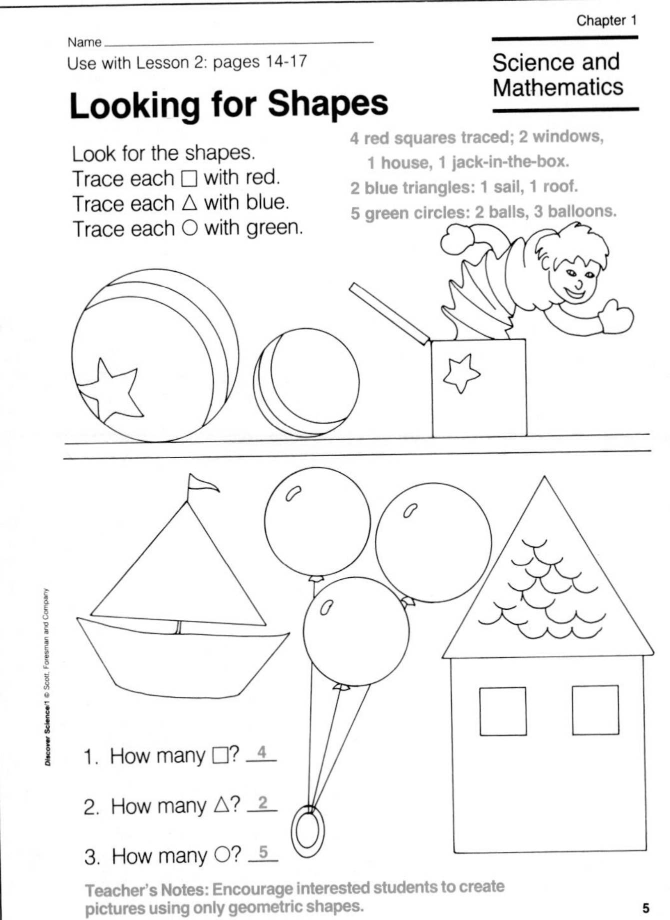

1. How many □? 4
2. How many △? 2
3. How many ○? 5

Teacher's Notes: Encourage interested students to create pictures using only geometric shapes.

Name ____________

Use with Lesson 2: pages 14-17

Chapter 1

Vocabulary Puzzle

Sense Wordsearch

Read the words in the word bank.
Write the words on the lines.
Then find each word in the puzzle below.

Word Bank
hearing
observe
seeing
senses
smelling
tasting
touching

hearing — observe
seeing — senses
smelling — tasting
touching

Circle the sense words.
Seven are hiding in the puzzle.
One is done for you.

s x b (t a s t i n g) p p s
d e g k (t o u c h i n g) e
w w a z (s m e l l i n g) e
e p s (h e a r i n g) q z n
s t (o b s e r v e) w z r g
(s e e i n g) x (s e n s e s)

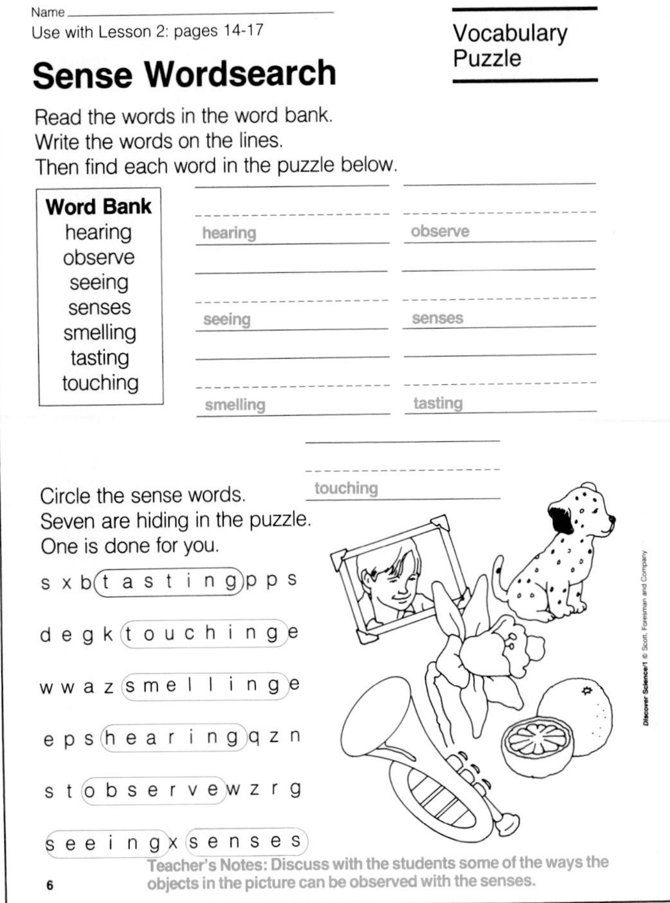

Teacher's Notes: Discuss with the students some of the ways the objects in the picture can be observed with the senses.

Name ____________

Chapter 1

Enrichment Experiment

A Hearing Experiment

Does using a paper horn help you hear better?

Circle your prediction. Yes No Accept any answer.

Do this experiment to find out.
1. Follow the steps in the pictures below.

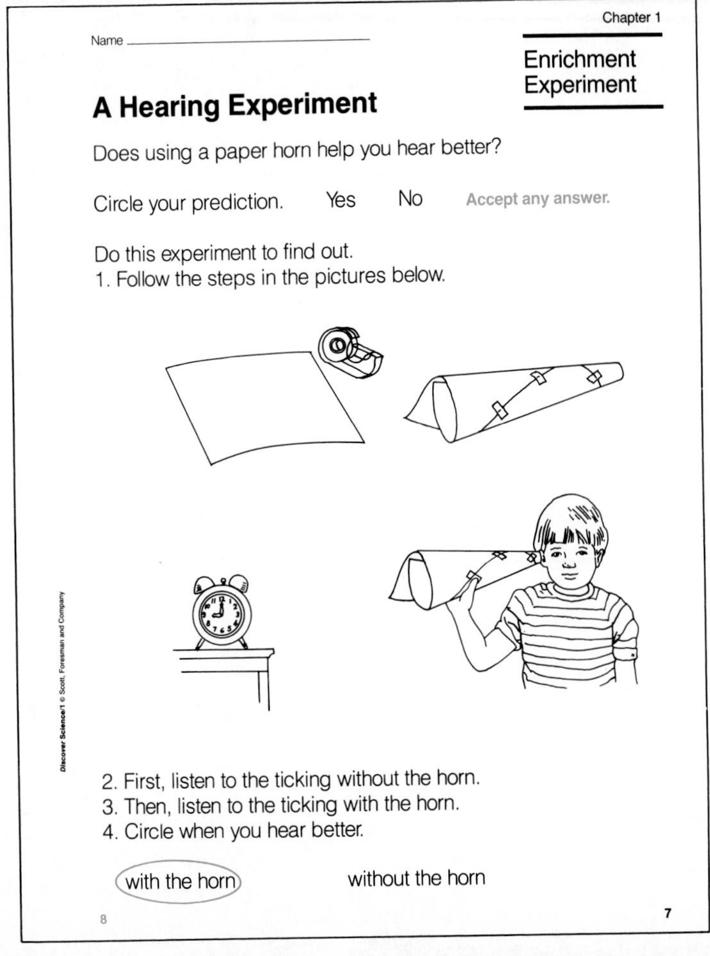

2. First, listen to the ticking without the horn.
3. Then, listen to the ticking with the horn.
4. Circle when you hear better.

(with the horn) without the horn

Name ____________

Chapter 1 Test

Your Senses

I. Write **Yes** or **No.**

1. Do you use body parts to learn? (1-1) Yes
2. Do you have six senses? (1-1) No
3. Are all of the senses the same? (1-1) No
4. Can you observe new things? (1-2) Yes
5. Can senses help keep you safe? (1-2) Yes

II. Draw a line from the word to the right picture.

1. smelling (1-1) 2. hearing (1-1) 3. touching (1-1) 4. tasting (1-1) 5. seeing (1-1)

The numbers in parentheses after each question refer to the chapter and lesson objective covered by that question.

TEACHING PLAN

INTRODUCING CHAPTER 1

Major Concepts

Lesson 1 Some learning takes place through the use of the five senses.
Lesson 2 The sense organs serve as major information-gathering sources for the body.

Vocabulary

feeling, hearing, observe, seeing, senses, smelling, tasting, touching

[1]how we use water; where it comes from
[2]your senses

Chapter 1

Your Senses

What can you learn about water?[1]
What parts of your body help you learn?[2]

8

Teaching Options

Blackline masters in every lesson are located where you use them.

Workbook page 1 *

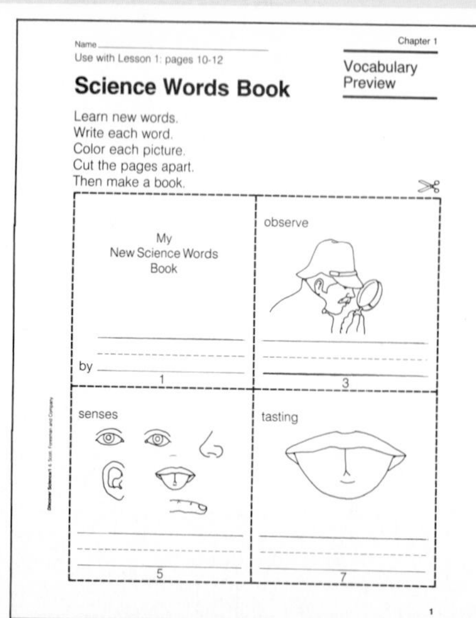

Name
Use with Lesson 1: pages 10-12
Chapter 1
Vocabulary Preview

Science Words Book

Learn new words.
Write each word.
Color each picture.
Cut the pages apart.
Then make a book.

My New Science Words Book
by
1

observe
3

senses
5

tasting
7

1

Workbook page 2 *

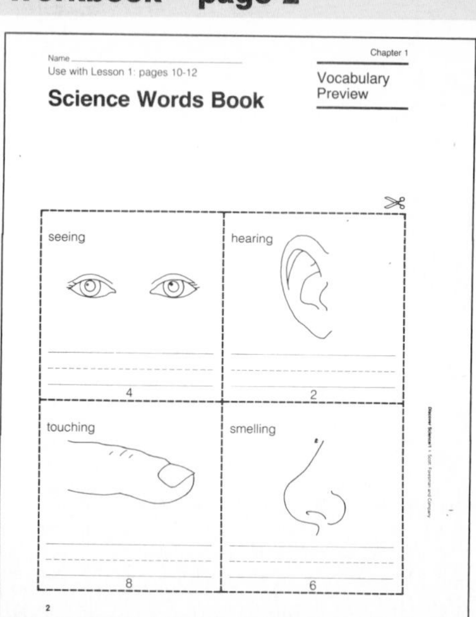

Name
Use with Lesson 1: pages 10-12
Chapter 1
Vocabulary Preview

Science Words Book

seeing
4

hearing
2

touching
8

smelling
6

2

♦ ***Suitable as a language development activity***

[1]by using senses

Starting the Chapter

How do you learn about things?[1]

You can use body parts to learn.

Find out how body parts help you learn.

Then read more about learning.

TRY THIS

Learning About Things

Have someone cover your eyes.
Have the person give you things.
Feel, listen, and smell each thing.
What body parts do you use?
What did you learn?

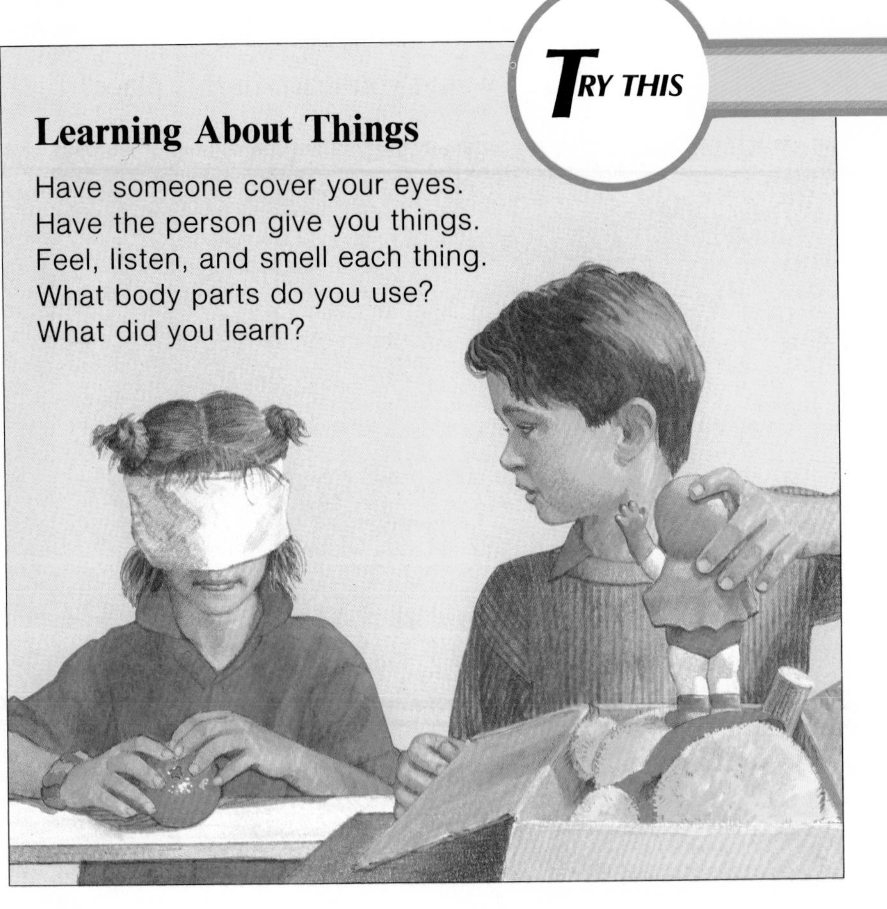

TRY THIS

Objective ◆
This optional *TRY THIS* activity will help students explore and build background information about the concept that the senses help people learn. Later in the chapter, students will be able to draw on this experience to help them assimilate the new information.

Science Process Skills
Observing

Materials
For each pair of students: 1 blindfold; 4 objects to feel, listen to, and smell

Safety Tips (See page T27.)
- Remind students to use caution when blindfolding their partners. Provide clean blindfolds, and provide assistance as necessary.
- When selecting items for students to feel, listen to, and smell, avoid items that may cause allergic reactions.

Teaching Tips
- Distribute objects to students, or allow one student from each pair to select objects from a table.
- You might wish to cut up various fruits, raw vegetables, cheeses, and crackers for students to taste. Encourage students to *describe* how each object tastes.

Resource Book page 3

↑ *Introductory activity provides a common background experience.*

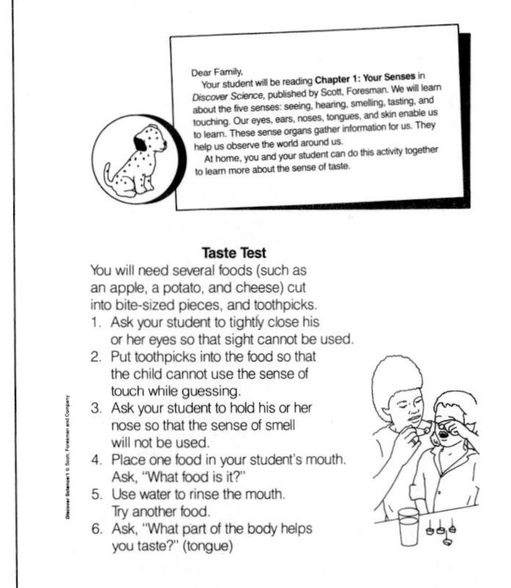

Dear Family,
Your student will be reading **Chapter 1: Your Senses** in *Discover Science*, published by Scott, Foresman. We will learn about the five senses: seeing, hearing, smelling, tasting, and touching. Our eyes, ears, noses, tongues, and skin enable us to learn. These sense organs gather information for us. They help us observe the world around us.
At home, you and your student can do this activity together to learn more about the sense of taste.

Taste Test

You will need several foods (such as an apple, a potato, and cheese) cut into bite-sized pieces, and toothpicks.

1. Ask your student to tightly close his or her eyes so that sight cannot be used.
2. Put toothpicks into the food so that the child cannot use the sense of touch while guessing.
3. Ask your student to hold his or her nose so that the sense of smell will not be used.
4. Place one food in your student's mouth. Ask, "What food is it?"
5. Use water to rinse the mouth. Try another food.
6. Ask, "What part of the body helps you taste?" (tongue)

3

SCIENCE BACKGROUND

Some parts of the body are more sensitive to touch because they contain more touch receptors than other parts of the body. For example, the fingers are more receptive than the back of the hand.

* Answers to masters on pages 8E–8F

TEACHING PLAN

LESSON 1
pages 10–12

Objectives correlate to lesson goals.

Lesson Objectives
- *Identify* the five senses.
- *Name* the parts of the body associated with each sense.
- *Explain* how each sense aids learning.

Lesson Vocabulary
feeling, hearing, seeing, senses, smelling, tasting, touching

1 MOTIVATE

Demonstration Activity ♦
Ask students to watch as you pour apple juice into a tinted pitcher. Pour a sample into a paper cup for each student to smell and taste. *CAUTION:* Remind students never to taste an unknown substance unless told that it is safe to do so by a responsible adult.

Discussion
Discuss what senses the students used to help them identify the apple juice. Questions: **What senses did you use to learn about the liquid?** (seeing, smelling, tasting) **What body parts helped you?** (eyes, nose, mouth)

Options provide added flexibility for your planning.

[1]learn about sights, sounds, and smells

Lesson 1 How Can You Learn?

You learn by using your **senses.**
Seeing and **hearing** are senses.
Touching and **tasting** are senses.
Smelling is another sense.
Pretend to use your senses.
What would you learn in this place? [1]

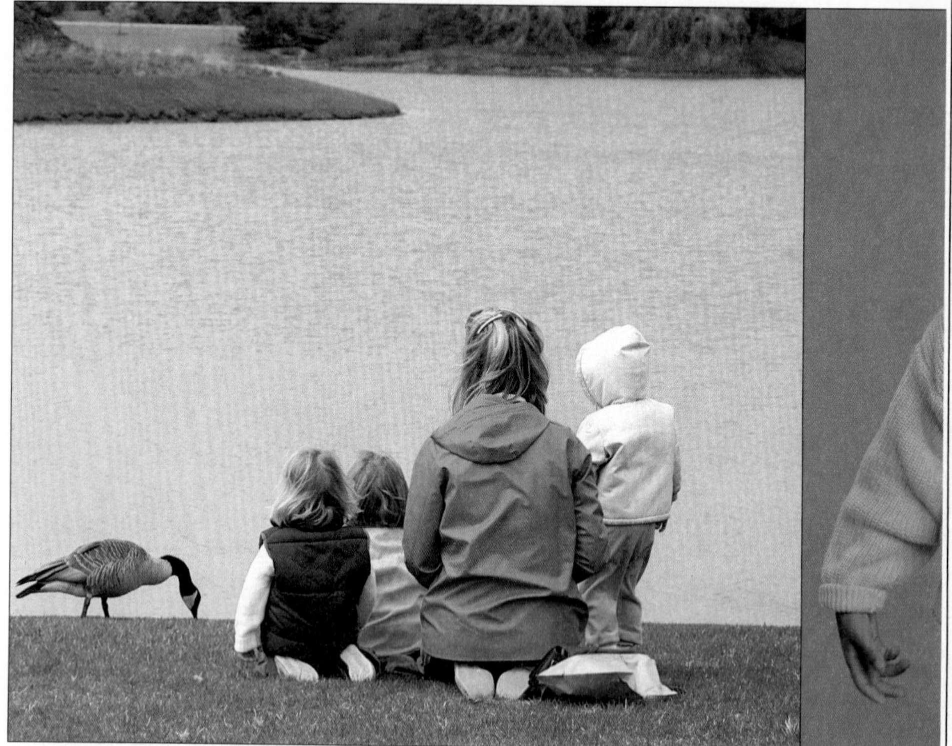

10

Teaching Options

SCIENCE BACKGROUND

The brain receives information from the external environment through the sense organs. The eyes detect light waves and transmit images and color to the brain. The ears detect vibrations (sound waves) that travel through the air. The brain perceives such qualities of sound as pitch and loudness. The nose detects airborne chemicals that enter the nostrils. Papillae on the surface of the tongue detect sourness, bitterness, sweetness, or saltiness in substances that come in contact with the tongue. The skin, which contains the sense of touch, detects texture and temperature, as well as pain.

Reinforcement

Provide objects that are hard or soft (rocks, beads, cotton balls, yarn); light-colored or dark-colored (try to use solid-colored objects); sour or salty (pretzels, pickles, salted nuts, lemons); sweet-smelling or spicy-smelling (perfume, flowers, garlic, cinnamon); and harsh-sounding or melodic (two blocks, tambourine, xylophone, bell). Ask students to use the senses of touch, sight, taste, smell, or hearing to determine how to *classify* the objects. *CAUTION:* Check for allergies to foods. Students should taste *only* the foods.

♦ ***Suitable as a language development activity***

[1]how things feel, smell, sound, and so on
[2]how animals look and sound; how horn sounds

What do you learn by using each sense?[1]

You learn by feeling with your skin.

You learn by hearing with your ears.

You learn by seeing with your eyes.

What are these children learning?[2]

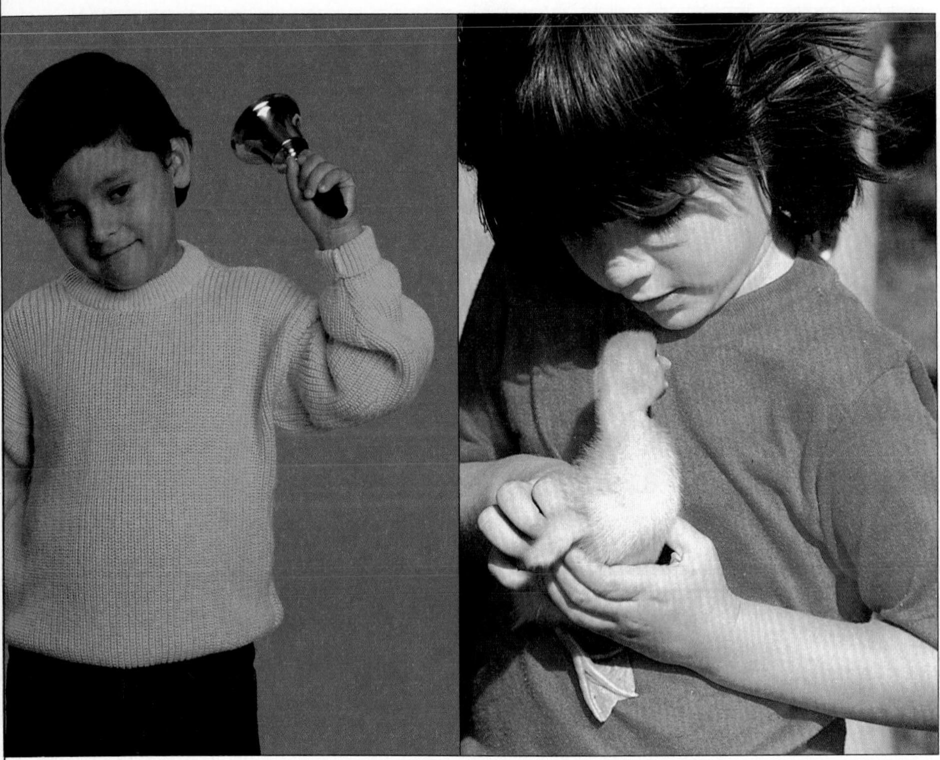

11

2 TEACH

Teaching Tips

- **Possible Misconception:** Some students might think that learning takes place only visually when, in fact, all five senses help us learn.
- Ask students to *name* the senses. Let volunteers *describe* what they like to see, smell, taste, touch, or hear. Direct students to look at the picture on page 10 and discuss what they could learn by using their senses in the situation shown.
- Remind students how they used senses other than sight to learn about things in the *TRY THIS* on page 9. Explain that when a person loses one of the senses, he or she makes up for the loss by using other senses to get needed information. To aid in clarification of this idea, provide students with sample situations. Questions: **If you could not see, how might you tell whether a greasy pan that you washed had gotten clean?** (by feeling it) **If you could not hear, how could you tell that a child next to you was crying?** (by seeing tears and watching the child's facial expressions)

Misconceptions are recognized and information is provided to clarify them.

Science and Language Arts

Give each student a piece of carrot. Have them use their senses to gather information about the carrot. Ask them to *describe* the carrot's characteristics, such as color, texture, and taste. Write these characteristics on the chalkboard. Next, give each student a piece of banana and repeat the procedure. Have students *compare* the information they obtained about each food. *CAUTION:* Make certain that students are not allergic to carrots or bananas.

Highlighted process and thinking skills help you plan to meet specific goals.

Special Education

To demonstrate the value of the sense of sight, show a filmstrip from start to finish without using a recording. Do not show the title of the filmstrip or any discernible words. Have students *describe* the pictures, frame by frame. Then let the class try to tell the story or guess what the filmstrip was about. Remind students that all of the information they related was gathered by using the sense of sight.

Enrichment

Help students understand what it would be like to do a few daily tasks without the benefit of sight. Ask for two volunteers, and have each of them sit in a chair. Blindfold them, and give them each a piece of paper and a pencil. Ask the first volunteer to write his or her name on a line you have drawn. Ask the second volunteer to draw a picture of a person's face. Then take the blindfolds off and let the volunteers look at their papers. Let other students close their eyes and try the activity at their desks.

TEACHING PLAN

Review questions correlate to lesson goals.

3 ASSESS

Lesson Review

1. The five senses are seeing, hearing, smelling, tasting, and touching.

2. The senses give you information about the world around you.

Challenge! Question: **Why do you think it helps to have most of your sense organs located on your head?** (Information that the senses gather goes directly to the brain.) **Thinking Skill:** *Inferring*

Find Out

Answers will vary. Students might say that they could learn who was speaking, if a door opened or closed, or if a schoolbell rang. **Thinking Skill:** *Making generalizations*

Additional opportunities to develop higher order thinking skills

[1]smell and taste the items pictured

Your nose and tongue help you learn.
You use your nose to help you smell.
You use your tongue to help you taste.
What could you smell and taste here?[1]

Lesson Review

1. What are your five senses?
2. How can your senses help you?

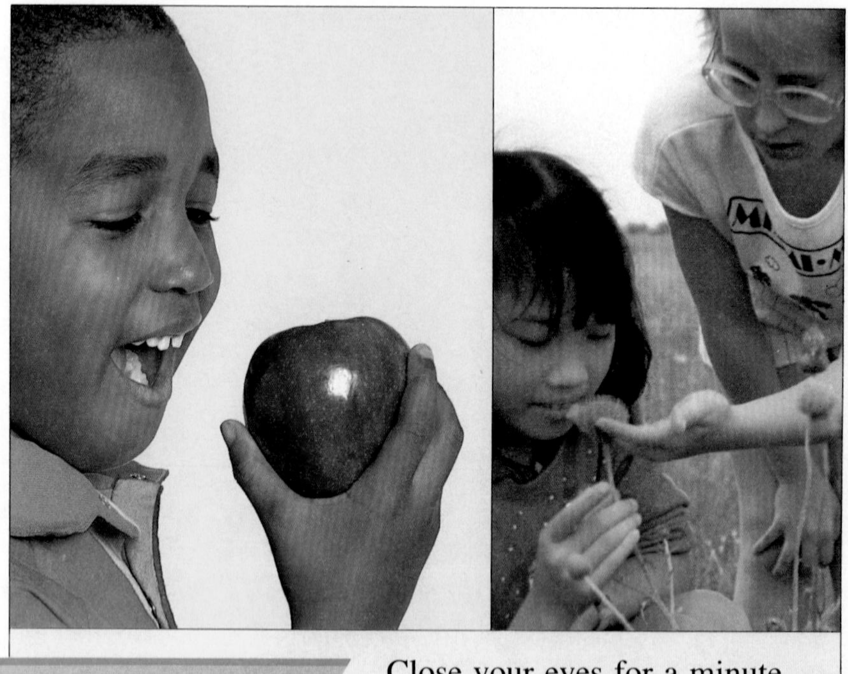

Find Out

Close your eyes for a minute.
What did you hear?

12

Teaching Options

SCIENCE ANECDOTE

Four types of taste buds are found on the top surface of the tongue. They enable us to distinguish between sweet, sour, salty, and bitter tastes. The tip of the tongue is more sensitive to the feeling of touch than any other part of the body.

Reteaching Suggestion ♦

Gather a variety of objects, such as a piece of fabric, sandpaper, a bell, a jar of paste, and a box of raisins. Allow students to examine the objects and then *describe* them. Ask students to *name* the senses and appropriate parts of the body they used to learn about each object.

Workbook page 3 *

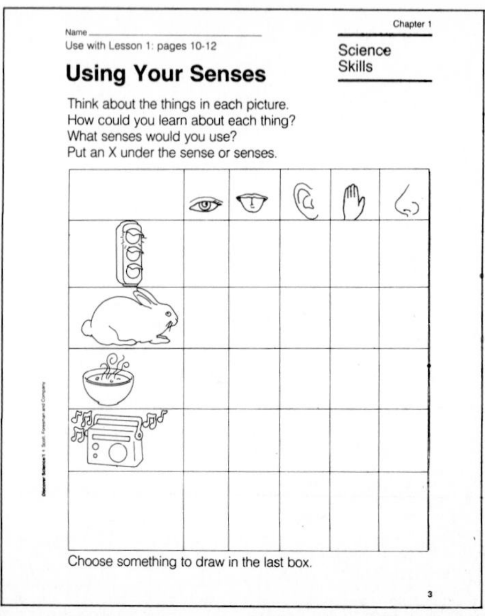

Name
Use with Lesson 1: pages 10-12

Chapter 1

Science Skills

Using Your Senses

Think about the things in each picture.
How could you learn about each thing?
What senses would you use?
Put an X under the sense or senses.

Choose something to draw in the last box.

3

♦ ***Suitable as a language development activity***

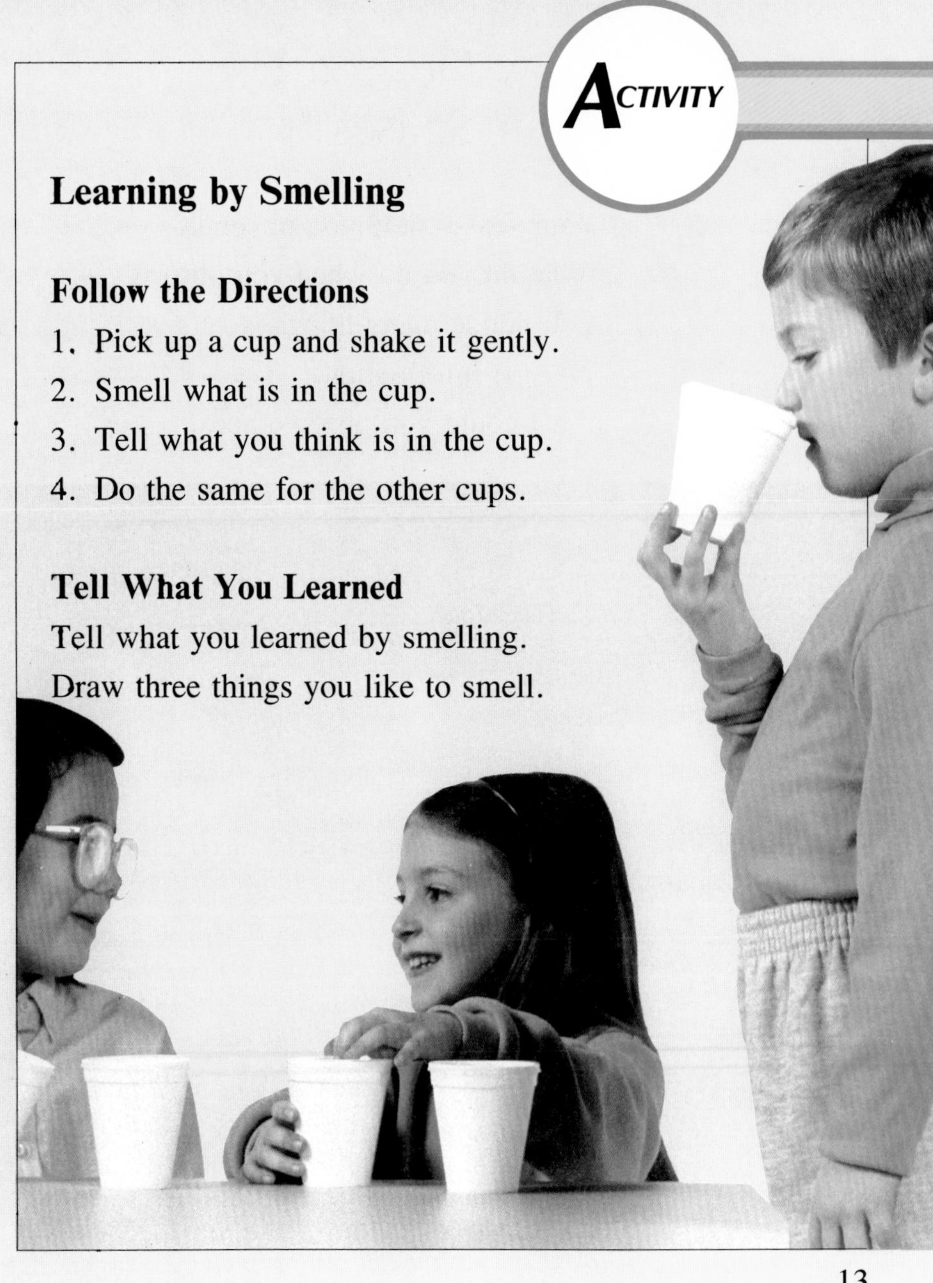

ACTIVITY
Learning by Smelling
Follow the Directions
1. Pick up a cup and shake it gently.
2. Smell what is in the cup.
3. Tell what you think is in the cup.
4. Do the same for the other cups.
Tell What You Learned
Tell what you learned by smelling.
Draw three things you like to smell.
13

ACTIVITY PLAN

Concept
Learning takes place through the sense of smell.

Objectives/Process Skills
- *Observe* various odors.
- *Infer* the identity of various substances by their odor.
- *Identify* objects with pleasing odors.

Time Allotment
Allow 15 minutes.

Materials
For the class: 10 plastic-foam cups with lids; 4 cotton balls, 1 soaked in 10 mL milk, 1 soaked in 10 mL lemon juice, 1 soaked in 10 mL cologne, 1 soaked in 10 mL white vinegar; 15 g ground pepper; 15 g chopped onion; 15 g chopped banana; 15 g chopped apple; 15 g ground cinnamon; 15 g ground coffee; 30 sheets drawing paper; 30 boxes crayons; 30 pencils

Safety Tip (See page T27.)
- Remind students to immediately wipe up any spills from the floor to prevent slipping accidents.

Teaching Tip
- Question: **What part of the body will you use to learn what is in the cups?** (the nose) Explain that the nose cannot identify an odor but rather gathers information that is sent to the brain, where the odor is identified.

Answers
Tell What You Learned
Students should try to identify each odor by naming it. They should draw three things they like to smell. **Thinking Skill:** *Identifying*

Objectives incorporate process skills to be developed.

Enrichment Activity
Have students hold their noses. While holding their noses, tell the students to taste a piece of raw potato and apple. Have the students try to distinguish the potato from the apple.

Activity Results
Students should be able to identify various substances by their odors.

LESSON 2
pages 14–17

Lesson Objectives
- *Identify* information that can be gathered by using the senses.
- *State* how sense organs can help people stay safe.

Lesson Vocabulary
observe

1 MOTIVATE

Demonstration Activity ♦
Bring an unusual fruit to class. Direct students to close their eyes, and allow each student to feel and smell the fruit. Cut it into pieces and let each student taste a sample. Instruct them to listen to the sound it makes as it is chewed. Allow students to look at the food, and tell them what it is. *CAUTION: Be sure to wash the fruit before cutting it.*

Discussion
Discuss the information that the students gathered about the fruit by using their senses. Questions: **What information did you get by using your senses?** (touching—texture, size, weight; tasting—salty, sour, sweet, or bitter; smelling—odor; seeing—size, color, shape)

[1]notice objects and actions around you
[2]sight, sound, and feel of water

Lesson 2 How Do You Use Your Senses?

Your senses help you **observe.**
What do you do when you observe?[1]
You notice many things.
You get information.
What could you observe here?[2]

14

Teaching Options

SCIENCE BACKGROUND

The amount of information the brain receives depends on the sensitivity of the sense organs. The more sensitive the sense organs are, the more information that is relayed to the brain. The ear operates within a range of frequency and loudness. Sounds that are too high in pitch or too low in volume cannot be heard by humans. Dogs have the ability to hear higher pitches than humans can perceive. Although the human brain can detect many odors, the nose of a human is not as sensitive as the nose of a dog or a deer. Vision is also variable. Nocturnal animals have better vision in the dark than other animals. The sense of taste also varies from person to person.

Reinforcement

Have each student think of an object and then ***describe*** how it looks, sounds, feels, smells, or tastes. Let the other students guess what is being described.

♦ ***Suitable as a language development activity***

[1]use senses to see, hear, and feel water

You use all your senses to observe.

You notice different sounds.

You notice different tastes.

How could you use your senses here?[1]

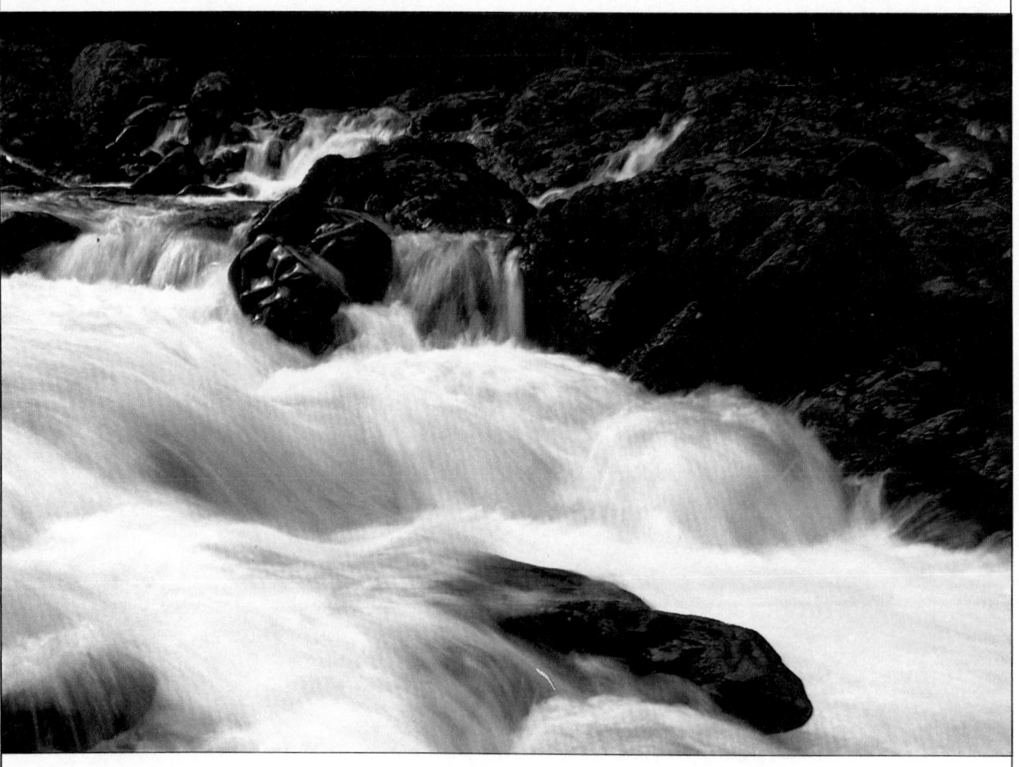

TEACH

Teaching Tips

- **Possible Misconception:** Many children expect animals to have the same sensory responses as people do, and to see and hear the same things in the same ways.
- Have students imagine that they are in the scene illustrated on page 14. Question: **What senses could you use to *observe* what was around you?** Remind students that senses other than seeing are used in the process of observing. Let students tell what they might ***observe*** in the scene illustrated.
- Ask students to look at the picture on page 15 and to ***describe*** the ways they could use their senses to learn about the objects shown. *CAUTION: Remind students not to taste anything that grows outdoors unless they have obtained permission to do so by a responsible adult.*

Special Education

Obtain or make a sound effects tape and collect pictures that illustrate each sound on the tape. Allow students to listen to the tape and try to ***identify*** the sounds. If students are unable to identify the sounds alone, provide corresponding pictures to assist them.

Workbook page 4 *

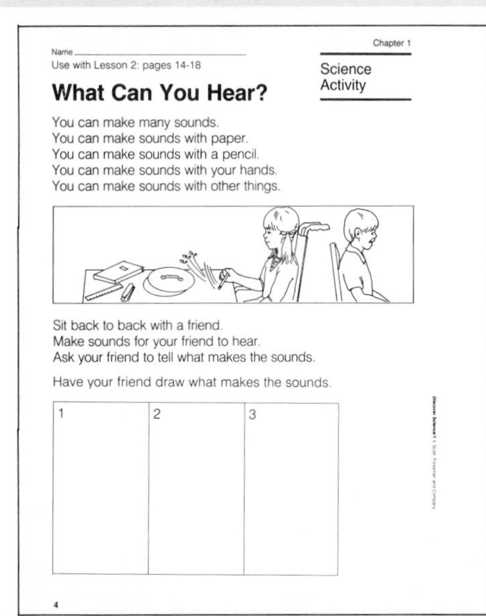

Name

Use with Lesson 2: pages 14-18

Chapter 1

Science Activity

What Can You Hear?

You can make many sounds.
You can make sounds with paper.
You can make sounds with a pencil.
You can make sounds with your hands.
You can make sounds with other things.

Sit back to back with a friend.
Make sounds for your friend to hear.
Ask your friend to tell what makes the sounds.

Have your friend draw what makes the sounds.

1	2	3

4

Workbook page 5 *

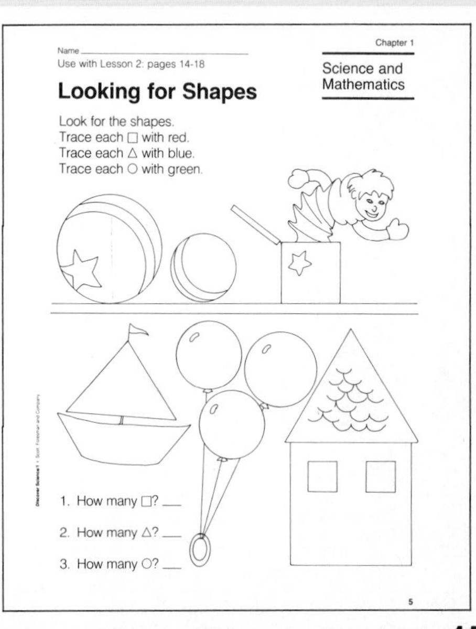

Name

Use with Lesson 2: pages 14-18

Chapter 1

Science and Mathematics

Looking for Shapes

Look for the shapes.
Trace each □ with red.
Trace each △ with blue.
Trace each ○ with green.

1. How many □? ___
2. How many △? ___
3. How many ○? ___

5

***** *Answers to masters on pages 8E-8F*

TEACHING PLAN

Teaching Tips

- Discuss with students stimuli that alert people to potential hazards. Question: **What are some colors, shapes, and sounds that warn you of danger or help you stay safe?** (Responses might include the color red in traffic signals and stop signs; the shape of a stop sign, yield sign, or railroad crossing sign; and the sound of sirens.) Write responses on the chalkboard. **How does the sense of smell help keep you safe?** (Answers may include that it can detect the smell of smoke.)
- Remind students of the importance of having emergency phone numbers near the phone. If your area has a 911 emergency system, discuss its use with students.

[1]sense of sight tells when it is safe to cross street

Senses can help keep you safe.

You can hear warning sounds.

You can see colors and signs.

You can see cars and animals.

How do senses help with safety here?[1]

16

Teaching Options

SCIENCE ANECDOTE

Balance enhances our ability to gather information about our environment. This sense depends on sight, as well as on stimuli from skeletal muscles, the soles of our feet, and parts of the inner ear that respond to changes in the position of the head.

Reinforcement

Have students work in pairs to draw a poster of warnings they can see, hear, or smell, such as signs, smoke, alarms, and sirens.

Enrichment

Talk to students about dangerous drugs, household chemicals, and cleansers that might be present in their homes. Ask students what special signs or warning labels they are familiar with. (Students might be familiar with Mr. Yuk, stop sign labels, or policeman labels.) Let students design and make their own warning labels that they can give to their parents to be placed on dangerous substances at home.

◆ ***Suitable as a language development activity***

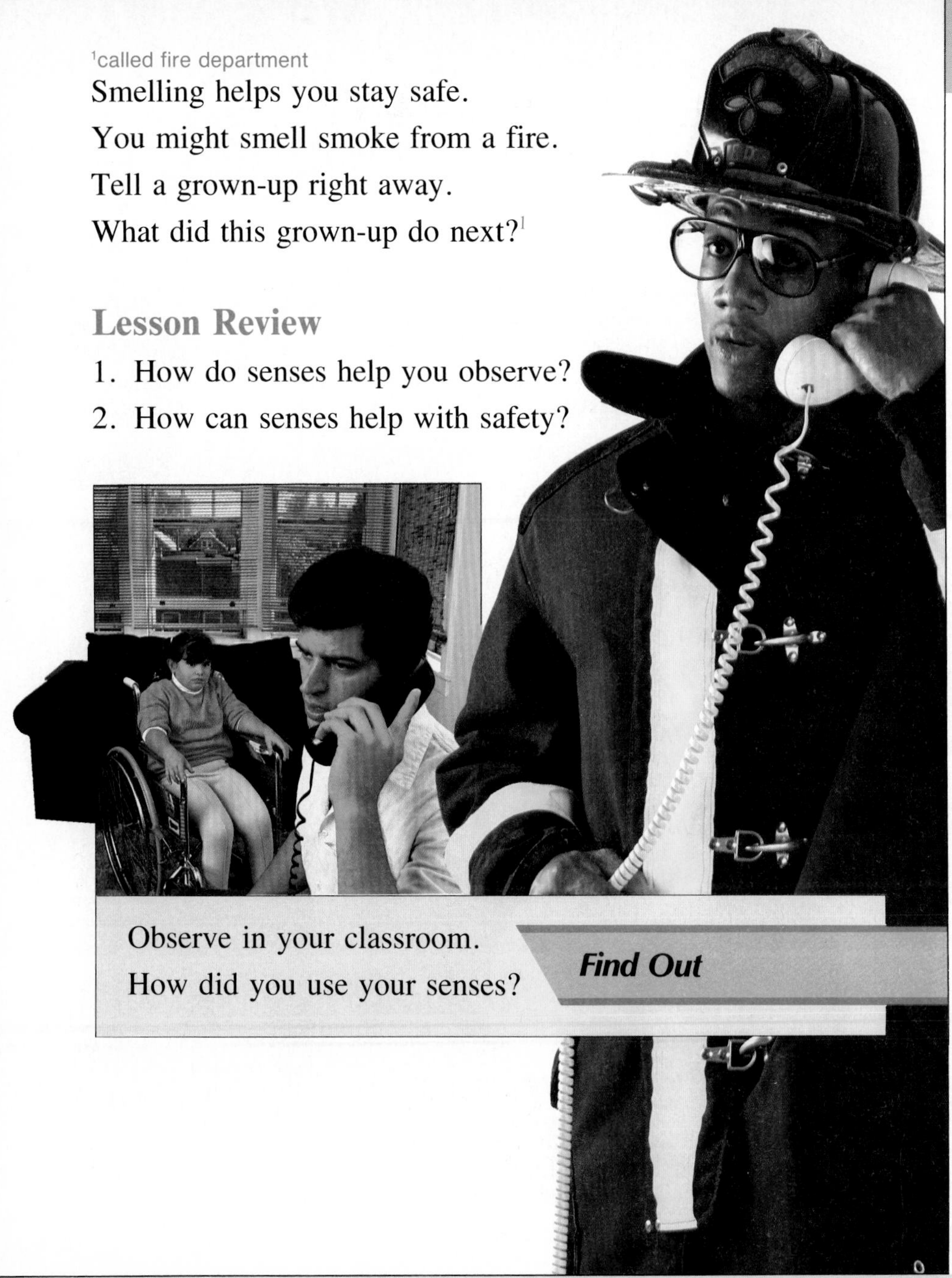

Smelling helps you stay safe.

You might smell smoke from a fire.

Tell a grown-up right away.

What did this grown-up do next?[1]

Lesson Review

1. How do senses help you observe?
2. How can senses help with safety?

Observe in your classroom.
How did you use your senses?

Find Out

[1]called fire department

3 ASSESS

Lesson Review

1. The senses help you observe by giving you information.
2. Senses help in safety by enabling people to see warning signs, hear warning sounds, and smell smoke that might come from a fire.
Challenge! Question: **If eyeglasses help in the sense of seeing what helps in the sense of hearing?** (hearing aid) **Thinking Skill:** *Identifying and suggesting alternatives*

Find Out

Answers will vary, but students should identify something they observed using their eyes, ears, nose, tongue, and hands. **Thinking Skill:** *Organizing information*

Workbook page 6 *

Name
Use with Lesson 2: pages 14-17

Chapter 1
Vocabulary Puzzle

Sense Wordsearch

Read the words in the word bank.
Write the words on the lines.
Then find each word in the puzzle below.

Word Bank
hearing
observe
seeing
senses
smelling
tasting
touching

Circle the sense words.
Seven are hiding in the puzzle.
One is done for you.

s x b t a s t i n g p p s
d e g k t o u c h i n g e
w w a z s m e l l i n g e
e p s h e a r i n g q z n
s t o b s e r v e w z r g
s e e i n g x s e n s e s

Game Suggestion ♦

Play a game of twenty questions. Think of a type of warning. Let the students ask questions and try to guess what you are thinking of. The student who guesses the correct answer gets to think of and be questioned about the next warning. (examples of warnings: stop signs, traffic signals, sirens, railroad crossing signs)

Reteaching Suggestion ♦

Describe a potentially dangerous situation to students, or show them pictures of such a situation. Ask students to tell what senses they could use to stay safe in each situation. Sample situations are:
1. crossing a street where there is no traffic light
2. crossing a street that has a traffic light
3. playing in a street when an ambulance is coming
4. cooking on a barbeque grill

***** *Answers to masters on pages 8E-8F*

ACTIVITY PLAN

Concept
The five senses provide useful information.

Objectives/Process Skills
- *Observe* a peanut by using the senses.
- *Gather information* about the peanut.
- *Describe* the peanut.

Time Allotment
Allow 15 minutes.

Materials
For each student: one whole peanut in the shell

Safety Tips (See page T27.)
- Direct students not to eat the peanuts.
- Warn students not to place peanuts in their noses or ears.
- Be certain to clean up any shells and peanuts that fall on the floor to prevent falls.

Teaching Tip
- Direct students to carefully investigate their peanuts, using their senses.

Answers
Tell What You Learned
Students should state that they used their senses to get information about how a peanut looks, smells, sounds, and feels. They should explain what they discovered: the peanut shell looks light brown, has texture (a bumpy surface), smells a little like wood, feels rough, and rattles, while the nuts inside are smooth and light brown. **Thinking Skills:** *Predicting, Inferring*

ACTIVITY

Using All Your Senses

Follow the Directions

1. Look at a peanut in a shell.
2. Smell the shell and feel it.
3. Shake the shell. Listen.
4. Open the shell.
5. Look at the peanuts.

Tell What You Learned

Tell how you used each sense.
Tell what you found out.

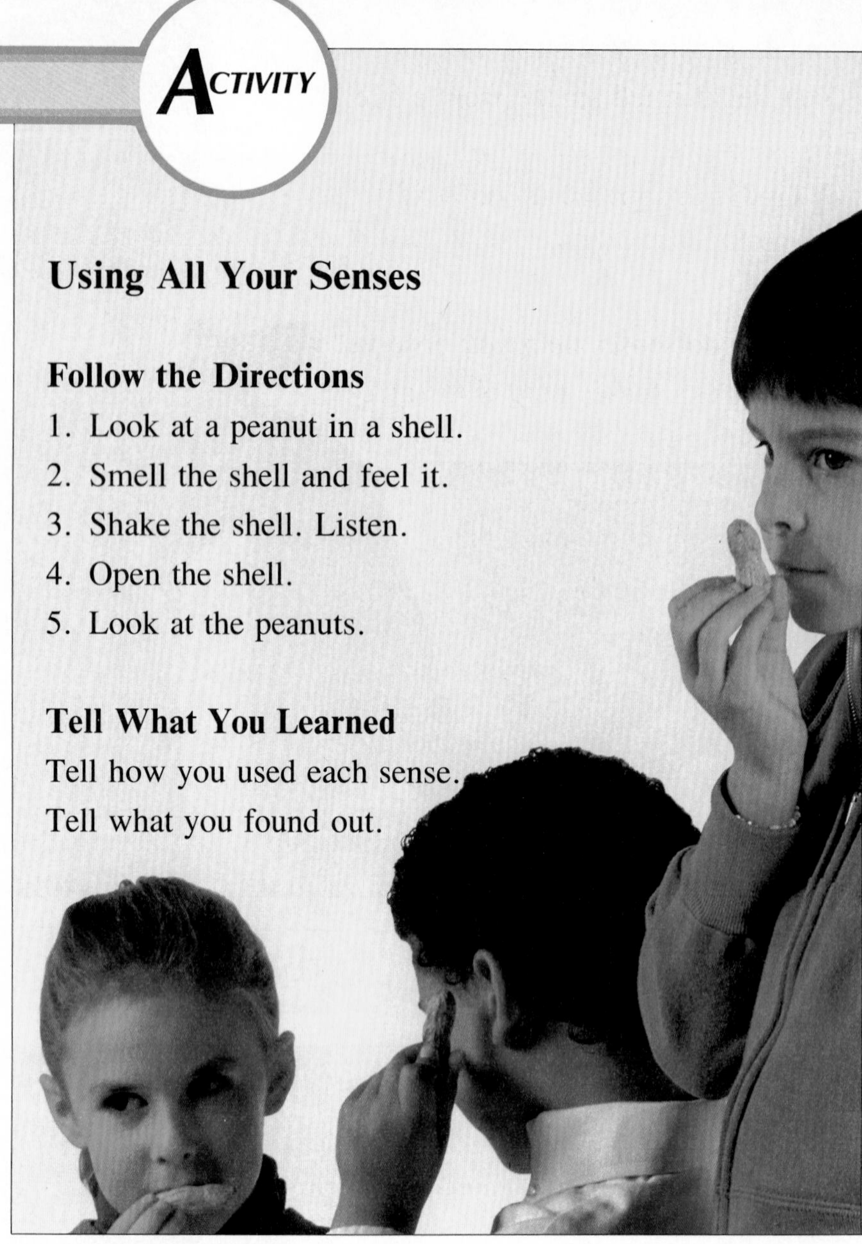

18

Activity Results

Students should be able to describe a peanut in terms of what they observed with each sense.

Enrichment Activity

Allow students to examine various objects, limiting the number of senses they can use. Let the students try to identify a rock, a can, and a penny by using only the sense of hearing. Have students use the sense of smell to try to identify food, a newspaper, or an unlit candle.

An Alarm to Help Smell Smoke

Fire can harm people.
Smoke from fires can warn people.
Suppose people do not smell the smoke.
Then this alarm can warn them.
It makes a noise when there is smoke.
Then people can go to a safe place.

What Do You Think?

Why would a person have this alarm?

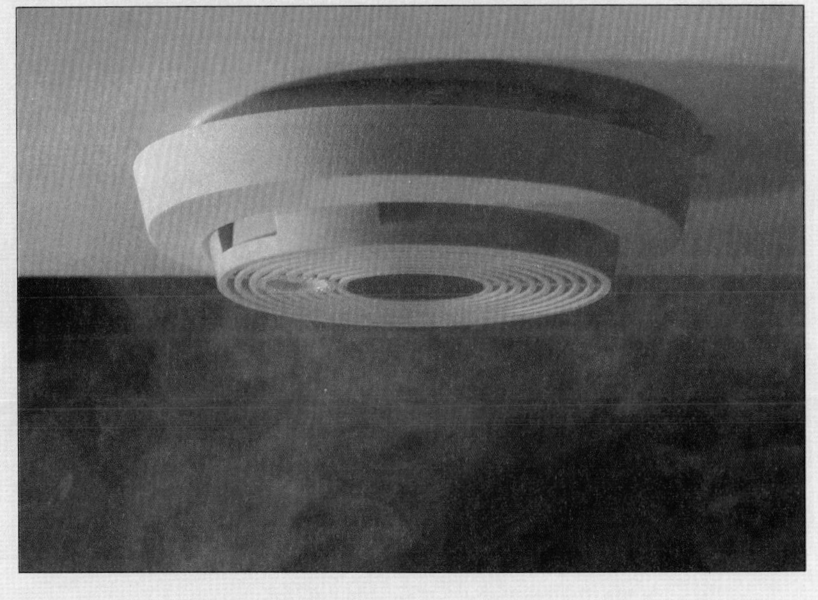

TEACHING PLAN

SCIENCE IN YOUR LIFE

Discussion

Discuss with students how machines help people do work. (vacuum picks up dirt, dishwasher cleans dishes, and so on) Tell students that machines help people in other ways. Question: **What machines help keep people safe?** (Answers might include traffic lights, warning sirens, automatic train gates, and so on.) Introduce the term *smoke alarm* if not mentioned by the students.

Teaching Tips

- Point out that fires sometimes start when people are asleep, and that smoke alarms can sense smoke before sleeping people might smell it.
- Discuss the safe procedure to follow if a smoke alarm sounds in a building. (Immediately leave the building, go a safe distance away, and do not reenter the building for any reason.)

Answers

What Do You Think?
The machine helps keep people safe from fires. **Thinking Skill:** *Drawing conclusions*

Teaching Options

SCIENCE BACKGROUND

Two kinds of smoke detectors are currently available. *Ionization detectors* use a tiny radioactive cell to electrically charge molecules of air. These charged particles, called ions, produce a flowing electric current. When smoke is present, its particles become attached to the ions and decrease the flow of the electric current. This, in turn, sets off the alarm. *Photoelectric detectors* contain a light that shines into a chamber, and a light-sensitive device called a photocell. Any smoke in the air scatters the light and reflects it onto the photocell. The photocell then triggers the alarm to sound.

TEACHING PLAN

Problem solving skills developed in every chapter

SKILLS FOR SOLVING PROBLEMS

pages 20–21

Purpose
This activity provides students with the opportunity to record information using a pictograph.

Materials
For each student: 20 small squares of construction paper (no larger than grid squares on pictograph)

1 MOTIVATE

Discussion
Direct students to look around the room and then tell you what objects they see. List the objects on the chalkboard. (Answers might include a clock, classroom plant, and so on.) Question: **What senses could you use to learn more about each of these things?** (Accept reasonable responses.) Instruct students to turn to page 20.

2 TEACH

Teaching Tip
- Ask students to *observe* each item in the picture and to *describe* what they see.

Skills for Solving Problems

Using a Pictograph

Which senses do you use to observe?

1. Look at the picture of the classroom.
   Find things to observe.
   Think of senses you would use.

20

Teaching Options

SCIENCE BACKGROUND

Scientists continuously use their skills of observation in their work. Their observations often help them to solve problems. Scientists are trained to keep track of all observations by recording them. They use various means of recording data, such as charts, graphs, and tables.

2. Fill in the pictograph.
Go across each row.
Use small paper squares.
Put one on each sense you would use.

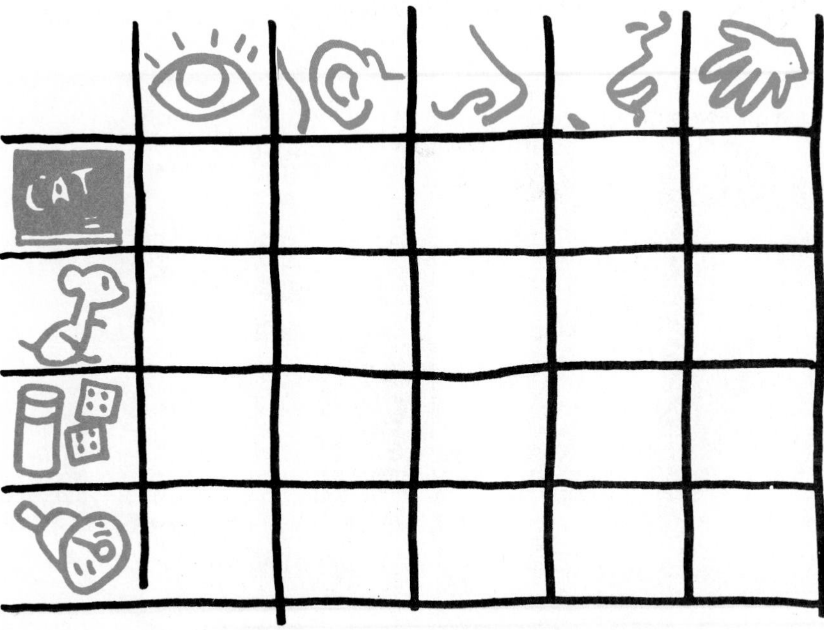

3. Look at your pictograph.
Which sense did you use most?

Teaching Tips

- Before students try to use the pictograph to plot their observations, explain the symbols used on the pictograph and make sure students understand how the columns are arranged: up and down (vertical), and across (horizontal).
- Explain that the students should mark which of the senses they used to ***observe*** each object. Students should use the small squares of paper to cover the grid square that corresponds to the object they are observing and the sense they used. Explain that they will use more than one sense to learn about some of the objects.
- Have students plot the pictograph for each object, and then count up the total number of times they used each sense to observe the objects.

3 ASSESS

Answer

The students' totals for each column of the grid should determine which sense they used most frequently (probably sight). Students might need help in computing their totals.

Resource Book page 7 *

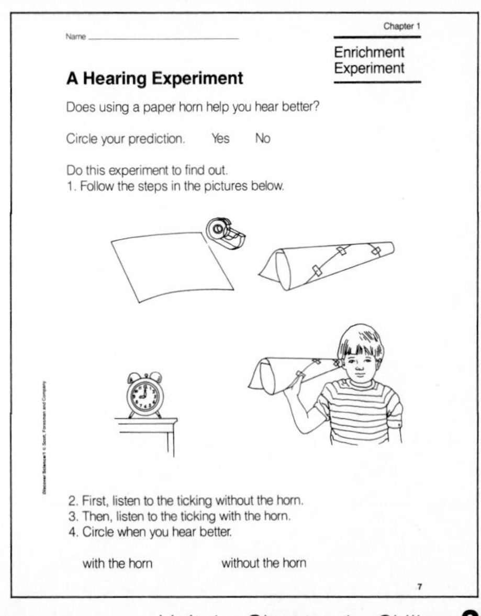

Name ____________

Chapter 1
Enrichment Experiment

A Hearing Experiment

Does using a paper horn help you hear better?

Circle your prediction. Yes No

Do this experiment to find out.
1. Follow the steps in the pictures below.

2. First, listen to the ticking without the horn.
3. Then, listen to the ticking with the horn.
4. Circle when you hear better.

with the horn without the horn

7

* *Answers to masters on pages 8E-8F*

REVIEW PLAN

CHAPTER 1 REVIEW

pages 22–23 *Check knowledge . . .*

Review Chapter Ideas

1. The senses are hearing, touching, smelling, tasting, and seeing.

2. Answers will vary, but may include that senses help you learn to read, help you discover different sounds, tastes, and smells, and let you know how things feel.

3. Your senses help you notice things and gather information.

4. Senses help with safety by helping people see and hear warning signs and signals and smell smoke.

5. Hearing, seeing, and smelling can help give warnings.

Chapter 1 Review

For further review, use Study Guide page 230.

Review Chapter Ideas

1. Name your senses.
2. Tell what senses help you learn.
3. Tell how senses help you observe.
4. Describe how senses help with safety.
5. Look at the pictures.
   Which senses give you warnings?

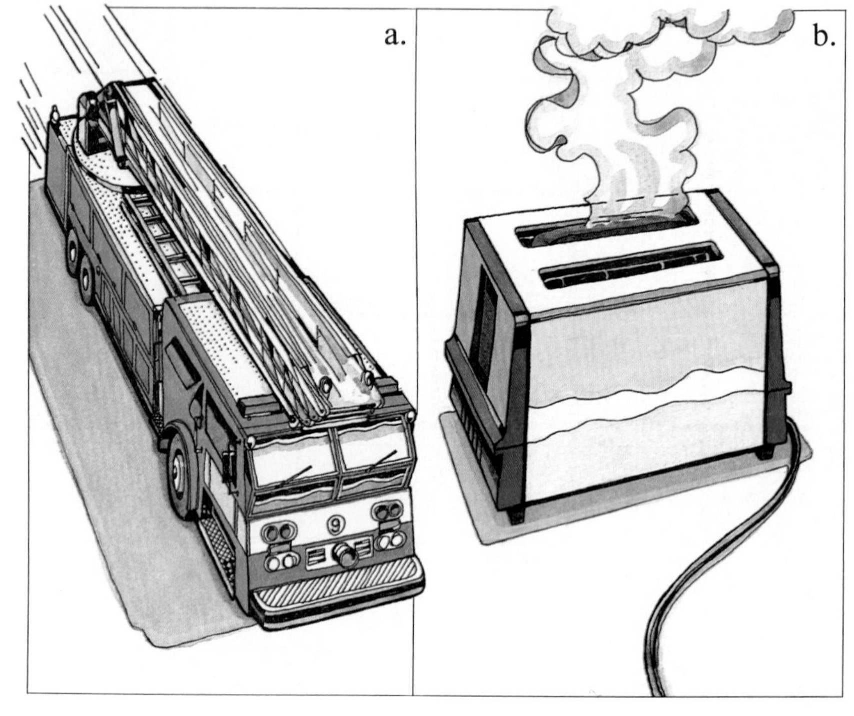

22

Review Options

Cooperative Learning ♦

STAD Format (See page T23.)
Assign students to work in four- to five-member teams to study Chapter 1 Review. Students should work together to make sure that they and their teammates know the material in the chapter. After students have had enough time to study together, give them a test to complete individually (Chapter 1 Test in the *Test Book*). Award Superteam certificates to teams whose average test scores exceed 90%, and Greatteam certificates to teams whose average test scores exceed 80%.

Optional tool in each chapter helps students help each other.

Test Book page 9 *

Name

Chapter 1 Test

Your Senses

I. Write **Yes** or **No.**

1. Do you use body parts to learn?
2. Do you have six senses?
3. Are all of the senses the same?
4. Can you observe new things?
5. Can senses help keep you safe?

II. Draw a line from the word to the right picture.

1. smelling 2. hearing 3. touching 4. tasting 5. seeing

9

♦ ***Suitable as a language development activity***

Review Science Words

Match the words and the pictures.

1. seeing
2. smelling
3. hearing
4. touching
5. tasting

a. b. c. d. e.

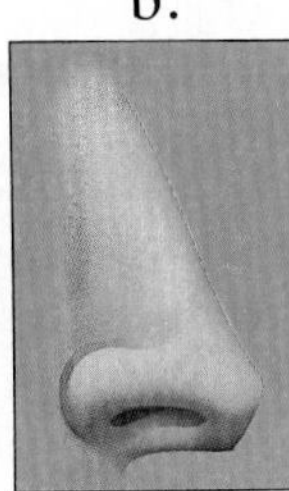
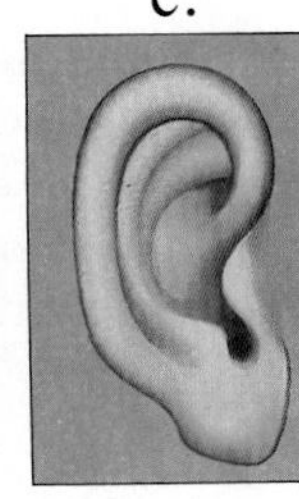
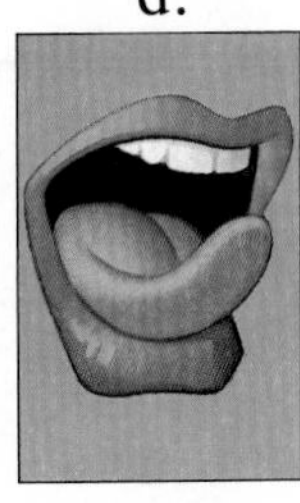
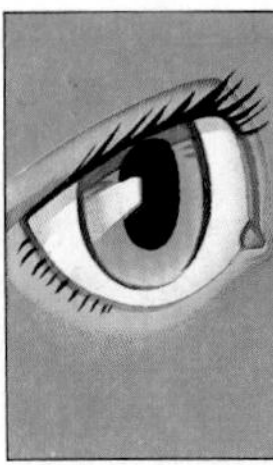

Tell what the words mean.

6. senses
7. observe

Use Science Ideas

What sense is being used for safety? How?

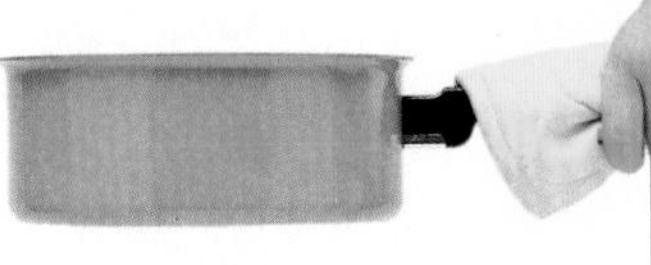

. . . Apply knowledge

Review Science Words

Match the words and the pictures.

1. seeing **4.** touching
2. smelling **5.** tasting
3. hearing

Tell what the words mean.
Thinking Skill: *Restating or explaining ideas.*
6. The senses are seeing, hearing, smelling, touching, and tasting.
7. When you observe, you notice things around you by getting information from your senses.

Use Science Ideas

The sense of touch; you would not touch a hot pot if you wanted to prevent yourself from being burned. **Thinking Skill:** *Recognizing cause and effect*

*** *Answers to masters on pages 8E-8F***

Teaching Plan

Chapter Components	Skills	Materials
Chapter Opener/*TRY THIS:* Matching Pictures pp. 24-25	***TRY THIS*** p. 25 **Science Process Skills** *Communicating, Observing*	***TRY THIS*** p. 25 (group of 30) one baby picture of each student
Lesson 1: How Do People Change? pp. 26-29	**Thinking Skills** Challenge!: *Predicting* Find Out: *Restating or explaining ideas*	**Demonstration** p. 26 1 kindergarten student, 1 fifth or sixth grade student
Activity: Getting New Teeth p. 30	**Science Process Skills** *Observing, Communicating*	(groups of 2) 15 small hand mirrors, 30 sheets drawing paper, 30 boxes crayons, 30 pencils
Science and People: Daniel A. Collins p. 31	**Thinking Skills** *Drawing Conclusions*	
Lesson 2: What Can Help You Grow? pp. 32-34	**Thinking Skills** Challenge!: *Making generalizations* Find Out: *Restating ideas*	**Demonstration** p. 32 1 puppet
Activity: Getting Clean p. 35	**Science Process Skills** *Observing, Communicating*	(individual) 3 bars hand soap, water, 1 roll paper towels, 1 small bag flour
Skills for Solving Problems: Measuring and Making a Chart pp. 36-37	**Problem Solving Skills** *Making decisions/Identifying and solving problems, Interpreting charts, maps, and graphs*	(individual) metric ruler, paper, colored pencils or crayons, blank chart to record measurements
Chapter Review pp. 38-39	**Thinking Skills** *Restating or explaining ideas, Recognizing factual and logical inconsistencies*	

Teaching Options

Strategies	Extensions		Resource Masters
			Family Letter: *Resource Book* p. 11 Vocabulary Preview: *Workbook* pp. 7-8
	Reinforcement pp. 26, 28 Special Education p. 27 Science and Math p. 27	Enrichment p. 28 Game Suggestion p. 29 Reteaching Suggestion p. 29	Science Activity: *Workbook* p. 9
	Enrichment Activity p. 30		
	Special Education p. 32 Enrichment p. 33	Reteaching Suggestion p. 34	Science Skills: *Workbook* p. 10 Science and Math: *Workbook* p. 11 Vocabulary Puzzle: *Workbook* p. 12
	Enrichment Activity p. 35		
			Enrichment Activity: *Resource Book* p. 15
Cooperative Learning p. 38 (Also see p. T23)			Chapter Test: *Test Book* p. 11

Preteaching Suggestions

For Advance Preparation

TRY THIS, page 25
Several days before you do this activity, remind students to look for baby pictures of themselves to bring to class.

Demonstration, page 26
Ask a kindergarten teacher and a fifth- or sixth-grade teacher to each ask a student who is of average height and weight to visit your class. Tell the teachers a few days in advance of when you want to do the demonstration, so they can make arrangements with the students.

Activity, page 30
Obtain one small, hand-held mirror for each group of students.

Demonstration, page 32
You may wish to bring a puppet for this demonstration.

Activity, page 35
Bring in one small bowl of white flour for each group of students.

For Vocabulary Review

Use the following sentences with your students to review the meanings of the underlined words.

1. When you think about how something might be, you are imagining.
2. Breakfast, lunch and dinner are meals.
3. A dentist checks your teeth to make sure they are healthy.

For High-Potential Students

Discuss with students the types of changes that can naturally occur in people's hair as a person gets older. Ask students to find out about these changes. They might talk to family members, barbers, or hairdressers or use library resources to find information. They should focus on such questions as: Does hair change color naturally? Does hair texture also change? Why do such changes occur? Encourage students to make a poster or bulletin-board display illustrating what they learned.

For Mainstreamed Students

Visually Impaired
Provide students with a doll that is similar in size and proportion to an infant. Have the students make a size comparison between the doll's hands and feet and those of a classmate. Also have students evaluate the doll's height, arm length, and leg length in comparison to those of a child their age.

For the *TRY THIS* on page 25 give visually handicapped students a verbal description of one of the pictures. Then describe the matching student's current appearance, and the appearance of two other students. Focus on the following features: eye color; hair color; skin color; shape of facial features; description of smile; any other obvious distinguishing features. Let visually impaired students try to tell who matches the description of the picture. Discuss measurable changes that occur during growth, such as changes in height, weight, and amount of hair.

Orthopedically Handicapped
Ask orthopedically handicapped students if they would be willing to share with the rest of the class the type of activities they do to keep fit. Students might describe doing specific exercises or playing certain sports. If students are reluctant to discuss this with the class, respect their wishes.

For Science Fair Projects

Encourage interested students to do one of the following projects:

1. Make a display of pictures taken during various stages of life. The display might include pictures of students or of students' family members. The display should include pertinent information about changes in size, physical abilities, and mental development.
2. Choose a favorite animal and learn how it grows and changes. Make a display of drawings or photographs to show how the animal changes from birth to maturity.

Classroom Resources

Bulletin Board
Encourage students to bring in pictures of themselves that show how they have grown and changed.

PEOPLE GROW AND CHANGE

Chapter 2 Poster

How will you change?

Science Discovery Center
Use pages from Chapter 2 in the *Science Discovery Center Book*. Place these worksheets in the appropriate pockets in the Science Discovery Center.

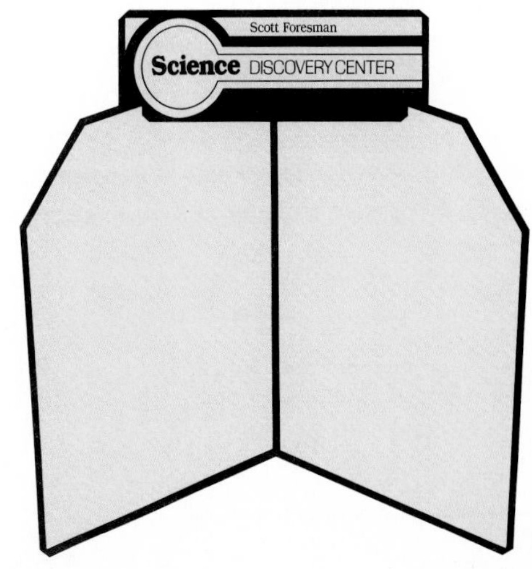
Scott Foresman
Science DISCOVERY CENTER

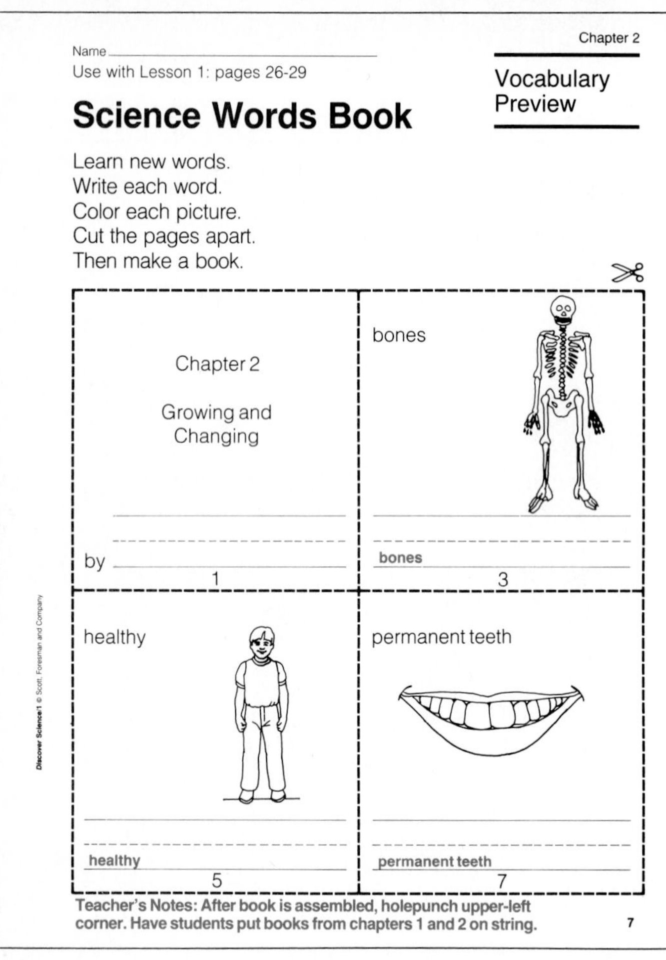

Chapter 2

Name ____________________

Use with Lesson 1: pages 26-29

Vocabulary Preview

Science Words Book

Learn new words.
Write each word.
Color each picture.
Cut the pages apart.
Then make a book.

Chapter 2 Growing and Changing by ________ 1	bones bones 3
healthy healthy 5	permanent teeth permanent teeth 7

Teacher's Notes: After book is assembled, holepunch upper-left corner. Have students put books from chapters 1 and 2 on string.

Chapter 2

Name ____________________

Use with Lesson 1: pages 26-29

Vocabulary Preview

Science Words Book

exercise exercise 4	2
	muscles muscles 6

Chapter 2

Name ____________________

Use with Lesson 1: pages 26-29

Science Activity

How Much Have You Grown?

Look at this hand of a baby.
Your hand was once this size.

Try this.
1. Put your hand over the baby's hand.
2. Trace around your hand with a pencil.
3. Color the baby's hand red.
4. Color your hand blue.

See how much you have grown.

Students will trace their hands over the baby's hand; then they will color the baby's hand red and their own hands blue.

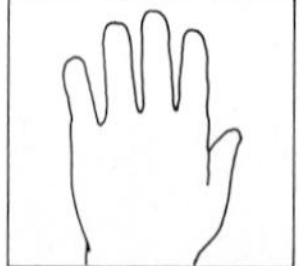

Teacher's Notes: Discuss how many years it has taken students to grow to be their current sizes. "How much more will you grow?"

Chapter 2

Name ____________________

Use with Lesson 2: pages 32-34

Science Skills

A Healthful Lunch

Look at the foods below.
Which foods will keep you healthy?
Make a healthful lunch.
Color and cut out the foods you want.
Then paste your foods on the tray.

Teacher's Notes: Balanced meals include: a fruit or a vegetable; a milk product; a bread; and meat, fish, poultry, or legume.

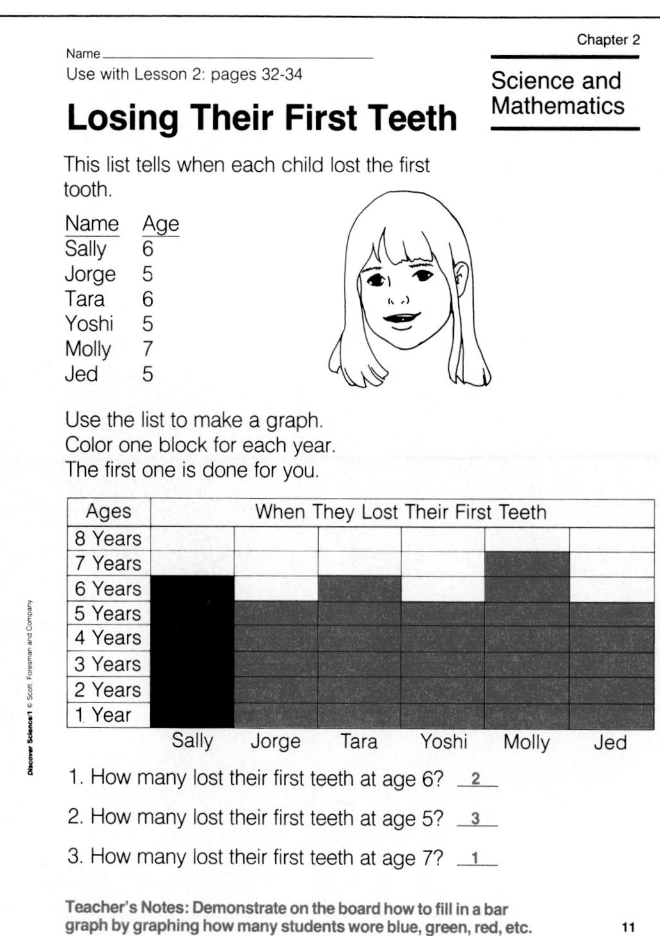

Name ______________________

Use with Lesson 2: pages 32-34

Chapter 2

Science and Mathematics

Losing Their First Teeth

This list tells when each child lost the first tooth.

Name	Age
Sally	6
Jorge	5
Tara	6
Yoshi	5
Molly	7
Jed	5

Use the list to make a graph.
Color one block for each year.
The first one is done for you.

Ages	When They Lost Their First Teeth					
8 Years						
7 Years						
6 Years						
5 Years						
4 Years						
3 Years						
2 Years						
1 Year						
	Sally	Jorge	Tara	Yoshi	Molly	Jed

1. How many lost their first teeth at age 6? 2
2. How many lost their first teeth at age 5? 3
3. How many lost their first teeth at age 7? 1

Teacher's Notes: Demonstrate on the board how to fill in a bar graph by graphing how many students wore blue, green, red, etc.

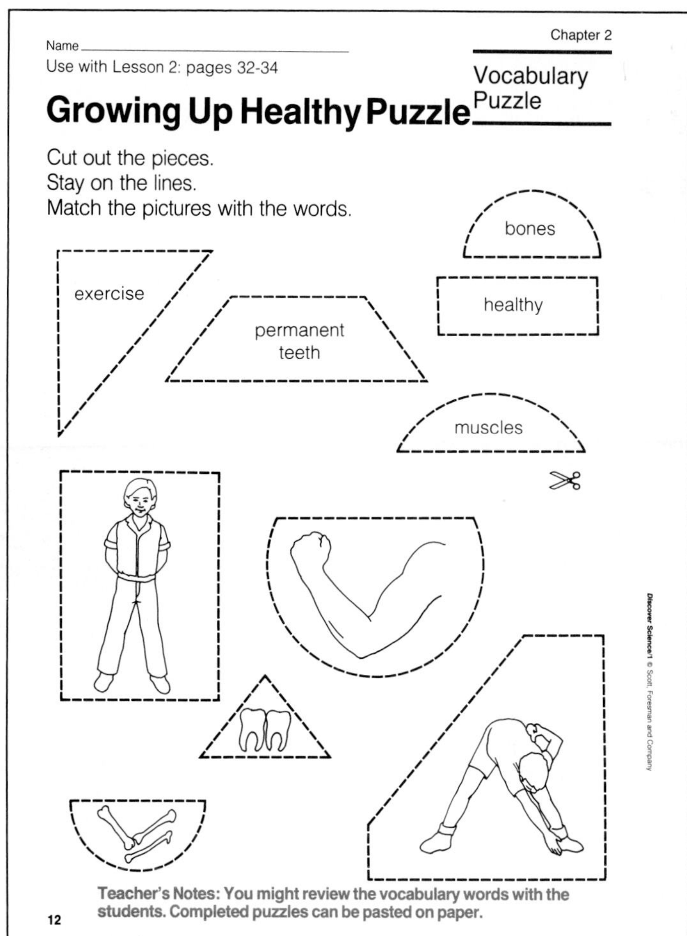

Name ______________________

Use with Lesson 2: pages 32-34

Chapter 2

Vocabulary Puzzle

Growing Up Healthy Puzzle

Cut out the pieces.
Stay on the lines.
Match the pictures with the words.

Teacher's Notes: You might review the vocabulary words with the students. Completed puzzles can be pasted on paper.

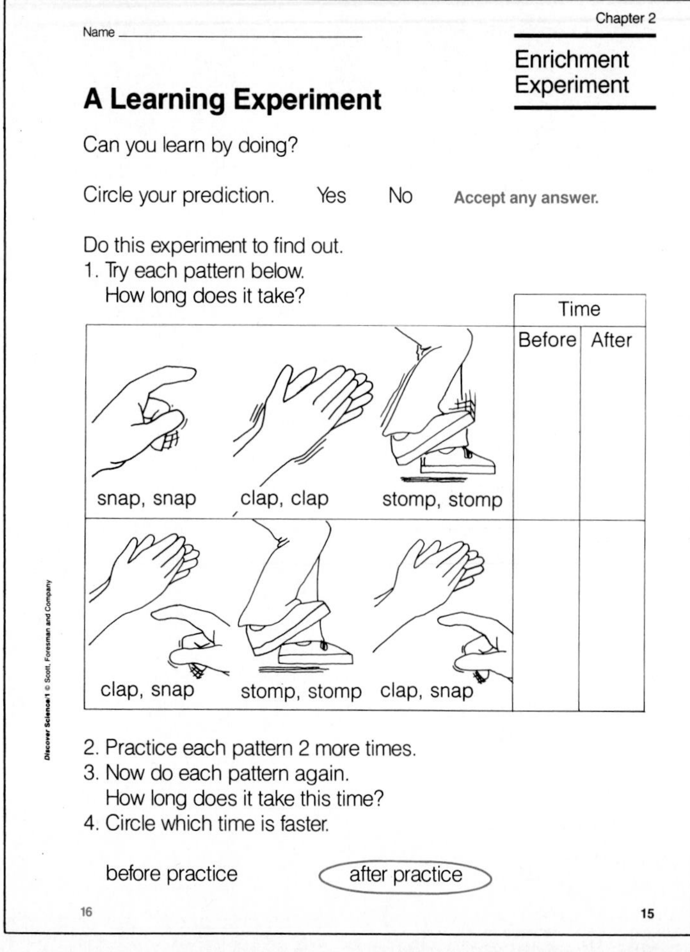

Name ______________________

Chapter 2

Enrichment Experiment

A Learning Experiment

Can you learn by doing?

Circle your prediction. Yes No **Accept any answer.**

Do this experiment to find out.

1. Try each pattern below.
   How long does it take?

Pattern			Time: Before	Time: After
snap, snap	clap, clap	stomp, stomp		
clap, snap	stomp, stomp	clap, snap		

2. Practice each pattern 2 more times.
3. Now do each pattern again.
   How long does it take this time?
4. Circle which time is faster.

before practice (after practice)

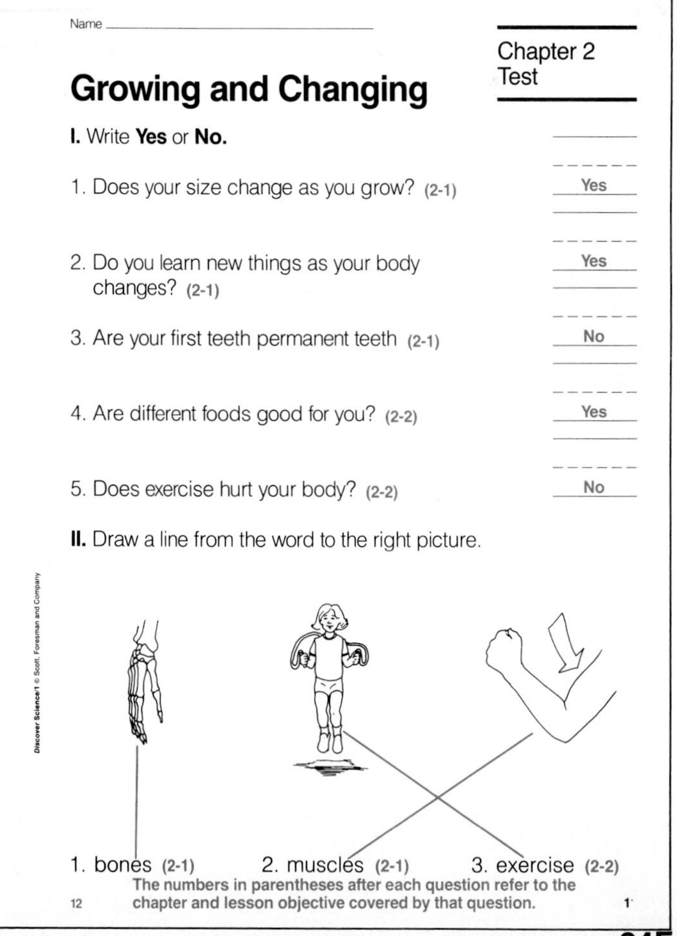

Name ______________________

Chapter 2 Test

Growing and Changing

I. Write **Yes** or **No.**

1. Does your size change as you grow? (2-1) Yes
2. Do you learn new things as your body changes? (2-1) Yes
3. Are your first teeth permanent teeth (2-1) No
4. Are different foods good for you? (2-2) Yes
5. Does exercise hurt your body? (2-2) No

II. Draw a line from the word to the right picture.

1. bones (2-1) 2. muscles (2-1) 3. exercise (2-2)

The numbers in parentheses after each question refer to the chapter and lesson objective covered by that question.

TEACHING PLAN

INTRODUCING CHAPTER 2

Major Concepts
Lesson 1 People change as they mature physically, mentally, and socially.
Lesson 2 Growth and change from infancy to adulthood can be affected by personal health-care practices.

Vocabulary
bones, exercise, muscles, permanent teeth

[1]changed and developed as she grew older
[2]will change, develop, and grow older

Chapter 2

Growing and Changing

How did this person grow and change?[1]
How will you grow and change?[2]

24

Teaching Options

Workbook page 7 *

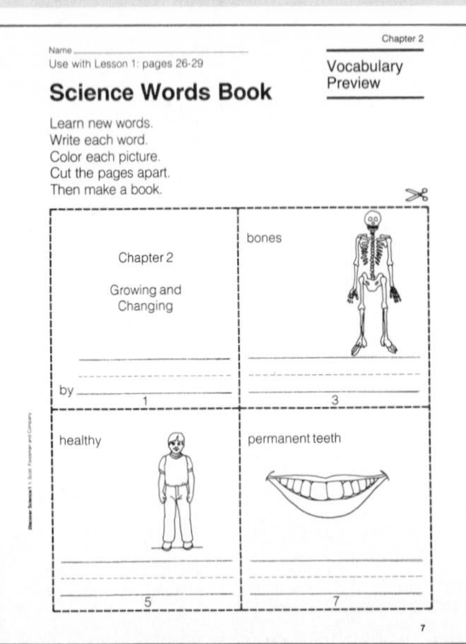
Name
Use with Lesson 1: pages 26-29
Chapter 2
Vocabulary Preview

Science Words Book

Learn new words.
Write each word.
Color each picture.
Cut the pages apart.
Then make a book.

Chapter 2
Growing and Changing
by
1

bones
3

healthy
5

permanent teeth
7

7

Workbook page 8 *

Name
Use with Lesson 1: pages 26-29
Chapter 2
Vocabulary Preview

Science Words Book

exercise
4

2

muscles
6

8

♦ ***Suitable as a language development activity***

[1] possibly

Starting the Chapter

Imagine your mother as a baby.
Could you pick out her picture?[1]
Match pictures of your classmates.
Notice how they have changed.
Read more about changing.

Matching Pictures

TRY THIS

Bring your baby picture to school.
Ask your classmates to do the same.
Mix up the pictures.
Pick one and match it to a classmate.
Take turns matching the pictures.
What helps you match them?

25

TRY THIS

Objective ♦

This optional *TRY THIS* activity will help students explore and build background information about the concept that people grow and change. Later in the chapter, students will be able to draw on this experience to help them assimilate the new content.

Science Process Skills

Communicating, Observing

Materials

For the class: one baby picture of each student

Teaching Tip

- After the students have had an opportunity to match students and baby pictures, pass your baby picture around the classroom. Let the students try to *identify* the person in the picture. If no one answers correctly, tell students that the person in the picture is you. Point out any similarities between your appearance as a child and as an adult.

Answer

Noticing similarities between students and their baby pictures helps in matching the correct picture with each person.

Resource Book page 11

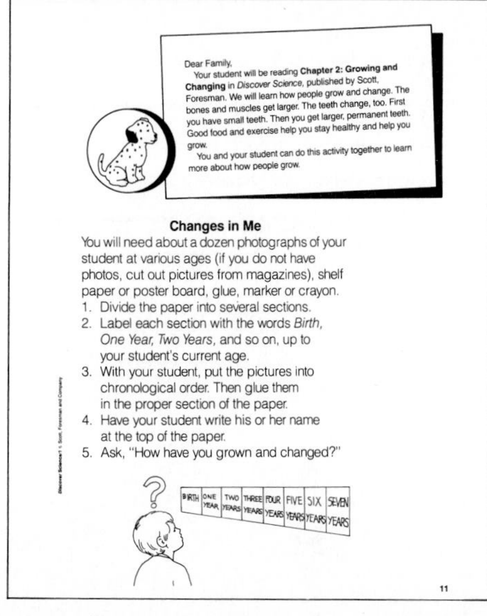

Dear Family,
Your student will be reading **Chapter 2: Growing and Changing** in *Discover Science*, published by Scott, Foresman. We will learn how people grow and change. The bones and muscles get larger. The teeth change, too. First you have small teeth. Then you get larger, permanent teeth. Good food and exercise help you stay healthy and help you grow.
You and your student can do this activity together to learn more about how people grow.

Changes in Me

You will need about a dozen photographs of your student at various ages (if you do not have photos, cut out pictures from magazines), shelf paper or poster board, glue, marker or crayon.

1. Divide the paper into several sections.
2. Label each section with the words *Birth, One Year, Two Years,* and so on, up to your student's current age.
3. With your student, put the pictures into chronological order. Then glue them in the proper section of the paper.
4. Have your student write his or her name at the top of the paper.
5. Ask, "How have you grown and changed?"

11

SCIENCE BACKGROUND

Growth is regulated by the pituitary gland located at the base of the brain. This gland produces growth hormone which, according to the amount produced, affects the way an individual grows. A child's self concept is often linked to his/her growth rate. Some children feel self-conscious, shy, or resentful if their growth does not match that of other children.

* *Answers to masters on pages 24E–24F*

TEACHING PLAN

LESSON 1
pages 26–29

Lesson Objective
• *Describe* several ways people change as they grow.

Lesson Vocabulary
bones, muscles, permanent teeth

1 MOTIVATE

Demonstration Activity ♦
Arrange for a kindergartener and a fifth- or sixth-grade student to visit the class. Choose one of the first-graders to stand in front of the class with the two visitors. (Do not choose students for this activity who are overweight, very thin, or exceptionally short or tall for their age. These students might be sensitive to being compared to others.) Tell the class to *observe* the three students carefully.

Discussion
Discuss how the students differ. Encourage students to notice differences in height, size of hands, and number of teeth. Point out that people grow at different rates, and no one rate is correct for all.

[1]child on the right

Lesson 1 How Do People Change?

Your body changes as you grow.
Your size and shape change.
Your **bones** grow and you get taller.
Your **muscles** grow larger.
Who has grown more here?[1]

26

Teaching Options

SCIENCE BACKGROUND

Before birth, humans grow in length at a rate of about 2 inches per month. During the first year, children grow at an average of 6 to 9 inches per year. Children from three to ten years of age slow down in growth—from about 7 centimeters (about 2.8 inches) per year at age three, to 5.3 centimeters (2.1 inches) per year at age ten. Most girls and boys have slow growth when they are in their mid-teens; some growth might continue to occur until a person is in his or her early twenties.

Reinforcement

Collect pictures of people of various ages—a baby, a toddler, a young child, a teenager, and an adult. Display the pictures in random order and have students rearrange them so that they show the proper progression. Encourage students to discuss how people grow and change.

♦ ***Suitable as a language development activity***

[1]child on the right

Your teeth change as you grow.
Your first teeth are small.
Your jaws get larger as you grow.
Then you get new, larger teeth.
The new teeth are **permanent teeth.**
Which child has permanent teeth?[1]

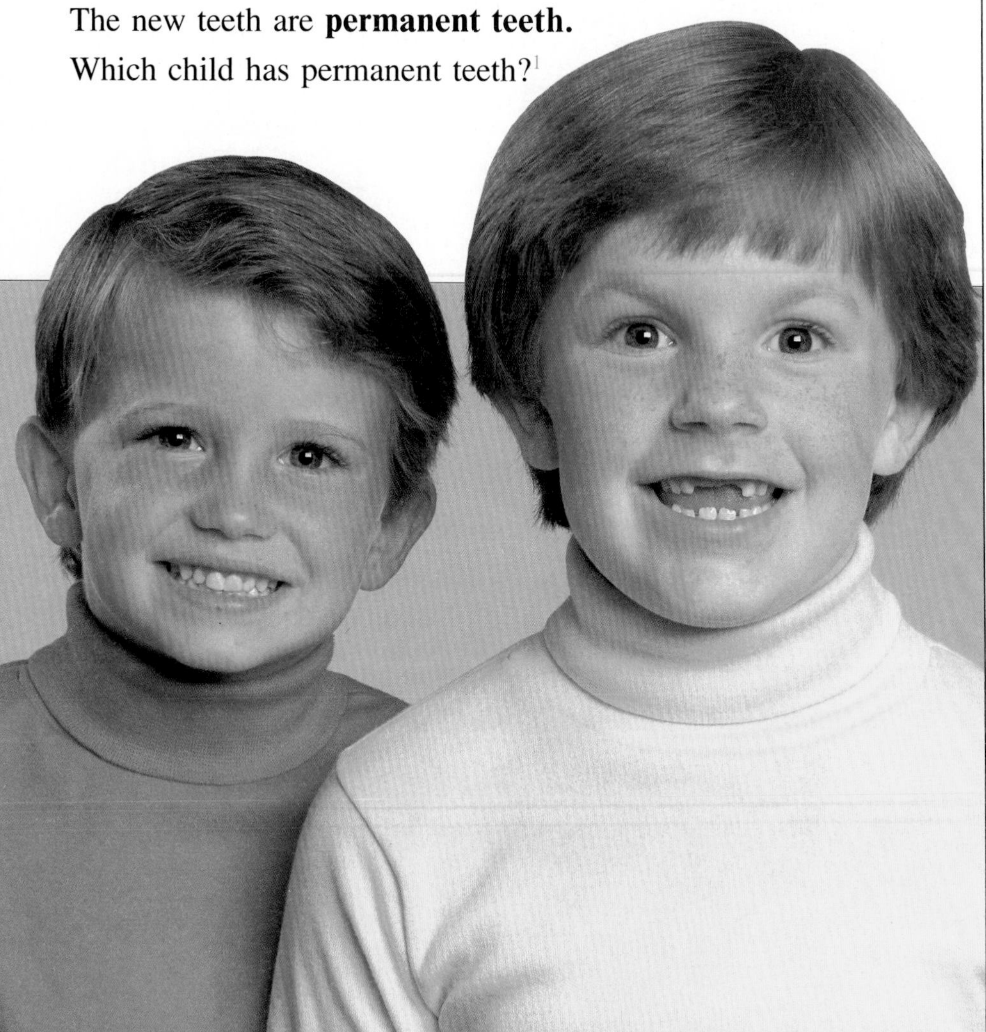

2 TEACH

Teaching Tips

- Refer students to the *TRY THIS* on page 25 in which they matched classmates to their baby pictures. Discuss the changes they observed in classmates from babyhood to present. Help students read page 26 to find out how people change as they grow.
- Have a discussion with students concerning the loss of primary teeth and the emergence of permanent teeth. Question: **How many of you have lost some of your teeth? Have many of you have loose teeth now, which will probably fall out soon?** (Answers will vary.) Have the students read page 27 to find out why children loose their teeth and get new teeth. Ask students to ***identify*** which child in the picture has permanent teeth. Discuss characteristics of baby teeth and permanent teeth.
- **Possible Misconception:** Many students think that they will have the same number of permanent teeth as primary teeth. Explain that all primary teeth are replaced by permanent teeth and that additional permanent teeth grow in at the back of the mouth as children get older.

Special Education

Obtain a baby toy and a toy that is suitable for first-graders. Discuss with students why they would or would not want to play with the baby toy. (Most will answer that they would quickly become bored.) Have students ***describe*** some of their toys and give reasons why they would not be good toys for babies. (Answers may include that they have small parts.) Ask students what they can learn from playing with their toys. (Accept reasonable responses.) Explain that babies learn some very important skills from playing with baby toys.

Science and Math

Give each child a piece of construction paper that has been cut into the shape of a tooth. On a large piece of poster board or paper, make a graph to show the number of teeth each student has lost. Have each student write his or her name on a paper tooth and place the tooth in the appropriate section of the graph.

TEACHING PLAN

Teaching Tips

- Ask the students to *describe* what they have learned since they have been in the first grade. Question: **What sports or activities do you participate in now that you could not or did not do when you were younger?** (Let volunteers answer.) Ask students to read page 28 and *discuss* what the children in the picture are learning.
- Tell students that very young children do not know how to play with others or share toys. Students who have younger siblings could tell the class what they have ***observed*** about how their younger brothers and sisters play. After students read page 29, discuss how the children are playing. (together) Let volunteers ***describe*** what kinds of games they like to play in large or small groups.

[1]how to play violin; how to play game

What do you learn as you grow?
You learn new games and sports.
You learn new things in school.
You can learn more all your life.
What are these children learning?[1]

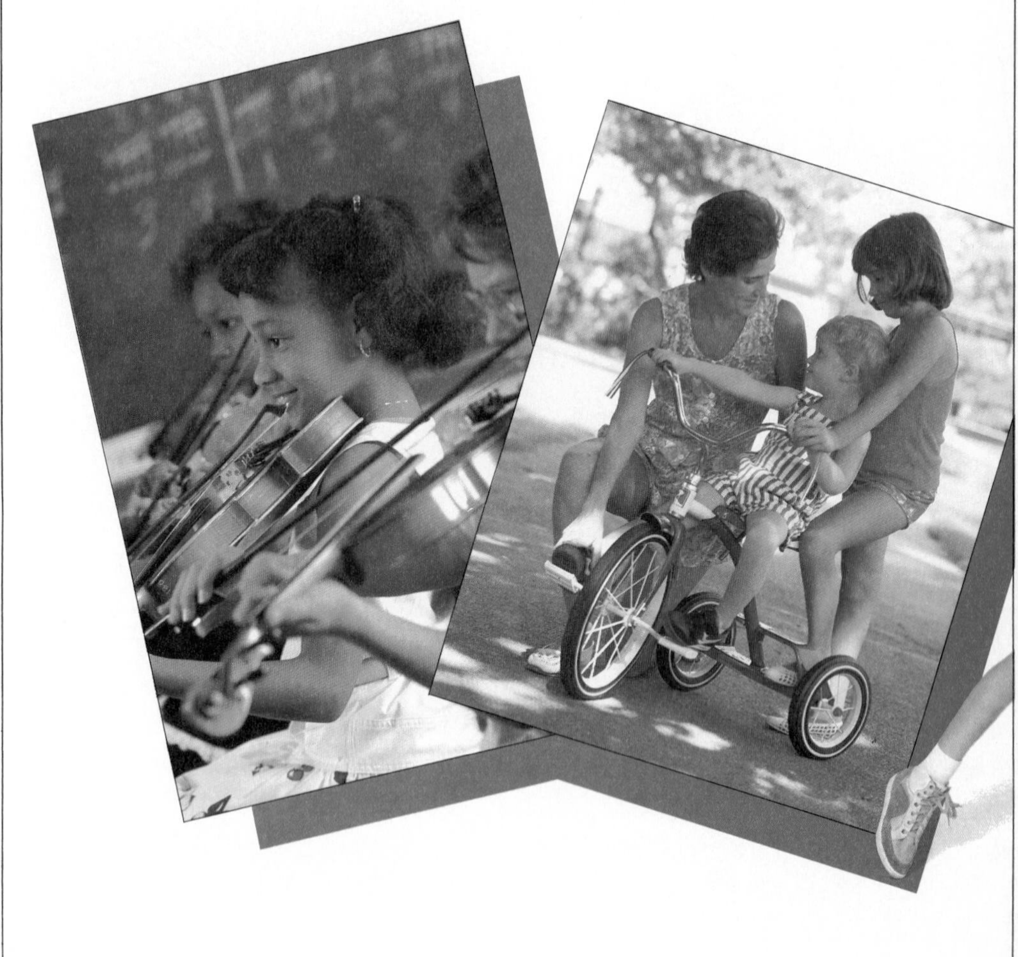

Teaching Options

Reinforcement

Have each student fold a piece of drawing paper in half. On one side, have the student draw a picture of what he or she looked like at a younger age. On the other side, have the student draw what he or she looks like now (or attach a recent school photo). On the bottom of their drawings, instruct students to ***list*** some things they learned to do as a younger child, and some of the things they are learning to do now.

Enrichment

Have students fold a sheet of paper into four sections. Tell them to label each section as follows:

1. *When I Was a Baby*
2. *Before I Started School*
3. *How I am Now*
4. *When I Grow Up*

Have students draw appropriate pictures in each section. Allow time for students to ***describe*** and discuss their pictures and ***explain*** how they have changed since they were babies.

SCIENCE ANECDOTE

Overall, the height of people in the United States has risen gradually in the past 100 years. Diets have become more nutritionally sound, enabling more people to grow to their genetic potential.

◆ ***Suitable as a language development activity***

[1]playing with a group, not separately

You play differently as you grow.
How are these children playing?[1]
You learn to get along with people.
Your family and friends help.

Lesson Review

1. How does your body grow and change?
2. What can you learn as you grow?

List ways you have changed.
Use words about learning.

Find Out

29

3 ASSESS

Lesson Review

1. A growing body gets bigger. Bones and muscles in the body grow. Small teeth fall out and larger new teeth grow in their place.

2. You can learn to do more things and to get along better with others as you grow.

Challenge! Question: **How do you think you will look and act when you grow up?** (Answers will vary , but will probably include the ideas of looking bigger, having a family, having a job, and making more decisions independently.) **Thinking Skill:** *Predicting*

Find Out

Answers will vary, but may include that students have learned to play and share with others, to play new games and sports, and to do new things at school. **Thinking Skill:** *Restating or explaining ideas*

Workbook page 9 *

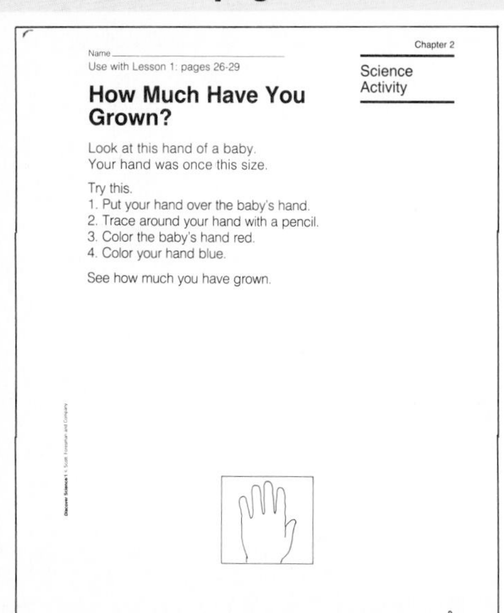

Name
Use with Lesson 1: pages 26-29

Chapter 2
Science Activity

How Much Have You Grown?

Look at this hand of a baby.
Your hand was once this size.

Try this.
1. Put your hand over the baby's hand.
2. Trace around your hand with a pencil.
3. Color the baby's hand red.
4. Color your hand blue.

See how much you have grown.

9

*** Answers to masters on pages 24E-24F**

Game Suggestion ♦

Make a gameboard by drawing a six-section grid on paper. Turning paper lengthwise, label the columns as follows: *Baby, Child,* and *Adult*. Photocopy for each student. Mount magazine pictures of toys, clothing, or activities appropriate to each age on cards cut to fit the gameboard sections. Place the pictures face down on a table. Let each student, in turn, turn over one card and place it in the appropriate section on his or her gameboard. If he/she turns over a card for a section that is already filled, he/she loses a turn. The first child to fill the grid wins.

Reteaching Suggestion ♦

Bring adult-sized articles of clothing, such as shoes, gloves, shirts, and slacks, to class and let students try them on. Also show students some baby clothing. Help students understand that they are much larger now than they were as a baby, but that they will grow much more before they are adults.

ACTIVITY PLAN

Concept
Permanent teeth demonstrate how the body changes during growth; children vary in the age at which they get permanent teeth.

Objectives/Process Skills
- *Observe* the teeth.
- *Identify* permanent teeth and the rate at which permanent teeth replace baby (primary) teeth.

Materials
For each pair of students: 1 small hand mirror, 2 sheets drawing paper, 2 boxes crayons, 2 pencils

Time Allotment
Allow 20 minutes

Safety Tip (See page T27.)
- Advise students to avoid putting their fingers in the mouths of other students when counting teeth, and direct them to wash their hands upon starting and completing this activity.

Teaching Tips
- Some students might not have any permanent teeth. Make sure that students understand that permanent teeth grow in at a different rate for each person.
- Show students your teeth and tell them that the teeth in your mouth are permanent. Ask a volunteer to show his permanent teeth and baby teeth to the class or show students a picture of a mouth that has both permanent and baby teeth.

Answers
Tell What You Learned
Students should draw a picture of how their permanent and baby teeth look. They should state that children get new teeth after they lose their first teeth. They might also give a length of time between when their classmates lost first teeth and when new teeth came in, or they might tell the age at which classmates got new teeth. **Thinking Skills:** *Inferring, Drawing conclusions*

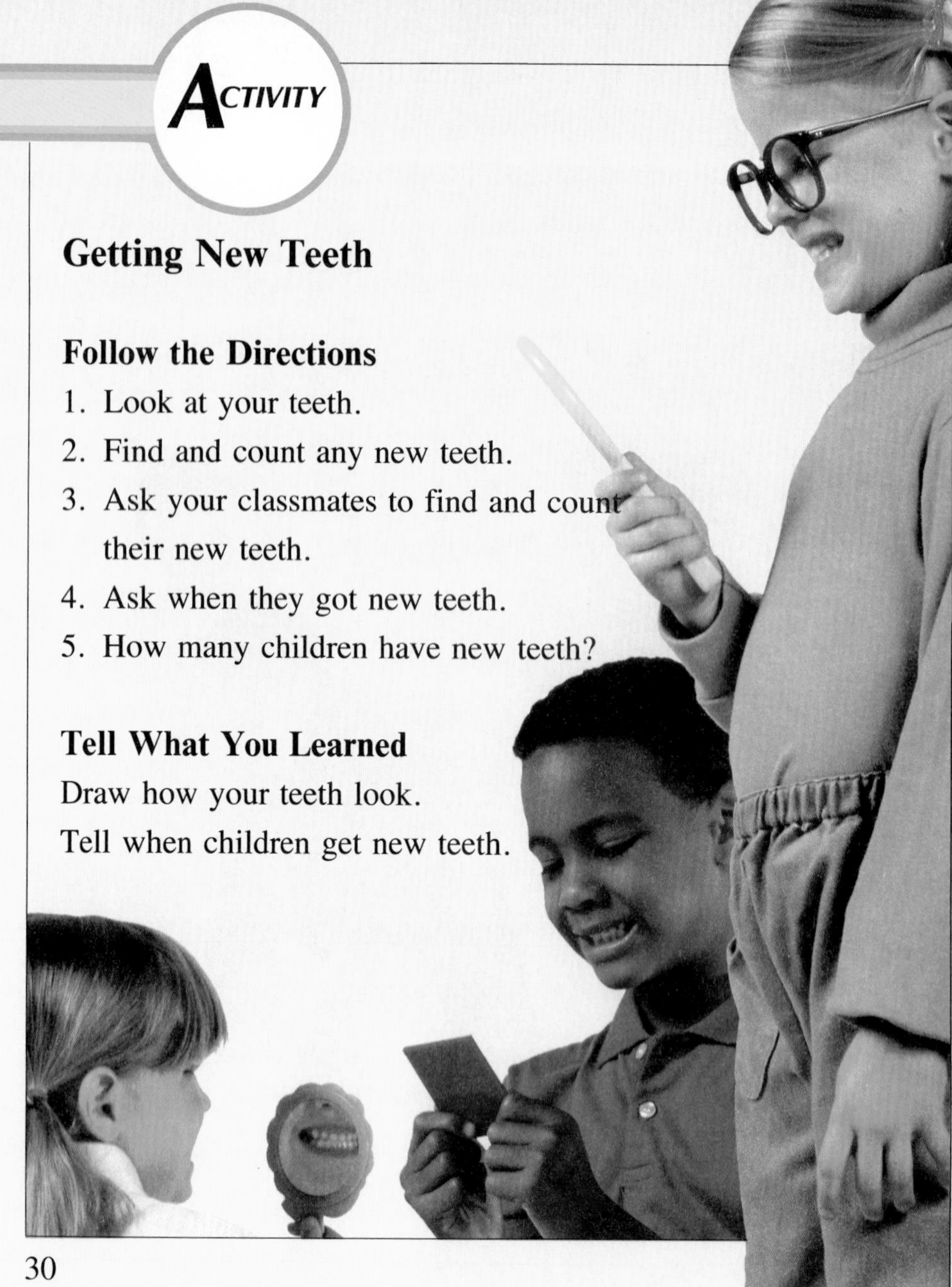

ACTIVITY

Getting New Teeth

Follow the Directions
1. Look at your teeth.
2. Find and count any new teeth.
3. Ask your classmates to find and count their new teeth.
4. Ask when they got new teeth.
5. How many children have new teeth?

Tell What You Learned
Draw how your teeth look.
Tell when children get new teeth.

30

Activity Results
Students should find out, and possibly record, how many other students in their class have permanent teeth.

Enrichment Activity
Make a poster that explains proper tooth care, including how to brush and floss teeth, what types of foods promote strong teeth, and when to visit the dentist. Discuss each part of the poster with students.

Daniel A. Collins

Dentists help us care for our teeth.
Daniel A. Collins is a dentist.
He has taught other dentists.
Some people had painful teeth and jaws.
Dr. Collins worked with other dentists.
They helped the people feel better.

What Do You Think?

Why do people study teeth?

TEACHING PLAN

SCIENCE AND PEOPLE

Discussion

Discuss with students the experiences they have had in a dentist's office. (Students may *describe* having their teeth X-rayed, cleaned, or filled.) Question: **Why is it important to see the dentist regularly?** (so that dental problems may be prevented and treated early)

Teaching Tips

- Point out that it is important to properly care for primary teeth, even though they are replaced by permanent teeth; if they are not properly cared for, the health of the jaws and permanent teeth may be adversely affected.
- Question: **What do you think might cause your teeth to become painful?** (Students might *identify* tooth decay as a factor causing oral pain.) Point out that jaw disorders may also result in painful teeth.
- Tell students that Daniel Collins was only a fair student, and was not interested in his studies until high school, when a math teacher encouraged him to study harder in his classes.

Answers

What Do You Think?
So that they can learn to take better care of their teeth. **Thinking Skill:** *Drawing conclusions*

Teaching Options

SCIENCE BACKGROUND

After receiving his master's degree in 1944, Daniel A. Collins became an instructor in the College of Dentistry at the University of California at San Francisco. There, he worked in the Institute of Experimental Biology, where he researched the effect of hormones on the head, face, jaw, and teeth. He found that too much or too little of certain hormones affects the jaw, causing pain and damaged teeth. He became so interested in the problems of pain in the face, teeth, and jaws that he and another dentist founded the Oral and Facial Pain service at the University of California Dental School.

TEACHING PLAN

LESSON 2
pages 32–34

Lesson Objective
- *Describe* the health care practices that promote good health.

Lesson Vocabulary
permanent teeth

1 MOTIVATE

Demonstration Activity ♦
Tell students that food is important to the body. Ask students to *name* their favorite kinds of food. Through the use of pantomine or puppetry, tell the story of a young child who does not want to eat anything except his or her favorite food. Show the child gradually eating smaller amounts of the food and eventually becoming very tired.

Discussion
Discuss with the students what happened to the child who ate only her or his favorite food. (child lost appetite and felt tired)

[1]fruits, vegetables, meat, bread, dairy products
[2]answers will vary

Lesson 2 What Can Help You Grow?

Food helps you grow.
It helps you stay **healthy.**
You need food every day.
You need different kinds of food.
What foods do you see here?[1]
Which of these foods do you like?[2]

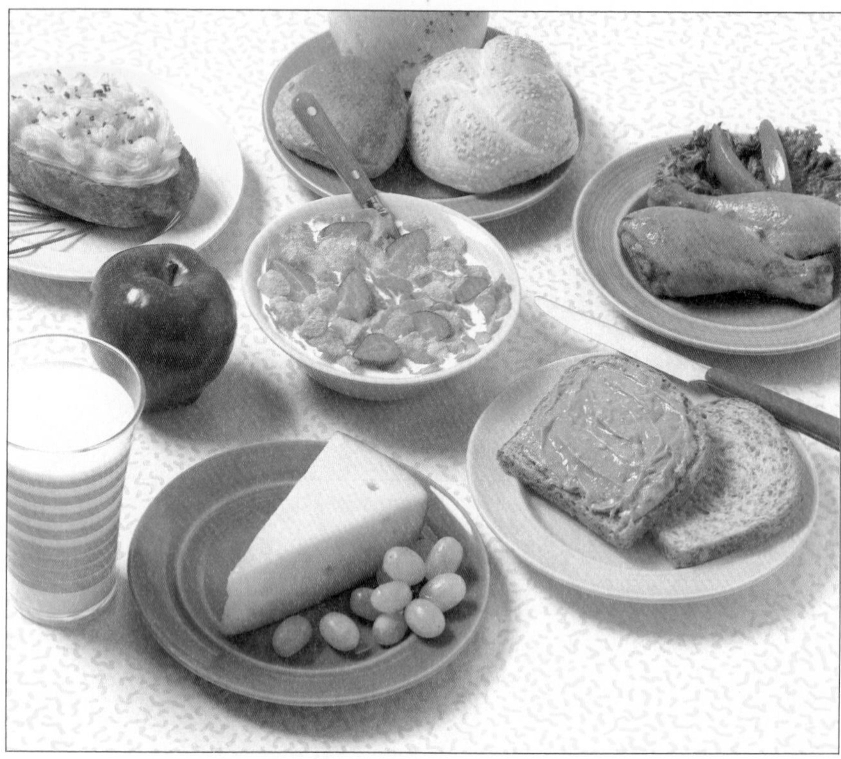

32

Teaching Options

SCIENCE BACKGROUND

People who are undernourished during early development often show signs of physical and mental deficiency. For example, a deficiency of vitamin D can result in a disease called *rickets*, which causes softening of the bones. Before 1919, doctors did not know that rickets could be prevented by eating foods rich in vitamin D, and the disease caused many children to become crippled. Most children now get sufficient vitamin D from milk, cereal, and exposure to sunlight. A proper diet should include foods with all of the six main nutrients: proteins which provide all essential amino acids, carbohydrates, vitamins, minerals, fats, and water.

Special Education

Have a "Health Day" in the classroom. Bring a few nutritious foods for students to eat. *CAUTION:* Make certain students are not allergic to foods. Obtain instructions for some simple exercises and let the students try the exercises in the classroom or gym. Designate a time for students to rest or read quietly. Set up an area of the classroom for students to use to check their appearance and wash their hands. (Provide a mirror, paper towels, and soap.)

♦ ***Suitable as a language development activity***

Exercise helps you grow.
Playing every day is good exercise.
Play the way these children do.
Run, jump, hop, and skip, too.
You also need rest to grow.
You need about ten hours of sleep.

2 TEACH

Teaching Tips

- **Possible Misconception:** Students might think that they have little control over their health. Explain that following the good health practices mentioned in this lesson can make a difference in how often students become ill.
- Write one day's school lunch menu on the chalkboard. Point out the variety of foods included. Question: **Why do you think different foods are served each day at school?** (because eating a variety of foods helps ensure that people get all the nutrients they need) Help the students read page 32 and *identify* the foods pictured.
- Ask students to *describe* what they like to do at recess and after school. Ask students to read page 33 to learn about different kinds of exercise they can do each day. Discuss the importance of getting enough sleep each night.

Workbook page 10 *

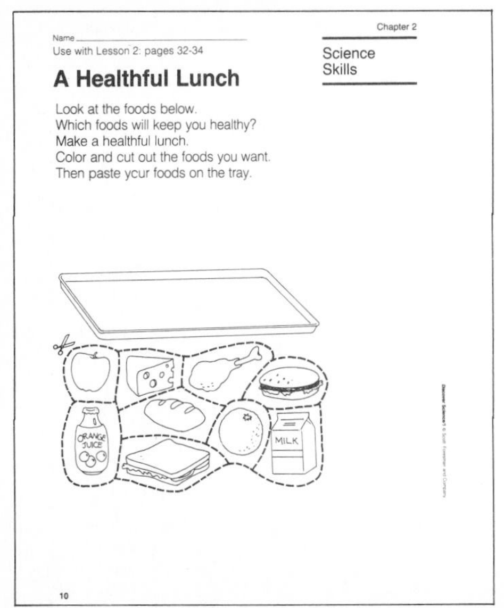

Name ______

Use with Lesson 2: pages 32-34

Chapter 2

Science Skills

A Healthful Lunch

Look at the foods below.
Which foods will keep you healthy?
Make a healthful lunch.
Color and cut out the foods you want.
Then paste ycur foods on the tray.

10

Workbook page 11 *

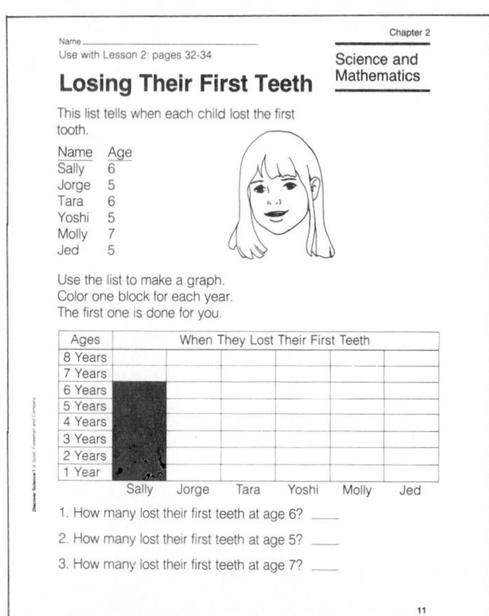

Name ______

Use with Lesson 2: pages 32-34

Chapter 2

Science and Mathematics

Losing Their First Teeth

This list tells when each child lost the first tooth.

Name	Age
Sally	6
Jorge	5
Tara	6
Yoshi	5
Molly	7
Jed	5

Use the list to make a graph.
Color one block for each year.
The first one is done for you.

Ages	When They Lost Their First Teeth					
8 Years						
7 Years						
6 Years						
5 Years						
4 Years						
3 Years						
2 Years						
1 Year						
	Sally	Jorge	Tara	Yoshi	Molly	Jed

1. How many lost their first teeth at age 6? ____
2. How many lost their first teeth at age 5? ____
3. How many lost their first teeth at age 7? ____

11

Enrichment

Introduce the four food groups (milk—cheese, vegetable—fruit, meat—poultry—fish—bean, and bread—cereal). Have each student choose one of the food groups and use construction paper, markers, wooden craft sticks, and string to make a mobile of the foods in that group.

* *Answers to masters on pages 24E–24F*

TEACHING PLAN

3 ASSESS

Lesson Review

1. You can help yourself grow by eating many different foods, resting, exercising, and keeping clean.
2. Keeping clean helps you stay well.
Challenge! Question: **What are some parts of your body that will never stop growing?** (hair, nails, skin) **Thinking Skill:** *Making Generalizations*

Find Out

Using magazines or food advertisements, students should find pictures, preferably in color, of meals that have foods from the four food groups. **Thinking Skill:** *Restating ideas*

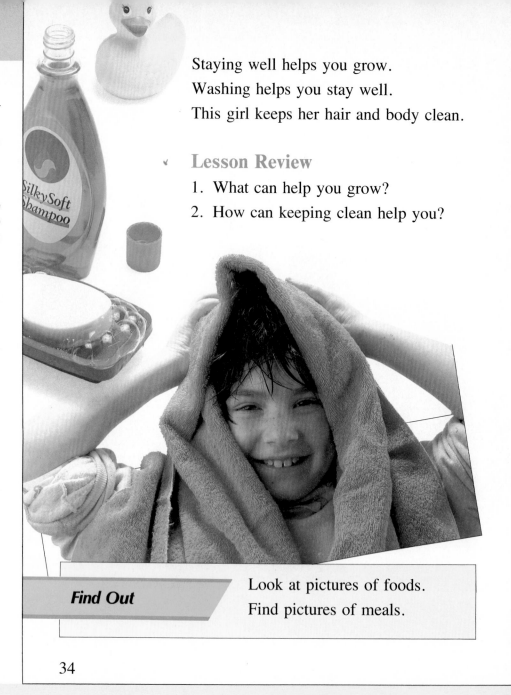

Staying well helps you grow.
Washing helps you stay well.
This girl keeps her hair and body clean.

Lesson Review

1. What can help you grow?
2. How can keeping clean help you?

Find Out

Look at pictures of foods.
Find pictures of meals.

34

Teaching Options

SCIENCE ANECDOTE

During growth spurts, children use energy just for the process of growing. Because of this, they need extra food and rest. During these periods, children may find that it is more difficult to study, pay attention, and cope with stress.

Reteaching Suggestion ♦

Have each student draw a self-portrait in the center of a large sheet of white paper. Ask students to look through magazines for pictures of foods that keep them healthy, people exercising or resting, and products that help keep people clean. Instruct students to cut the pictures out and paste them around their drawings.

Workbook page 12 *

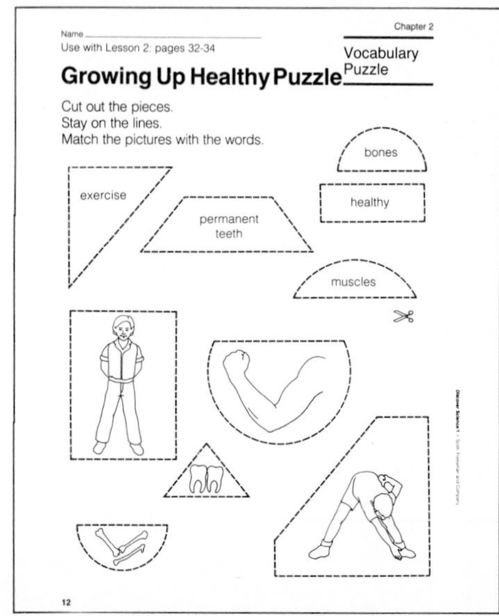

Name ______ Chapter 2
Use with Lesson 2: pages 32-34
Vocabulary Puzzle

Growing Up Healthy Puzzle

Cut out the pieces.
Stay on the lines.
Match the pictures with the words.

bones
exercise
permanent teeth
healthy
muscles

12

♦ ***Suitable as a language development activity***

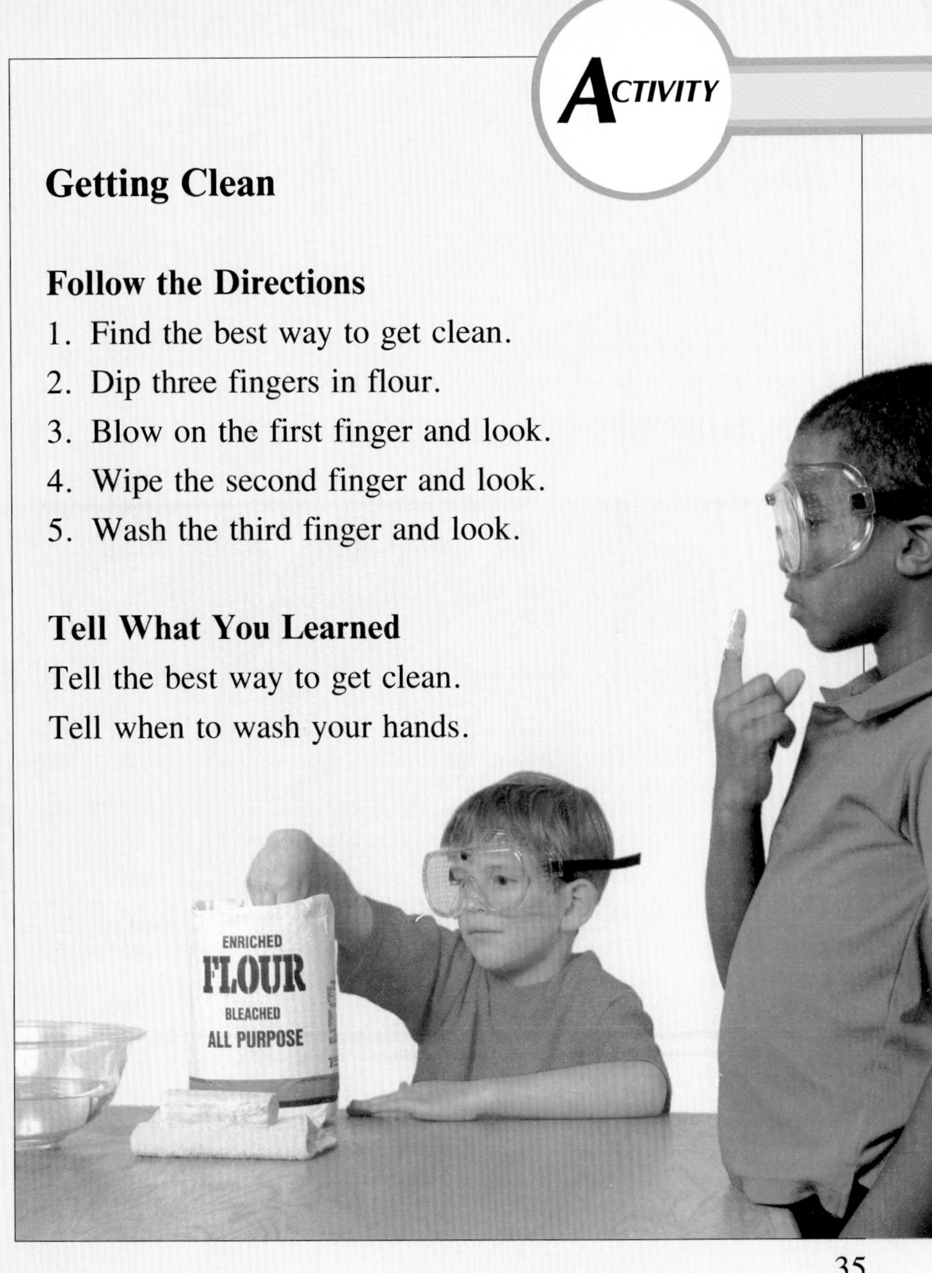

ACTIVITY

Getting Clean

Follow the Directions

1. Find the best way to get clean.
2. Dip three fingers in flour.
3. Blow on the first finger and look.
4. Wipe the second finger and look.
5. Wash the third finger and look.

Tell What You Learned

Tell the best way to get clean.

Tell when to wash your hands.

35

Concept

Washing with soap and water is the best way to remove dirt that contains germs that might cause illness.

Objectives/Process Skills

- *Observe* each finger after using a different cleaning method.
- *Compare* the cleaning methods.
- *Identify* the best way to remove dirt so that the germs it contains might not cause illness.

Materials

For each student: hand soap, water, paper towels, flour

Time Allotment

Allow 20 minutes.

Safety Tips (See page T27.)

- For students with wheat allergies, substitute corn starch for flour.
- Instruct students to wash their hands upon completing this activity.
- Remind students to immediately wipe up any water that spills on the floor to avoid slipping accidents.

Teaching Tip

- Ask students to *pretend* that the bowl of flour is a bowl of dirt.

Answers

Tell What You Learned

Students should state that the best way to get clean is to wash with soap and water. Students might state that a person should wash before meals, after using the bathroom, or after petting an animal.

Thinking Skill: *Drawing conclusions*

Enrichment Activity

Explain that germs can enter the body when the household items a person uses are dirty, even if the person's hands are clean. Discuss the importance of having clean towels, washcloths, and dishes to use. Then divide students into three groups. Let each group perform a comparative consumer test on a different type of cleaning product, such as laundry detergent, dishwashing liquid, and shampoo. Students should *evaluate* features of the product such as smell, cleaning ability, and price.

Activity Results

After students dip their hands in the flour, they should discover that washing their hands removes the flour better than any of the other methods do.

*** *Answers to masters on pages 24E-24F***

TEACHING PLAN

SKILLS FOR SOLVING PROBLEMS
pages 36–37

Purpose
To develop the skills of collecting and organizing information using metric rulers and charts to solve problems.

Materials
For each student: metric ruler, paper, colored pencils or crayons, blank chart to be used for recording measurements

1 MOTIVATE

Discussion
Tell students to pretend that they are buying new gloves. Discuss with students what they must consider before making their purchase. (glove size) Question: **How can you find out what size glove you need?** (measure your hand)

2 TEACH

Teaching Tip
- Point out the units of measurement on the ruler. Demonstrate the correct way to use the ruler by measuring a book, desk top, or any appropriate object.

Skills for Solving Problems

Measuring and Making a Chart
What can you learn from measuring?

1. Use a ruler.
   Measure your hand.
   Ask two friends to measure their hands.
   Write the numbers on your paper.

Teaching Options

SCIENCE BACKGROUND

The tendency to be tall or short is influenced by a variety of environmental factors. Most markedly, malnutrition can interrupt normal growth. Tobacco, alcohol, and drug use all interfere with adequate nutrition. Babies born to mothers who smoke tobacco may be shorter and smaller than their peers throughout childhood. People who use tobacco, drugs, and alcohol may suffer from malnutrition because these substances leach important nutrients from the body. In addition, drug and alcohol abusers tend to neglect their health and may fail to eat an adequate diet. Children are especially vulnerable to the effects of these substances, as their bodies are still growing.

2. Make a chart like the one shown.
   Use the numbers on your paper.
   Color in the chart.
   Show how long your hand is.
   Color in the chart for your friends.

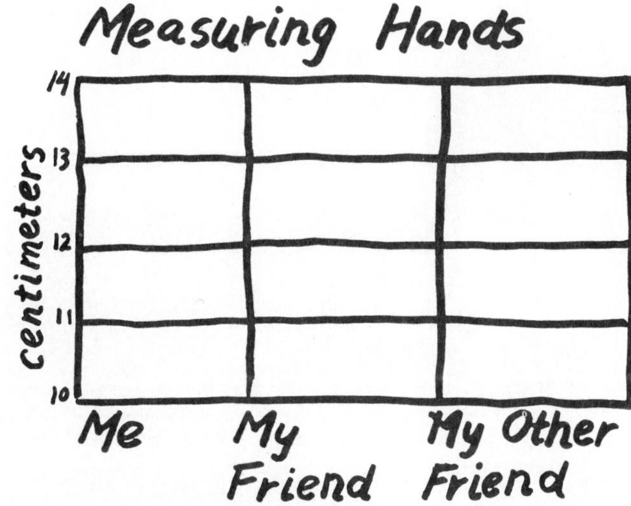

3. Look at the chart.
   What did measuring show?
   Does everyone grow the same?

37

Teaching Tips

- Make sure students align the end of their ruler with the top of their longest finger when measuring their hands.
- You might wish to draw the chart and make copies for students with coordination problems.

3 ASSESS

Measuring showed that students have different hand sizes. Everyone does not grow at the same rate or to the same size; growth is individual and varies from person to person.

Resource Book page 15 *

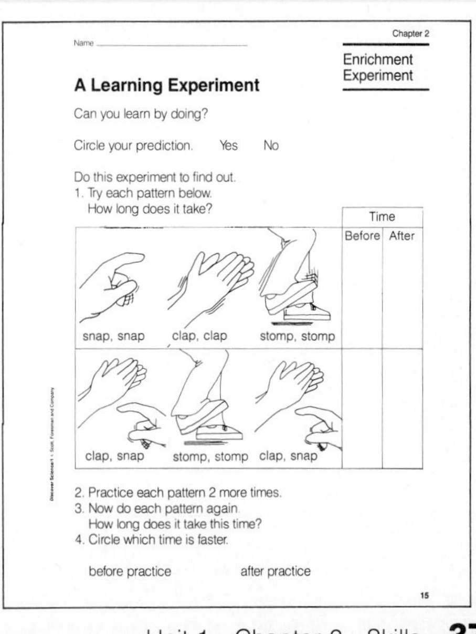

Name

Chapter 2

Enrichment Experiment

A Learning Experiment

Can you learn by doing?

Circle your prediction. Yes No

Do this experiment to find out.
1. Try each pattern below.
   How long does it take?

	Time Before	Time After
snap, snap / clap, clap / stomp, stomp		
clap, snap / stomp, stomp / clap, snap		

2. Practice each pattern 2 more times.
3. Now do each pattern again.
   How long does it take this time?
4. Circle which time is faster.

before practice after practice

15

* *Answers to masters on pages 24E-24F*

REVIEW PLAN

CHAPTER 2 REVIEW

pages 38–39

Review Chapter Ideas

1. The baby will grow in size. The baby's muscles and bones will grow larger, and he or she will get first teeth. As the baby grows into a child, he/she will learn to play with others.
2. First, you have small teeth; then, you get new, larger teeth to fit into your larger jaw.
3. As you grow, you learn new skills and games, and discover how to play together with others.
4. Eating a variety of foods, having enough rest, getting exercise, and staying clean can help you grow.
5. Good exercise involves playing actively. Running, jumping, hopping, and skipping are active exercises.
6. Keeping clean helps you stay well.

Chapter 2 Review

For further review, use Study Guide pages 230—231.

Review Chapter Ideas

1. Tell how this baby will change.
2. Tell how teeth change as you grow.
3. Explain what you learn as you grow.
4. Tell what helps you grow.
5. Tell what good exercise is.
6. Tell how keeping clean helps you.

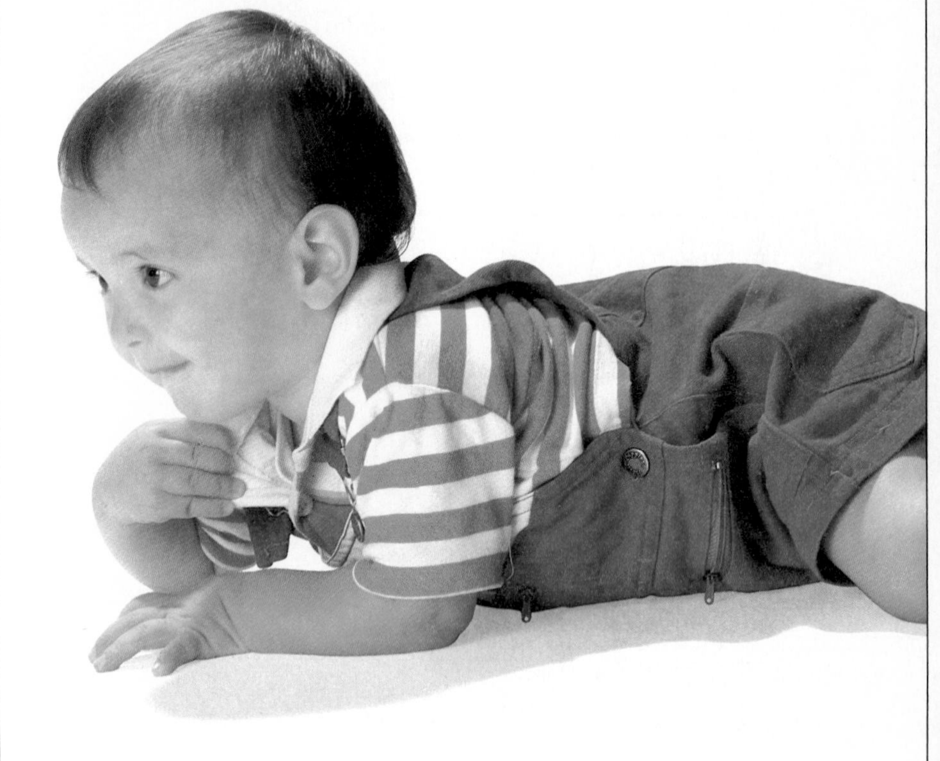

38

Review Options

Cooperative Learning ♦

STAD Format (See page T24.)
Assign students to work in four- to five-member teams to study Chapter 2 Review. Students should work together to make sure that they and their teammates know the material in the chapter. After students have had enough time to study together, give them a test to complete individually (Chapter 2 Test in the *Test Book*). Award Superteam certificates to teams whose average test scores exceed 90%, and Greatteam certificates to teams whose average test scores exceed 80%.

Test Book page 11 *

Name ______________

Chapter 2 Test

Growing and Changing

I. Write **Yes** or **No.**

1. Does your size change as you grow?
2. Do you learn new things as your body changes?
3. Are your first teeth permanent teeth
4. Are different foods good for you?
5. Does exercise hurt your body?

II. Draw a line from the word to the right picture.

1. bones 2. muscles 3. exercise

11

♦ ***Suitable as a language development activity***

Review Science Words

Match the words and the pictures.

1. bones
2. exercise
3. muscles
4. permanent teeth

a. 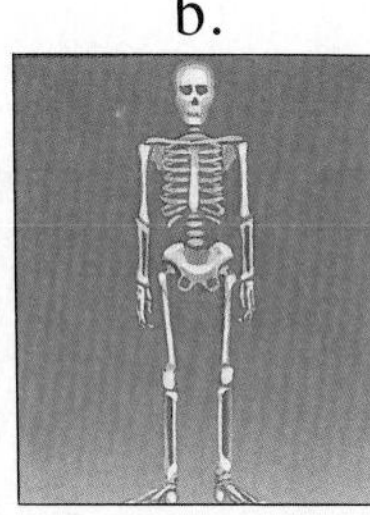

b. 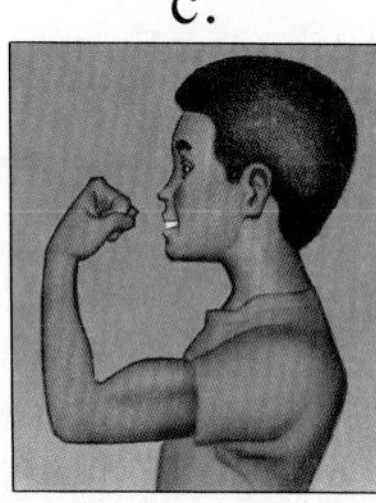

c. 

d.

Tell what the word means.

5. healthy

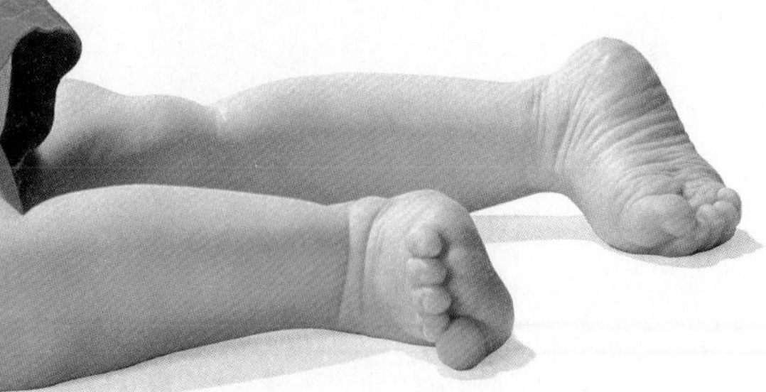

Use Science Ideas

What can help this baby stay healthy?

Review Science Words

Match the words and pictures.

1. b **2.** a
3. c **4.** d

Tell what the words mean.
Thinking Skill: *Restating or explaining ideas*
5. Healthy means to be in good health, not to be sick.

Use Science Ideas

Food, soap, and water will help the baby stay healthy. **Thinking Skill:** *Recognizing factual and logical inconsistencies*

*** Answers to masters on pages 24E-24F**

TEACHING PLAN

CAREERS

Purpose

This feature explains how dentists and dental assistants care for teeth. Children should begin regular visits to the dentist at age two or three. If children begin their visits at an early age, they will establish good dental habits.

Teaching Tips

- Discuss the procedure dental professionals follow when checking a patient's teeth. (A dental professional looks at the teeth, uses dental instruments to check for flaws, takes X rays when necessary, and so on.)
- Have students *name* the machines and tools they recognize in the picture. Discuss the function of each.
- Question: **What are some other careers that involve taking care of your health?** (Students might mention doctors, nurses, paramedics, and so on.)

Careers

Dentists and Helpers

Dentists and their helpers study teeth.
They clean teeth and fix them.
They use special machines and tools.
They show people how to brush.
They show people how to floss.
Dentists help people care for teeth.

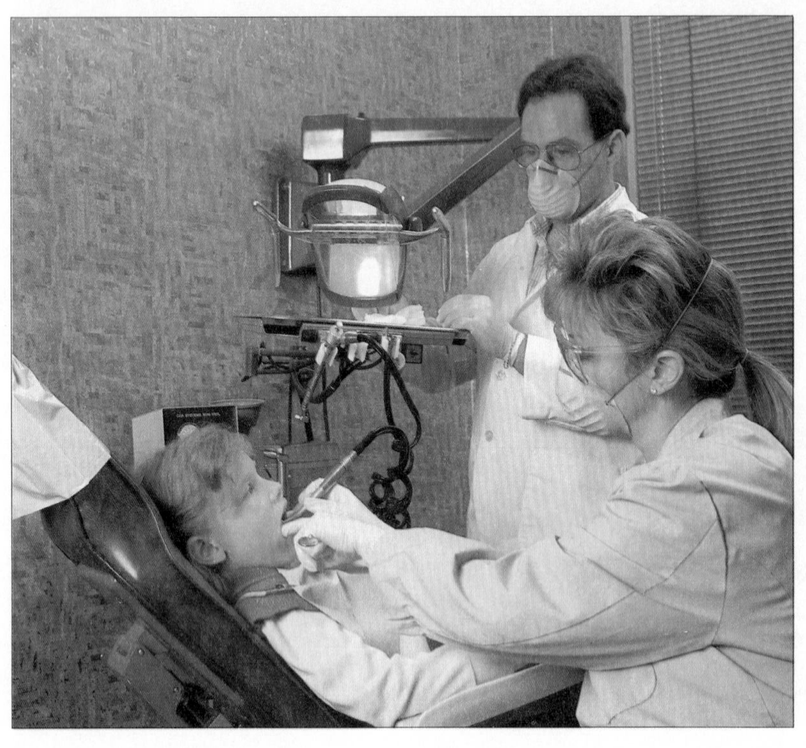

Teaching Options

Enrichment

Read the following sentences aloud to the class. Tell students to clap their hands if the sentence describes a good dental practice, and to remain silent if the sentence describes a dental practice that should be avoided.

1. Brush your teeth after meals.
2. Use your teeth to help you open a package.
3. Eat raw vegetables as snacks.
4. Eat sweet, sticky foods as snacks.
5. Grind your teeth.
6. Eat and drink dairy products every day.
7. Brush and floss your teeth every day.

Where to Write

For additional information about these careers contact:
American Dental Hygienists Association, 444 N. Michigan Avenue, Chicago, Illinois 60611.
National Dental Hygienists Association, 5506 Connecticut Avenue NW, Washington, DC 20015.
American Dental Association, 211 E. Chicago Avenue, Chicago, Illinois 60611.

How It Works

Stethoscope

This doctor uses a stethoscope.
It helps him hear body sounds.

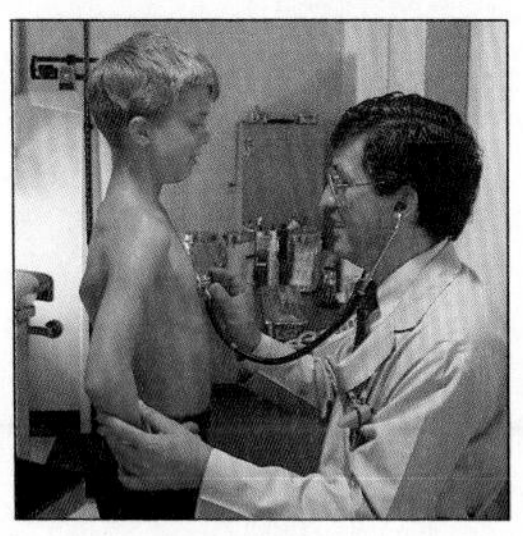

A stethoscope has two sides.
The smaller side is for low sounds.
The larger side is for higher sounds.

The sounds travel through the tubes.
Then the doctor can hear the sounds.

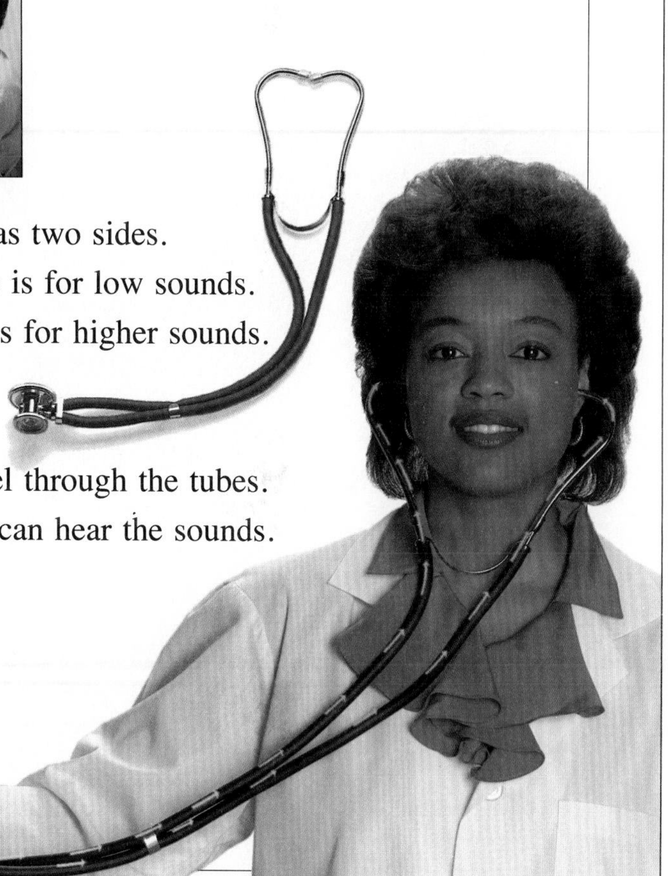

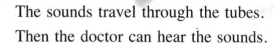

HOW IT WORKS

Teaching Tips

- After students read page 41, lead a discussion about medical checkups. Question: **Did you ever listen to your heartbeat through a stethoscope?** Let any student who has had the experience *describe* the sounds.
- A cardboard tube, such as the one inside a roll of paper towels, can function as a stethoscope. Bring in some tubes and let students work in pairs listening to one another's heartbeat. Explain that the stethoscope makes the heartbeat sound much louder and clearer than the tubes can.
- You might fashion a stethoscope that amplifies sound by attaching a small funnel to a piece of rubber tubing. Place the funnel over a volunteer's heart while another volunteer listens by putting the free end of the tube near his or her outer ear. *CAUTION:* Remind students to never put anything into their ears.
- Question: **What other tools does a doctor use to examine a person?** (Students might mention instruments used for looking into ears, eyes, and throats.)

SCIENCE BACKGROUND

A French physician, René Laënnec, invented the stethoscope in 1816. Before then, physicians listened to the heartbeat by placing their ear directly on the patient's chest. Physicians use stethoscopes to listen to the lungs, intestines, and blood vessels as well as to the heart. The stethoscope makes the sounds easier to hear because it picks up just the sounds made by the organs being examined and excludes other sounds.

REVIEW PLAN

UNIT 1 REVIEW

Answer the Questions

1. You use the five senses for hearing, seeing, tasting, smelling, and touching.
2. Your eyes, ears, nose, skin, and tongue help you learn.
3. As you grow, you will get bigger, grow new teeth, and learn new skills.
4. The baby in the picture has a few first teeth. The six-year-old is missing some first teeth, and the adult has only permanent teeth.
5. A variety of foods, sleep, exercise, and cleanliness help you grow.

Study the Picture

You could see everything; you could hear the sound of the fire and the birds; you could smell the smoke; you could touch the dog and the cat, and feel the heat from the fire. (Accept other reasonable answers.) The senses you could use for safety include seeing, hearing, and smelling. **Thinking Skill:** *Applying information to new situations*

Unit 1 Review

Answer the Questions

1. How do you use your five senses?
2. What body parts help you learn?
3. How will you change as you grow?
4. Look at the picture.
   What changes in teeth do you see?
5. What helps you grow?

Study the Pictures

How could you use your senses here?

a. b. c. d.

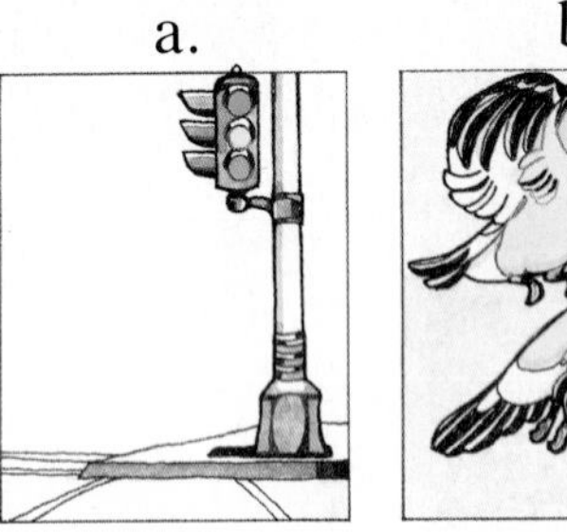

42

Review Options

Test Book page 13

Name ____________

Unit Test

Human Body

I. Write **Yes** or **No.**

1. Are different foods good for you?
2. Does your size change as you grow?
3. Does exercise hurt your body?
4. Are your first teeth permanent teeth?
5. Do you learn new things as your body changes?

II. Draw a line from the word to the right picture.

1. seeing 2. hearing 3. touching 4. smelling 5. tasting

13

What to Do

1. Look at the picture.
   Play the game.
   Ask a friend to put things in a box.
   Touch each thing and tell what it is.
   Put different things in the box.
   Ask a friend to guess.

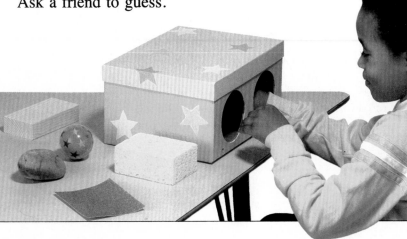

2. Work with your classmates.
   Make up a poem about hearing.
   Describe sounds you like to hear.
3. Draw a picture of yourself.
   Show a way you help yourself grow.

UNIT PROJECTS

Teaching Tips

1. Collect a variety of objects that have different textures. In addition to the objects shown in the illustration, include classroom objects such as paper clips, crayons, a paint brush, and so on.
2. Read several poems to the students. Point out that some poems rhyme, and some do not. Emphasize to the students that our hearing allows us to enjoy poetry and music. Ask students to ***name*** some sounds they like to hear. Give students time to work together and make up a poem about hearing.
3. Have students ***recall*** what they can do to help themselves grow. (eat a variety of foods, exercise, rest, and keep clean)

Books in Spanish

Oxenbury, Helen. Series of books that encourages young children to explore new experiences with hearing, touch, and sight. Ediciones Alta, 1985. (grades ps–k) *Oiga con mis oidos* (hearing). *Toco con mis manos* (touch). *Veo, veo* (sight).
Parramon, J.M. and Ruis, Maria. Series of five books each of which explores one of the senses. Barron, 1983. (grade ps–k) *El oido* (hearing). *La vista* (sight). *El olfato* (smell). *El gusto* (taste). *El tacto* (touch).
Selsam, Millicent E. *Como crecen los perritos.* (How puppies grow.) Scholastic, 1986. (grades k–3)

Books for Students

Gaskin, John. *The Senses.* Watts, 1985. Discusses the five senses in simple terms. (grades 3–4)
Iveson-Iveson, Joan. *Your Health.* Bookwright, 1985. Explains the importance of cleanliness, proper foods, exercise, and sleep in staying healthy.
Krementz, Jill. *Taryn Goes To the Dentist.* Crown, 1986. Records a first visit to a pediatric dentist. (grades ps–k)
Richardson, Joy. *What Happens When You Grow?* Gareth Stevens, 1986. Traces the process of growth from infancy to adulthood. (grades 3–4)

Planning Guide

Unit Components			Pages
Unit Overview			44–45
Chapter 3 Living and Nonliving	**Lesson 1** What Is a Living Thing? **Lesson 2** What Do Living Things Need?	**Lesson 3** What Are Nonliving Things Like?	46–63
Chapter 4 Learning About Plants	**Lesson 1** How Are Plants Alike and Different? **Lesson 2** How Do Plants Grow?	**Lesson 3** What Do Plants Need To Grow? **Lesson 4** Why Do People Need Plants?	64–83
Chapter 5 Learning About Animals	**Lesson 1** What Ways Are Animals Different? **Lesson 2** How Do Animals Grow?	**Lesson 3** Why Do People Need Animals? **Lesson 4** How Can You Care for a Pet?	84–101
Careers	pet store worker		102
How It Works	Fireflies		103
Unit Review			104
Unit Projects			105

Science Process Skills Book
The Science Process Skills Book contains worksheets that can be used to teach and then assess student mastery of the basic science process skills. In addition, other worksheets in this book teach students the manipulative skills they will need to use basic science equipment. Assign these worksheets whenever you think it fits in your curriculum.

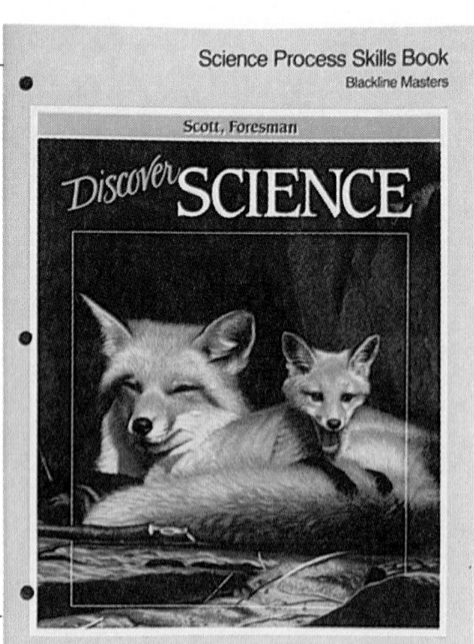

Science Resources for the Unit

Resource Books

MacFarlane, & Alford, Ruth B. *Collecting and Preserving Plants for Science and Pleasure*. Arco, 1985. Offers guidance on methods for gathering, preserving, identifying, mounting, storing, and displaying a variety of plants.

Silver, Donald M. *The Animal World: From Single-Cell Creatures to Giants of the Land and Sea*. Random, 1987. The book covers all the major animal groups: one-celled animals, sponges, jellyfish, corals, mollusk, worms, insects, fishes, amphibians, reptiles, birds, and mammals.

Wilson, Jennifer Bauer. *A Naturalist's Teaching Manual: Activities and Ideas for Teaching Natural History*. Prentice-Hall, 1986.

Community Resources

Take students on a tour of a nursery. Ask the nurseryman to tell the class about caring for plants. Discuss the various ways plants can be purchased, such as seeds, bulbs, seedlings, or small plants.

Visit a pet shop or an animal hospital. Ask the veterinarian or another person who provides animal care to speak to the students about how to take care of pets.

Audio-Visual Resources

Animal Babies. National Geographic. Film or video, 15 minutes. Introduces a variety of familiar and exotic animals and their offspring.

Animal Homes. Churchill. Film, 10 1/2 minutes. Shows a variety of animals living in their homes and using them for safety, for shelter, for food storage, and for raising their young.

Animals Are Different and Alike. Coronet. Film, 11 minutes. Jimmy's observations on a farm lead him to group animals by characteristics.

Animals Growing Up. Britannica. Film, 11 minutes. Shows the growth and development of puppies, a calf, and chicks during the first weeks of life.

Care of Pets. Britannica. Film, 13 minutes. Shows that proper feeding, grooming, shelter, exercise, and training of pets helps ensure their health.

Harold and His Amazing Green Plants. Walt Disney Educational Media. Film or video, 8 minutes. A basic botany lesson follows the life cycle of a green plant from seed to maturity.

Insects in a Garden. Britannica. Film, 11 minutes. Reveals aphids, green lacewings, ladybugs, and ants living on a rose bush.

Living or Nonliving? National Geographic. Film or video, 16 minutes. The film explores examples of how living things are nourished, how they grow and respond to the world around them, and how they produce other living things like themselves.

Putting Animals in Groups. International. Film, 13 minutes. Describes clearly and simply the characteristics of groups of animals.

The World of Plants. National Geographic. Filmstrips with cassettes, 12–13 minutes each. *The Parts of a Plant, How Plants Grow, Kinds of Plants, Where Plants Grow,* and *Plants and People*.

Computer Software

All About Dinosaurs. Orange Cherry Media. Apple II+, IIe. General information and descriptions of various types of dinosaurs.

Animals and Insects. Scott, Foresman. Apple II+, IIe. Introduces children to the language associated with familiar objects and activities.

Plants and How They Grow. Right-On. Apple II. Basic introduction to the parts of plants and trees.

INTRODUCING UNIT 2

Unit Overview

This unit is about living things and how they differ from nonliving things. Living things grow and maintain themselves by taking in nutrients. They respond to stimuli, and they reproduce themselves. Plants, as living organisms, have special parts for absorbing and making energy, and for reproduction. Animals have different characteristics and patterns of growth.

About the Photograph

The picture of a frog and lily pads illustrates the vast differences in living things. However, all living things are alike in many ways. For example, all organisms exhibit six basic life processes—taking in nutrients and energy, releasing energy, eliminating wastes, growing, reproducing, and responding to stimuli.

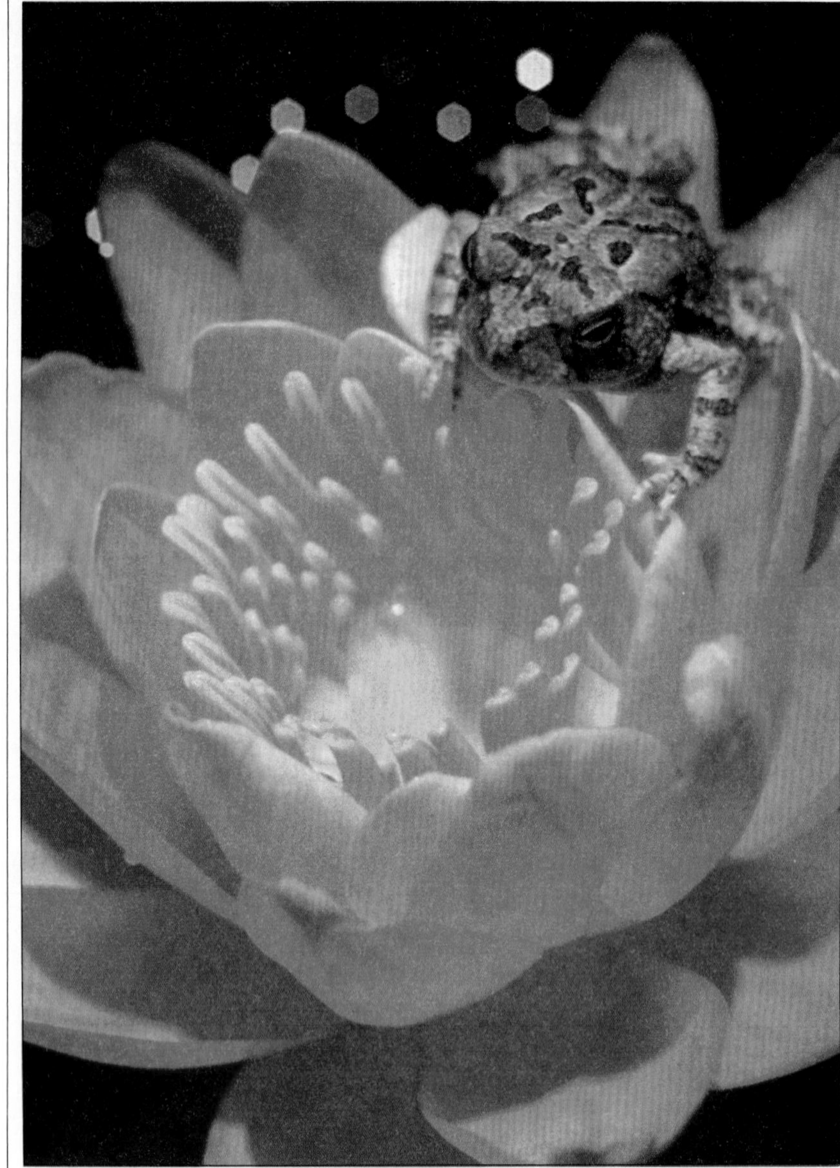

44

Teaching Options

Chapter 3 Preview

Living and Nonliving

This chapter discusses the activities that living things can do. Living things grow and change, respond to stimuli, move on their own, and reproduce themselves. All living things are interdependent—animals need plants, and plants need animals.

Chapter 4 Preview

Learning About Plants

The chapter focuses on the similarities and differences in plants. Students will learn that plants have roots, stems, leaves, and flowers. Students will observe leaves, and classify them by shape. They , also, will learn that some plants grow from seeds, and that plants grow in a variety of habitats. Students will explore the ways plants can be useful to people.

[1]answers will vary

Unit 2

Life Science

This frog and flower are living things.
They both need air to live.
The frog and flower need water, too.

What other living things can you name?[1]
Work with someone in your class.
Think of other living things.

Teaching Tips

- Ask students if they have ever seen a department store mannequin that looked like a real person. Ask: **How could you tell that the mannequin was not alive?** (Students might say that it felt cold, did not breathe, did not move, and that it felt hard when touched.) Explain that Unit 2 will discuss some differences between living and nonliving things.
- After reading the text and studying the picture, have volunteers ***describe*** how the lily and the frog are alike. (For example, they both take in nutrients, reproduce, need water, and so on.)
- After the class discussion, have the students write a story about a day in the life of a frog. Encourage the students to include such topics as what kind of food it would eat, how it gets food and water, and where it would live.

Chapter 5 Preview

Learning About Animals
This chapter focuses on animals and how they are different in size, shape, covering, and the ways they move. Students will learn which animals care for their young and which animals have babies that look like their parents. The chapter further explains how animals are benefical to people, and which animals make good pets.

Teaching Plan

Chapter Components	Skills	Materials
Chapter Opener/*TRY THIS*: Drawing What You Do pp. 46-47	***TRY THIS*** p. 47 **Science Process Skills** *Communicating, Inferring*	***TRY THIS*** p. 47 (individual) 30 sheets drawing paper, 30 boxes crayons, 30 pencils
Lesson 1: What Is a Living Thing? pp. 48-50	**Thinking Skills** Challenge!: *Comparing* Find Out: *Making generalizations, Collecting information*	**Demonstration** p. 48 dolls or stuffed animals
Activity: Observing Mealworms p. 51	**Science Process Skills** *Observing, Communicating*	(groups of 2) 15 mealworms, 15 flashlights, 1 box oatmeal
Lesson 2: What Do Living Things Need? pp. 52-54	**Thinking Skills** Challenge!: *Making inferences* Find Out: *Making inferences*	**Demonstration** p. 52 live nontoxic plant and plastic plant
Science in Your Life: Traveling in Space p. 55	**Thinking Skill** *Inferring*	
Lesson 3: What Are Nonliving Things Like? pp. 56-58	**Thinking Skills** Challenge!: *Contrasting, Making inferences* Find Out: *Generalizing, Restating information*	**Demonstration** p. 56 several objects (rock, toy car, doll, jar of paste, crayons)
Activity: Discovering What is Alive p. 59	**Science Process Skill** *Observing*	(groups of 2) 3 bags light brown aquarium stones, 400 grams mung beans, 15 plastic trays, water, 30 sheets drawing paper, 30 boxes crayons, 30 pencils
Skills for Solving Problems: Observing and Making a Graph pp. 60-61	**Problem Solving Skills** *Making decisions/Identifying and solving problems, Interpreting charts, maps, and graphs*	(individual) drawing paper and crayons, colored pencils, or colored markers
Chapter Review pp. 62-63	**Thinking Skills** *Restating or explaining ideas, Recognizing factual and logical inconsistencies*	

Teaching Options

Strategies	Extensions		Resource Masters
			Family Letter: *Resource Book* p. 19 Vocabulary Preview: *Workbook* pp. 13-14
	Enrichment p. 48 Science and Language Arts p. 49 Special Education p. 49	Reinforcement p. 49 Reteaching Suggestion p. 50	Science Skills: *Workbook* p. 15
	Enrichment Activity p. 51		
	Science and Math p. 52 Special Education p. 53 Reinforcement p. 53	Enrichment p. 53 Reteaching Suggestion p. 54	Science and Language Arts: *Workbook* p. 16
	Enrichment p. 56 Game Suggestion p. 57 Special Education p. 57 Reteaching Suggestion p. 58		Science Activity: *Workbook* p. 17 Vocabulary Puzzle: *Workbook* p. 18
	Enrichment Activity p. 59		
			Enrichment Activity: *Resource Book* p. 23
Cooperative Learning p. 62 (Also see p. T23)			Chapter Test: *Test Book* p. 15

Preteaching Suggestions

For Advance Preparation

Activity, page 51

Obtain 2–3 dozen mealworms from a pet store. Have oatmeal or bran and apple pieces available for food. Hand lenses or hand mirrors for each group are optional, but helpful. (The mealworms can be kept dormant for 2–3 weeks and used again for the activity in Chapter 5. Keep the dormant mealworms in a glass container with oatmeal or bran and apple pieces.)

Activity, page 59

Obtain 2 lbs. tan-colored aquarium gravel, 1/4 lb. each of 4–5 different types of dry beans, 2–3 dozen shallow plastic or plastic-foam containers, and containers for pouring.

For Vocabulary Review

Use the following sentences with your students to review the meanings of the underlined words.

1. You feel air moving when the wind blows.
2. The stars are far away in space.
3. Observing ants can teach you where ants live and what they eat.
4. The girl touched the elephant to feel its rough skin.

For High-Potential Students

Further students' understanding of how living processes, such as growth and decay, and nonliving processes, such as freezing, melting, and rusting, can change things over time. Ask students to make lists of "things that change," "things that do not change," and "things that might or might not change." (The last category is for things students cannot decide about.) Discuss the items in each category. Be aware that students may not realize that items such as large trees, bushes, and rocks change. Discuss whether the changes that occurr involve living or nonliving processes.

Mainstreamed Students

Emotionally Handicapped

Let emotionally handicapped students care for a living pet, such as fish. Make sure to supervise their care of the living organisms. Have the students describe differences in the amount and type of care each pet needs.

Hearing Impaired

Because some hearing-impaired students will have difficulty understanding abstract concepts initially, try to give concrete examples of the concepts of "living" and "not living." For example, you could compare a real puppy to a stuffed puppy by hugging, walking, and feeding the puppy, and ignoring the stuffed animal. You may wish to bring in pictures of these actions if it is inconvenient to bring in a pet. Stress that the living thing requires certain care, different from the nonliving thing.

For Science Fair Projects

Encourage interested students to do one of the following projects:

1. Choose a living thing (plant or animal) and care for it over a period of time. Keep a journal that describes how the plant or animal was cared for each day. Take photographs or make drawings of how the plant or animal changed over time.
2. Make a display by taking photographs of various things and classifying them as living or nonliving.
3. Observe the life cycle of a living thing such as a caterpillar, which makes a cocoon and then turns into a butterfly. Make drawings that illustrate the life cycle.

Classroom Resources

Bulletin Board
After students identify which things are living and which are nonliving, have them bring in pictures of living and nonliving things to add to the bulletin board.

WHICH ONES ARE LIVING?

Chapter 3 Poster

What will your pet need?

Science Discovery Center
Use pages from Chapter 3 in the *Science Discovery Center Book*. Place these worksheets in the appropriate pockets in the Science Discovery Center.

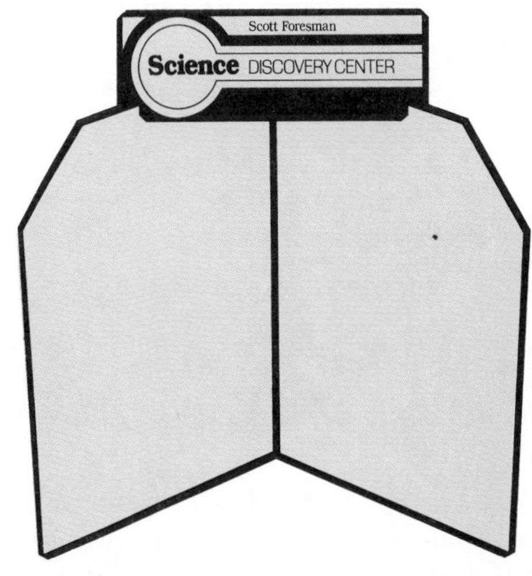
Scott Foresman
Science DISCOVERY CENTER

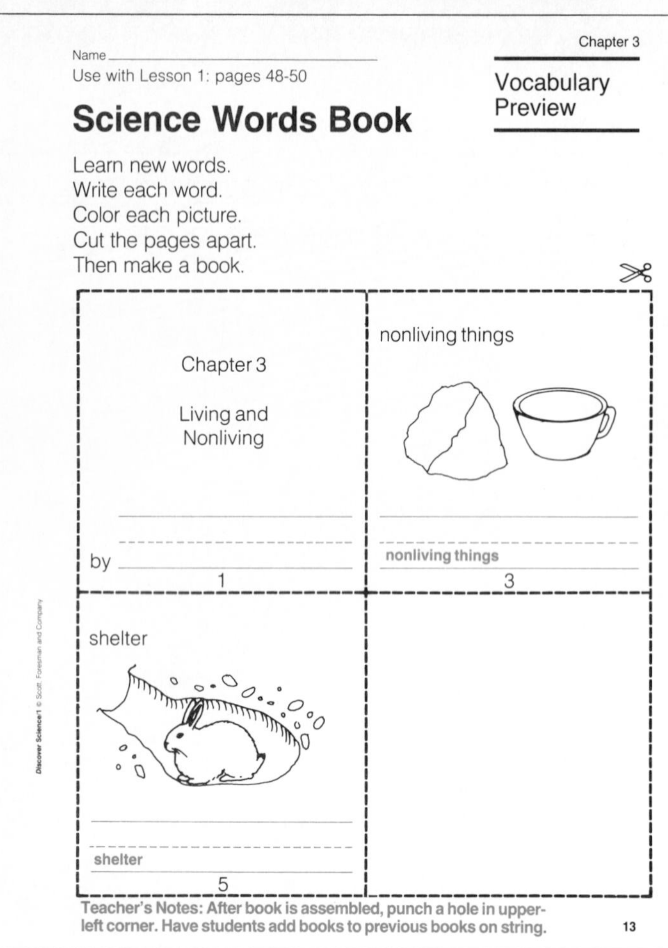

Name ______________________

Use with Lesson 1: pages 48-50

Chapter 3

Vocabulary Preview

Science Words Book

Learn new words.
Write each word.
Color each picture.
Cut the pages apart.
Then make a book.

Chapter 3

Living and Nonliving

by ______________

1

nonliving things

nonliving things

3

shelter

shelter

5

Teacher's Notes: After book is assembled, punch a hole in upper-left corner. Have students add books to previous books on string.

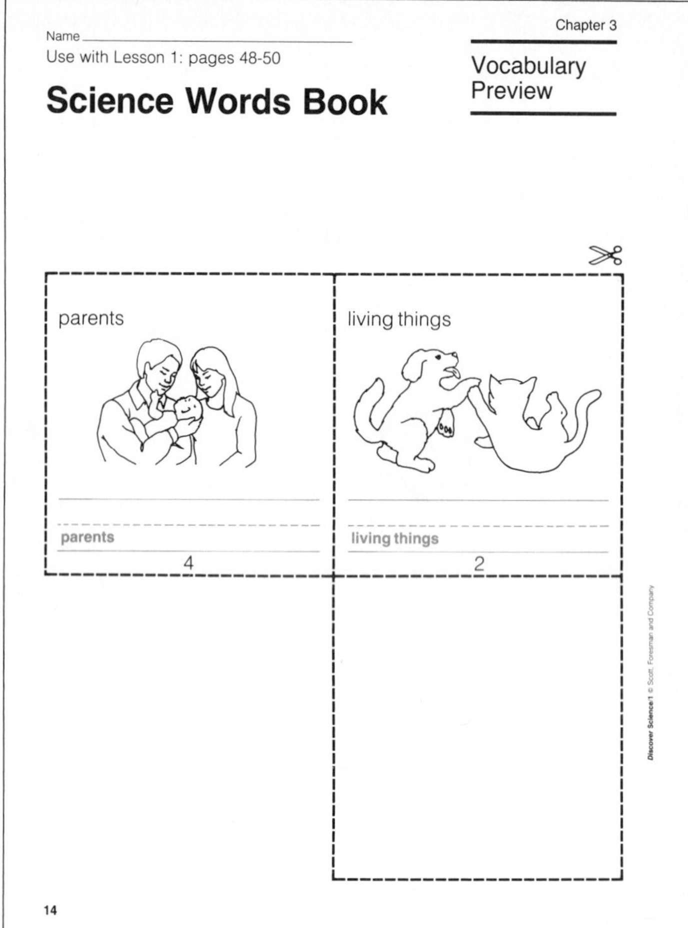

Name ______________________

Use with Lesson 1: pages 48-50

Chapter 3

Vocabulary Preview

Science Words Book

parents

parents

4

living things

living things

2

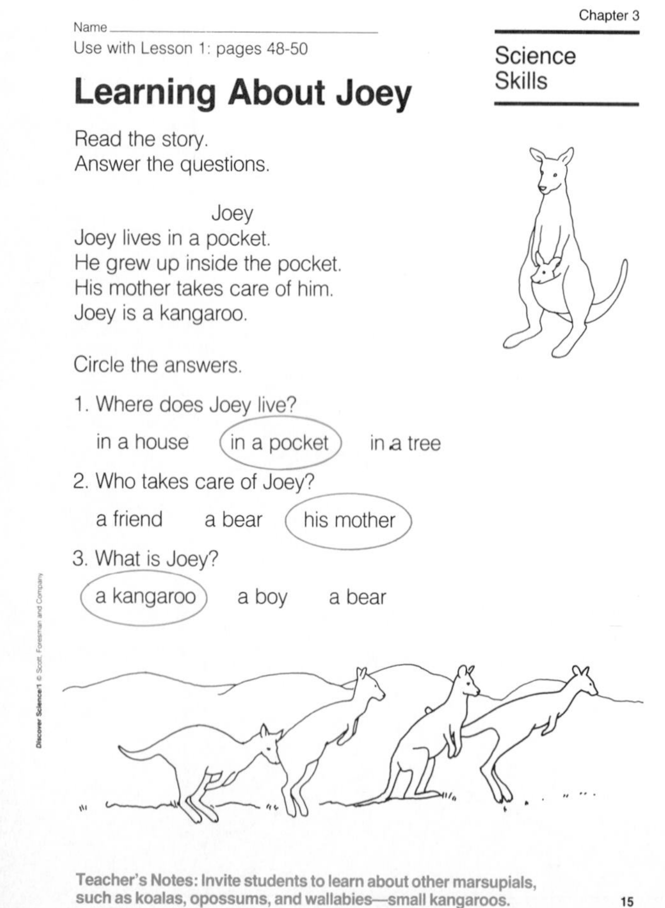

Name ______________________

Use with Lesson 1: pages 48-50

Chapter 3

Science Skills

Learning About Joey

Read the story.
Answer the questions.

Joey

Joey lives in a pocket.
He grew up inside the pocket.
His mother takes care of him.
Joey is a kangaroo.

Circle the answers.

1. Where does Joey live?
   in a house   (in a pocket)   in a tree
2. Who takes care of Joey?
   a friend   a bear   (his mother)
3. What is Joey?
   (a kangaroo)   a boy   a bear

Teacher's Notes: Invite students to learn about other marsupials, such as koalas, opossums, and wallabies—small kangaroos.

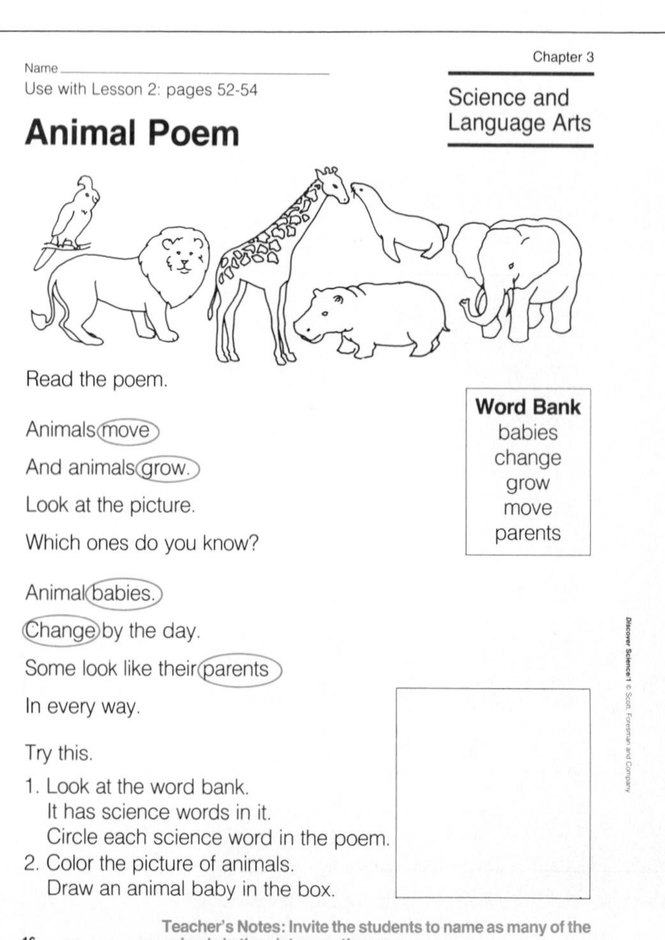

Name ______________________

Use with Lesson 2: pages 52-54

Chapter 3

Science and Language Arts

Animal Poem

Read the poem.

Word Bank
babies
change
grow
move
parents

Animals (move)
And animals (grow.)
Look at the picture.
Which ones do you know?

Animal (babies.)
(Change) by the day.
Some look like their (parents)
In every way.

Try this.

1. Look at the word bank.
   It has science words in it.
   Circle each science word in the poem.
2. Color the picture of animals.
   Draw an animal baby in the box.

Teacher's Notes: Invite the students to name as many of the animals in the picture as they can.

Name ____________________

Use with Lesson 3: pages 52-54

Chapter 3

Science Activity

Living or Nonliving?

Look at the things around you.
Draw pictures of living things you see.
Draw pictures of nonliving things you see.

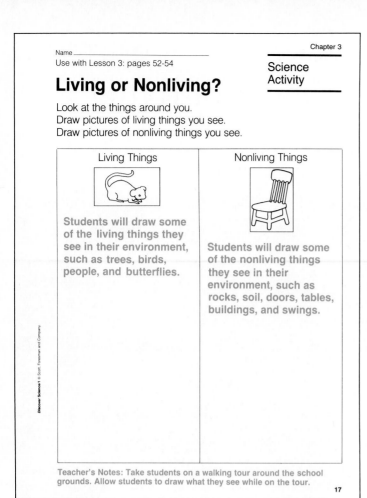

Living Things	Nonliving Things
Students will draw some of the living things they see in their environment, such as trees, birds, people, and butterflies.	Students will draw some of the nonliving things they see in their environment, such as rocks, soil, doors, tables, buildings, and swings.

Teacher's Notes: Take students on a walking tour around the school grounds. Allow students to draw what they see while on the tour.

Name ____________________

Use with Lesson 3: pages 56-58

Chapter 3

Vocabulary Puzzle

Puzzle

Read the words in the word bank.
Match each word with a picture.
Write the word in the puzzle.
Write one letter in each box.

Word Bank
living things
nonliving things
parents
shelter

Across: n o n l i v i n g t h i n g s; p a r e n t s

Down: l i v i n g t h i n g s; s h e l t e r

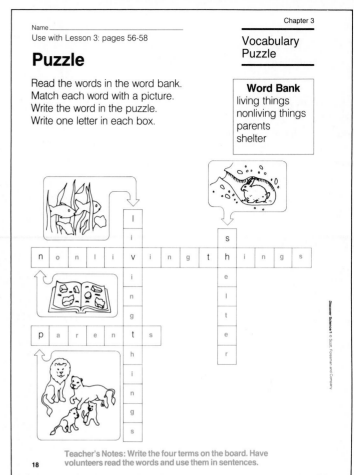

Teacher's Notes: Write the four terms on the board. Have volunteers read the words and use them in sentences.

Name ____________________

Chapter 3

Enrichment Experiment

An Earthworm Experiment

Does an earthworm go to light?

Circle your prediction. Yes No Accept any answer.

Do this experiment to find out.

1. Make an earthworm home like the one below.

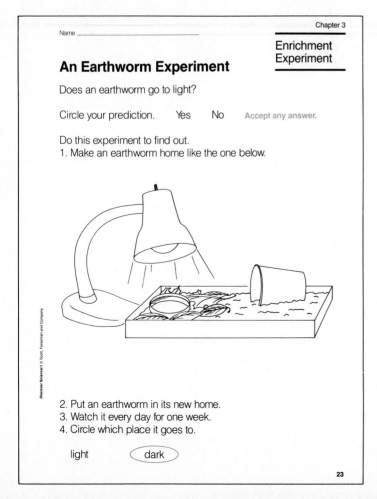

2. Put an earthworm in its new home.
3. Watch it every day for one week.
4. Circle which place it goes to.

light (dark)

Name ____________________

Chapter 3 Test

Living and Nonliving

I. Write **Yes** or **No.**

1. Is a plant a living thing? (3-1) Yes
2. Do living things stay the same size? (3-1) No
3. Do people need air to stay alive? (3-2) Yes
4. Is a rock a nonliving thing? (3-3) Yes
5. Do nonliving things eat or drink? (3-3) No

II. Draw a line from the word to the right picture.

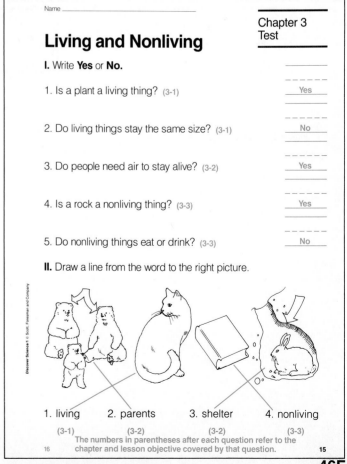

1. living (3-1) 2. parents (3-2) 3. shelter (3-2) 4. nonliving (3-3)

The numbers in parentheses after each question refer to the chapter and lesson objective covered by that question.

TEACHING PLAN

INTRODUCING CHAPTER 3

Major Concepts

Lesson 1 Living things grow and reproduce. Living things also can move on their own.
Lesson 2 Living things require water, food, air, and shelter.
Lesson 3 Nonliving things do not grow and do not move on their own.

Vocabulary

living things, nonliving things, parents, shelter

[1]figure can only be moved by someone else
[2]does not move, breathe, or grow

Chapter 3

Living and Nonliving

This figure looks alive.
What do you think it can do?[1]
How can you tell it is not alive?[2]

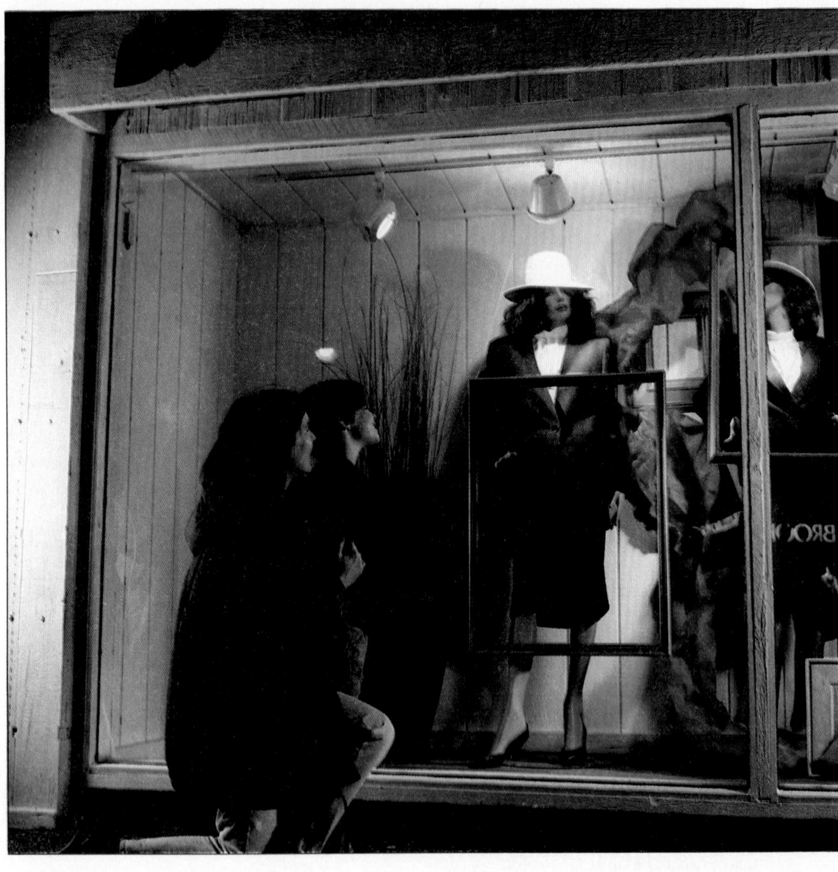

46

Teaching Options

Workbook page 13 *

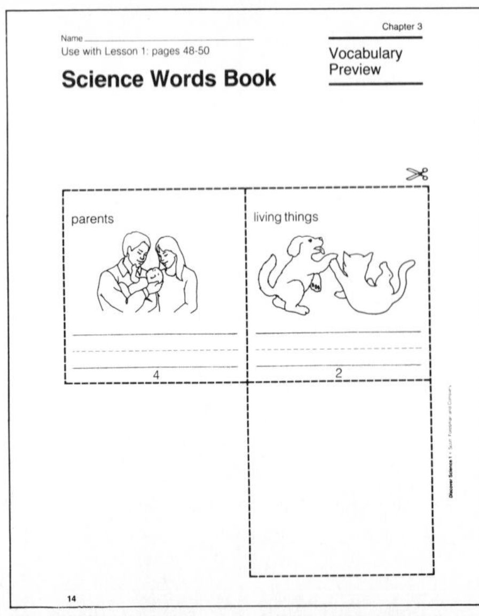

Name ____________
Use with Lesson 1: pages 48-50

Chapter 3
Vocabulary Preview

Science Words Book

parents	living things
4	2

14

Workbook page 14 *

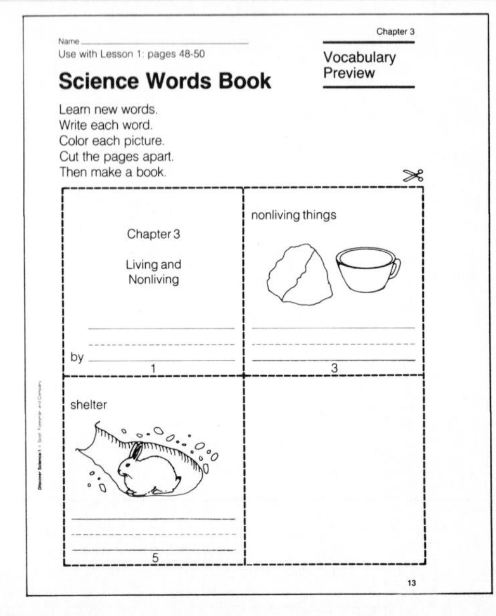

Name ____________
Use with Lesson 1: pages 48-50

Chapter 3
Vocabulary Preview

Science Words Book

Learn new words.
Write each word.
Color each picture.
Cut the pages apart.
Then make a book.

Chapter 3 Living and Nonliving by ______	nonliving things
1	3
shelter	
5	

13

♦ ***Suitable as a language development activity***

Starting the Chapter

You are alive.

You can do many things.

You can draw what you do.

Then read more about living things.

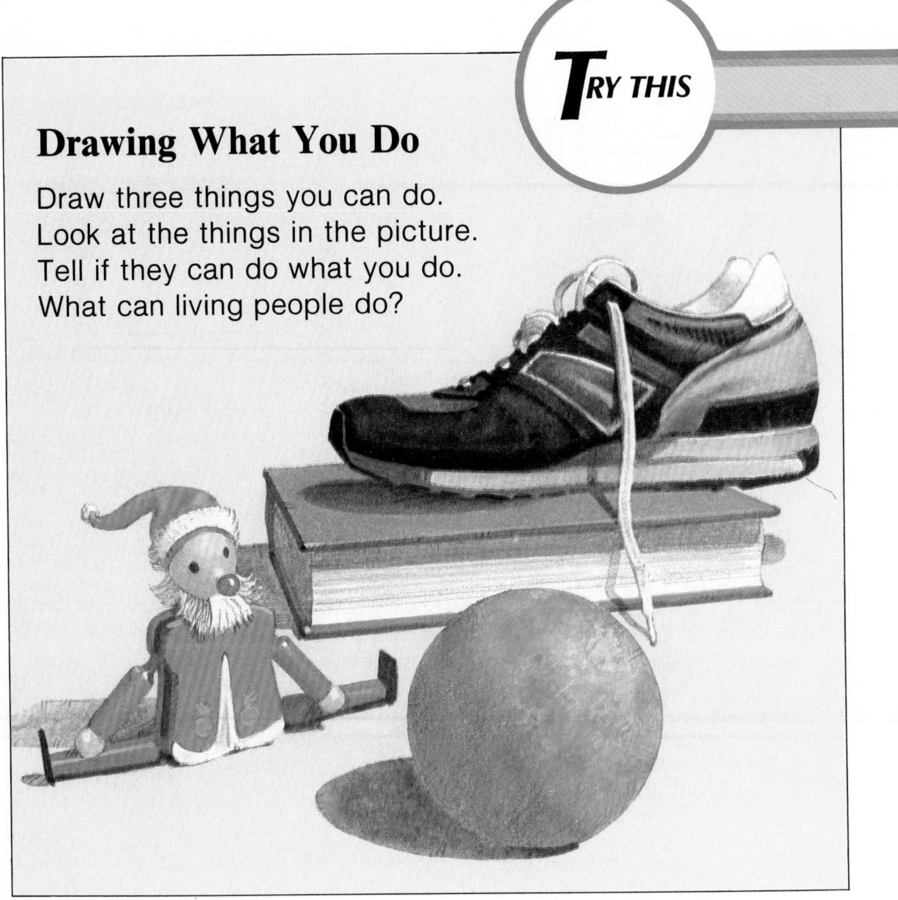

TRY THIS
Drawing What You Do
Draw three things you can do.
Look at the things in the picture.
Tell if they can do what you do.
What can living people do?

47

TRY THIS

Objective ♦

This optional *TRY THIS* activity will help students explore and build background information about the concept of what living things can do. Later in the chapter students will be able to draw on this experience to help them assimilate the new content.

Science Process Skills

Communicating, Inferring

Materials

For each student: drawing paper, crayons or colored markers

Teaching Tips

- Have the students think about all of the things they can do. List the activities on the chalkboard. Ask the students to choose three things from the list to draw. Allow each student to ***describe*** his or her drawing.
- Ask the students to ***compare*** what people can do with what the things in the picture on page 47 can do.
- Question: **What do things that are not living do?** (Answers might include: do nothing by themselves; might roll when pushed; metal might rust.)

Answer

Answers might include: play, work, walk, eat, sleep, learn, and so on.

Resource Book page 19

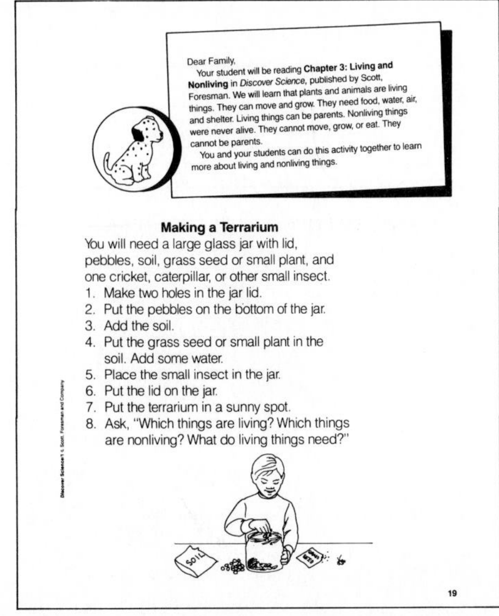

Dear Family,

Your student will be reading **Chapter 3: Living and Nonliving** in *Discover Science*, published by Scott, Foresman. We will learn that plants and animals are living things. They can move and grow. They need food, water, air, and shelter. Living things can be parents. Nonliving things were never alive. They cannot move, grow, or eat. They cannot be parents.

You and your students can do this activity together to learn more about living and nonliving things.

Making a Terrarium

You will need a large glass jar with lid, pebbles, soil, grass seed or small plant, and one cricket, caterpillar, or other small insect.

1. Make two holes in the jar lid.
2. Put the pebbles on the bottom of the jar.
3. Add the soil.
4. Put the grass seed or small plant in the soil. Add some water.
5. Place the small insect in the jar.
6. Put the lid on the jar.
7. Put the terrarium in a sunny spot.
8. Ask, "Which things are living? Which things are nonliving? What do living things need?"

19

SCIENCE BACKGROUND

Between the ages of six and seven, a child begins to develop systematic reasoning about familiar situations. Children this age are learning about cause and effect, and are developing abilities for logical reasoning.

* *Answers to masters on pages 46E–46F*

TEACHING PLAN

LESSON 1
pages 48–50

Lesson Objectives
- *Identify* living things.
- *Describe* some activities that living things perform.

Lesson Vocabulary
living things, parents

1 MOTIVATE

Demonstration Activity ♦
Ask students to bring dolls or stuffed animals to class. Display the dolls and animals and list special features of each, such as "talks," "walks," "barks."

Discussion
Have students *compare* the toys with themselves. Questions: **What can these toys do that a dog can do? What can you do that they cannot do? How are you different now than you were in the past? How will you change? How will the toys change? How many different ways can a dog move? How can the toys move? Do you have parents? Do dolls and stuffed animals have parents?** Guide students to understand that nonliving things do not grow, do not require food, are not born, and do not have parents.

[1]will grow and become more like parents

Lesson 1 What Is a Living Thing?

People are **living things.**
Animals and plants are living.
Many living things move on their own.
Living things can grow.
How will these animals grow?[1]

48

Teaching Options

SCIENCE BACKGROUND

Life is characterized by the ability of organisms to maintain themselves. Living things collect and eat food, which supplies them with energy for activity, and materials (molecules) for growth and development. Life processes include maintaining a steady internal environment, response to stimuli, and reproduction of offspring. All living things contain the same kinds of chemicals and are made up of one or more cells.

Enrichment

Obtain tadpoles and have students *observe* as they turn into frogs. Have students draw pictures of each stage of the tadpoles' development and write the date on each drawing. Help students make a booklet that organizes the drawings by dates.

♦ ***Suitable as a language development activity***

[1]leaves have died and dropped from tree

Living things can change.

You can change and grow bigger.

Plants and animals grow bigger.

Some trees change and grow bigger.

How has this tree changed?[1]

49

2 TEACH

Teaching Tips

- Remind students of the drawings they made of things they could do, in the *TRY THIS* activity on page 47. Discuss the fact that people are living things. Point out that other living things can do some of these activities.
- Draw students' attention to the mother dog and her puppies. Question: **How can dogs move?** (run, jump, wag tail, open mouth, move ears, and so on)
- **Possible Misconception:** Students might think that some inanimate objects, such as clouds and buildings, are alive because they sometimes grow. However, growth materials in these objects are added on from the outside.

Science and Language Arts

Have students think of stuffed animals, dolls, or toys they have at home. Have the students tell stories about how these nonliving things would be different if they were alive.

Special Education

To ensure that children with learning disabilities understand the concepts of living and not living, have these students list things that are alive. If a student names something that is not alive, question him or her as to whether the object eats, grows, or moves by itself. Review the characteristics of living things, and describe what they need and do.

Reinforcement

Have each child choose a living thing to study. Give each child a booklet made from several sheets of paper with a construction paper cover. Encourage the students to illustrate how the living thing they have selected moves, grows, and changes. Students could draw both the parents and the young of the species they choose. Some children might choose to study a pet. Encourage other children to choose living things they can *observe* in their area, such as ants, squirrels, trees, or birds.

3 ASSESS

Lesson Review
1. Plants, animals, and people are living things.
2. Living things can move, grow, change, and be parents.
Challenge! Question: **How are a dog and a plant alike?** (need food, grow and change, respond, reproduce) **Thinking Skill:** *Comparing*

Find Out
Students should cut out some pictures of plants, animals, or people and explain what the pictures show about living things. **Thinking Skills:** *Making generalizations, Collecting information*

[1]smaller, baby animals

Where do new living things come from?
They come from other living things.
Living things can be **parents.**
Which are the new living things here?[1]

Lesson Review

1. What are living things?
2. What can living things do?

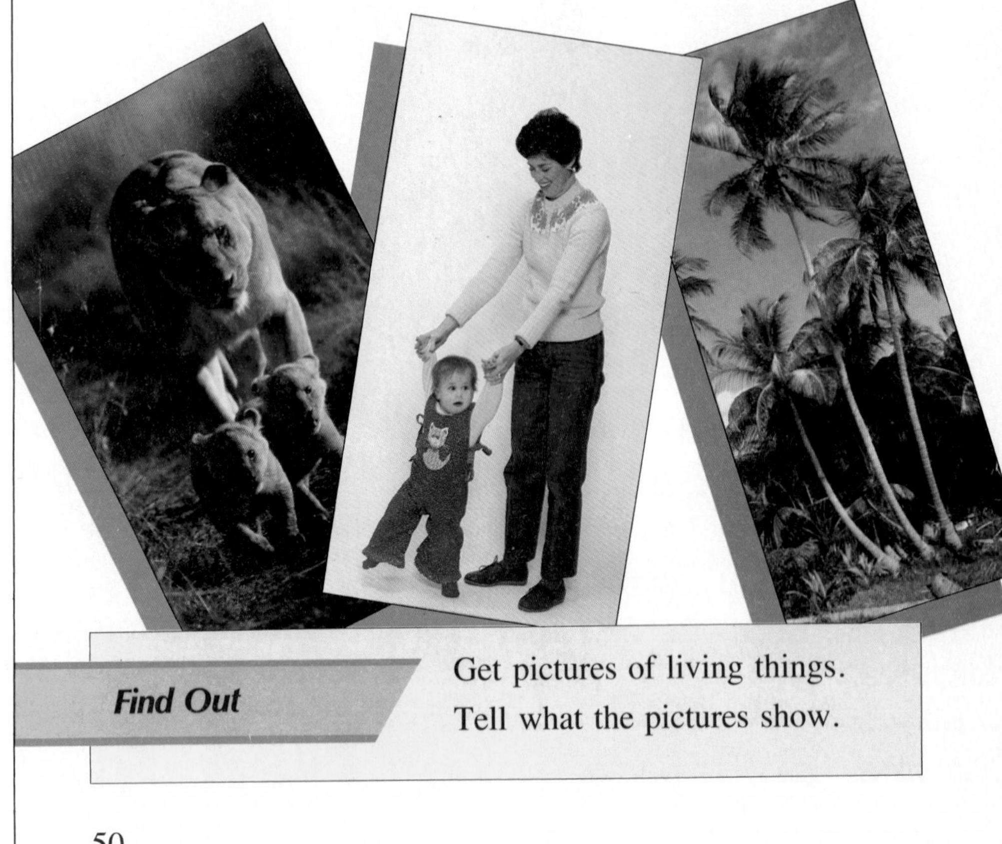

Find Out Get pictures of living things.
Tell what the pictures show.

50

Teaching Options

SCIENCE ANECDOTE

Scientists do not consider viruses to be living organisms. By themselves, viruses do not reproduce, respond to changes, use energy, or grow. Viruses enter host cells and use parts of the cells to reproduce themselves.

Reteaching Suggestion ♦

Have students bring in pictures of themselves (as babies, participating in activities, with their parents, and so on). Allow time for the students to tell about the pictures. Help students understand that they, like other living things, grow, move, change, and have parents.

Workbook page 15 *

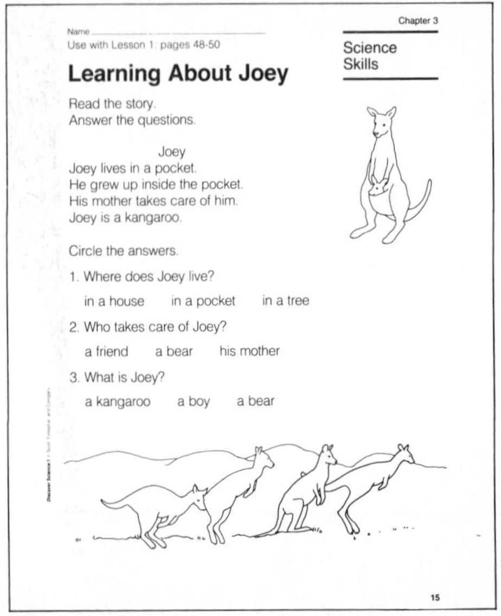
Name
Use with Lesson 1: pages 48-50

Chapter 3
Science Skills

Learning About Joey

Read the story.
Answer the questions.

Joey
Joey lives in a pocket.
He grew up inside the pocket.
His mother takes care of him.
Joey is a kangaroo.

Circle the answers.

1. Where does Joey live?
in a house in a pocket in a tree
2. Who takes care of Joey?
a friend a bear his mother
3. What is Joey?
a kangaroo a boy a bear

15

♦ ***Suitable as a language development activity***

ACTIVITY

Observing Mealworms

Follow the Directions

1. Put a mealworm on your desk.
2. Put food near the mealworm.
3. Touch it and give it light.
4. Observe how the mealworm moves.

Tell What You Learned

Tell what your mealworm did.

Tell what another animal can do.

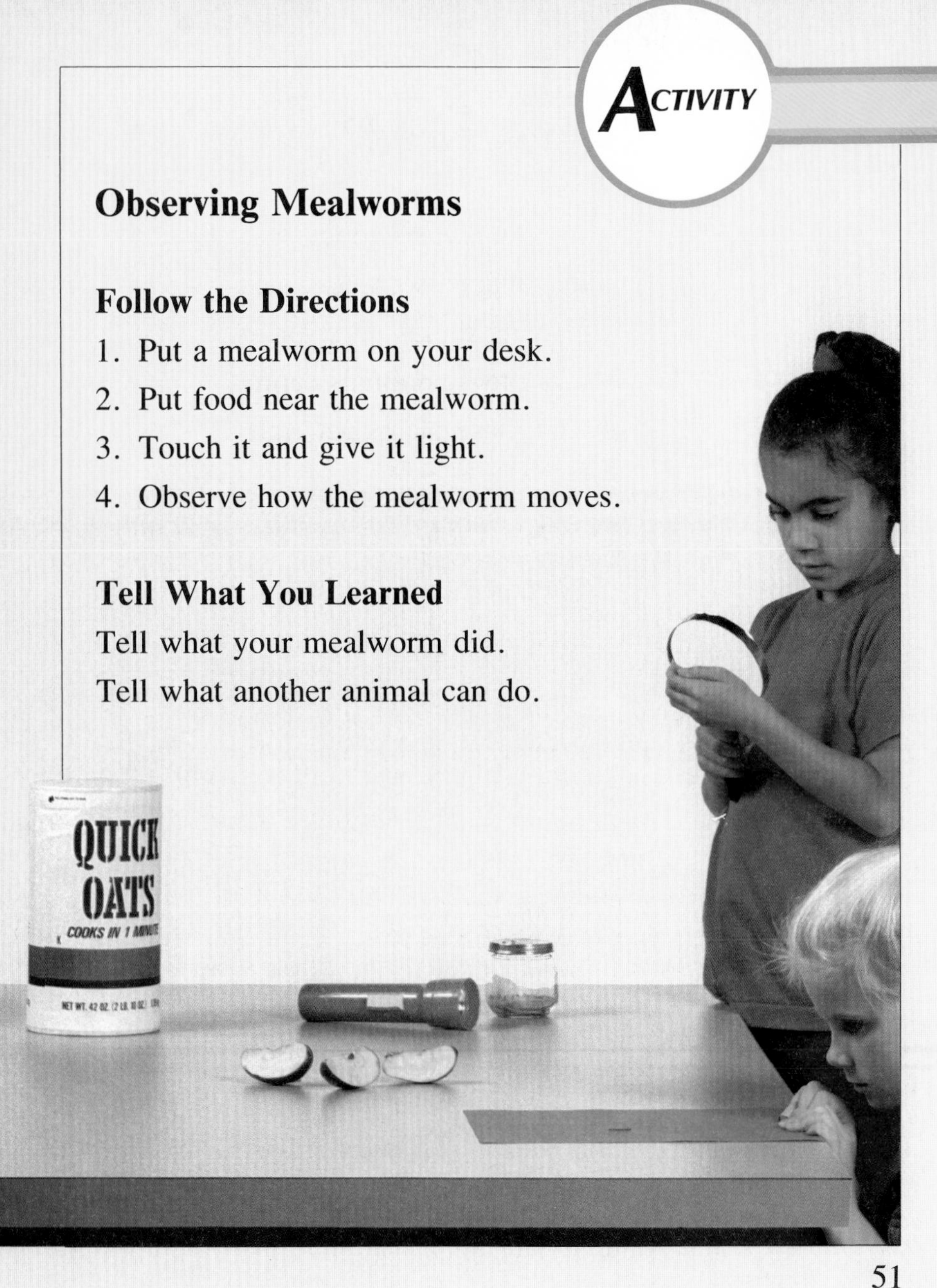

51

Concept

Observing gives information about living things.

Objectives/Process Skills

- *Describe* how a mealworm moves.
- *Observe* how a mealworm reacts to touch, to the texture of different surfaces, and to light.

Time Allotment

Allow 20 minutes.

Materials

For each group of 3: mealworm, 22.4 grams of oatmeal (about one tablespoon), flashlight

Safety Tips (See page T27.)

- Tell students not to put their hands or the mealworms into their mouths.
- Instruct students to wash their hands after the activity.
- Students who use hand lenses to observe mealworms should handle the lenses carefully.

Teaching Tips

- Before students begin the activity, explain that mealworms do not bite or sting, but they should be handled gently.
- Have students ***observe*** how the mealworms react to touch, to light from a flashlight, to sandpaper, and to food. (Results might vary significantly from mealworm to mealworm. Make sure you have extra mealworms to replace those that are "sleepy" or do not seem to respond to stimuli.)

Answers

Tell What You Learned

The students should *describe* what the mealworms did (crawled around, moved away from light, looked for food, ate food, and so on). Second statement—the answer will vary depending on students' backgrounds. **Thinking Skill:** *Applying information to new situations*

Enrichment Activity

Allow students to ***experiment*** to learn more about mealworms. Questions students might try to answer by experimenting are: Do mealworms like light or dark places? Do they crawl uphill or downhill when placed on a book that is held at an angle to the floor? Can mealworms move on mirrors? Can they crawl on a pencil?

Activity Results

Results will vary. Most mealworms will probably retreat from light and touch. They avoid extremes of temperature and moisture, and seek out food.

***** Answers to masters on pages 46E–46F**

LESSON 2
pages 52–54

Lesson Objective
- *List* what living things require to stay alive.

Lesson Vocabulary
shelter

1 MOTIVATE

Demonstration Activity ♦
Bring a plastic plant and a live plant to school for students to *observe.*

Discussion
Have students *identify* the living plant and *compare* it with the nonliving (plastic) plant. Question: **What are the differences in the plants' needs?** (Students might say that the living plant needs water, air, and nutrients from the soil in order to grow. They should realize that the plastic plant will not grow and does not have needs.)

[1]grasses, leaves, and so on
[2]from lakes, rivers, streams, and rain

Lesson 2 What Do Living Things Need?

Living things need food.
Living things also need water.
Most living things need air.
What are these animals eating?[1]
How do these plants get water?[2]

52

Teaching Options

SCIENCE BACKGROUND

Water and air are two substances that are necessary to support life. Water covers about three-quarters of the earth's surface. The cells of most living things contain about 80-90% water, and most of the chemical reactions within cells need to occur in watery solutions. Therefore, most living things die if deprived of water over a period of time. Humans can survive without water for less than a week. Air contains gases necessary for life—oxygen, nitrogen, and carbon dioxide. The gases in air dissolve in water, just as sugar dissolves when mixed in water. Aquatic organisms, not humans, have special body parts that help them take in gases from water.

Science and Math

Suggest that students make graphs illustrating the number of different types of living things in their homes (1 dog, 3 people, 1 fish). Let the students display their graphs on a bulletin board.

♦ ***Suitable as a language development activity***

[1]a space between rocks

Some living things need **shelter.**

A home gives shelter.

Some birds have homes in trees.

Some ants build homes in the ground.

What shelter does this animal have?[1]

2 TEACH

Teaching Tips

- **Possible Misconception:** From cartoons and fairy tales, children might think that animals live like humans. All animals, including humans, require special and distinct forms of nutrition and shelter.
- Discuss different types of human homes and what they are made of. Question: **What materials do we use to build homes?** (brick, wood, concrete block) Explain that a long time ago some homes were made of mud and grass (especially in the plains).
- Ask the students what kinds of shelters animals use. (Students might mention a bee hive, gopher hole, or the inside of a tree.)

Special Education

Have students with learning disabilities describe activities that are necessary for life, such as eating, drinking, sleeping, and playing outdoors. Help students understand why eating the right foods is important for life. Explain that playing outdoors helps them get fresh air. Explain that sleeping comfortably is possible because they have shelter. Have the students draw pictures of some of the things they do that are important for living.

Reinforcement

Obtain a living thing (small mammal, plant, fish, and so on) to keep in the classroom for several days. Write *air, water, food,* and *shelter* on the chalkboard. Discuss how the students can provide what the living thing needs. Make a schedule of the tasks involved in caring for the organism, and assign students to each task. *CAUTION:* Make certain students wash their hands after handling the organism. Tell students to report any bites to you immediately.

Enrichment

Obtain a library book or encyclopedia that describes how certain animals build their own shelters (beavers build lodges, birds build nests, bees make hives.) Share the information with students and let them draw pictures to illustrate what they have learned.

3 ASSESS

Lesson Review

1. Plants and animals need air, food, and water. Some animals need shelter.

2. People need the same things that all living things need (air, water, food). They also need homes for shelter and people to care about them.

Challenge! Question: **Since living things need air, water, and food, where do you think plants that grow at the bottom of a lake get air?** (They get air that is dissolved in the water.) **Thinking Skill:** *Making inferences*

Find Out

Students should recommend places for animal homes that would be sheltered from the weather and would provide safety for animals. **Thinking Skill:** *Making inferences*

[1]by working together

People need food.
They need air, water, and homes.
People also need to help each other.
How do these people help each other?[1]

Lesson Review

1. What do plants and animals need?
2. What do people need?

Find Out

Get pictures of animal homes.
Tell what the pictures show.

Teaching Options

SCIENCE ANECDOTE

Koala bears and some other animals do not drink water. They get water they need from food they eat.

Reteaching Suggestion ♦

Provide clay and let each student make a model of a living thing. (The clay models can be painted and fired if you use ceramic clay and your school has a kiln.) Ask the students to find out about the needs of the living things they have modeled. Let each student display his or her model and tell the class what that living thing needs. (If you do not want your students to make models, have them draw a living thing.)

Workbook page 16 *

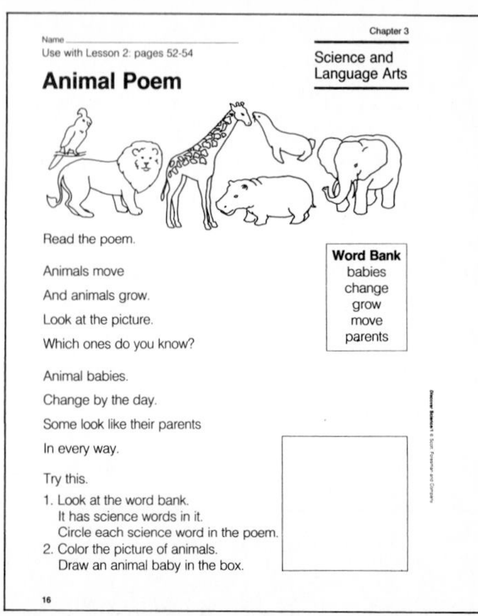

Name
Use with Lesson 2: pages 52-54

Chapter 3

Science and Language Arts

Animal Poem

Read the poem.

Animals move
And animals grow.
Look at the picture.
Which ones do you know?

Animal babies.
Change by the day.
Some look like their parents
In every way.

Word Bank
babies
change
grow
move
parents

Try this.

1. Look at the word bank.
   It has science words in it.
   Circle each science word in the poem.
2. Color the picture of animals.
   Draw an animal baby in the box.

16

♦ ***Suitable as a language development activity***

Science in Your Life

Traveling in Space

People travel in space.
Space has no air, water, or food.
People travel in spacecraft.
The craft have air, water, and food.
Then people can live and work in space.

What Do You Think?

What is shelter for people in space?

55

SCIENCE IN YOUR LIFE

Discussion

Discuss with students trips they have taken or heard about for which people had to take along food, water, air, and shelter. (Students might tell about bringing food and water on a camping trip, or they might tell about a scuba diver carrying air tanks.) Explain that sometimes people travel to places where they cannot get air, water, or food, and so they need to take these things along.

Teaching Tips

- Explain that a spacecraft contains air, and without this air, people in space would die. Question: **How do people get air in space when they are outside the spacecraft?** (Spacesuits provide them with air.)
- Tell students that before scuba gear was invented, people who stayed under water for long periods of time wore diving suits that were attached to air hoses. Explain that in some ways, those diving suits were similar to spacesuits.

Answer

What Do You Think?
A spacecraft or a spacesuit is shelter for people living in space. **Thinking Skill:** *Inferring*

Books To Read

Billings, Charlene W. *Space Station: Bold New Step Beyond Earth.* Dodd, Mead, 1986. (grades 4–6)
Lord, Suzanne. *A Day In Space.* Scholastic, 1986. (grades 3–4)
Allen, Joseph P. *Entering Space: An Astronaut's Odyssey.* Tabori and Chang, 1985. (for the teacher)

SCIENCE BACKGROUND

Scientists are developing ways to aid space travelers in the future. Some of the experiments scientists are conducting involve growing plants in space, without the use of soil. This type of growth is called *hydroponics*. Experiments during space shuttle missions have shown that seedlings can be grown in zero gravity for a short period of time. The nutrients that the seedlings need can be provided by using a nutrient solution in agar—a gelatinlike substance used as a culture medium. Scientists hope that plants will be grown eventually in space stations, but many more experiments will be done before this type of gardening is feasible.

* ***Answers to masters on pages 46E–46F***

TEACHING PLAN

LESSON 3
pages 56–58

Lesson Objectives
- *Identify* nonliving things.
- *List* characteristics of nonliving things.

Lesson Vocabulary
nonliving things

1 MOTIVATE

Demonstration Activity ♦
Display several objects such as a rock, a toy car, a doll, a jar of paste, and some crayons. Ask the students to *observe* the objects.

Discussion
Have the students *describe* the objects. Questions: **Can these objects eat? Can they grow? Do they move? How do they move?** Explain that all of the objects are nonliving things—they are not alive (and never were alive). Instruct students to name other nonliving things in the classroom.

[1]no
[2]nonliving

Lesson 3 What Are Nonliving Things Like?

Nonliving things were never alive.
They cannot do what living things do.
Nonliving things cannot eat food.
Can these things grow?[1]
Are they living or nonliving?[2]

56

Teaching Options

SCIENCE BACKGROUND

All living organisms carry out certain life processes; they grow, respond, use energy, and reproduce. Nonliving things can carry on some of these processes, but not all of them. Living things grow by using food and changing it into more of themselves. Nonliving things, such as clouds, can get bigger, but cannot grow as a result of using nutrients. Nonliving things, such as smoke detectors, can respond, but cannot protect themselves through the responses (which living things can do). Nonliving things can use energy, but that energy is provided by living things. Living things can reproduce themselves; nonliving things can be copied, but cannot reproduce on their own.

Enrichment

Make a tape recording of sounds made by living and nonliving things (a dog barking, a person talking, a telephone ringing, a horn honking, and so on). Have the students listen to the tape and try to identify the source of the sounds. Ask the students to tell whether the sounds were made by living or nonliving things.

♦ ***Suitable as a language development activity***

[1]everything pictured is nonliving
[2]they can all move, but not by themselves

Some nonliving things can move.

They do not move on their own.

Something makes nonliving things move.

What nonliving things do you see here?[1]

Which ones can move?[2]

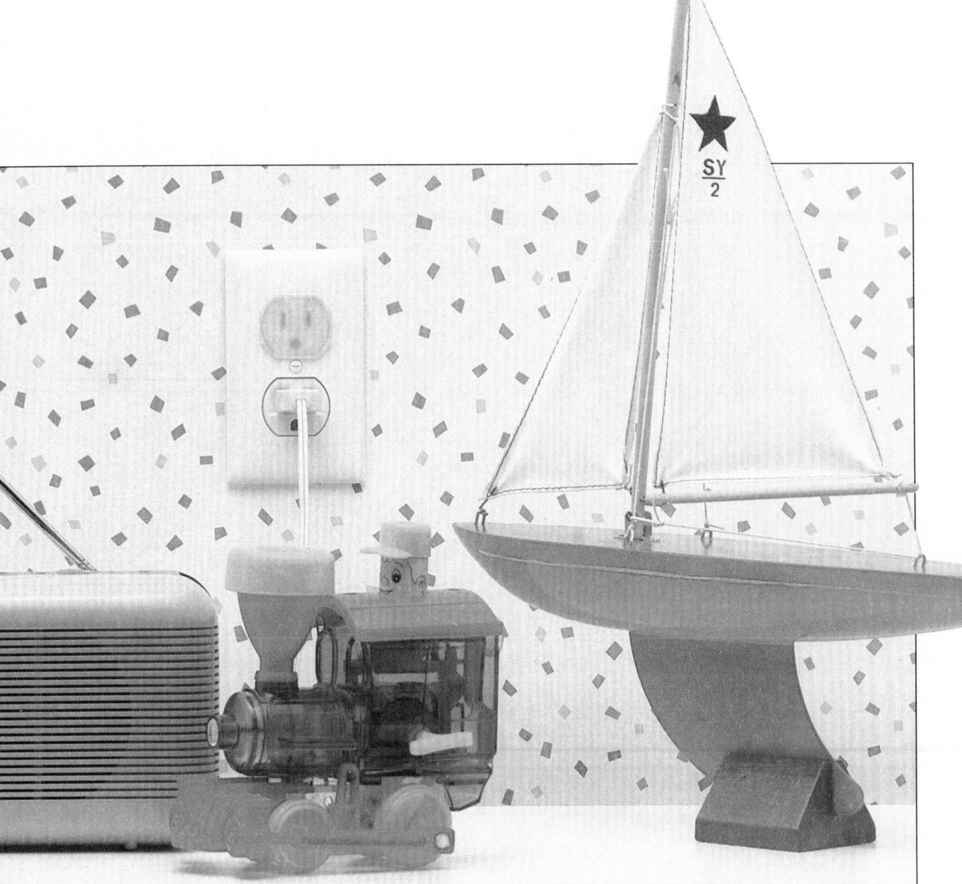

2 TEACH

Teaching Tips

- Help students *identify* the living and nonliving things in the pictures on pages 56, 57, and 58.
- Discuss with students how some of the nonliving objects move. Question: **What makes each one move?** (sailboat—wind, locomotive—windup machine)
- Encourage students to bring in nonliving things that move. Have the students tell the class what makes the objects move. If students do not have such objects at home, ask them to draw pictures of nonliving things that move, and tell how they move.
- **Possible Misconception:** Children might confuse nonliving things with living things that have died. Emphasize that nonliving things were never living things.

Workbook page 17 *

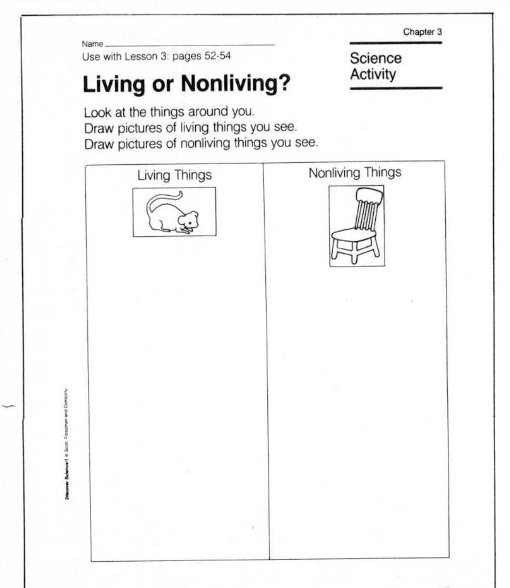
Name
Use with Lesson 3: pages 52-54

Chapter 3

Science Activity

Living or Nonliving?

Look at the things around you.
Draw pictures of living things you see.
Draw pictures of nonliving things you see.

Living Things	Nonliving Things

17

*** Answers to masters on pages 46E–46F**

Game Suggestion ♦

Play "I am thinking of an object." Have one student describe an object in the classroom. Ask the other students to guess what the object is and tell whether it is living or nonliving. The student who guesses correctly gets a chance to describe the next item.

Special Education

Provide an aquarium and some living and nonliving things that can be found in an aquarium. Supervise and instruct as children with learning disabilities put the aquarium together by adding one layer at a time, beginning with the gravel. After the addition of a layer, ask whether the object added is living or nonliving. Have the students justify their answers by telling what the object can or cannot do.

TEACHING PLAN

3 ASSESS

Lesson Review

1. Nonliving things do not eat, drink, or grow.
2. Nonliving things do not move on their own. Electricity, wind, and mechanical parts (windup keys and so on) help nonliving things move.
Challenge! Question: **What is the difference between a rock and a dead flower?** (The rock was never alive; the flower was once alive.) **Thinking Skills:** *Contrasting, Making inferences*

Find Out

Answers will vary. Students should *describe* the characteristics of the nonliving things they find. **Thinking Skills:** *Generalizing, Restating information*

[1]the woman and child
[2]they grow, breathe, and move

Only living things can be parents.
Who are the living things here?[1]
How do you know they are living?[2]

Lesson Review

1. What does not eat, drink, or grow?
2. How do nonliving things move?

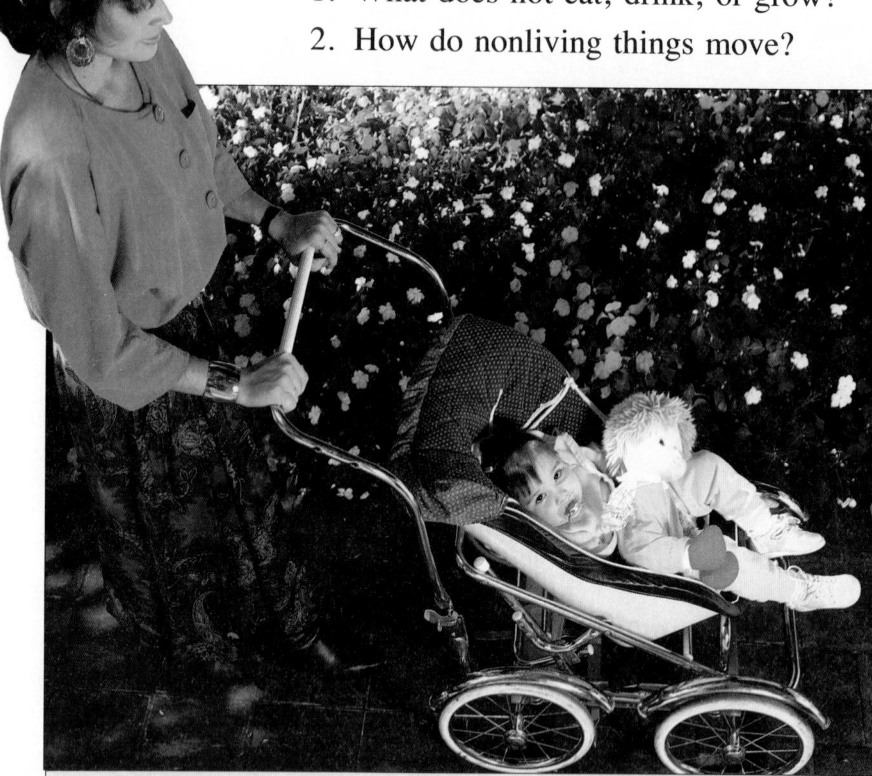

Find Out

Find some nonliving things.
Tell what they are like.

58

Teaching Options

SCIENCE ANECDOTE

People use computers to program robots to do many tasks without additional human help. Robots are used in industry to do jobs that are repetitious, dangerous, or require heavy lifting. They also do "intelligent" tasks, such as welding and drilling.

Reteaching Suggestion ♦

Provide magazines and have the students look for and cut out pictures of nonliving things. Let each student *describe* the pictures he or she has cut out and identify the characteristics of the nonliving things pictured. Display all of the pictures on a bulletin board.

Workbook page 18 *

Name
Use with Lesson 3: pages 56-58
Chapter 3
Vocabulary Puzzle

Puzzle

Read the words in the word bank.
Match each word with a picture.
Write the word in the puzzle.
Write one letter in each box.

Word Bank
living things
nonliving things
parents
shelter

18

♦ ***Suitable as a language development activity***

Discovering What is Alive

Follow the Directions

1. Put some stones and beans on a tray.
2. Cover them with water.
3. Leave them alone for three or four days.
4. Tell what happens.

Tell What You Learned

Draw what was alive and not alive.
Draw another living thing.

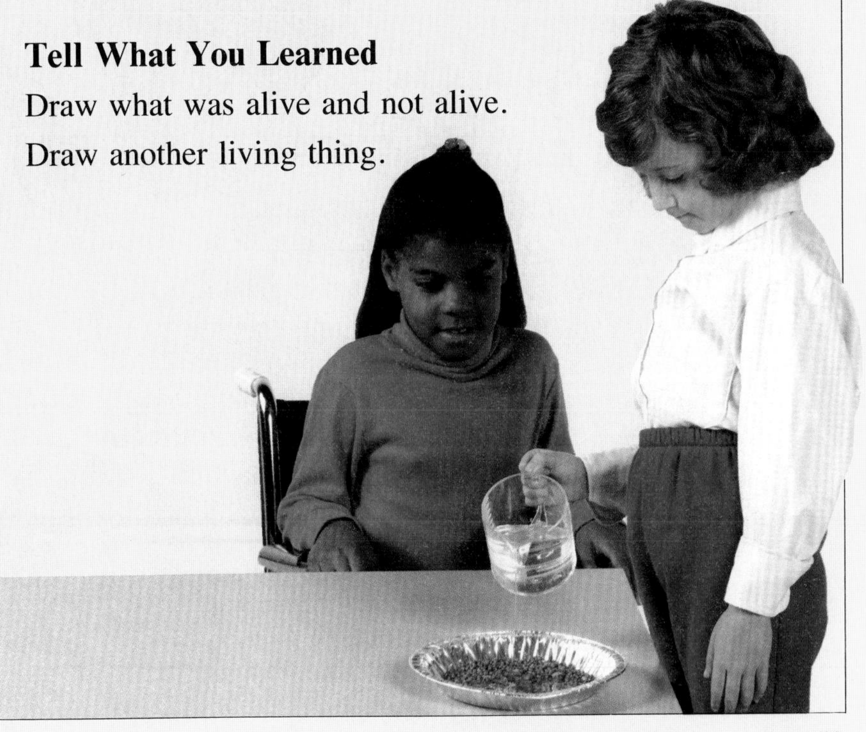

59

Enrichment Activity

Students might want to plant the seeds that have germinated. Others might want to make a garden area near the classroom or at home for the new plants. If such an area is not available, students could plant the seeds in a large pot.

Activity Results

Students should discover that beans begin to germinate, thus showing growth and change, which are characteristics of living things.

Concept

Living things grow and change.

Objectives/Process Skills

- *Observe* beans and stones placed in water.
- *Compare* beans and stones after three or four days.
- *Identify* living and nonliving things.

Time Allotment

Allow 20 minutes, plus observation.

Materials

For each group of three: 112 grams (about 4 ounces) of tan-colored aquarium gravel, four or five *untreated* fresh beans (such as mung beans, soy beans, alfalfa seeds, or lentils), small, shallow, metal or plastic container, water

Safety Tips (See page T27.)

- Instruct students not to put beans or stones in their mouth, nose, or ears.
- Wipe up water spills to prevent falls.

Teaching Tips

- **Helpful Hint:** Place trays away from direct light. Seeds usually germinate better away from light.
- The water should cover the bean/rock mixture; students should add water as necessary for several days.

Answers

Tell What You Learned
Students should draw the beans (which were alive) as they changed over time. They should draw the gravel (which was not alive). Students should state that the beans were alive because they began to change and grow. Second statement—students' drawing will vary. **Thinking Skill:** *Applying information to new situations*

*** Answers to masters on pages 46E–46F**

SKILLS FOR SOLVING PROBLEMS
pages 60–61

Purpose
To develop the skills of collecting and organizing information using a bar graph to solve problems.

Materials
For each student: drawing paper and crayons, colored pencils, or colored markers.

1 MOTIVATE

Discussion
Choose two main colors of clothing that students are wearing. Without stating why, ask students wearing one color to stand in one part of the room, and students wearing the other color to stand in another area. Questions: **In what way are the students in each group alike? Which group has more students? Is it easier to see the way the students are alike when they are together in a group?** Explain that scientists sometimes put information into groups.

Skills for Solving Problems

Observing and Making a Graph

What can a graph show?

1. Observe the picture.
   Count the living things.
   Count the nonliving things.
   Write each number on your paper.

60

Teaching Options

SCIENCE BACKGROUND

In the scientific method, scientists use many different processes as they perform research. These processes help scientists discover new information and formulate new theories. The processes include observation, forming a hypothesis that can make predictions and be tested, conducting experiments, classifying data, expressing findings mathematically, and using logic to draw conclusions. As early as 3000 B.C., early civilizations followed this method to predict flooding, predict eclipses, or acquire other types of knowledge.

2. Copy the graph you see.
   Use the paper with the numbers you wrote.
   Use two colors.
   Color how many things are alive.
   Color how many things are not alive.

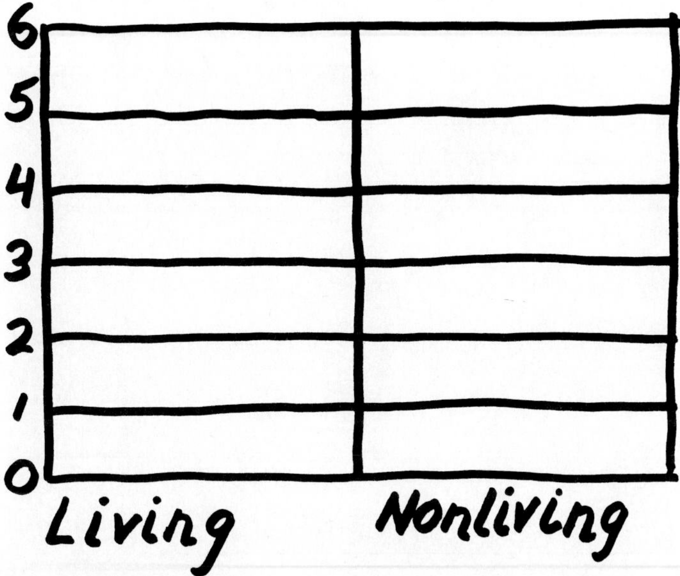

3. Observe the colors in your graph.
   What do they show about the groups?

61

2 TEACH

Teaching Tips

- Explain that a bar graph is one way that scientists show how they organize information into groups. After the students have copied the graph, have them color in one square for each object in the group they are counting (living or nonliving). Instruct students to use a different colored crayon to color each column. You might want to demonstrate how the graph is to be completed by filling in a similar graph using an overhead projector or large poster.
- Have students count the colored squares in each column to make sure they match the numbers students wrote on their papers. Ask students to determine which column (group) has the greatest number of objects.

3 ASSESS

The graph should show that the number difference between living and nonliving things is one. (There is one more living object than the nonliving objects shown.)

Resource Book page 23

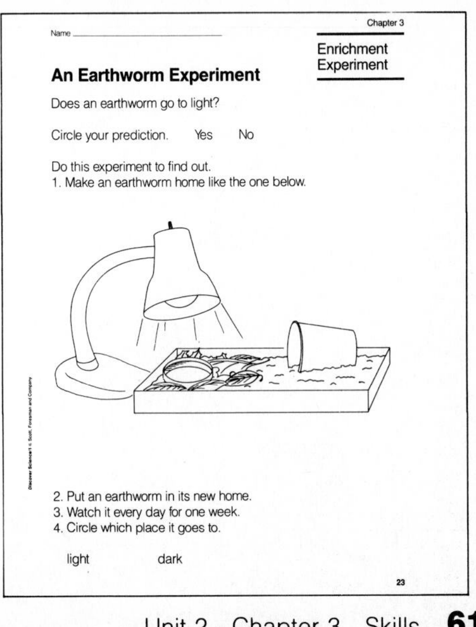
Name ____________________

Chapter 3

Enrichment Experiment

An Earthworm Experiment

Does an earthworm go to light?

Circle your prediction. Yes No

Do this experiment to find out.
1. Make an earthworm home like the one below.

2. Put an earthworm in its new home.
3. Watch it every day for one week.
4. Circle which place it goes to.

light dark

23

REVIEW PLAN

CHAPTER 3 REVIEW

pages 62–63

Review Chapter Ideas

1. Living things can grow and change. They can be parents, and usually they can move.

2. Living things are the girl, the fish, and the dog.

3. Living things need food, air, and water. Some living things need shelter.

4. Students might mention food, air, water, a home for protection and shelter, and a family or other people to help them.

5. Accept reasonable answers that show an understanding of the characteristics of nonliving things. Generally, nonliving things cannot eat, grow, or be parents; nonliving things have never been alive.

6. Accept reasonable answers. Some nonliving things students might mention include toys, boats, cars, rocks, and furniture.

Chapter 3 Review

For further review, use Study Guide page 231.

Review Chapter Ideas

1. Tell what living things can do.
2. Look at the picture.
   Name the living things you see.
3. Explain what living things need.
4. Tell what people need.
5. Tell what nonliving things are like.
6. Name six nonliving things.

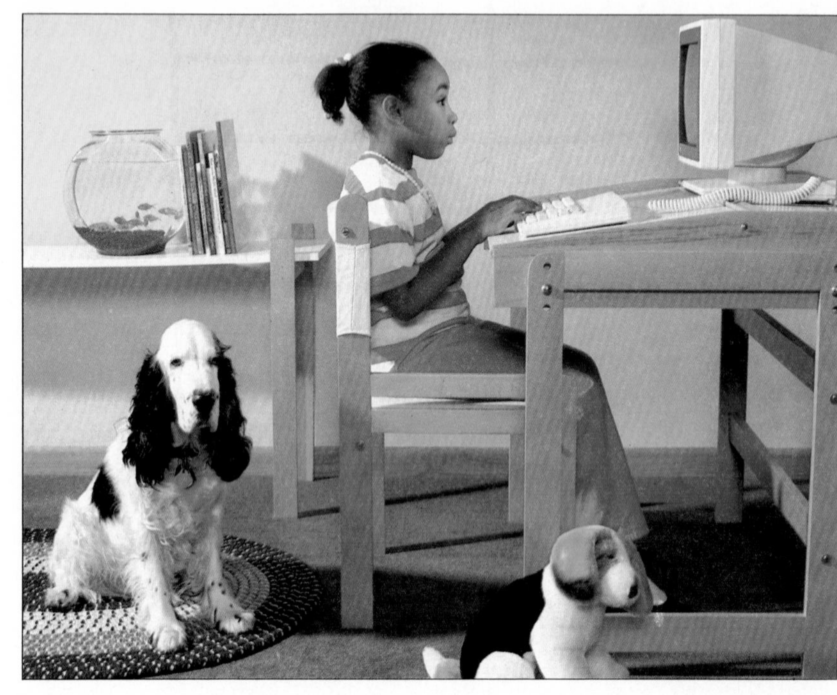

62

Review Options

Cooperative Learning ♦

STAD Format (See page T23.)
Assign students to work in four- to five-member teams to study Chapter 3 Review. Students should work together to make sure that they and their teammates know the material in the chapter. After students have had enough time to study together, give them a test to complete individually (Chapter 3 Test in the *Test Book).* Award Superteam certificates to teams whose average test scores exceed 90%, and Greatteam certificates to teams whose average test scores exceed 80%.

♦ ***Suitable as a language development activity***

Review Science Words

Match the words and the pictures.

1. parents
2. shelter

a.

b.

Tell what the words mean.

3. living things
4. nonliving things

Use Science Ideas

What picture does not belong?

a. b. c.

63

Review Science Words

Match the words and the pictures.

1. a
2. b

Tell what the words mean.
Thinking Skill: *Restating or explaining ideas*

3. Living things are things that can grow, change, and be parents. Living things need air, water, and food.

4. Nonliving things are things that were never alive and cannot be parents. They cannot move on their own, eat, grow, or change.

Use Science Ideas

The picture of the pencil does not belong because it shows a nonliving thing.
Thinking Skill: *Recognizing factual and logical inconsistencies*

Test Book page 15 *

Name

Chapter 3 Test

Living and Nonliving

I. Write **Yes** or **No**.

1. Is a plant a living thing?
2. Do living things stay the same size?
3. Do people need air to stay alive?
4. Is a rock a nonliving thing?
5. Do nonliving things eat or drink?

II. Draw a line from the word to the right picture.

1. living 2. parents 3. shelter 4. nonliving

15

* ***Answers to masters on pages 46E–46F***

CHAPTER 4

Teaching Plan

Chapter Components	Skills	Materials
Chapter Opener/*TRY THIS*: Telling About Plants pp. 64-65	***TRY THIS*** p. 65 **Science Process Skills** *Classifying, Observing*	***TRY THIS*** p. 65 (individual) no materials needed
Lesson 1: How Are Plants Alike and Different? pp. 66-68	**Thinking Skills** Challenge!: *Drawing conclusions* Find Out: *Comparing*	**Demonstration** p. 66 potted nontoxic plant, hand shovel
Activity: Grouping Leaves p. 69	**Science Process Skills** *Observing, Classifying, Communicating*	(individual) assorted nontoxic leaves
Lesson 2: How Do Plants Grow? pp. 70-72	**Thinking Skills** Challenge!: *Making generalizations* Find Out: *Contrasting*	**Demonstration** p. 70 seeds (coconut, peach pit, almond, apple seeds, and peas)
Activity: Looking At Seeds p. 73	**Science Process Skills** *Observing, Measuring, Predicting*	(groups of 2) 30 wedges of orange, 30 wedges of apple, 30 wedges of lemon, 30 sheets drawing paper, 30 boxes crayons, 30 pencils
Lesson 3: What Do Plants Need to Grow? pp. 74-76	**Thinking Skills** Challenge!: *Inferring* Find Out: *Recognizing cause and effect*	**Demonstration** p. 74 clear-plastic shallow pan of soil, water
Science in Your Life: Bringing Water to Plants p. 77	**Thinking Skill** *Drawing conclusions*	
Lesson 4: Why Do People Need Plants? pp. 78-79	**Thinking Skills** Challenge!: *Identifying and suggesting alternatives* Find Out: *Restating or explaining ideas*	**Demonstration** p. 78 cotton towel, cotton clothing, wooden toy, newspaper
Skills for Solving Problems: Using a Hand Lens pp. 80-81	**Problem Solving Skills** *Making decisions/Identifying and solving problems, Interpreting charts, maps, and graphs*	(individual) hand lens, small nontoxic leaf
Chapter Review pp. 82-83	**Thinking Skills** *Restating or explaining ideas, Drawing conclusions*	

Teaching Options

Strategies	Extensions	Resource Masters
		Family Letter: *Resource Book* p. 27 Vocabulary Preview: *Workbook* pp. 19-20
	Game Suggestion p. 67 Science and Art p. 67 Reteaching Suggestion p. 68 Special Education p. 68	
	Enrichment Activity p. 69	
	Reinforcement p. 71 Special Education p. 71 Science and Art p. 71 Reteaching Suggestion p. 72	Science Skills: *Workbook* p. 21
	Enrichment Activity p. 73	
	Enrichment p. 74 Reinforcement p. 75 Special Education p. 75 Science and Language Arts p. 75 Reteaching Suggestion p. 76	Science Activity: *Workbook* p. 22
	Special Education p. 78 Reteaching Suggestion p. 79	Science and Social Studies: *Workbook* p. 23 Vocabulary Puzzle: *Workbook* p. 24
		Enrichment Activity: *Resource Book* p. 31
Cooperative Learning p. 82 (Also see p.T23)		Chapter Test: *Test Book* p. 17

Preteaching Suggestions

For Advance Preparation

Demonstration, page 66
Obtain a potted plant for the class to observe.

Activity, page 69
Supply a variety of leaves for each group of students or ask students to collect leaves for the class. If leaves are not available, you can make cardboard cutouts or cut out pictures of leaves in magazines.

Demonstration, page 70
Obtain a variety of seeds including a coconut, a peach pit, an almond, apple seeds, and peas.

For Vocabulary Review

Use the following sentences with your students to review the meanings of the underlined words.

1. Apples, oranges, grapes, and bananas are types of fruit.
2. Air is all around you even though you cannot see it.
3. The children ran indoors when it began to rain.
4. The trunk and branches of trees are made of wood.

For High-Potential Students

Carefully uproot several grass plants from different areas of the school grounds. Using hand lenses and tweezers, students should examine and draw the different parts of the plant.

Encourage students to conduct experiments with grass or bean plants grown from seed to find out how variations of soil, water, and sunlight affect the growth of these plants. Explain to students the important of changing only one variable at a time.

For Mainstreamed Students

Emotionally Handicapped
Provide the opportunity for students to care for flowering plants in the classroom. Help them set up a watering schedule for the plants.

Visually Handicapped
Encourage students to use their sense of touch to "observe" plants of various kinds, indoors and outdoors. *CAUTION:* Be sure that plants students touch are not poisonous and that they put no plants to their mouths.

Orthopedically Handicapped
Be aware of special arrangements that might have to be made for orthopedically handicapped students if you have any outdoor experiences planned for this chapter. Choose outdoor areas that are accessible to all students.

For Science Fair Projects

Encourage interested students to do one of the following projects:

1. Collect a variety of foods that are parts of plants. Tell what part of the plant each food comes from.
2. Care for two plants over a certain length of time. Deprive one plant of water or sunlight and keep a record of what happens to each plant. This project is a simpler version of that suggested for high-potential students.
3. Make a poster display of the most common plants in your area. Use a field guide to find out the plant name, where it grows, and some unique fact about it. You may want to concentrate on certain kinds of plants, such as trees or woodland wildflowers.

Classroom Resources

Bulletin Board
Ask students to bring in pictures of as many different kinds of plants as they can find. Encourage students to describe the differences among the plants.

DESCRIBE THESE PLANTS

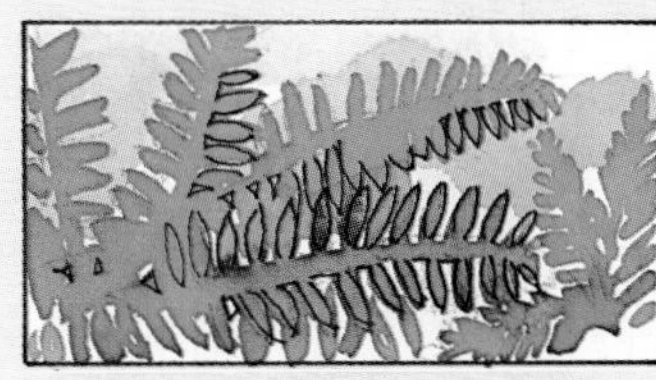

Chapter 4 Poster

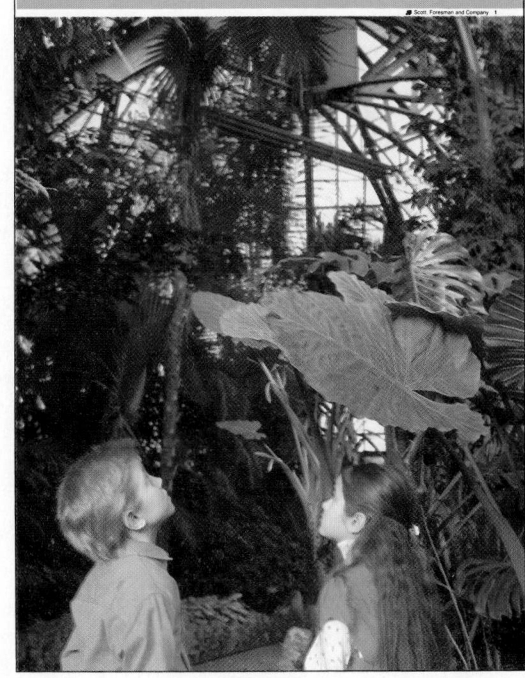
What do these plants need?

Science Discovery Center
Use pages from Chapter 4 in the *Science Discovery Center Book*. Place these worksheets in the appropriate pockets in the Science Discovery Center.

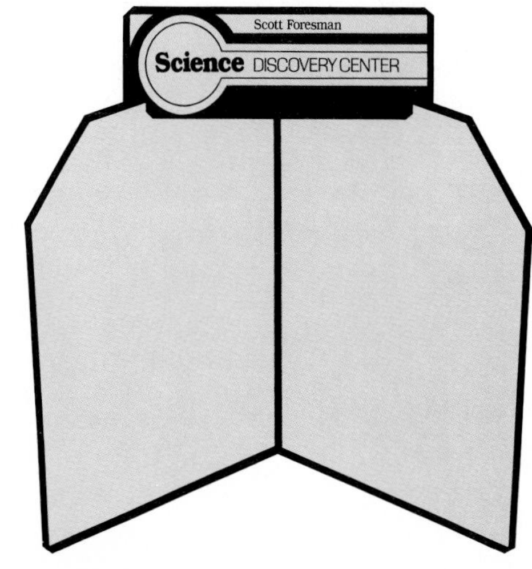
Scott Foresman
Science DISCOVERY CENTER

CHAPTER 4 COPY MASTERS

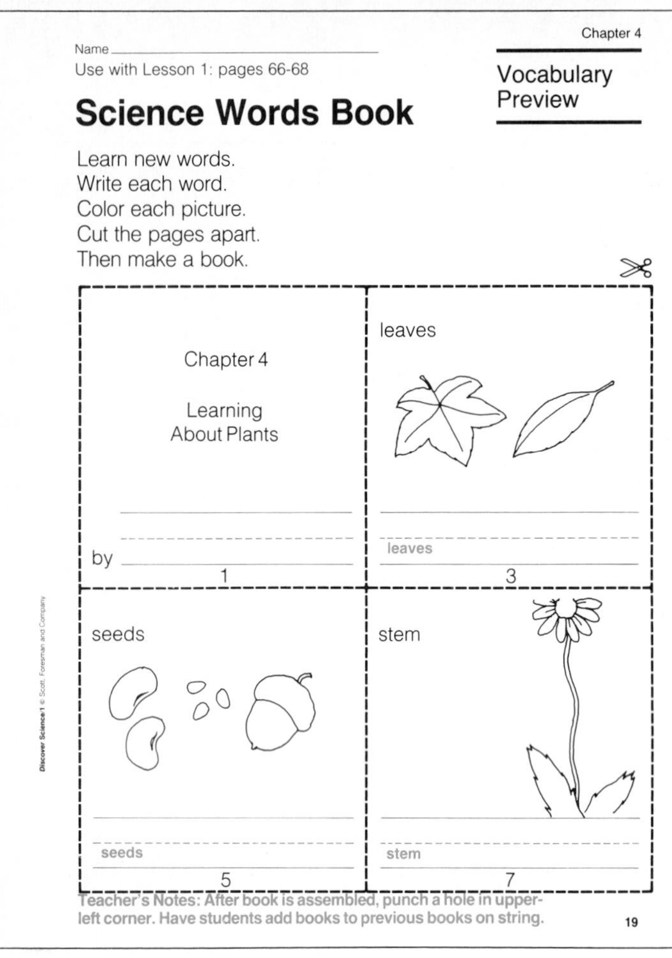

Name ____________________

Use with Lesson 1: pages 66-68

Chapter 4

Vocabulary Preview

Science Words Book

Learn new words.
Write each word.
Color each picture.
Cut the pages apart.
Then make a book.

Teacher's Notes: After book is assembled, punch a hole in upper-left corner. Have students add books to previous books on string.

19

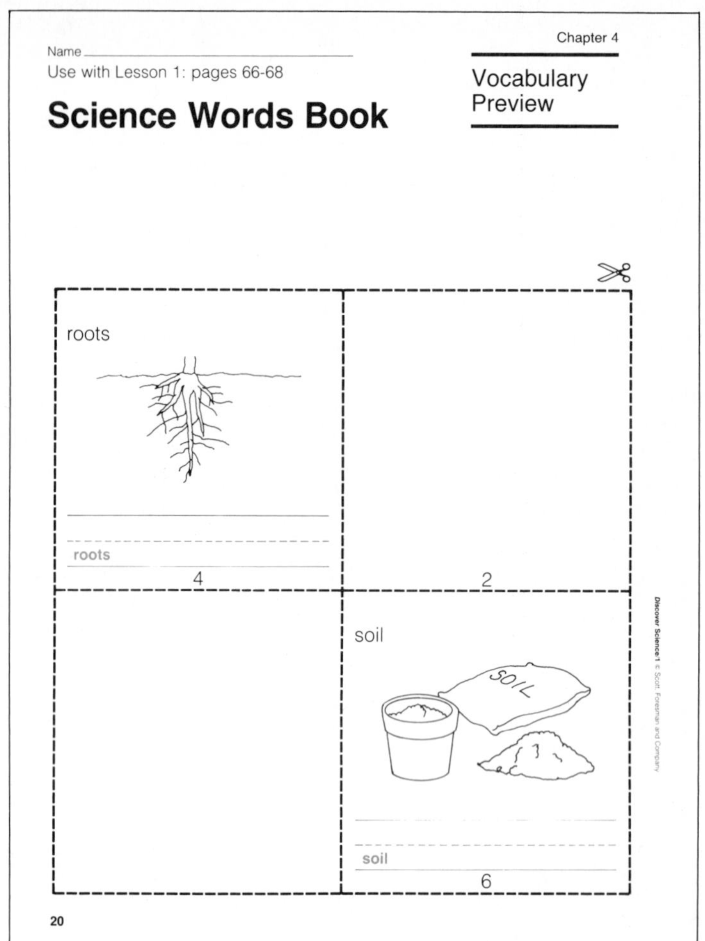

Name ____________________

Use with Lesson 1: pages 66-68

Chapter 4

Vocabulary Preview

Science Words Book

20

Name ____________________

Use with Lesson 2: pages 70-72

Chapter 4

Science Skills

The Life of a Tree

Look at pictures of a growing plant.
Number the pictures in order.
The proper order shows the life of the tree.
Color the pictures.

Teacher's Notes: Take students on a walking tour to identify plants in various stages of growth in your environment.

21

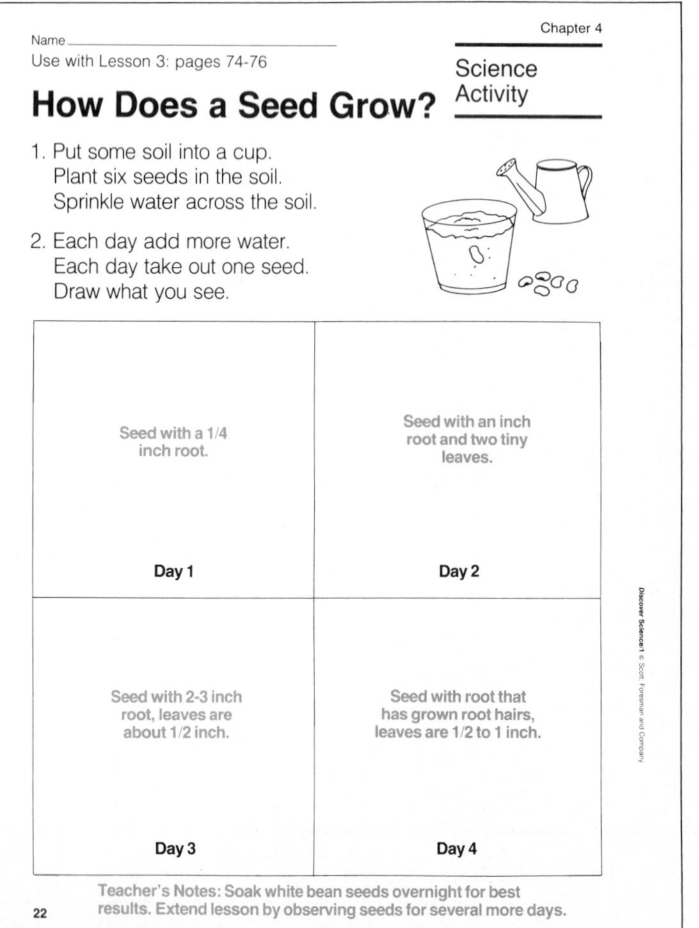

Name ____________________

Use with Lesson 3: pages 74-76

Chapter 4

Science Activity

How Does a Seed Grow?

1. Put some soil into a cup.
   Plant six seeds in the soil.
   Sprinkle water across the soil.
2. Each day add more water.
   Each day take out one seed.
   Draw what you see.

Seed with a 1/4 inch root. **Day 1**	Seed with an inch root and two tiny leaves. **Day 2**
Seed with 2-3 inch root, leaves are about 1/2 inch. **Day 3**	Seed with root that has grown root hairs, leaves are 1/2 to 1 inch. **Day 4**

22

Teacher's Notes: Soak white bean seeds overnight for best results. Extend lesson by observing seeds for several more days.

Name ______________________

Use with Lesson 4: pages 78-79

Chapter 4

Science and Social Studies

Using Parts of Trees

We use trees in many ways.
We eat fruit from many trees.
We use wood from trees.
Color the things that come from trees.

Students will color the chair, table, apple, and pencil.

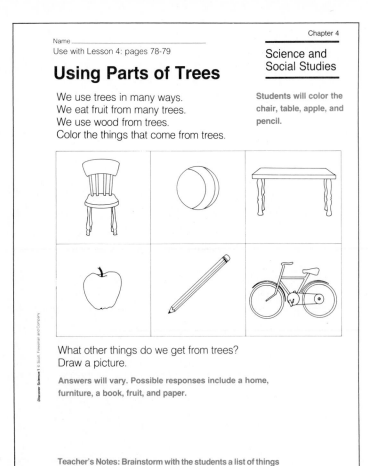

What other things do we get from trees?
Draw a picture.

Answers will vary. Possible responses include a home, furniture, a book, fruit, and paper.

Teacher's Notes: Brainstorm with the students a list of things that come from parts of trees, including maple syrup and nuts.

Name ______________________

Use with Lesson 4: pages 78-79

Chapter 4

Vocabulary Puzzle

Building a Plant Puzzle

Answer the question.
What do roots grow in?

s o i l

Color each plant part.
Cut out its name.
Paste the name on the line.
Cut out all the plant parts.
Paste them on paper to make a plant.

flower	
stem	leaf
roots	leaf
seeds	leaf

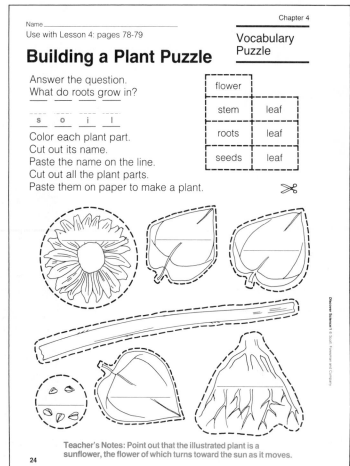

Teacher's Notes: Point out that the illustrated plant is a sunflower, the flower of which turns toward the sun as it moves.

Name ______________________

Chapter 4

Enrichment Experiment

A Seed Experiment

Do lima bean seeds grow better with soil?

Circle your prediction. Yes No **Accept any answer.**

Do this experiment to find out.
1. Plant six seeds like the picture below.

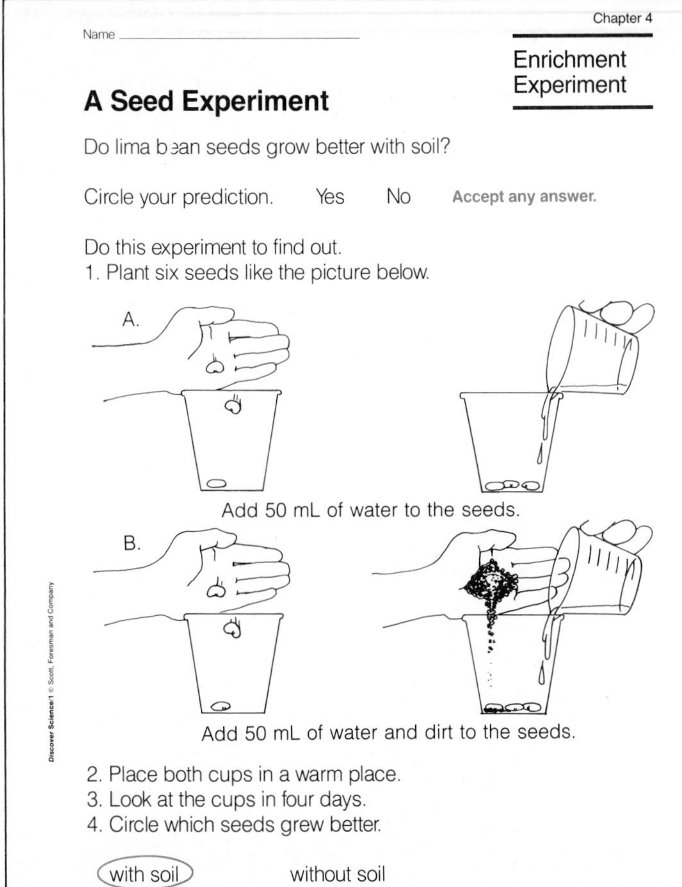

Add 50 mL of water to the seeds.

Add 50 mL of water and dirt to the seeds.

2. Place both cups in a warm place.
3. Look at the cups in four days.
4. Circle which seeds grew better.

(with soil) without soil

Name ______________________

Chapter 4 Test

Plants

I. Write **Yes** or **No.**

1. Can plants be different shapes and sizes (4-1) **Yes**
2. Are stems, roots, and leaves parts of plants? (4-1) **Yes**
3. Will plants only grow in warm places? (4-2) **No**
4. Can a plant grow without any water? (4-3) **No**
5. Do people eat plant stems? (4-3) **Yes**

II. Draw a line from the word to the right picture.

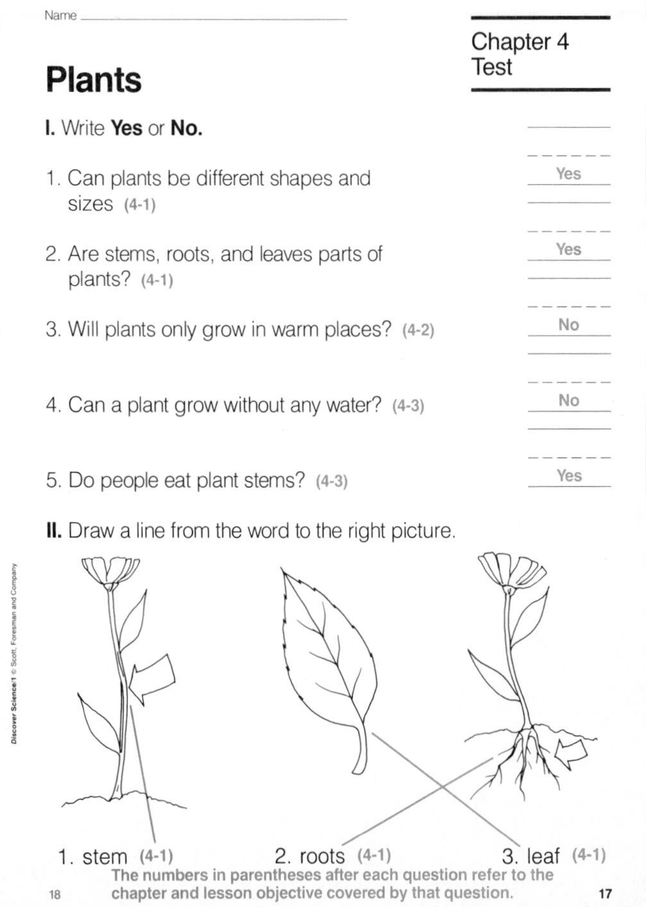

1. stem (4-1) 2. roots (4-1) 3. leaf (4-1)

The numbers in parentheses after each question refer to the chapter and lesson objective covered by that question.

INTRODUCING CHAPTER 4

Major Concepts

Lesson 1 Plants have similarities and differences.

Lesson 2 Plants grow in a variey of habitats and in an orderly way.

Lesson 3 Plants need air, water, food, and light to grow.

Lesson 4 Plants provide food and materials for such items as cloth and paper.

Vocabulary

leaves, roots, seeds, soil, stem

[1] Plant looks like a face.

Chapter 4

Learning About Plants

Look at the plant in the picture.
What does the plant look like?[1]

64

Teaching Options

Workbook page 19 *

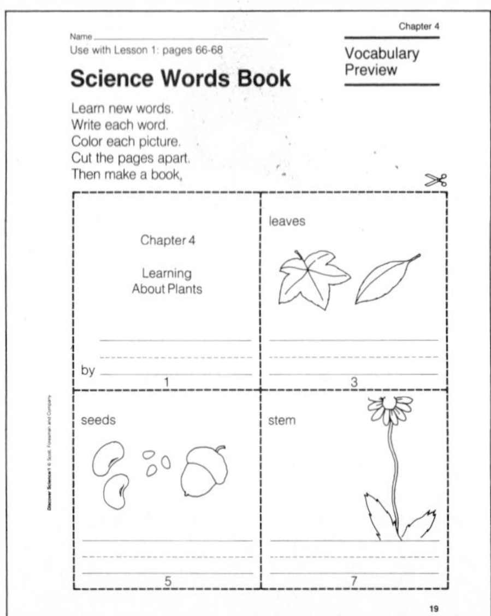

Workbook page 20 *

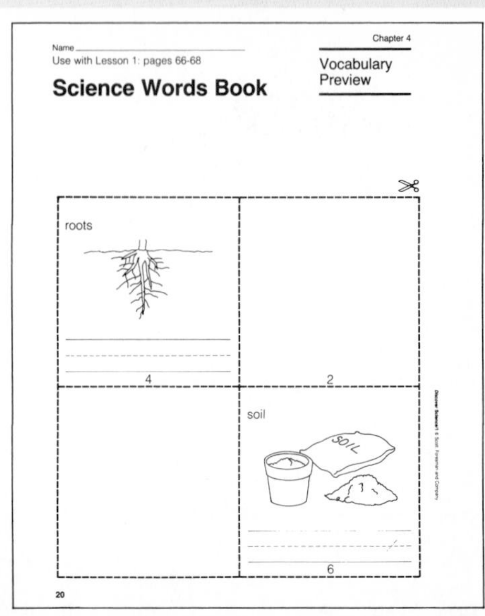

♦ ***Suitable as a language development activity***

Starting the Chapter

Do you enjoy seeing pretty plants?
Many kinds of plants are pretty.
You can learn how these plants are alike.
Then read more about plants.

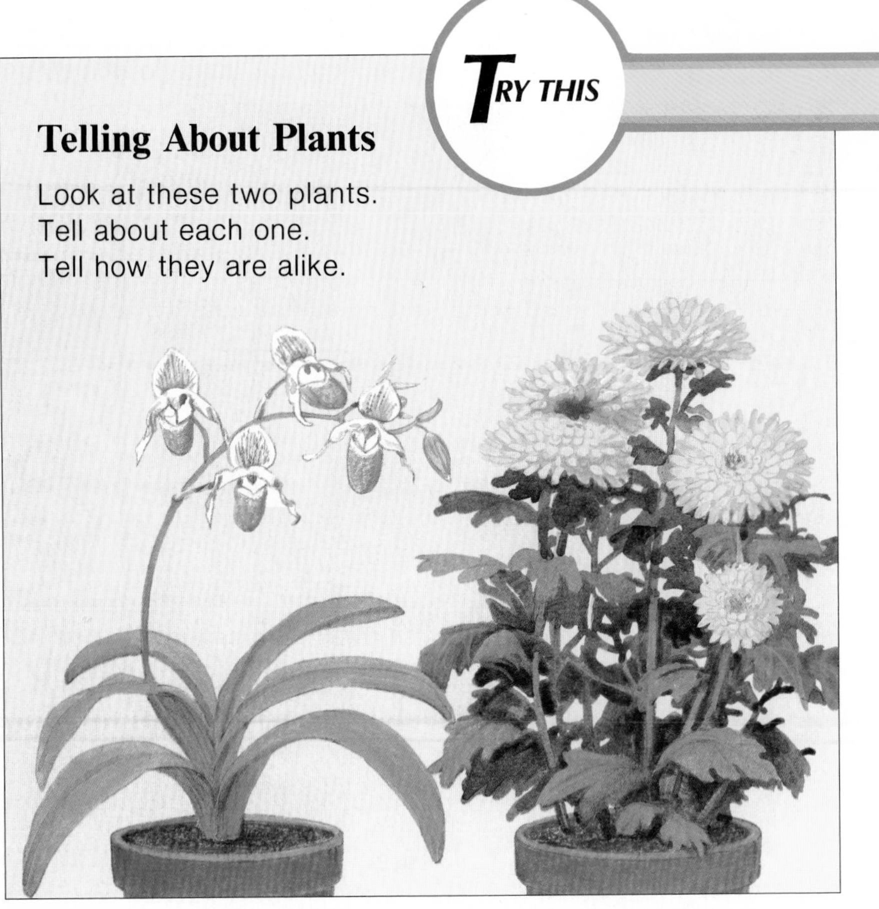
TRY THIS
Telling About Plants
Look at these two plants.
Tell about each one.
Tell how they are alike.

65

TRY THIS

Objective ♦

This optional *TRY THIS* activity will help students explore and build background information about the concept of differences and similarities among plants. Later in the chapter, students will be able to draw on this experience to help them assimilate the new content.

Science Process Skills

Classifying, Observing

Teaching Tips

- Ask the students to ***observe*** the plants. Explain to students that although the plants are very different, they are alike in many ways.
- If you have a plant in the classroom, have students compare it to the plants in the picture. *CAUTION:* Use only a nontoxic plant. If students handle the plant, have them wash their hands after completing the activity.

Answer

Students should describe the size, shape, and color of each plant. They should state that both plants grow roots in soil and have leaves, flowers, and stems.

Resource Book page 27

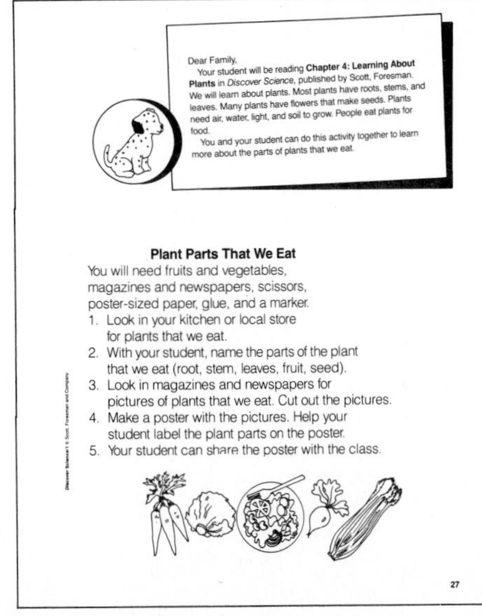

Dear Family,
Your student will be reading **Chapter 4: Learning About Plants** in *Discover Science*, published by Scott, Foresman. We will learn about plants. Most plants have roots, stems, and leaves. Many plants have flowers that make seeds. Plants need air, water, light, and soil to grow. People eat plants for food.
You and your student can do this activity together to learn more about the parts of plants that we eat.

Plant Parts That We Eat

You will need fruits and vegetables, magazines and newspapers, scissors, poster-sized paper, glue, and a marker.

1. Look in your kitchen or local store for plants that we eat.
2. With your student, name the parts of the plant that we eat (root, stem, leaves, fruit, seed).
3. Look in magazines and newspapers for pictures of plants that we eat. Cut out the pictures.
4. Make a poster with the pictures. Help your student label the plant parts on the poster.
5. Your student can share the poster with the class.

27

SCIENCE BACKGROUND

The group of flowering vascular plants that produce seeds within flowers are angiosperms. As the seeds develop, they are covered by seed coats and fruits. Today, flowering plants are the most common of all land plants. There are over 250,000 species of angiosperms, and they are found in all climates.

* ***Answers to masters on pages 64E–64F***

TEACHING PLAN

LESSON 1
pages 66–68

Lesson Objectives
- *Identify* size, shape, and color as differences among plants.
- *Identify* plant parts such as roots, stems, leaves, and flowers as similarities among plants.

Lesson Vocabulary
leaves, roots, stem

1 MOTIVATE

Demonstration Activity ♦
Bring a potted plant to school for students to examine. *CAUTION:* Use only nontoxic plants. Ask students to ***name*** the parts of the plant. Expose the plant's roots for students to ***observe***. *CAUTION:* If students handle the plant or soil, have them wash their hands thoroughly after completing the activity.

Discussion
Discuss similarities and differences among plants with students. Ask students to ***name*** some flowering plants. (Answers will vary.) Questions: **How are these plants alike?** (They all have roots, leaves, and stems.) **How are they different?** (Answers may include color, stem length, size, and so on.)

[1] different sizes, colors, leaf shapes

Lesson 1 How Are Plants Alike and Different?

Plants are alike and different.
Plants have different colors.
Plants have different shapes.
How are these plants different?[1]

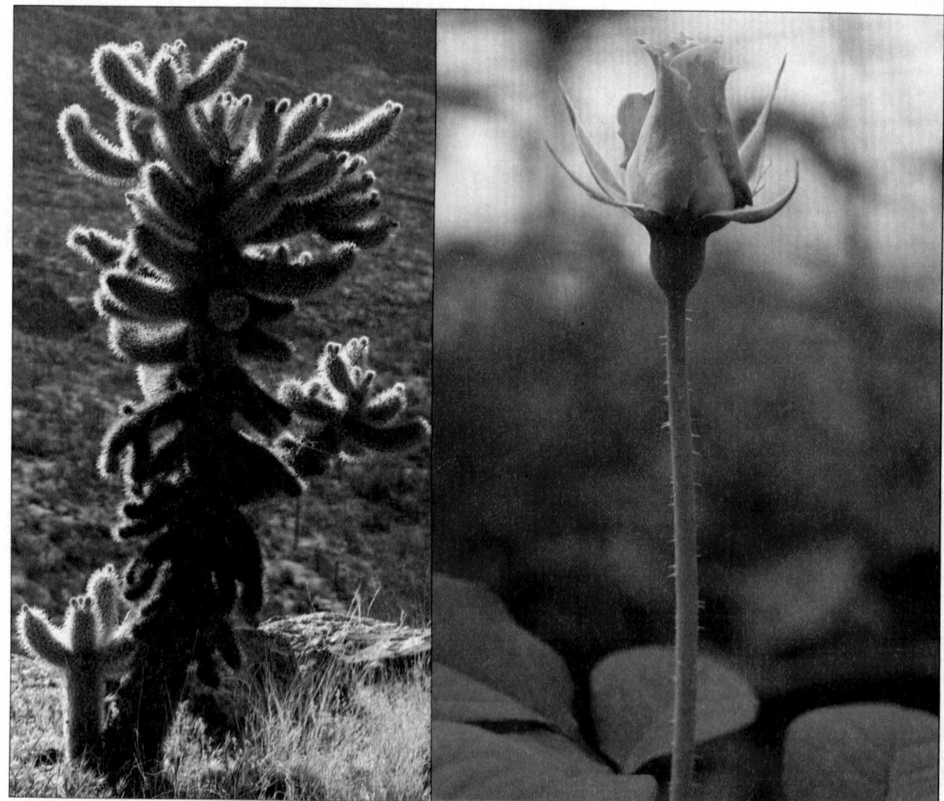

Teaching Options

SCIENCE BACKGROUND

Over a period of many years, diversity in the size and shape of plants has evolved in response to the needs of plants to obtain light under various conditions. Deciduous trees form canopies, exposing much of their leaves to the sun. Vines climb to the tops of trees to find needed sunlight. Plants on the forest floor have developed large leaves, which gather the little available light from a wide area. Water, wind, soil, and temperature also affect how a plant adapts in terms of size, shape, and color.

♦ ***Suitable as a language development activity***

Plants are also alike.

Most plants have the same parts.

Plants have **leaves.**

Plants have **roots.**

Find the leaves and roots here.

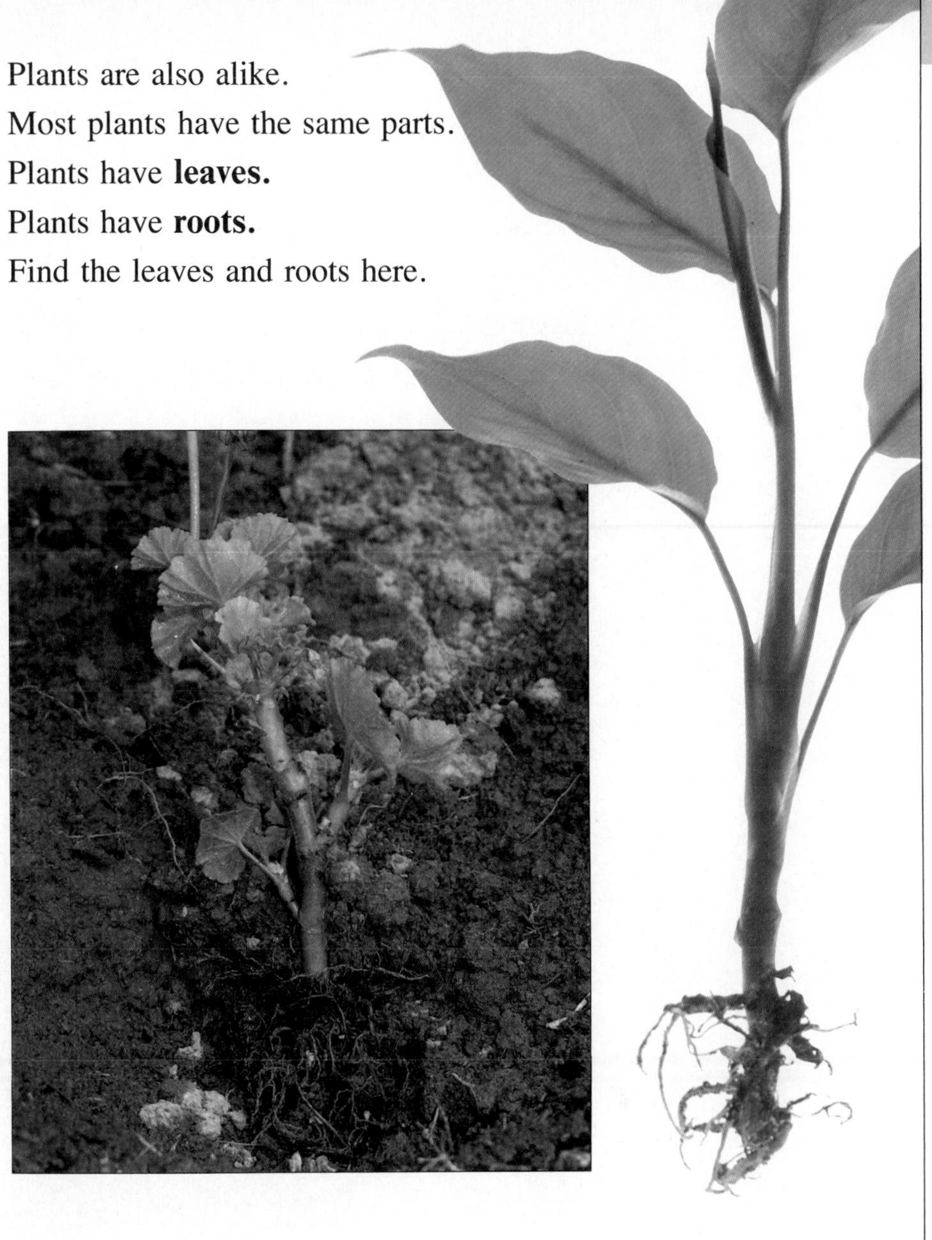

67

2 TEACH

Teaching Tips

- Ask students to look at the pictures on page 66 and 67 and *identify* the plant parts shown.
- Encourage students to describe any experiences they have had with growing and caring for plants.

Game Suggestion ♦

Make plant puzzles from magazine pictures of several different flowering plants. Let students work in groups to cut out and glue the pictures onto lightweight cardboard. They should cut each plant picture into several pieces. Let students put their plant puzzles together and then trade puzzles with other students.

Science and Art

Have students make leaf rubbings by placing a leaf under a sheet of paper and rubbing a crayon across the paper. Taping the leaf in place makes the rubbing process easier. Display the finished pictures and encourage students to notice and *describe* the differences in the patterns of the leaves.

TEACHING PLAN

Teaching Tips

• Refer students to the *TRY THIS* activity on page 65. Ask them to again tell how the plants shown on that page are alike.
• Questions: **What would happen if plants that have very long stems, such as tall trees, had very soft stems?** (The plants would droop.)
• **Possible Misconception:** Students might not think of a tree as a plant. Compare the parts of a tree to those of other plants. Point out that the trunk of a tree is its stem.

3 ASSESS

Lesson Review

1. Plants have leaves, flowers, stems, and roots.
2. Plants are different in size, shape, and color.
Challenge! Question: **How do stems that bend help to protect a plant?** (The stems will not break when the wind blows them.) **Thinking Skill:** *Drawing conclusions*

Find Out

Students should discover similarities in the plants outside their homes. Examples of similarities include the presence of leaves, stems, flowers, roots, and similarities in color, shape, or size. **Thinking Skill:** *Comparing*

[1] Tree has hard stems. Other plant has softer stems.

A plant has a **stem.**
Some plant stems are soft.
Trees are plants with hard stems.
What kinds of stems do you see here?[1]

Lesson Review

1. What parts do plants have?
2. How are plants different?

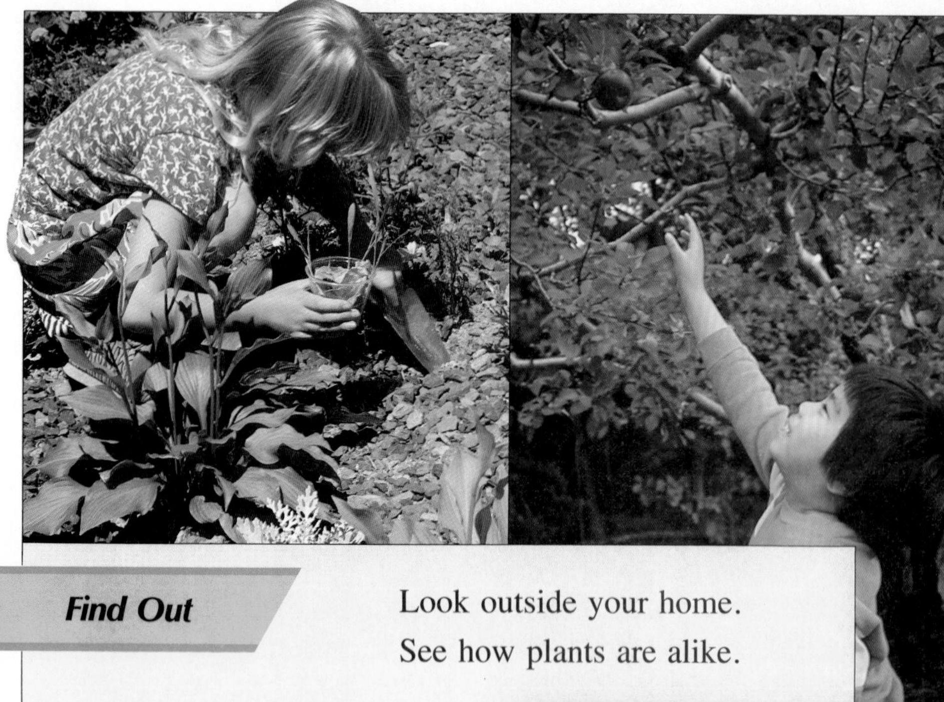

Find Out

Look outside your home.
See how plants are alike.

68

Teaching Options

SCIENCE ANECDOTE

It is not always easy to identify the parts of a plant. For example, the bright red parts of a poinsettia plant are actually the leaves of the plant, not the flowers. Poinsettia flowers are the small greenish-yellow parts of the plant that are found in the center of the bright red leaves.

Reteaching Suggestion ♦

Have students draw two different plants. Ask students to explain the similarities and differences in the plants they have drawn. You might also want students to bring leaves to class to discuss their similarities and differences.

Special Education

Have students with learning disabilities help other members of the class to transplant a flowering plant from one pot to another. *CAUTION:* Use a nontoxic plant. Remind students not to place plant parts in their mouths.Have the students find the four parts of the plant. Unpot the plant and expose the roots. Discuss the parts of the plant before students help you repot it. *CAUTION:* Direct students to wash their hands thoroughly after completing this activity.

♦ ***Suitable as a language development activity***

Grouping Leaves

Follow the Directions

1. Make two groups of leaves.
2. Find leaves with the same shape.
3. Put them in one group.
4. Find leaves with another shape.
5. Put them in a second group.

Tell What You Learned

Tell how your leaves are shaped alike.
Group your leaves a new way.

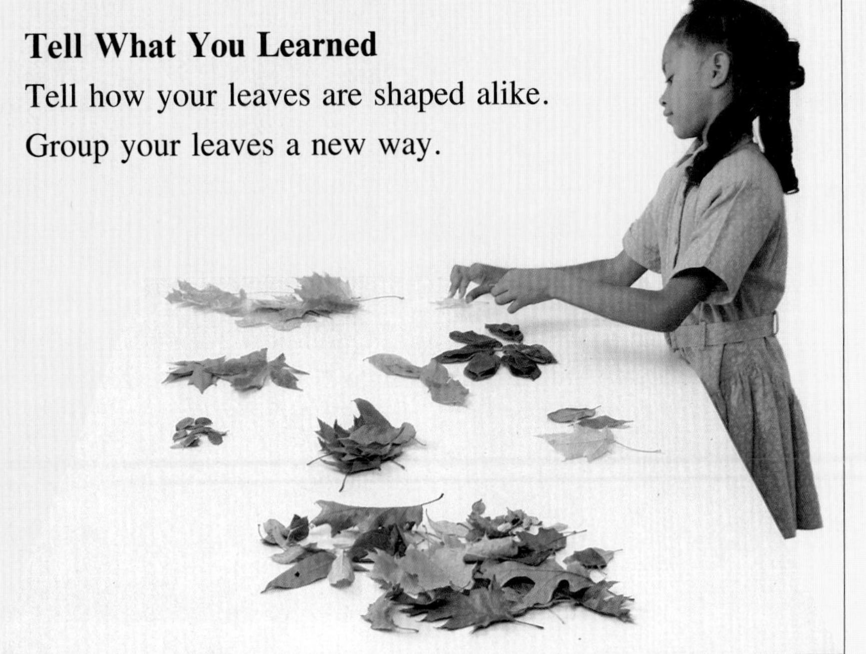

69

Enrichment Activity

Ask students to group other objects according to similar properties. Students could group buttons (size, shape, color), books (size, subject, length), or cloth (color, texture, pattern).

Activity Results

Leaves should be grouped by shapes. In most cases pinnate leaves will not be grouped with palmate leaves.

ACTIVITY PLAN

Concept
Leaves can be classified by their shape.

Objectives/Process Skills
- *Observe* a variety of leaves.
- *Classify* leaves according to shape.
- *Describe* how leaves in each group are alike.

Time Allotment
Allow 10 minutes.

Materials
For each student: assorted palmate and pinnate leaves

Safety Tips (See page T27.)
- Use only leaves of nontoxic plants.
- Remind students not to put leaves into their mouths.

Teaching Tip
- Ask students to look at the picture on page 69 and to notice differences in the leaves. Discuss how the leaves are alike and different. Have students describe the shape of the leaves.

Answers
Tell What You Learned
Students should describe similarities in the general shape or outline of their leaves. Students could regroup their leaves according to color, texture, type of edges, or type of vein pattern. **Thinking Skill:** *Comparing, Contrasting*

TEACHING PLAN

LESSON 2
pages 70–72

Lesson Objectives
- *Describe* the development of a plant from a seed.
- *Identify* different types of places where plants grow.

Lesson Vocabulary
seeds

1 MOTIVATE

Demonstration Activity ♦
Bring a variety of seeds to school and allow students to observe them closely. You might include a coconut, a peach pit, an almond, apple seeds, and peas. Do not identify the seeds for students. *CAUTION:* If students handle seeds, remind them not to place seeds in their mouths, noses, or ears.

Discussion
After showing students the seeds, explain that each one is an important part of a plant. Let students try to *identify* each seed.

Lesson 2 How Do Plants Grow?

Many plants grow from **seeds.**
Look at the plant flowers.
Flowers of plants make seeds.
Find the seeds in this flower.

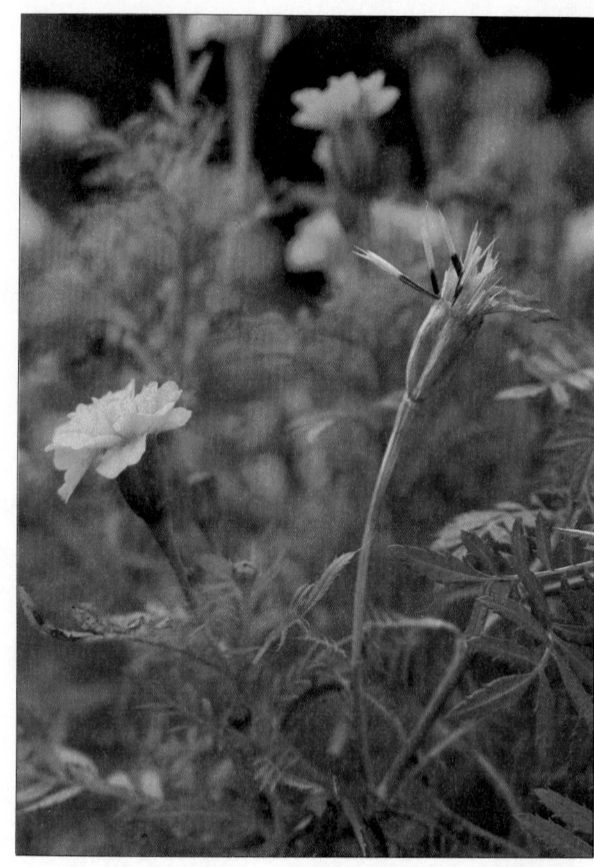

70

Teaching Options

SCIENCE BACKGROUND

Several factors help determine where a plant will grow. One of those factors is seed dispersal. When a mature plant is fertilized and develops seeds, the seeds are dispersed, or spread to other areas, in several different ways. Some plants propel their seeds. Some seeds are carried away by water. Some seeds have prickly, thornlike structures that attach to the fur of animals, which carry the seeds to new locations. Bird sometimes disperse the seeds of fruits that they eat. Some seeds are especially adapted to being dispersed by wind. The winged, whirlybird structure that carries a maple tree seed and the fluffy, white fibers that carry a dandelion seed are examples.

♦ ***Suitable as a language development activity***

[1] bean plants

A seed opens when it begins to grow.
A plant grows from the open seed.
A growing plant makes more seeds.
Look at the seeds in the picture.
What plants will grow from the seeds?[1]

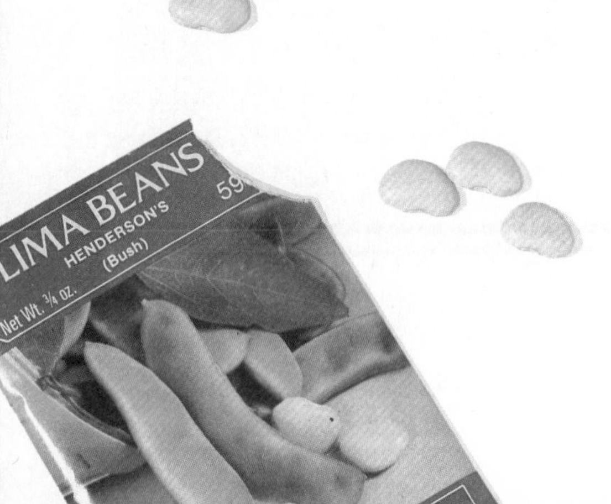

2 TEACH

Teaching Tips

- Help students read the lesson pages and direct their attention to the bean seed, sprout, and plant. Have students ***describe*** what is happening in the growing process.
- Point out the seed package. Help students understand that seeds can be purchased or collected from mature plants.

Reinforcement

Help students plant bean seeds. Have students put a bean on top of a damp ball of cotton in a plastic foam cup. When beans sprout (in 4-5 days) instruct students to add dirt to the cup. Give each student a large sheet of paper and instruct students to divide the paper into eight spaces, either by folding or drawing lines. Have the students ***observe, measure, describe,*** and draw pictures of their plant every three days. Students should use the eight spaces on their paper for their observations over a 24-day period. *CAUTION:* Remind students not to place seeds in their mouths, noses, or ears. Have students wash their hands thoroughly after handling soil.

Special Education

For more concrete experience for student with learning disabilities, provide a variety of seeds in seed packets. Show students each type of seed and the picture of what it will become. Have the students ***describe*** the variety of seeds by size, shape, and color. Ask them to ***describe*** the plants that will grow from each type of seed. *CAUTION:* Remind students not to place seeds in their mouths, noses, or ears.

Science and Art

Provide a variety of seeds, small pieces of poster board, and glue. Instruct students to make mosiacs with the seeds. The mosaics can be a design or a picture of something. *CAUTION:* Remind students not to place seeds in their mouths, noses, or ears.

TEACHING PLAN

Teaching Tips

- Ask students to look at the pictures on page 72. Discuss the characteristics of the plants in the habitats shown. On a map, point out places in the country and around the world that have habitats similar to those shown.
- **Possible Misconception:** Some students might think that trees die when the temperature turns cold and the leaves fall. Point out that trees with broad leaves, such as maple, oak, and birch, become dormant during the cold months. You can loosely compare this dormancy to the hibernation of a woodchuck.

3 ASSESS

Lesson Review

1. A plant grows from a seed that opens.
2. Plants can grow in dry, wet, hot, or cold places.

Challenge! Question: **Why are flowers important for more plants to grow?** (Flowers make seeds, which will grow into more plants.) **Thinking Skill:** *Making generalizations*

Find Out

Answers should refer to abundance, size, shape, and color. **Thinking Skill:** *Contrasting*

[1] variety of areas

Where can plants grow?
Plants grow in dry or wet places.
Plants grow in hot or cold places.
Where are these plants growing?[1]

Lesson Review

1. How does a plant grow?
2. In what places can plants grow?

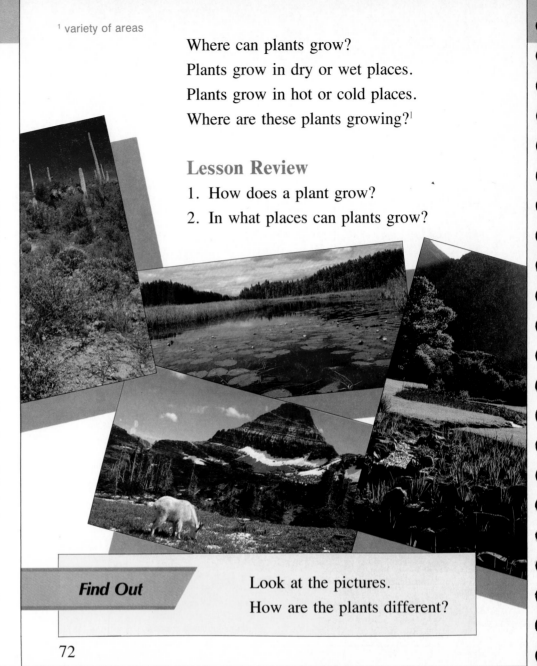

Find Out

Look at the pictures.
How are the plants different?

72

Teaching Options

SCIENCE ANECDOTE

John Chapman (1774–1845), better known as Johnny Appleseed, was a pioneer in the Ohio River Valley. As he traveled westward from Pennsylvania to Illinois, he planted apple seeds, which gave rise to orchards throughout that part of the country.

Reteaching Suggestion ♦

Combine the use of photographs and a fruit with seeds to reteach some of the basic concepts of how plants grow. For example, show students pictures of of a blossoming apple tree in spring and an apple tree with growing fruit in summer and fall. Ask students to *explain* what is happening as you show each picture. Then show students an apple. Cut the apple open to reveal the seeds. Point out that the seeds can be planted to grow new trees.

Workbook page 21 *

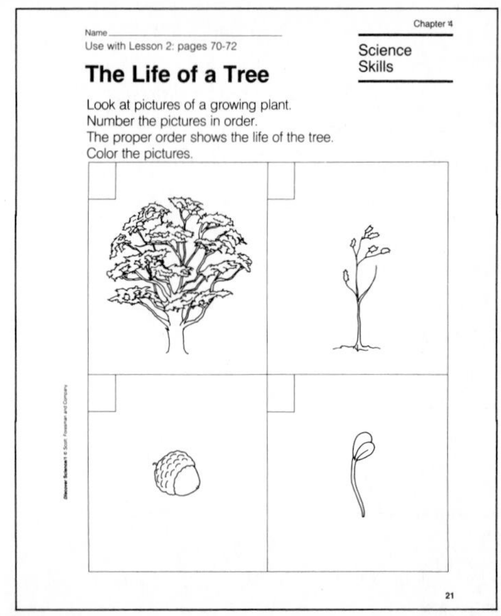
Name
Use with Lesson 2: pages 70-72
Chapter 4
Science Skills

The Life of a Tree

Look at pictures of a growing plant.
Number the pictures in order.
The proper order shows the life of the tree.
Color the pictures.

21

♦ ***Suitable as a language development activity***

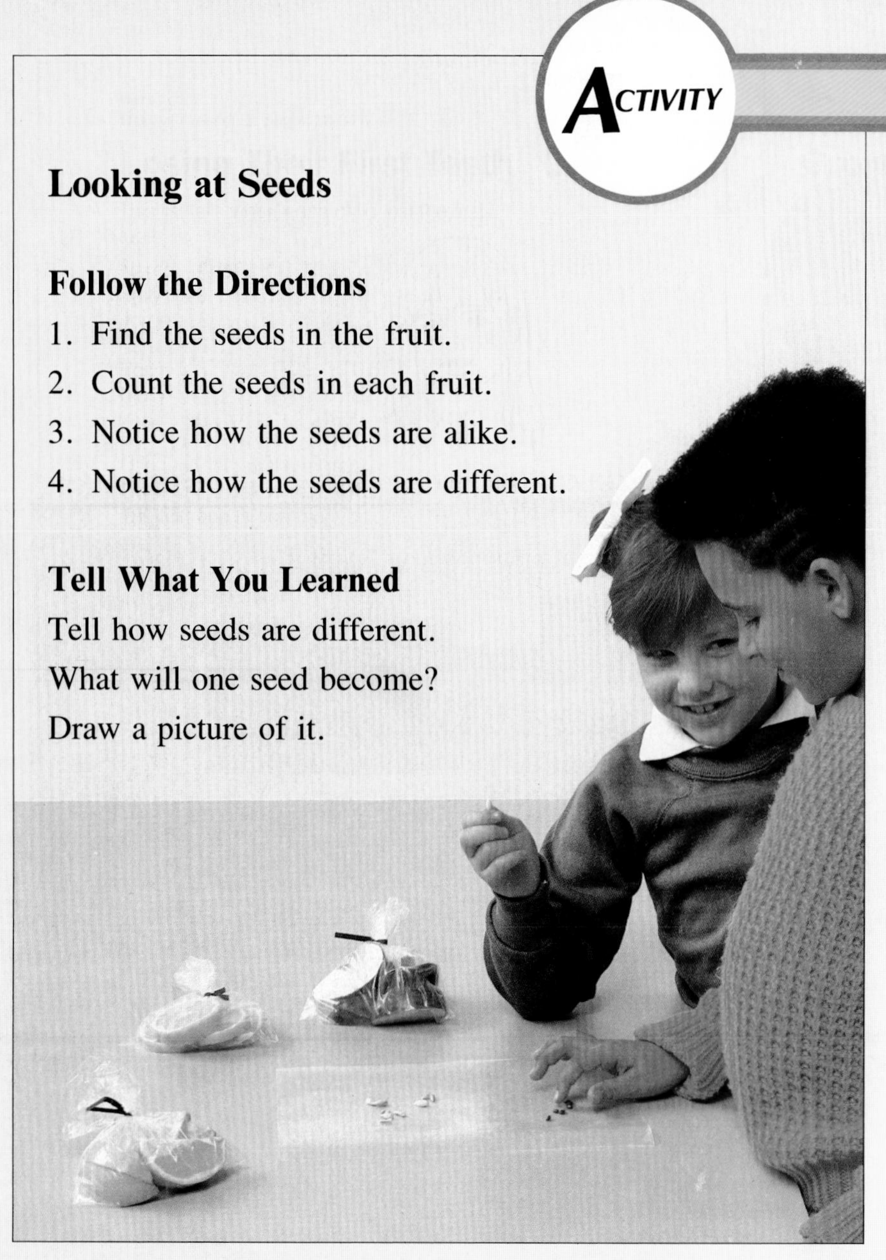

ACTIVITY

Looking at Seeds

Follow the Directions

1. Find the seeds in the fruit.
2. Count the seeds in each fruit.
3. Notice how the seeds are alike.
4. Notice how the seeds are different.

Tell What You Learned

Tell how seeds are different.
What will one seed become?
Draw a picture of it.

73

ACTIVITY PLAN

Concept
Seeds have different sizes, shapes, and colors.

Objectives/Process Skills
- *Observe* seeds in fruits.
- *Count* the seeds in each fruit.
- *Compare* and *contrast* the seeds.
- *Predict* what one seed will become.

Time Allotment
Allow 15 minutes.

Materials
For each student: a wedge (with seeds) of orange, apple, lemon; drawing paper, crayons, pencil

Safety Tips (See page T27.)
- Instruct students not to eat the fruit.
- Remind students not to put seeds into their mouths, noses, or ears.

Teaching Tips
- Before students begin the activity, discuss the types of fruits that students will be observing. Questions: **Do these fruits all have a skin?** (yes) **Is the fruit firm or soft? Are any of the fruits similar?**
- Ask students to complete the activity. If you are using more than one kind of citrus fruit for the activity, you might want to explain that the seeds in these fruits are similar in many ways, but usually differ in size according to the size of the fruit.

Enrichment Activity

Ask students to collect seeds from some of the foods they eat at home. Allow students to grow the seeds they collect, and report to the class about the progress of their plants.

Activity Results

Number of seeds will vary. The lemon and orange seeds will be somewhat similar in appearance. Both are whitish on the outside and somewhat rounded. The apple seeds are brown on the outside and comparatively flat.

Answers
Tell What You Learned
For the first statement, students should point out differences in the sizes, shapes, colors, and textures of seeds. For the second statement, students should draw an appropriate picture to correspond with one type of seed they have been observing. **Thinking Skill:** *Comparing, Contrasting*

***** *Answers to masters on pages 64E–64F***

LESSON 3
pages 74–76

Lesson Objective
- *Identify* what plants need for growth.
- *Describe* how plants can be cared for indoors.

Lesson Vocabulary
soil

1 MOTIVATE

Demonstration Activity ♦
Bring to class a shallow pan of soil. The pan should be clear plastic, if possible. Sprinkle the soil with water so that the soil is wet to the touch. *CAUTION:* Immediately wipe up any soil or water that spills on the floor to prevent slipping accidents.

Discussion
Allow students to touch the soil and *describe* how it feels. (wet) Questions: **What do you think plants need in order to grow?** (Students should mention water, among other things.) **How do you think plants get the water?** (Lead students to *conclude* that the water enters the plants' roots from the soil.) *CAUTION:* Direct students to wash their hands thoroughly after touching the soil.

[1] from the sun
[2] from rain, lakes, rivers, and other sources

Lesson 3 What Do Plants Need to Grow?

Plants need air to grow.
Plants also need water to grow.
Green plants need light.
How do these plants get light?[1]
How do they get water?[2]

74

Teaching Options

SCIENCE BACKGROUND

Flowering plants have only a few basic parts: leaves, supported by stems, manufacture food for the plant; roots absorb water and minerals; flowers, which form seeds, are the plant's reproductive organs. Green plants make nutrients using the two-stage process of photosynthesis. First, light energy from the sun is absorbed by the chlorophyll in the leaves. This energy is changed to chemical energy and stored. Next, the plant uses the stored chemical energy to change carbon dioxide and water into glucose.

Enrichment

Give each student a copy of the school lunch menu for the week. Read each day's lunch menu together and determine which items come from plants. Have the students circle these items. Have students locate items in the classroom that come from plants.

♦ ***Suitable as a language development activity***

[1] roots

Most plants grow in the ground.
They need **soil** to grow.
Soil holds plants in place.
Soil also holds water plants use.
What part of the plant grows in soil?[1]

2 TEACH

Teaching Tips

- If there are plants in the classroom, have students explain how they get light. Then have the students look at the plants in the pictures and discuss how these plants get light.
- **Possible Misconception:** Many students will likely think that plants take in water through their leaves, since they have seen raindrops on leaves. Point out that the water enters the plant through the roots from the soil. Question: **When watering plants, is it more important for the plants to get wet or for the soil around the plants to get wet?** (soil around the plants)

Reinforcement

Obtain two healthy bean plants and have students care for them in exactly the same way, with one exception—keep one plant in a dark closet and the other plant in sunlight. Let students ***observe*** and ***compare*** the plants daily. Repeat the activity with two other bean plants, but deprive one plant of water instead of sunlight.

Special Education

Ask students with learning disabilities to ***recall*** the four things green plants need to grow. (air, water, light, soil) Have the students ***predict*** what might happen to a plant that was suddenly deprived of one or more of these factors. (The plant might die or not grow as well.)

Science and Language Arts

Tell students to pretend that they are giving a plant to a friend, as a gift. Ask the students to write directions that explain how to take care of the plant.

TEACHING PLAN

Teaching Tip

- Have students discuss what can be done to care for indoor plants. Explain that, in addition to water and sunlight, plants needs minerals which they usually get from the soil. Tell students that it is sometimes necessary to give these minerals to indoor plants in another way. You might want to bring some examples of different types of plant foods to class.

3 ASSESS

Lesson Review

1. Plants need air, water, light, and soil.
2. Indoor plants need care from people.
Challenge! Question: **How can you tell that a plant is getting its water from deep in the ground?** (The plant grows long roots.) **Thinking Skill:** *Inferring*

Find Out

When students keep a plant in a dark place, the plant's leaves and flowers might droop or bend over, and the flowers might fall off of the plant. **Thinking Skill:** *Recognizing cause and effect*

[1] watering the plant

Plants need care to grow indoors.
People can care for indoor plants.
People give plants what they need.
What is this girl doing?[1]

Lesson Review

1. What are four needs of plants?
2. What plants need care from people?

Find Out

Keep a plant in a dark place.
See what happens to it.

76

Teaching Options

SCIENCE ANECDOTE

Recently, researchers have been experimenting with hydroponic gardening—growing plants without using soil. Instead, plants grow in nutrient-rich water. With hydroponics, crops can be grown without the space, weeds, and pests that are characteristic of farmland.

Reteaching Suggestion ♦

Bring a plant to school and help students plan how to care for it. Tell students how much light and water that type of plant needs, and let students decide where to place the plant, and how often to water it. *CAUTION:* Immediately wipe up any water that spills on the floor.

Workbook page 22 *

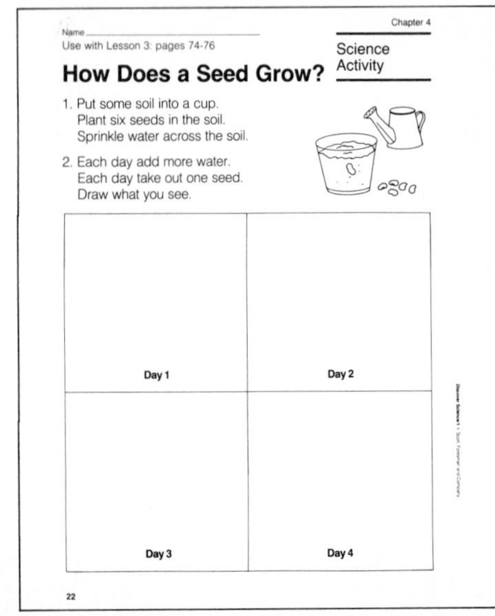

Name ____ Chapter 4
Use with Lesson 3: pages 74-76
Science Activity

How Does a Seed Grow?

1. Put some soil into a cup. Plant six seeds in the soil. Sprinkle water across the soil.
2. Each day add more water. Each day take out one seed. Draw what you see.

Day 1	Day 2
Day 3	Day 4

22

♦ ***Suitable as a language development activity***

Science in Your Life

Bringing Water to Plants

This place is hot and dry.
Rain hardly ever falls here.
Few plants could grow here.
The plants did not get water.
Now machines pump in water.
How do the machines help plants?

What Do You Think?

How does water help dry places?

77

SCIENCE IN YOUR LIFE

Discussion

Ask students if they have ever seen sprinklers watering grass. Ask students why people water grass. (Sometimes an area does not get enough rain to keep the grass alive or as healthy as people would like.) Ask what happens when grass does not get enough water (It turns yellow or brown and eventually dies.) If any of the students live in rural areas, ask them to relate their observations of crop irrigation.

Teaching Tips

- Help students read the page. Discuss the differences in the irrigated and nonirrigated portions of the desert area in the illustration. Guide students to understand that water can make desert areas useful for growing crops.
- Discuss the problems that many parts of the country, especially the Southwest, are having with irrigated water. The huge amounts of water required to irrigate arid lands makes water a scarce resource for other uses, such as washing and flushing.

Answers

What Do You Think?
Watering dry places enables those places to grow crops that could not be grown without water. **Thinking Skill:** *Drawing conclusions*

SCIENCE BACKGROUND

Plants in desert regions have special adaptations that allow them to survive the dry conditions. For example, cactuses have thick, fleshy stems that retain water for long periods of time. Also, their spiny leaves lose less water to the air than broad leaves do. Other plants, such as a jade plant, have thick, water-retaining leaves with a waxy coating. The coating helps keep water inside the leaves. Some desert plants bloom only after heavy rains. They can sprout, bloom, and produce seeds in one or two weeks. Thereafter, the plants die, but the seeds remain alive in the ground, ready for the next rainfall.

*** Answers to masters on pages 64E–64F**

TEACHING PLAN

LESSON 4
pages 78–79

Lesson Objective
- *Name* ways that people use plants.

1 MOTIVATE

Demonstration Activity ♦
Bring a cotton towel, an article of clothing made from cotton, a wooden toy, and a newspaper to school. Pass the items around the classroom and let students observe them closely.

Discussion
Allow time for the students to identify and discuss the differences in each of the objects. Explain that, although the objects are very different, they are all alike in one way. Let students try to guess how the objects are alike. (They are all made from plants.)

[1] roots, stems, leaves, fruit
[2] answers will vary

Lesson 4 Why Do People Need Plants?

People need plants for food.
People eat different plants.
Look at the farm plants here.
What parts of plants do people eat?[1]
What plant parts do you like?[2]

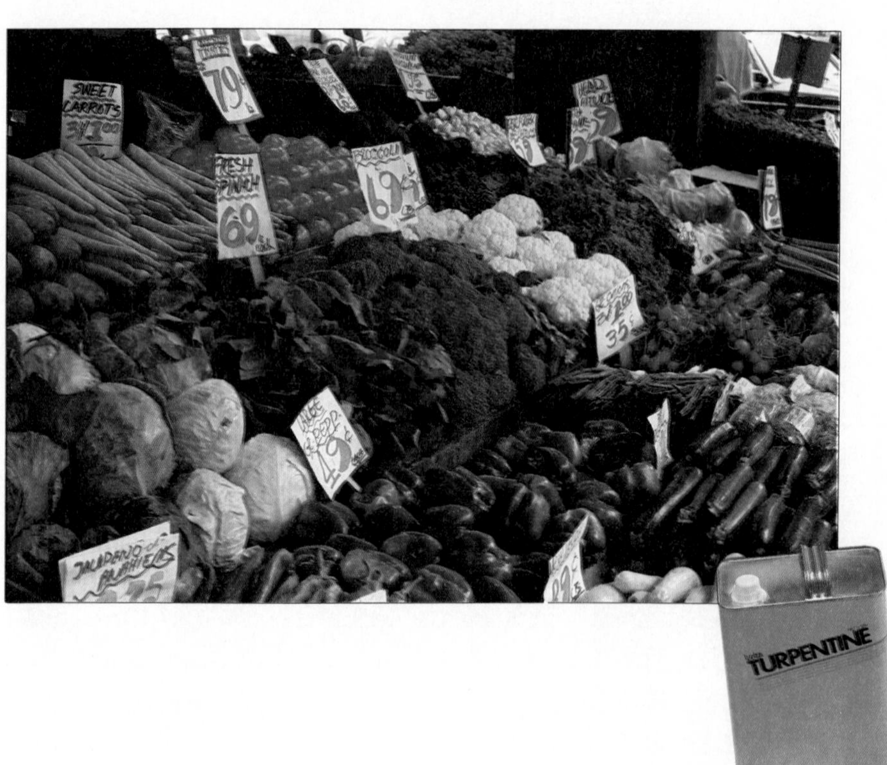

78

Teaching Options

SCIENCE BACKGROUND

Foods that are commonly called fruits and vegetables come from different parts of plants. Apples, oranges, strawberries, tomatoes, cucumbers, string beans, and squash are some edible fruits of their respective plants. Peanuts, peas, corn, and kidney beans are examples of seeds. Edible roots include sweet potatos, radishes, carrots, beets, and turnips. Asparagus and white potatoes are edible stems. People are eating leaves when they eat lettuce, cabbage, spinach, and Brussels sprouts. Broccoli and cauliflower are the flower buds of their respective plants.

Special Education

Help students with learning disabilities point out items in the classroom that are made from plants. Remind students that trees are plants. Help students point out items made of wood, clothing made of cotton, and paper products. Briefly explain how the plant material is processed to make these products. For example, explain that wooden chips are pulverized, washed, and pressed into flat sheets—paper.

♦ ***Suitable as a language development activity***

What comes from plants?
Cloth is made from parts of some plants.
Wood comes from trees.
People can make paper from wood.

Lesson Review

1. What plant parts can people eat?
2. What can people make from plants?

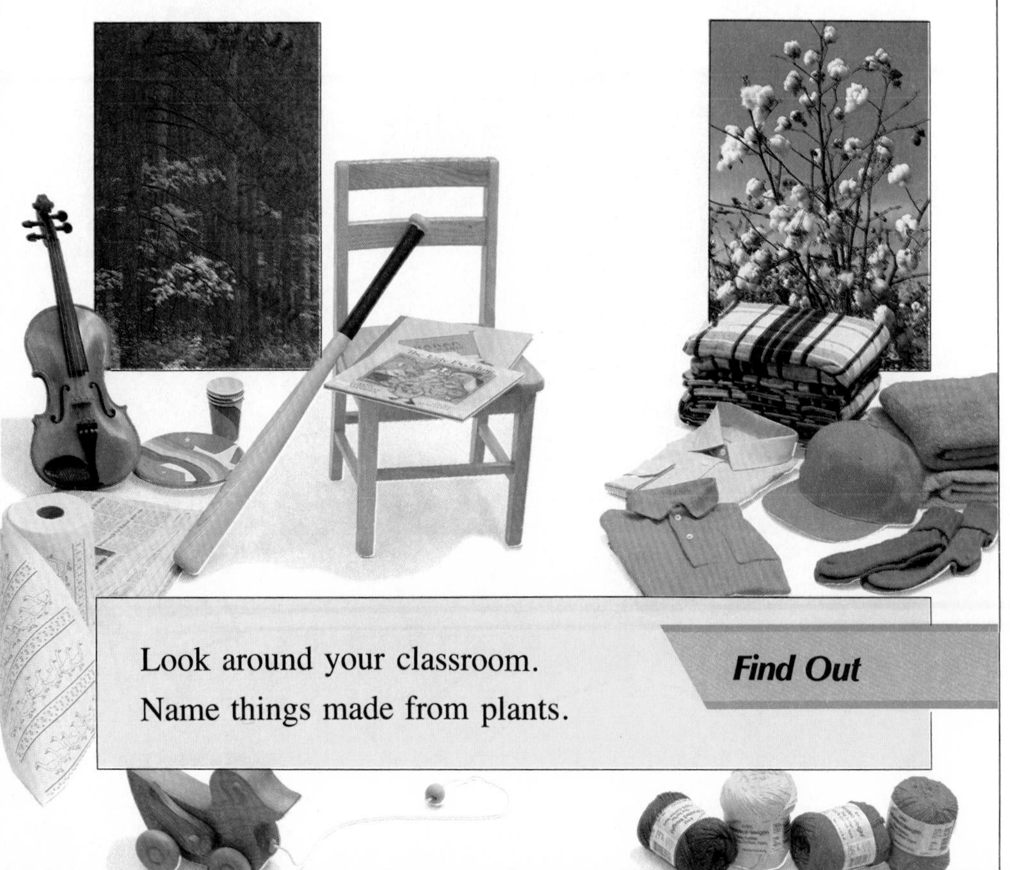

Look around your classroom.
Name things made from plants.

Find Out

2 TEACH

Teaching Tip

• **Possible Misconception:** Students might mention mushrooms as being a plant part that people eat. Explain that mushrooms are not considered to be plants because they cannot make their own food. Mushrooms are fungi.

3 ASSESS

Lesson Review

1. People can eat roots, stems, flowers, leaves, seeds, and fruits of certain plants.
2. Answers may differ but should include items made from wood and cloth.
Challenge! Question: **Name some things that are made of paper. Think of a new way to use paper.** (Items may include writing tablets, napkins, cups, plates, newspapers, and facial tissue. New uses might refer to using paper to make objects for games.) **Thinking Skill:** *Identifying and suggesting alternatives*

Find Out

Students might name paper, furniture, clothing, and baskets. **Thinking Skill:** *Restating or explaining ideas*

Workbook page 23 *

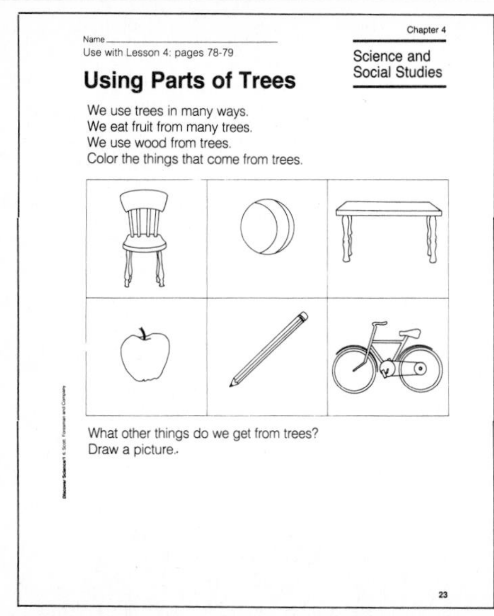

Name
Use with Lesson 4: pages 78-79

Chapter 4
Science and Social Studies

Using Parts of Trees

We use trees in many ways.
We eat fruit from many trees.
We use wood from trees.
Color the things that come from trees.

What other things do we get from trees?
Draw a picture.

23

Workbook page 24 *

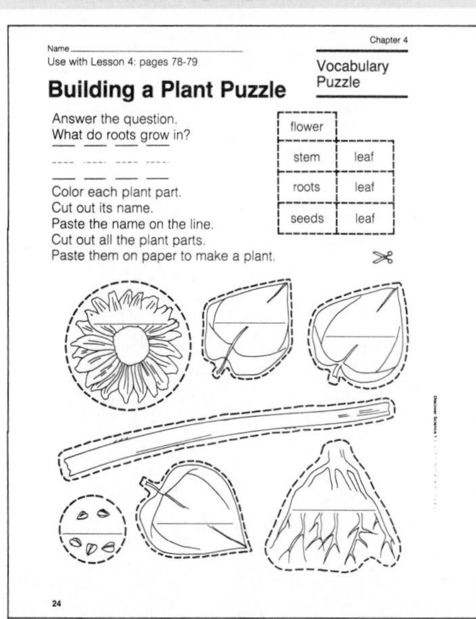

Name
Use with Lesson 4: pages 78-79

Chapter 4
Vocabulary Puzzle

Building a Plant Puzzle

Answer the question.
What do roots grow in?

Color each plant part.
Cut out its name.
Paste the name on the line.
Cut out all the plant parts.
Paste them on paper to make a plant.

flower	
stem	leaf
roots	leaf
seeds	leaf

24

Reteaching Suggestion ♦

Collect pictures of various types of products—those that come from plants and those that do not. Include food items. Glue each picture to a flash card. Hold up the cards and let students state if the item is made from plants or not. You might also suggest students play "Go Fish." The first student to get four cards of items made from plants is the winner.

*** Answers to masters on pages 64E–64F**

TEACHING PLAN

SKILLS FOR SOLVING PROBLEMS

pages 80–81

Purpose
To develop the skills of collecting and organizing information using hand lenses and drawings to solve problems.

Materials
For each student: hand lens , small nontoxic leaf

1 MOTIVATE

Discussion
Ask students if they have ever used a hand lens. Discuss its purpose of making an object appear larger so it can be seen more easily and in greater detail. Place a drop of water on a newspaper over some of the type and let students *observe* how the drop acts as a magnifier. *CAUTION:* Immediately wipe up any water that spills on the floor to prevent slipping accidents.

Skills for Solving Problems

Using a Hand Lens

How does a hand lens help you see?

1. Look at a leaf.
   Then use a hand lens to look at a leaf.
   Place the lens near the leaf.
   Stop when you see clearly.
   Tell what you see each time.

Teaching Options

SCIENCE BACKGROUND

A hand lens that magnifies only ten times is an important tool for many scientists. For example, a geologist on a field trip commonly uses a hand lens to examine rocks. In the laboratory, a thin slice of rock can be viewed under a microscope at hundreds of times magnification. The upper limit of magnification for a microscope using ordinary light is about 2,000X. Microscopes using only ultraviolet light, however, can magnify up to 3,000X. The most powerful microscopes are electron microscopes, which use beams of electrons rather than beams of light to magnify objects. Electron microscopes can magnify objects hundreds of thousands of times.

2. Draw two large boxes like this.
   Draw a leaf seen without a hand lens.
   Draw a leaf seen with a hand lens.

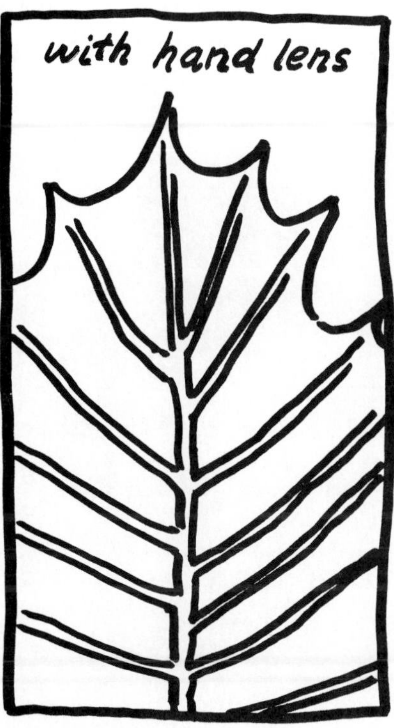

3. How does using a hand lens help you?

81

2 TEACH

Teaching Tips

- Help students to move the hand lens farther from and closer to the object to focus the image. *CAUTION:* Tell students not to use the hand lens to concentrate the sun's rays on skin or paper. Tell them to notice the position that gives the sharpest image and use that position as a guide when viewing other objects.
- Have students ***describe*** some of the details that can be seen when the leaf is in focus under the hand lens.

3 ASSESS

A hand lens helps people see things that are too small to be seen with their eyes alone.

Resource Book page 31

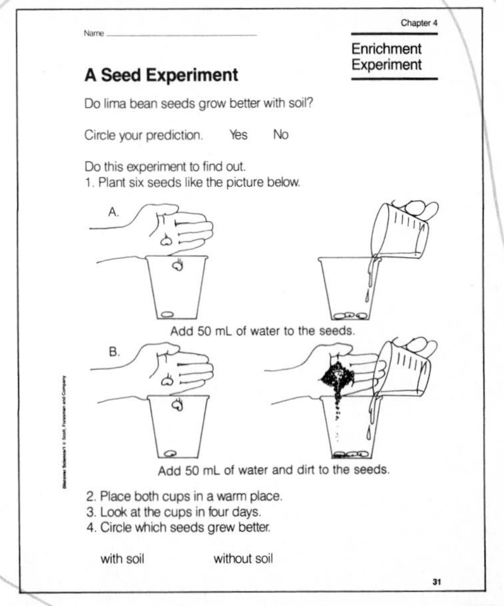

Name ____________ Chapter 4

Enrichment Experiment

A Seed Experiment

Do lima bean seeds grow better with soil?

Circle your prediction. Yes No

Do this experiment to find out.
1. Plant six seeds like the picture below.

A.

Add 50 mL of water to the seeds.

B.

Add 50 mL of water and dirt to the seeds.

2. Place both cups in a warm place.
3. Look at the cups in four days.
4. Circle which seeds grew better.

with soil without soil

31

*** Answers to masters on pages 64E–64F**

REVIEW PLAN

CHAPTER 4 REVIEW
pages 82–83

Review Chapter Ideas
1. Plants have similar parts.
2. Plants differ in size, shape, and color. They grow in different ways.
3. A plant grows from a seed that opens in soil.
4. Plants can grow in hot, dry, wet, and cold places.
5. Plants need air, light, water, and soil to grow.
6. The girl is using furniture made from plants. The book, pencils, and paper are made of materials that come from plants. The food comes from plants.

For further review, use Study Guide page 232.

Chapter 4 Review

Review Chapter Ideas
1. Tell how plants are alike.
2. Tell how plants are different.
3. Explain how a plant grows.
4. Name places where plants can grow.
5. Tell what plants need to grow.
6. Look at the picture.
   Tell how the girl is using plants.

82

Review Options

Cooperative Learning ♦

STAD Format (see page T23)
Assign students to work in four- to five-member teams to study Chapter 4 Review. Students should work together to make sure that they and their teammates know the material in the chapter. After students have had enough time to study together, give them a test to complete individually (Chapter 4 Test in the *Test Book*). Award Superteam certificates to teams whose average test scores exceed 90% and Greatteam certificates to teams whose average test scores exceed 80%.

Test Book page 17 *

Name ____________

Chapter 4 Test

Plants

I. Write **Yes** or **No.**

1. Can plants be different shapes and sizes ______
2. Are stems, roots, and leaves parts of plants? ______
3. Will plants only grow in warm places? ______
4. Can a plant grow without any water? ______
5. Do people eat plant stems? ______

II. Draw a line from the word to the right picture.

1. stem 2. roots 3. leaf

17

♦ ***Suitable as a language development activity***

Review Science Words

Match the words and the pictures.

1. leaves
2. stem
3. roots

a.

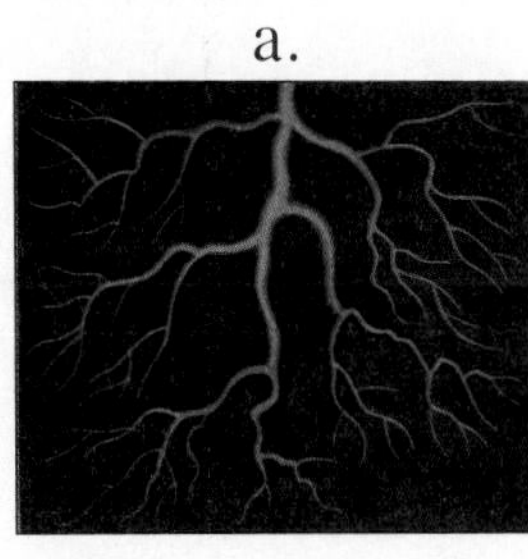

b.

c.

Tell what the words mean.

4. seeds
5. soil

Use Science Ideas

Tell what will happen next.

83

Review Science Words

Match the words and the pictures.

1. b
2. c
3. a

Tell what the words mean.

Thinking Skill: *Restating or explaining ideas*

4. Seeds—parts of a plant made by flowers that grow into new plants.

5. Soil—material on the ground that plants grow in.

Use Science Ideas

The seed will begin to grow and then become a larger plant. **Thinking Skill:** *Drawing conclusions*

***** *Answers to masters on pages 64E–64F***

Teaching Plan

Chapter Components	Skills	Materials
Chapter Opener/*TRY THIS:* Touching Animals pp. 84-85	***TRY THIS*** p. 85 **Science Process Skills** *Classifying, Observing*	***TRY THIS*** p. 85 no materials needed
Lesson 1: What Ways Are Animals Different? pp. 86-87	**Thinking Skills** Challenge!: *Making analogies* Find Out: *Inferring*	**Demonstration** p. 86 2 pictures of very different animals
Lesson 2: How Do Animals Grow? pp. 88-90	**Thinking Skills** Challenge!: *Applying information to new situations* Find Out: *Restating or explaining ideas*	**Demonstration** p. 88 Mother with her baby
Activity: Observing Growing and Changing p. 91	**Science Process Skills** *Observing, Predicting*	(groups of 2) 30 mealworms, water, 15 small boxes, 1 box oatmeal, 30 sheets drawing paper, 30 boxes crayons, 30 pencils
Lesson 3: Why Do People Need Animals? pp. 92-93	**Thinking Skills** Challenge!: *Applying information to new situations* Find Out: *Restating or explaining ideas*	**Demonstration** p. 92 no materials needed
Activity: Using Something from Animals p. 94	**Science Process Skills** *Communicating, Observing, Measuring*	(groups of 2) 15 jars (baby-food size) with lids, 1 liter whipping cream, 30 sheets drawing paper, 30 boxes crayons, 30 pencils
Science and People: Gerald Durrell p. 95	**Thinking Skill** *Drawing conclusions*	
Lesson 4: How Can You Care for a Pet? pp. 96-97	**Thinking Skills** Challenge!: *Inferring* Find Out: *Restating or explaining ideas*	**Demonstration** p. 96 pictures of students' pets
Skills for Solving Problems: Making Charts About Animals pp. 98-99	**Problem Solving Skills** *Making decisions/Identifying and solving problems, Interpreting charts, maps, and graphs*	(individual) paper, pencil
Chapter Review pp. 100-101	**Thinking Skills** *Restating or explaining ideas, Applying information to new situations*	

Teaching Options

Strategies	Extensions	Resource Masters
		Family Letter: *Resource Book* p. 35 Vocabulary Preview: *Workbook* pp. 25-26
	Special Education p. 86 Game Suggestion p. 87 Reteaching Suggestion p. 87	Science and Math: *Workbook* p. 27
	Special Education p. 88 Reinforcement p. 89 Science and Reading p. 89 Reteaching Suggestion p. 90	Science Skills: *Workbook* p. 28
	Enrichment Activity p. 91	
	Special Education p. 92 Reteaching Suggestion p. 93 Science and Social Studies p. 93	Science Activity: *Workbook* p. 29
	Enrichment Activity p. 94	
	Reinforcement p. 96 Reteaching Suggestion p. 97	Vocabulary Puzzle: *Workbook* p. 30
		Enrichment Activity: *Resource Book* p. 39
Cooperative Learning p. 100 (Also see p. T23)		Chapter Test: *Test Book* p. 19

Preteaching Suggestions

For Advance Preparation

Demonstration, page 88
Arrange for the mother or father and baby brother or sister of one of the students to visit the class to discuss parent/infant similarities and parental care of infants. You may want to arrange for non-relatives to visit the classroom instead.

Activity, page 91
Obtain 1–2 dozen mealworms from a pet store or use those from Chapter 3. Keep them in the refrigerator until you are ready to use them. Obtain a shoe box or other container that will keep the light out but will allow air to circulate. Have oatmeal and apple slices available.

Activity, page 94
Obtain 2 or 3 half pints of whipping cream and crackers. Keep the cream cold until it is to be used.

For Vocabulary Review

Use the following sentences with your students to review the meanings of the underlined words.

1. An ant is a kind of animal called an insect.
2. Shirts, pants, skirts, and stockings are types of clothing.
3. When you expect something to happen, you think it is going to happen.

For High-Potential Students

Encourage students to look through magazines about animals to find information that would extend the content of this chapter. Such magazines as *Your Big Backyard* and *Ranger Rick,* both published by the National Wildlife Federation, would be appropriate. You may wish to have students use the information they find to answer each of the Lesson Review questions more completely.

Ask students to think about what animals would not make good pets. Instruct them to explain why in a few sentences. Students might refer to dangerous animals, large animals, or animals that need special conditions to live, such as large bodies of water and certain temperature controls.

For Mainstreamed Students

Emotionally Handicapped
Provide a classroom pet for students to care for. Work out a routine for appropriate care and post the schedule near the animal's dwelling.

Make an effort to include emotionally handicapped students in discussions about students' pets.

Visually Impaired
Provide examples of totally blind or visually impaired people who have benefited from the use of seeing-eye dogs. Organizations such as The Seeing Eye in Morristown, New Jersey, provide information to educators.

Point out that many animals rely on their senses of smell and hearing rather than sight to gain information about their surroundings. In fact, cave salamanders and cave fish have no sight at all. Emphasize that relying on these other senses sharpens them.

Hearing Impaired
Explain that some chimpanzees have learned to use sign language to communicate with deaf people.

For Science Fair Projects

Encourage interested students to do one of the following projects:

1. Obtain and care for an animal over a period of time. Keep a journal that describes your animal care.
2. Collect seashells and group them according to color, shape, and type of animal they came from.
3. Find out about wild animals that live in your area. Make a display including a poster showing what the animals look like and where they live, such as in fields, woods, swamps, and urban areas.

Classroom Resources

Bulletin Board
Ask students to draw pictures of some different kinds of animals and describe the body coverings of the animals.

MATCH THE ANIMALS WITH THEIR COVERINGS

Chapter 5 Poster

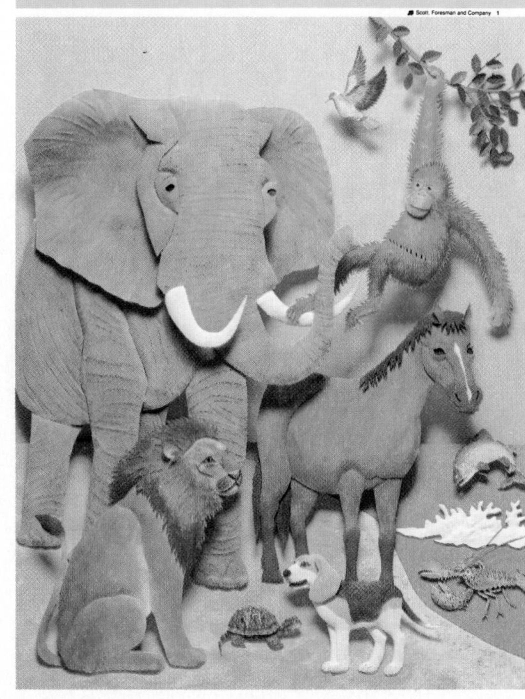
How are these animals different?

Science Discovery Center
Use pages from Chapter 5 in the *Science Discovery Center Book*. Place these worksheets in the appropriate pockets in the Science Discovery Center.

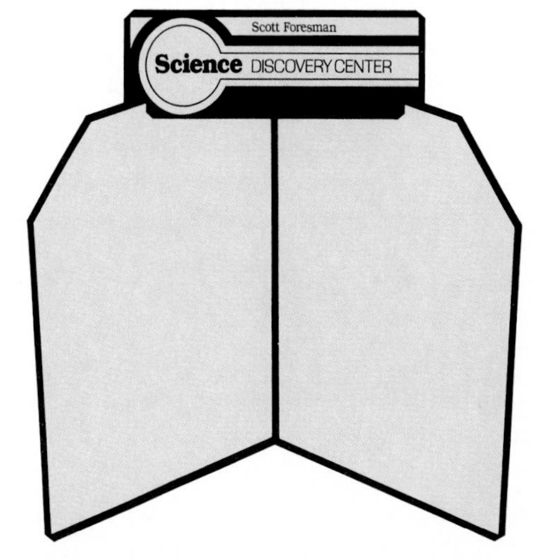
Scott Foresman
Science DISCOVERY CENTER

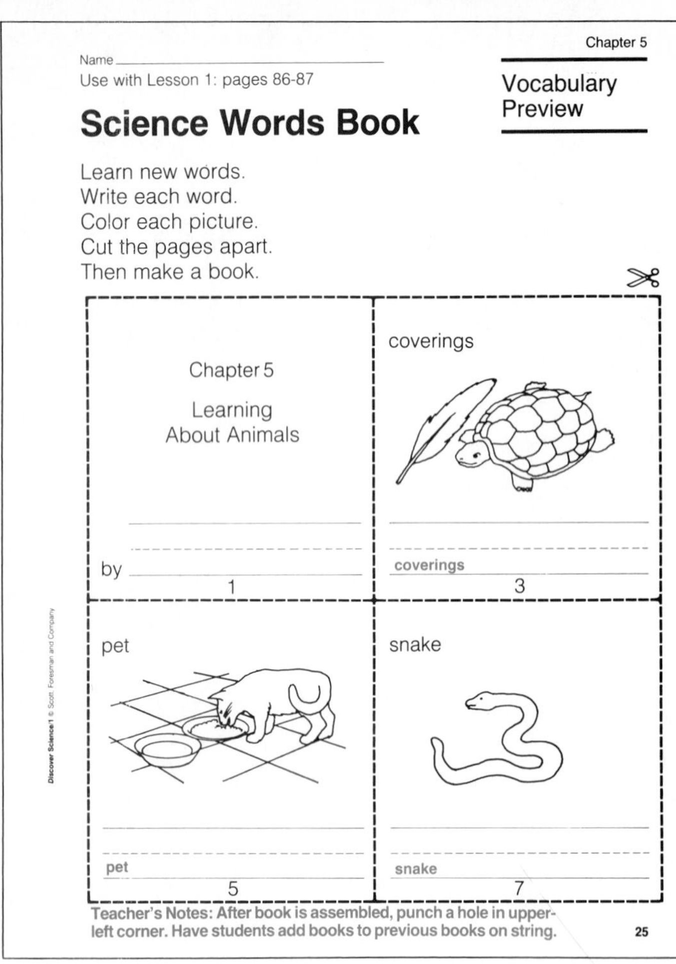
Chapter 5

Name

Use with Lesson 1: pages 86-87

Vocabulary Preview

Science Words Book

Learn new words.
Write each word.
Color each picture.
Cut the pages apart.
Then make a book.

Chapter 5

Learning About Animals

by

1

coverings

coverings

3

pet

pet

5

snake

snake

7

Teacher's Notes: After book is assembled, punch a hole in upper-left corner. Have students add books to previous books on string.

25

Discover Science 1 © Scott, Foresman and Company

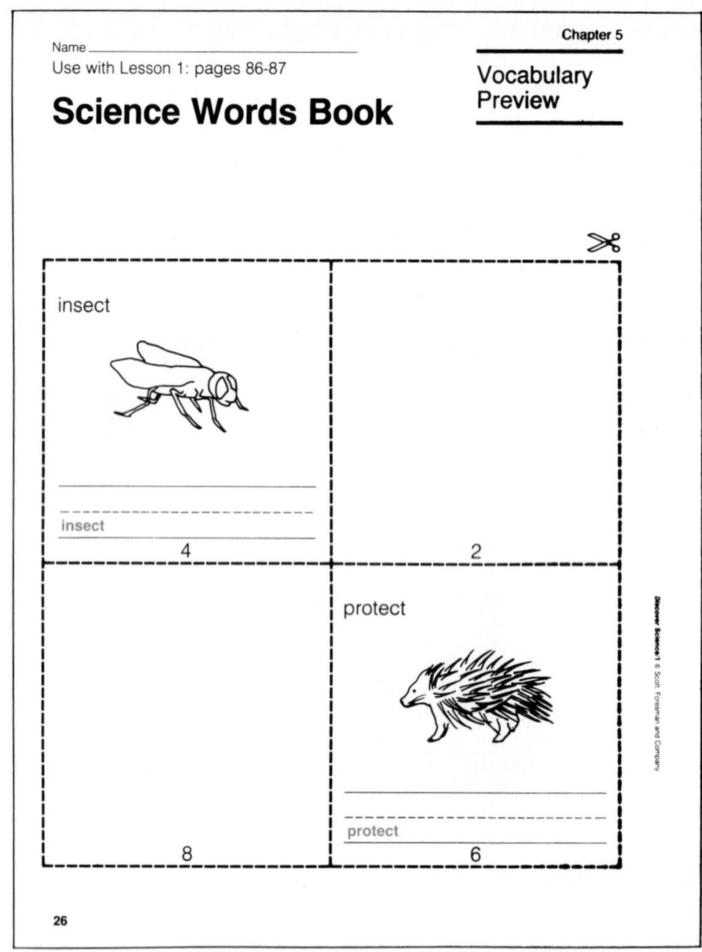
Chapter 5

Name

Use with Lesson 1: pages 86-87

Vocabulary Preview

Science Words Book

insect

insect

4

2

protect

protect

8

6

26

Discover Science 1 © Scott, Foresman and Company

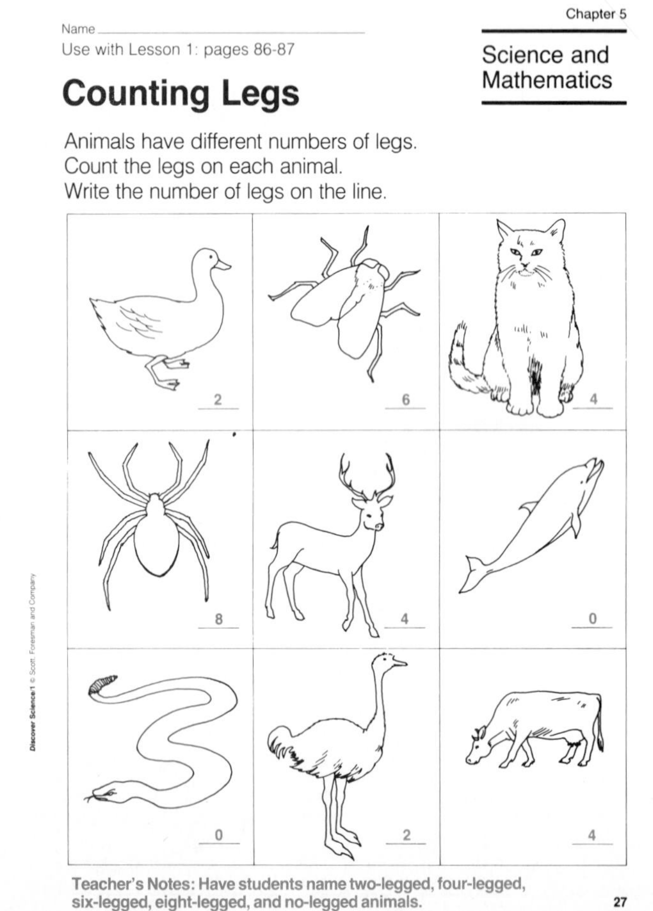
Chapter 5

Name

Use with Lesson 1: pages 86-87

Science and Mathematics

Counting Legs

Animals have different numbers of legs.
Count the legs on each animal.
Write the number of legs on the line.

2	6	4
8	4	0
0	2	4

Teacher's Notes: Have students name two-legged, four-legged, six-legged, eight-legged, and no-legged animals.

27

Discover Science 1 © Scott, Foresman and Company

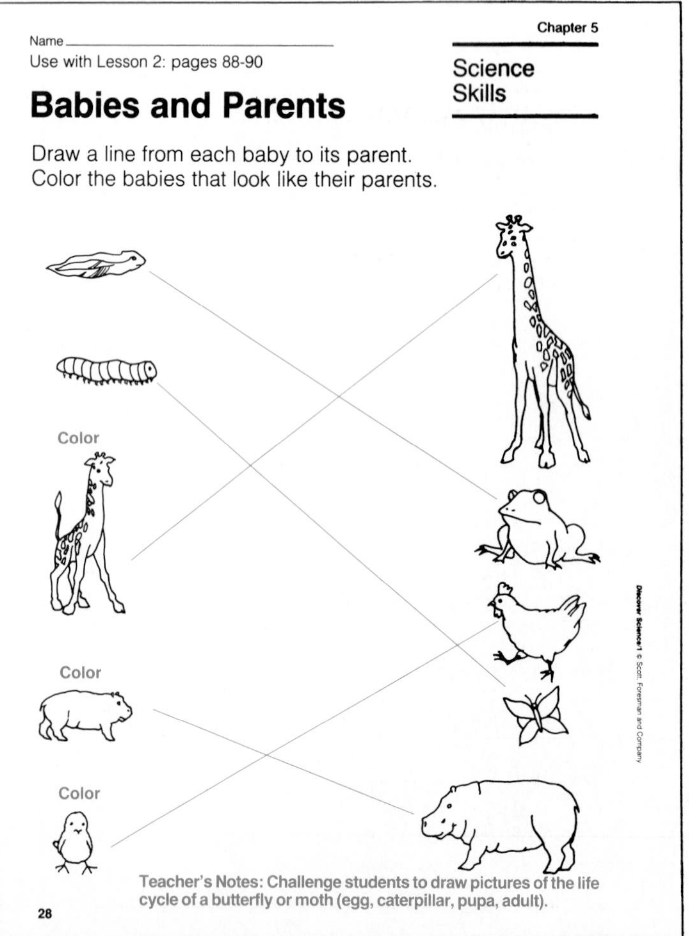
Chapter 5

Name

Use with Lesson 2: pages 88-90

Science Skills

Babies and Parents

Draw a line from each baby to its parent.
Color the babies that look like their parents.

Color

Color

Color

Teacher's Notes: Challenge students to draw pictures of the life cycle of a butterfly or moth (egg, caterpillar, pupa, adult).

28

Discover Science 1 © Scott, Foresman and Company

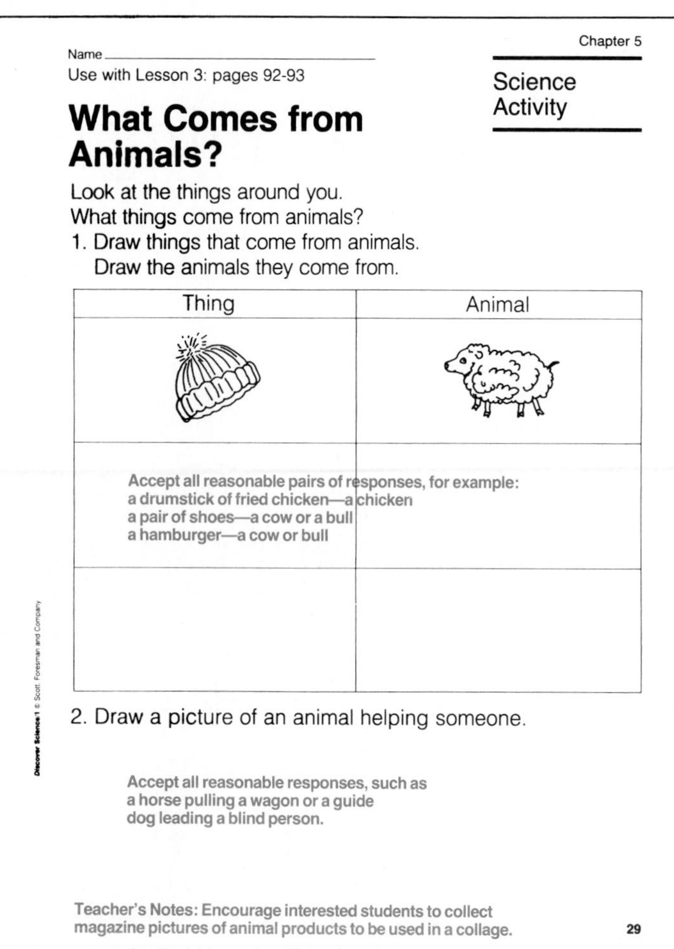

Name ______________________

Use with Lesson 3: pages 92-93

Chapter 5

Science Activity

What Comes from Animals?

Look at the things around you.
What things come from animals?

1. Draw things that come from animals.
   Draw the animals they come from.

Thing	Animal
Accept all reasonable pairs of responses, for example: a drumstick of fried chicken—a chicken; a pair of shoes—a cow or a bull; a hamburger—a cow or bull	

2. Draw a picture of an animal helping someone.

Accept all reasonable responses, such as a horse pulling a wagon or a guide dog leading a blind person.

Teacher's Notes: Encourage interested students to collect magazine pictures of animal products to be used in a collage.

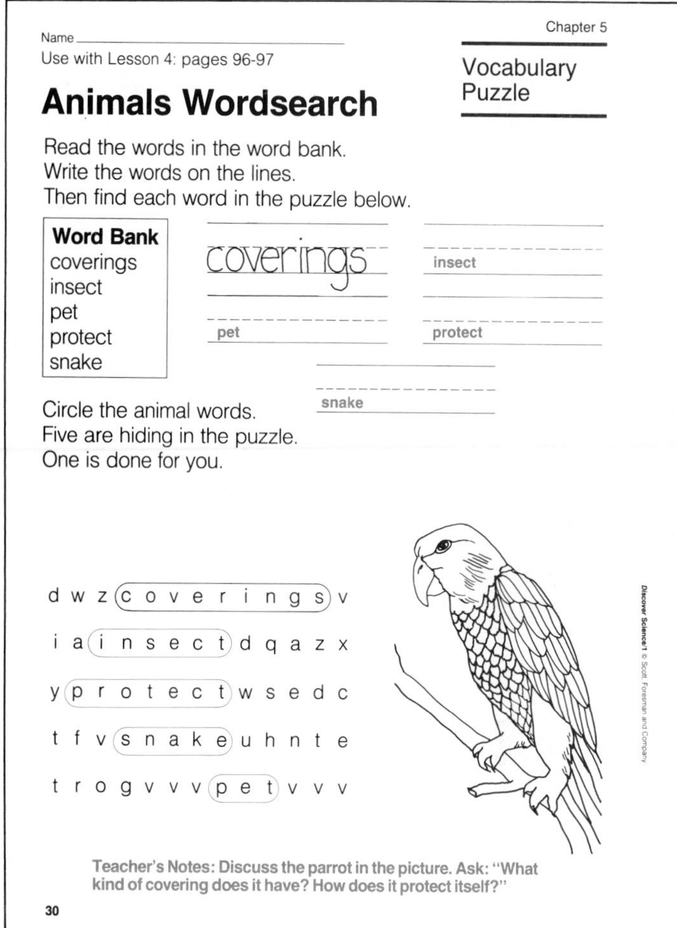

Name ______________________

Use with Lesson 4: pages 96-97

Chapter 5

Vocabulary Puzzle

Animals Wordsearch

Read the words in the word bank.
Write the words on the lines.
Then find each word in the puzzle below.

Word Bank
coverings
insect
pet
protect
snake

coverings
insect
pet
protect
snake

Circle the animal words.
Five are hiding in the puzzle.
One is done for you.

d w z (c o v e r i n g s) v
i a (i n s e c t) d q a z x
y (p r o t e c t) w s e d c
t f v (s n a k e) u h n t e
t r o g v v v (p e t) v v v

Teacher's Notes: Discuss the parrot in the picture. Ask: "What kind of covering does it have? How does it protect itself?"

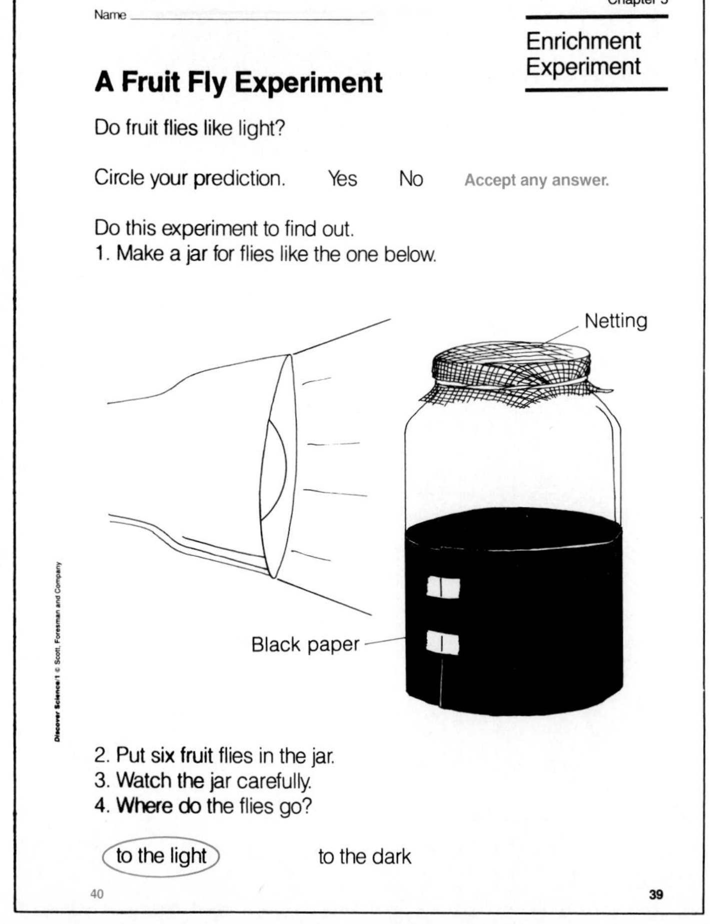

Name ______________________

Chapter 5

Enrichment Experiment

A Fruit Fly Experiment

Do fruit flies like light?

Circle your prediction. Yes No Accept any answer.

Do this experiment to find out.

1. Make a jar for flies like the one below.

2. Put six fruit flies in the jar.
3. Watch the jar carefully.
4. Where do the flies go?

(to the light) to the dark

Name ______________________

Chapter 5 Test

Animals

I. Write **Yes** or **No.**

1. Do coverings help protect animals? (5-1) Yes
2. Do animals move in the same ways? (5-1) No
3. Do all baby animals need care? (5-2) No
4. Can animals help people? (5-3) Yes
5. Do people need to care for pets? (5-4) Yes

II. Draw a line from the word to the right picture.

1. insect (5-2) 2. snake (5-2) 3. pet (5-4)

The numbers in parentheses after each question refer to the chapter and lesson objective covered by that question.

TEACHING PLAN

INTRODUCING CHAPTER 5

Major Concepts
Lesson 1 Animals differ in size, shape, covering, and means of movement.
Lesson 2 Most animals change as they grow; some require care from their parents and others do not.
Lesson 3 People use animals for food, for products such as clothing, and for work and transportation.
Lesson 4 Animal pets have certain needs and require care.

Vocabulary
coverings, insects, pets, protect, snake

[1] like a mask or face

Chapter 5

Learning About Animals

Look at the animal in the picture.
What does the animal look like?

84

Teaching Options

Workbook page 25 *

Name
Use with Lesson 1: pages 86-87

Chapter 5
Vocabulary Preview

Science Words Book

Learn new words.
Write each word.
Color each picture.
Cut the pages apart.
Then make a book.

Chapter 5
Learning About Animals
by
1

coverings
3

pet
5

snake
7

25

Workbook page 26 *

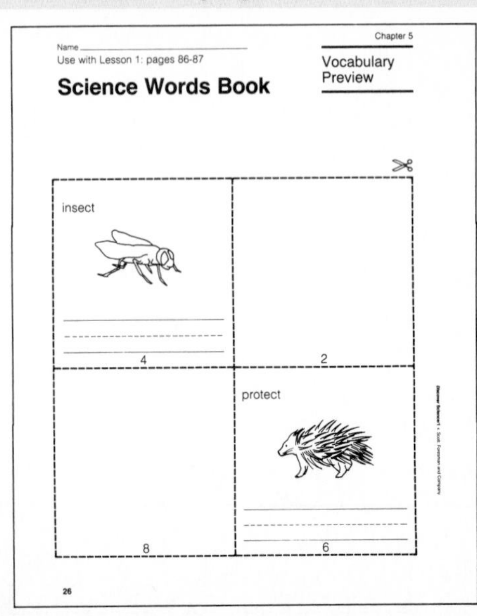

Name
Use with Lesson 1: pages 86-87

Chapter 5
Vocabulary Preview

Science Words Book

insect
4

2

8

protect
6

26

♦ ***Suitable as a language development activity***

Starting the Chapter

Maybe you have touched some animals.
Point to parts of animals here.
Then read more about animals.

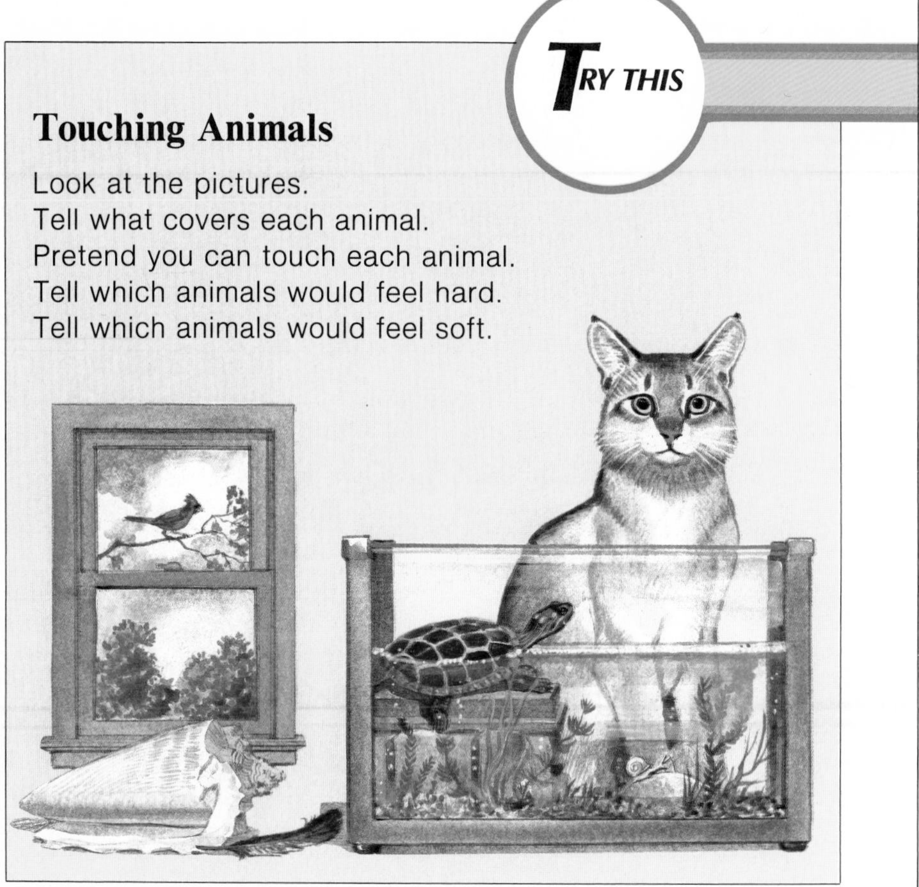

Touching Animals

Look at the pictures.
Tell what covers each animal.
Pretend you can touch each animal.
Tell which animals would feel hard.
Tell which animals would feel soft.

85

TRY THIS

Objective ♦
This optional *TRY THIS* activity will help students explore and build background information about the concept that animals have different coverings. Later in the chapter, students will be able to draw on this experience to help them assimilate the new content.

Science Process Skills
Classifying, Observing

Safety Tip (See page T27.)
- If students handle actual animal coverings, have them wash their hands thoroughly after this activity.

Teaching Tips
- Students should look at the pictures of the animal coverings and tell how they think the animals would feel.
- Bring to class several examples of animal coverings, such as a shell, a fake fur, and a feather. Instruct students to touch the different objects and *describe* how they feel. You might want students to close their eyes when they do this.

Answers
Students should state that feathers cover the bird, fur covers the kitten, and shells cover the snail, the conch, and the turtle. Students should state that the feather and fur feel soft, and the shells feel hard.

Resource Book page 35

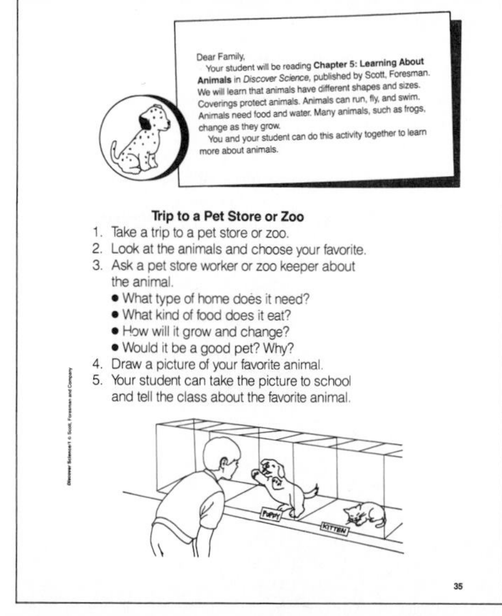

Dear Family,
Your student will be reading **Chapter 5: Learning About Animals** in *Discover Science*, published by Scott, Foresman. We will learn that animals have different shapes and sizes. Coverings protect animals. Animals can run, fly, and swim. Animals need food and water. Many animals, such as frogs, change as they grow.
You and your student can do this activity together to learn more about animals.

Trip to a Pet Store or Zoo

1. Take a trip to a pet store or zoo.
2. Look at the animals and choose your favorite.
3. Ask a pet store worker or zoo keeper about the animal.
   - What type of home does it need?
   - What kind of food does it eat?
   - How will it grow and change?
   - Would it be a good pet? Why?
4. Draw a picture of your favorite animal.
5. Your student can take the picture to school and tell the class about the favorite animal.

35

SCIENCE BACKGROUND

Some animals' coverings have unusual characteristics that help them survive. A porcupine fish inflates its body to look like a spiny ball to ward off enemies. Some animals, such as chameleons, can change their body color to blend in with their surroundings.

* *Answers to masters on pages 84E–84F*

TEACHING PLAN

LESSON 1
pages 86–87

Lesson Objectives
- *Identify* differences in animals.
- *Discuss* ways animals move.

Lesson Vocabulary
coverings, protect

1 MOTIVATE

Demonstration Activity ♦
Show students two pictures, each of a very different animal, such as a bird and a lion.

Discussion
Question: **How are these two animals different?** (Students might mention differences in size, shape, body covering, sounds made, and way of moving.)

2 TEACH

Teaching Tip
- Help students *identify* the animals in the illustration. Then have students *describe* the coverings of the animals pictured. Question: **How does a porcupine protect itself?** (It uses its covering of bony spines or quills to keep harmful animals away.)

[1] protect animals from enemies and other dangers

Lesson 1 What Ways Are Animals Different?

Animals can be big or small.
They have different shapes.
Animals have different **coverings.**
Coverings help **protect** the animals.
How do coverings protect these animals?[1]

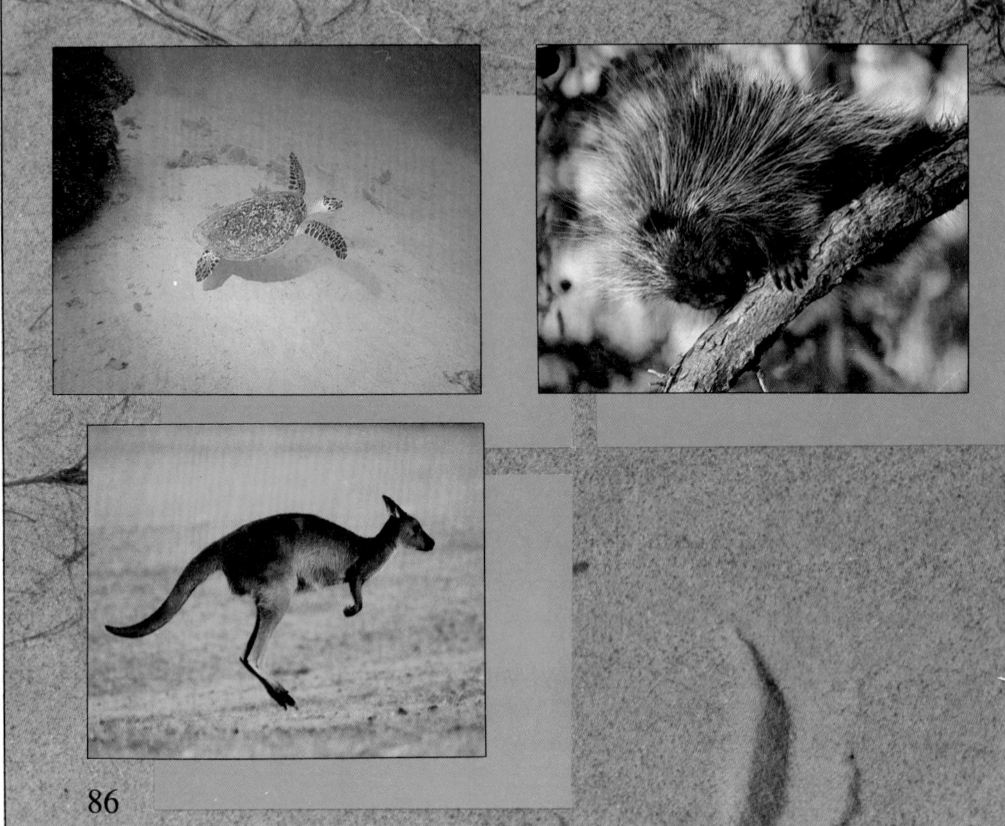

86

Teaching Options

SCIENCE BACKGROUND

Different animal coverings help animals survive in their surroundings. Some animals have coverings that help them stay warm. Polar bears have thick, oily fur. The fur traps a layer of air that keeps the bear's body heat inside, making it possible for polar bears to swim and hunt in icy water. Penguins have closely packed, scale-like feathers that trap body heat and make it possible for them to live in extremely cold climates. Birds have feathers that trap warm air next to their skin. Birds cool off by extending their feathers.

Special Education

Use chalk to draw life-sized outlines of various animals on the chalkboard, classroom floor, or playground. Have students with learning disabilities *compare* the animals. Ask each student to choose one of the animals and draw a picture of it. Then have the students discuss which animals are similar and group their pictures according to the animals' similarities (those that can fly, those that have fur, and so on). Display students' pictures by groups (according to the type of animal the students have drawn).

♦ ***Suitable as a language development activity***

[1] turtle swims; porcupine walks; kangaroo hops; snake crawls; bird flies

Animals move in different ways.

Some animals walk, fly, or swim.

Which animals walk, fly, or swim?

What ways do these animals move?[1]

Lesson Review

1. How are animals different?
2. What ways can animals move?

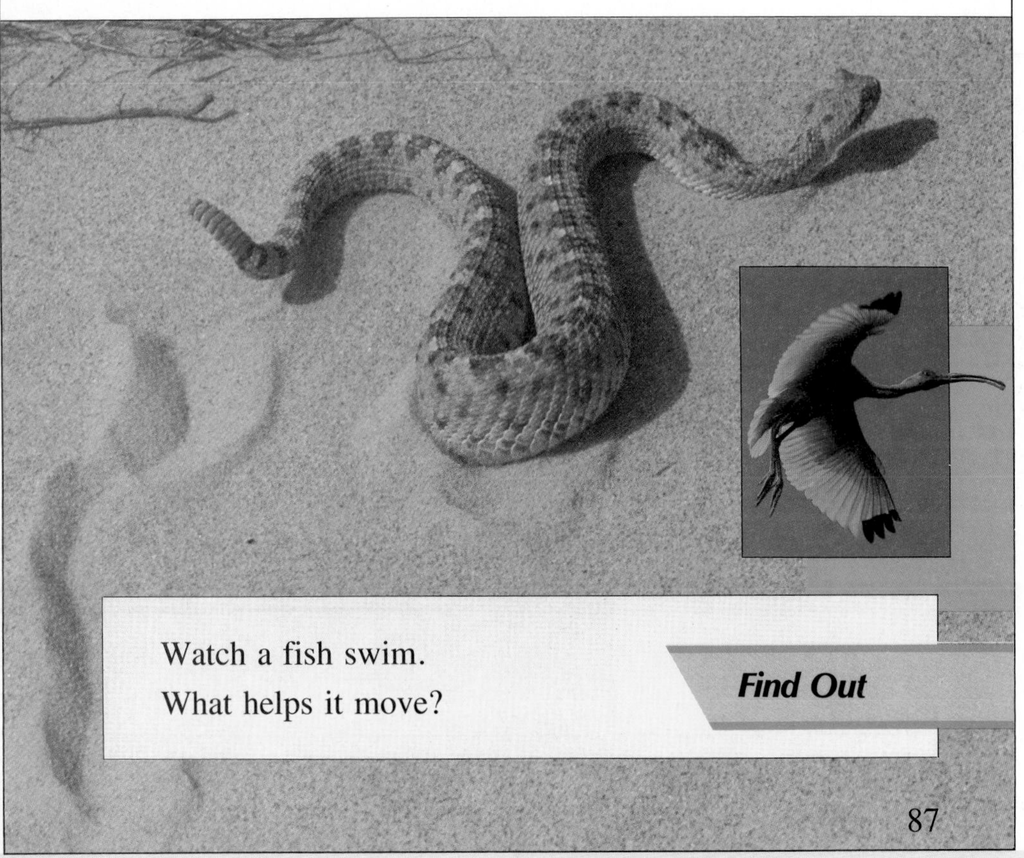

Find Out

Watch a fish swim.

What helps it move?

Teaching Tips

- After students have read page 87, ask how animals can move. (Students should ***describe*** animal movements such as swimming, walking, flying, and so on.) Have students act out some of the ways that animals move.
- **Possible Misconception:** Children often do not think of human skin and hair as being similar to the skin and fur of other animals. Point out this similarity.

3 ASSESS

Lesson Review

1. Animals have different coverings, sizes, shapes, and ways of moving.

2. Animals can move by walking, flying, swimming. Students might also mention running, hopping, swinging, or crawling.

Challenge! Question: **How do your hair and skin act like fur, feathers, and skin on animals?** (They protect your body and help keep it warm.) **Thinking Skill:** *Making analogies*

Find Out

Fins help a fish move. **Thinking Skill:** *Inferring*

Workbook page 27 *

Name ____________

Use with Lesson 1: pages 86-87

Chapter 5

Science and Mathematics

Counting Legs

Animals have different numbers of legs.
Count the legs on each animal.
Write the number of legs on the line.

27

* ***Answers to masters on pages 84E–84F***

Game Suggestion ♦

Make two sets of cards—one with pictures of animals and one with the names of various types of animal coverings. Have students play Old Maid by matching an animal card with the correct covering card. Be sure to include one card that does not match, to substitute for the Old Maid card.

Reteaching Suggestion ♦

Display pictures of several different animals. Have the students identify each animal and tell whether it is big or small, what type of covering it has, and how the covering protects the animal. Have students tell how each animal moves.

TEACHING PLAN

LESSON 2
pages 88–90

Lesson Objectives
- *Identify* ways that animals change and grow, including growing to resemble parents.
- *Identify* which animals need care from their parents.

Lesson Vocabulary
insect, snake

1 MOTIVATE

Demonstration Activity ♦
If possible, arrange for the mother and a baby brother or sister of one of the students to visit the class. Have the students observe how the mother and the baby are alike or different. Ask the mother to describe some of the things she does to take care of the baby. This activity can be done using pictures.

Discussion
Lead a discussion of how adult and baby humans are alike and different. Ask students to describe what kind of care they think human babies need. Let students whose pets have had young tell how the mother took care of them.

[1] changed from egg, to caterpillar, to cocoon, to butterfly

Lesson 2 How Do Animals Grow?

Many animals change when they grow.
Animals change in size.
Many animals change in color.
Some animals also change in shape.
How did this butterfly change?[1]

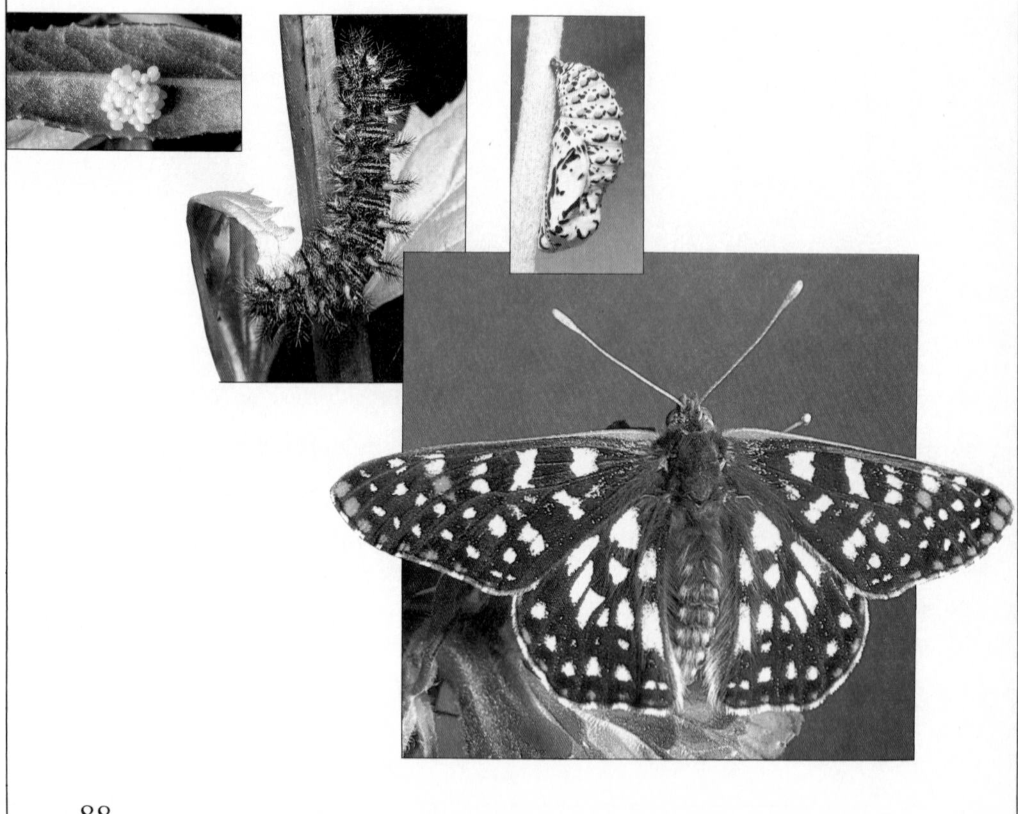

88

Teaching Options

SCIENCE BACKGROUND

Animals such as frogs and many kinds of insects have independent-living larval stages in their life cycle. The larvae (tadpoles and caterpillers) follow different lifestyles than the adults and do not resemble the adults. Frog larvae eat submerged plants. Adult frogs eat insects on land. Frog larvae have gills and a tail so they can live and swim in water; frogs have lungs and four legs. In addition to beetle larvae, the larvae of moths and butterflies also are caterpillars. In birds and mammals the young develop through their early (larval) stages inside the mother's body or within an egg.

Special Education

Witnessing the events described in the text and illustrations will make a lasting impression on all students, but will be especially helpful for those with learning disabilities. Set up an aquarium to provide an environment in which to show the development of tadpoles. Use sand or gravel on the bottom and only half fill the aquarium with water. *CAUTION:* Immediately wipe up any water that spills on the floor to prevent accidents. Use driftwood and a larger rock that break the surface, providing a habitat for the adult frogs. Tadpoles can be obtained at a pet shop.

♦ ***Suitable as a language development activity***

[1] yes
[2] food, water, shelter, and protection from enemies.

Baby animals have parents.

Some look like their parents.

Do these baby animals look like their parents?[1]

Some baby animals need care to grow.

Parents protect and feed them.

What care do these baby animals get?[2]

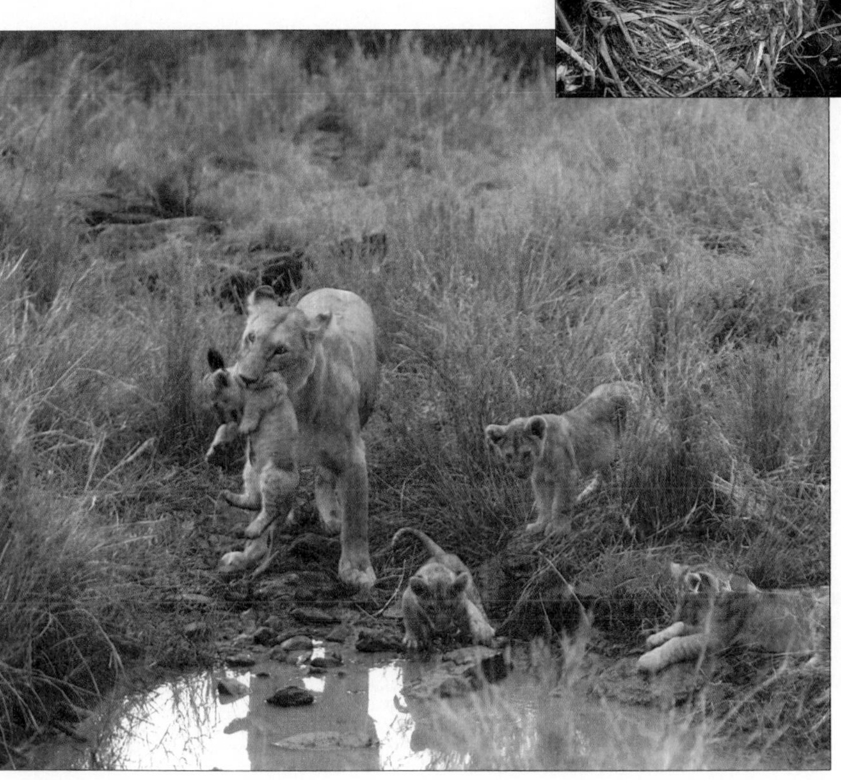

89

2 TEACH

Teaching Tips

- Have the students discuss how they have grown and changed since they were babies. Question: **What can you do now that you could not do as a baby?** (Students should *describe* ways that they have changed and new abilities that they have.) Instruct students to look at the picture of the life cycle of a butterfly. Question: **How is the way that butterflies grow and change different from the way that you grow and change?** (Humans do not completely change in their form or the way they look.)
- **Possible Misconception:** Most students probably think that caterpillars and butterflies are completely different animals, unrelated to one another. Emphasize that caterpillars represent one stage in the life cycle of a butterfly, moth, or other insect.
- Have students *describe* the care they have seen given to some baby animals. Have the students read page 89 and *describe* the care the young receive from the parents.

Reinforcement

Encourage students to find a picture showing an adult animal caring for its young. Show each picture to the class and discuss how the young are being cared for.

Science and Reading

Read to students a story about wild animals and how they care for their young. You might want to concentrate on how kangaroos and opossums care for their young.

Teaching Tip

- **Possible Misconception:** Many students will think that the parent-young relationship exhibited by humans and other animals applies to all animals. Point out that most snakes and insects care for themselves.

3 ASSESS

Lesson Review

1. Animals grow in size. Some change in shape and color; some grow to look like their parents and others do not.
2. Baby animals such as birds and cats need care. (Accept other reasonable answers.)
Challenge! Question: **Is a cow more like a person or a frog in the way its young grow and develop?** (A cow is more like a person because its young look like the parents. Young frogs—tadpoles— do not look like the parents and do not need care from parents.) **Thinking Skill:** *Applying information to new situations*

Find out

Answers will vary. Students might draw themselves being fed, put to bed, played with, or protected from something dangerous when they were babies. **Thinking Skill:** *Restating and explaining ideas*

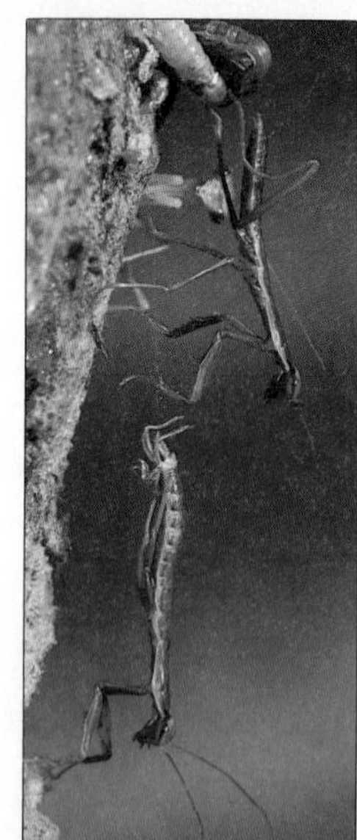

What baby animals do not need care?
Look at the **snake** and **insects.**
They do not need care from parents.
Snakes and insects care for themselves.

Lesson Review

1. How do animals change and grow?
2. What baby animals need care to grow?

Find Out

What did you need as a baby?
Draw a picture.
Show someone caring for you.

90

Teaching Options

SCIENCE ANECDOTE

A baby kangaroo is born just 32 days after gestation. It must crawl up the mother's abdomen to the pouch, where it stays attached to a teat for 144 days, developing further. A baby kangaroo begins to leave the pouch for short periods of time when it is about 190 days old. At about 8 months, it leaves the pouch permanently.

Reteaching Suggestion ♦

Use the aquarium of tadpoles suggested in the *Special Education* in the *Teaching Options* on page 88 as a reteaching tool. The main ideas of the lesson will become clearer as students observe the metamorphosis of tadpoles into frogs. If you do not use an aquarium, have students draw pictures of tadpoles changing into frogs.

Workbook page 28 *

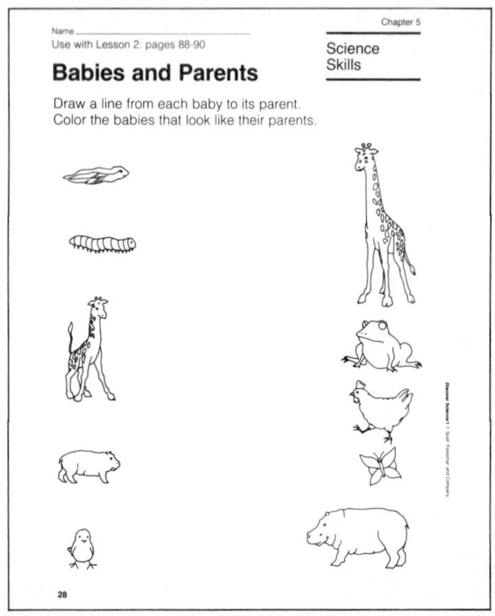

Name

Use with Lesson 2: pages 88-90

Chapter 5

Science Skills

Babies and Parents

Draw a line from each baby to its parent.
Color the babies that look like their parents.

28

♦ ***Suitable as a language development activity***

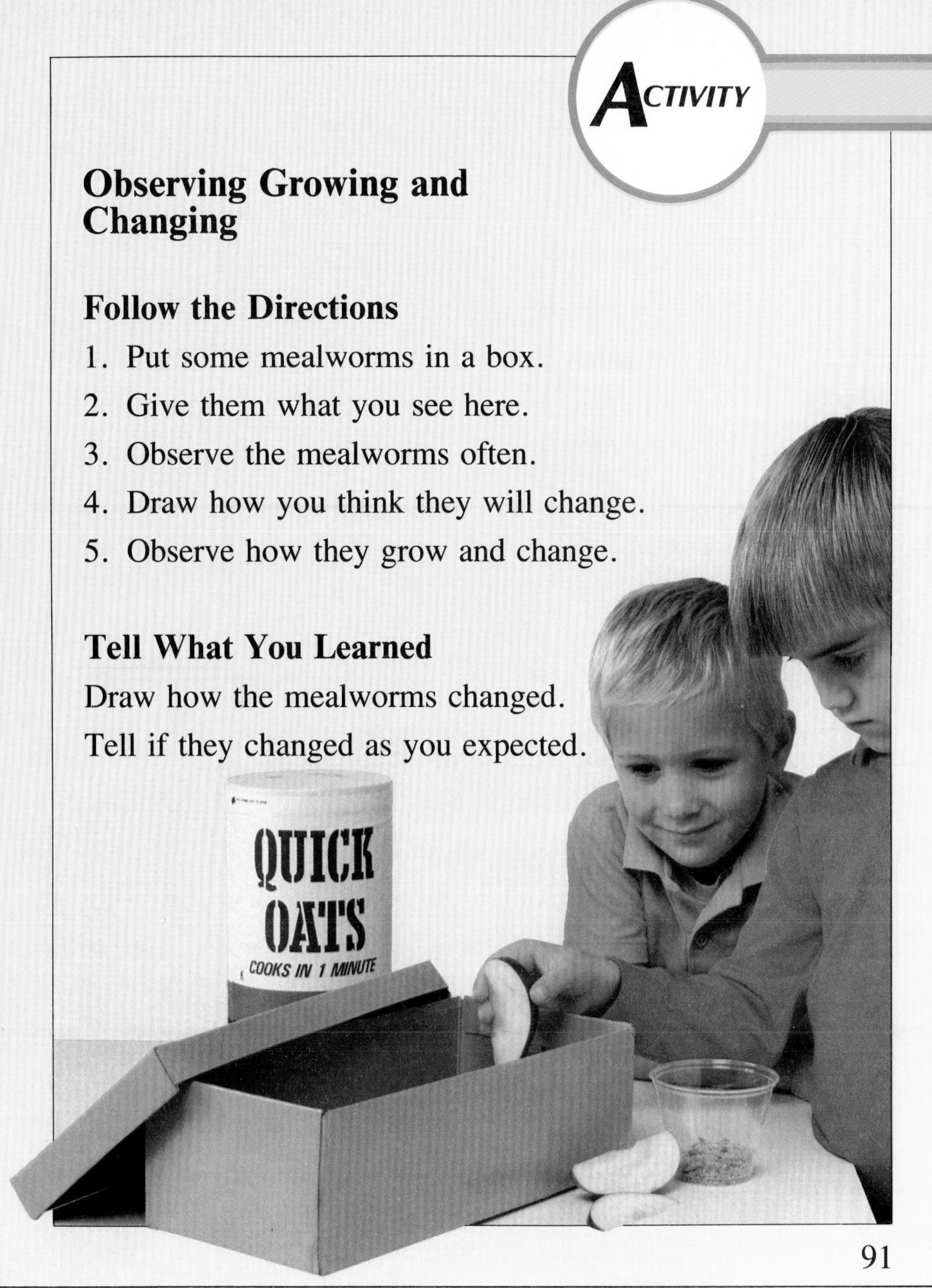

ACTIVITY

Observing Growing and Changing

Follow the Directions

1. Put some mealworms in a box.
2. Give them what you see here.
3. Observe the mealworms often.
4. Draw how you think they will change.
5. Observe how they grow and change.

Tell What You Learned

Draw how the mealworms changed.

Tell if they changed as you expected.

91

Enrichment Activity

Help students find out about the different kinds of beetles that exist. Use an encyclopedia or other book to show a sample of the various sizes, shapes, and colors of beetles.

Activity Results

The mealworms should grow and change as they mature.

ACTIVITY PLAN

Concept

Some animals go through changes in body form as they grow.

Objectives/Process Skills

- *Predict* how mealworms will change as they grow.
- *Observe* the changes in mealworms.
- *Describe* how a mealworm changes as it grows.

Time Allotment

Allow a couple minutes twice a day for observations.

Materials

For each pair of students: empty shoe box, 3-4 mealworms, oatmeal or other dry cereal, slices of apple

Teaching Tips

- Explain that mealworms grow and change in a way similar to the way a butterfly grows and changes. Instruct students to follow the directions in the text and write down what they observe about how a mealworm grows and changes.
- Tell students that they should give their mealworms apple slices and oatmeal. The students can change the apple slices as necessary, but they should not disturb the oatmeal.

Answers

Tell What You Learned

Students should draw the stages of a mealworm's development—larva (worm), pupa (worm beginning to change to a beetle), adult beetle. You might want to tell students that the worms came from eggs which are usually too small to be seen. **Thinking Skill:** *Inferring*

*** Answers to masters on pages 84E–84H.***

LESSON 3
pages 92–93

Lesson Objective
- *Identify* products and services obtained from animals.

1 MOTIVATE

Demonstration Activity ♦
On a bulletin board, show pictures of foods that are on the school lunch menu. If your school does not have a hot lunch program, show foods that might appear on a typical family restaurant menu.

Discussion
Ask students to *identify* the items that come from animals. Discuss the choices students make. Make a class list of the animal products that are on the menu. Tell students that food is only one of many products we get from animals. Question: **What are some other products that come from animals?** (Students might name products such as leather belts, shoes, and purses; clothing; and feather pillows.)

[1] Leather goods come from livestock; woolen goods come from sheep. Milk, cheese, and yogurt come from cows.

Lesson 3 Why Do People Need Animals?

People need animals for food.
People need animals for clothing.
Look at what comes from animals.
Look at the food, clothing, and shoes.
What animal does each thing come from?[1]

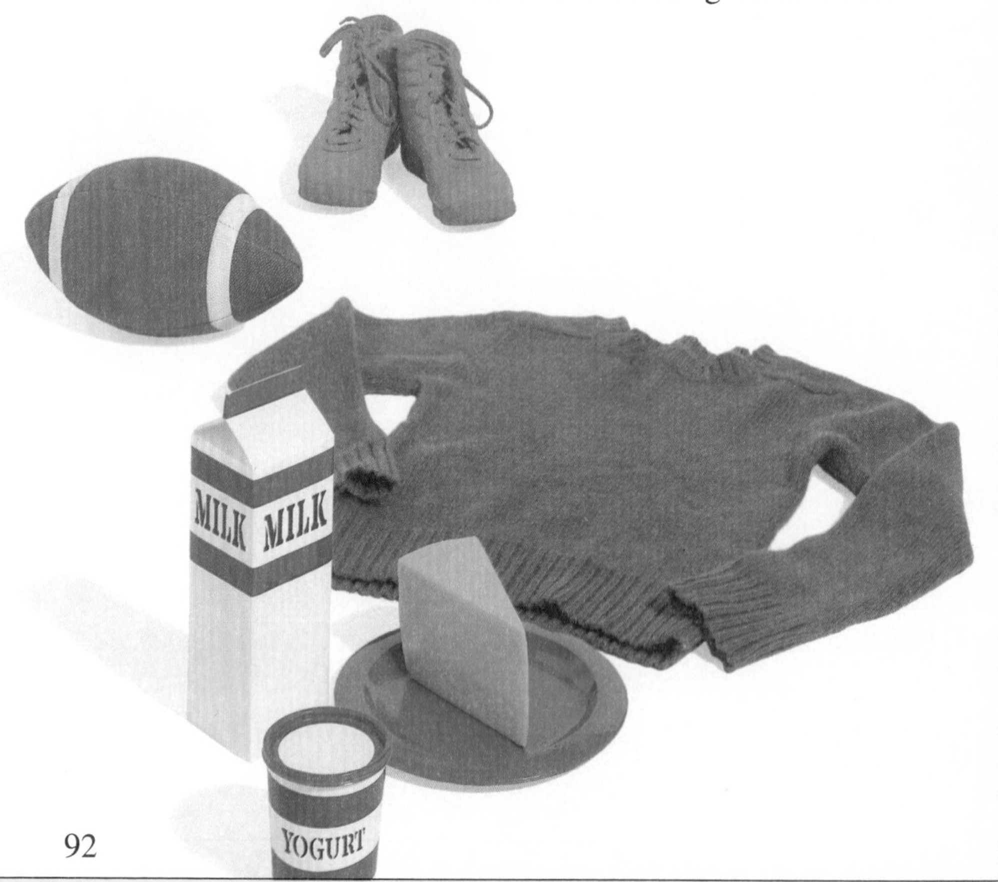

92

Teaching Options

Special Education

Ask students with learning disabilities to draw a picture of a type of food they like to eat. Help the students identify whether the food is from an animal, and, if so, what type of animal.

SCIENCE BACKGROUND

Domestic animals such as dogs, cats, cattle, sheep, goats, pigs, horses, chickens, and elephants have been kept for thousands of years. The ancestors of dogs were first domesticated for their ability to work. As people gave up the nomadic life and settled into agriculture, other animals were domesticated for food (cattle, pigs, sheep, chickens); clothing (sheep); work (elephants, dogs, horses); protection (dogs); and companionship (dogs, cats).

♦ *Suitable as a language development activity*

[1] The dog pulls the boy's wheelchair and carries things for him.

People enjoy animals.
Animals can help people.
Some animals can help people work.
How does this dog help the boy?[1]

Lesson Review

1. What things come from animals?
2. How can animals help people?

Find Out

Look in magazines and books.
Find pictures of animals
helping people.

2 TEACH

Teaching Tips

- Help students *identify* the items in the picture on page 92. Have students differentiate between items that come from parts of an animal (leather, meat, fish) and items that animals produce (honey, milk).
- **Possible Misconception:** Try to elicit misconceptions students have about wild animals, such as *wolves are bad.* Discuss the root of some of these misconceptions, such as *Little Red Riding Hood* and other stories in which an animal is the antagonist or protagonist.

3 ASSESS

Lesson Review

1. food and clothing
2. by doing work, protecting people, providing companionship

Challenge! Question: **Why were animals especially important to people before cars and tractors were invented?** (Animals were used more for transportation and for pulling plows on farms.) **Thinking Skill:** *Applying information to new situations*

Find Out

Students should explain what the pictures show. **Thinking Skill:** *Restating or explaining ideas*

Workbook page 29 *

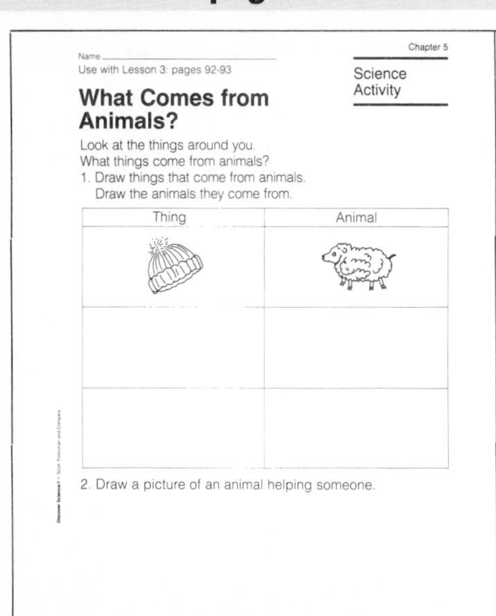

Name ____ Chapter 5
Use with Lesson 3: pages 92-93
Science Activity

What Comes from Animals?

Look at the things around you.
What things come from animals?
1. Draw things that come from animals.
Draw the animals they come from.

Thing	Animal

2. Draw a picture of an animal helping someone.

29

*** Answers to masters on pages 84E–84F***

Reteaching Suggestion ♦

Have students act out situations in which animals are helping people. Let students try to guess what each animal is and how it is being helpful.

Science and Social Studies

Help students find out what types of animals are raised for food in your state or what type of industry in your state depends on products that come from animals (dairy industry, meat-packing industry, and so on).

Concept
People use products from animals to make food.

Objectives/Process Skills
- *Observe* cream before and after shaking.
- *Measure* the time while shaking.
- *Describe* how butter can be used.

Time Allotment
Allow 30 minutes: 10 minutes to shake the jars and 20 minutes to draw the pictures.

Materials
For each pair of students: whipping cream, small plastic containers with lids, measuring cup, drawing paper, crayons or nontoxic markers

Safety Tip (See page T27.)
- Do not allow students with milk or wheat allergies to taste the butter or crackers. Warn students to be careful when using glass containers.

Teaching Tips
- Show students a carton of whipping cream. Question: **What animal does cream come from?** (Guide students to *infer* that cream comes from a cow.) Distribute cream, a container, and a measuring cup to each group. Help each group measure 1/4 cup of cream to place in their container. Place the lids tightly on each container.
- Have students take turns shaking the container for about 10 minutes. Students should notice the cream beginning to thicken and begin to resemble very small grains of butter.

Answers
Tell What You Learned
Students should state that they used cream from a cow to make butter. Students should draw three ways to use butter, such as on toast, on potatoes, and when baking a cake. **Thinking Skills:** *Restating or explaining ideas*

Using Something from Animals

Follow the Directions
1. Put some cold, fresh cream in a small jar.
2. Cover the jar tightly.
3. Shake it for about 10 minutes.
   Take turns shaking.
4. Observe how the cream changes.
   It is starting to become butter.

Tell What You Learned
Tell how you used cream from an animal.
Draw three ways to use butter.

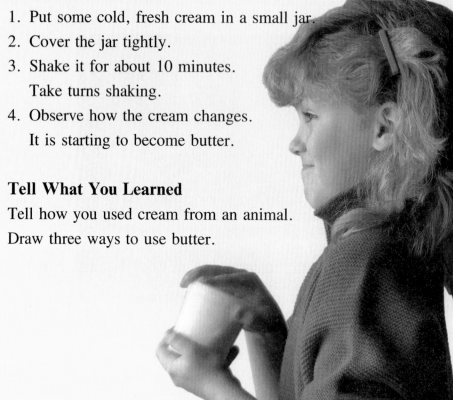

94

Activity Results
The cream should be slightly thickened after shaking. Small grains of butterfat (butter) might be visible.

Enrichment Activity
Allow students to taste other dairy products such as cheese, yogurt, and cottage cheese. *CAUTION:* Students with diary product allergies should not eat or taste any of these products.

Gerald Durrell

Gerald Durrell cares about animals.
He loved animals when he was young.
He began to study animals.
He collected many kinds of animals.
Later, he started a special zoo.
His zoo protects animals.

What Do You Think?

How could a zoo help animals?

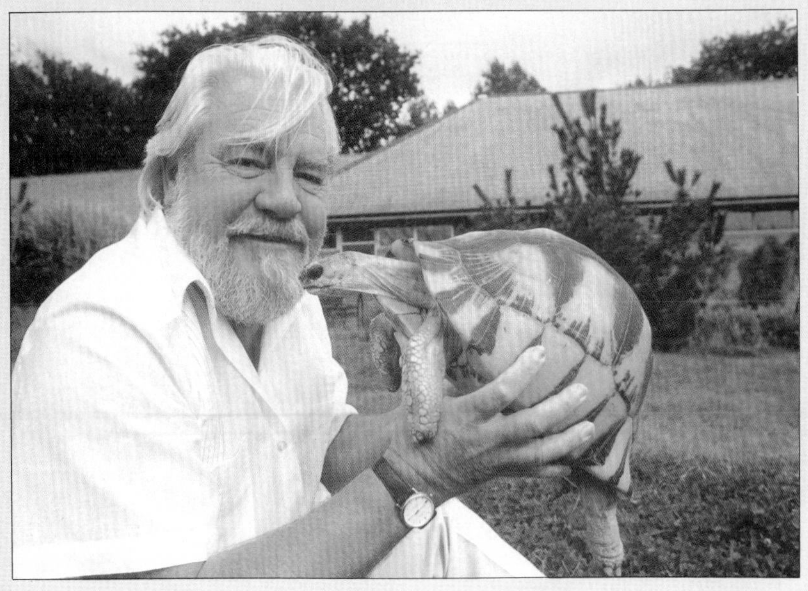

95

TEACHING PLAN

SCIENCE AND PEOPLE

Discussion

Questions: **How are animals sometimes harmed?** (Help students understand that some animals are hunted, some are hit by cars, and some animals are harmed because the land they lived on was used for other purposes.) **Have you ever visited a zoo?** (Have students describe their experiences.) Discuss how people in a zoo care for animals properly. Tell students that they will be reading about a man who started his own zoo.

Teaching Tip

- Write the name Gerald Durrell on the chalkboard and pronounce it for students. Have students read page 95 and identify the animals in Gerald's zoo. Question: **Which animals would you like to have if you could start your own zoo?** (Answers will vary.) Discuss what the students would need to know about their zoo animals in order to keep the animals healthy.

Answers

What do you think?
A zoo could help an animal that needs protection (from being hunted, hit by cars, and so on). **Thinking Skill:** *Drawing conclusions*

Teaching Options

SCIENCE BACKGROUND

Gerald Durrell was born in Jamshedpur, India, in 1925. As a child he lived in France, Italy, Switzerland, and Greece. It was in Greece, when Durrell was between the ages of 10 and 14, that he developed his life-long involvement with animals. Durrell observed, wrote about, and collected animals. Between 1945–46, he was a student keeper at the Whipsnade Zoological Park in England. His collecting expeditions took him to Africa, South America, Australia, and Southeast Asia. In 1959 he established Zoological Park in Jersey, Channel Islands, which later became the Jersey Wildlife Perservation Trust—a scientific non-profit organization that fosters animal conservation through controlled breeding.

LESSON 4
pages 96–97

Lesson Objectives
- *List* kinds of pets.
- *Describe* the care pets need.

Lesson Vocabulary
pets

1 MOTIVATE

Demonstration Activity ♦
Ask students to bring photographs or drawings of their pets to school. (Students who do not have pets could bring pictures of animals they would like to have as pets.) Allow time for students to tell about their pets or the pets they would like to have.

Discussion
Have the students who own pets discuss some of the things they do for their pets or *describe* the care that their pets need. Have the other students tell what kind of care they think the pet they have chosen would need.

[1] Boy provides food, water, shelter, and identification on dog's collar.

Lesson 4 How Can You Care for a Pet?

People keep some animals as **pets.**
People take care of pets.
Pets need food and water.
They need a place to live.
How does this boy care for his pet?[1]

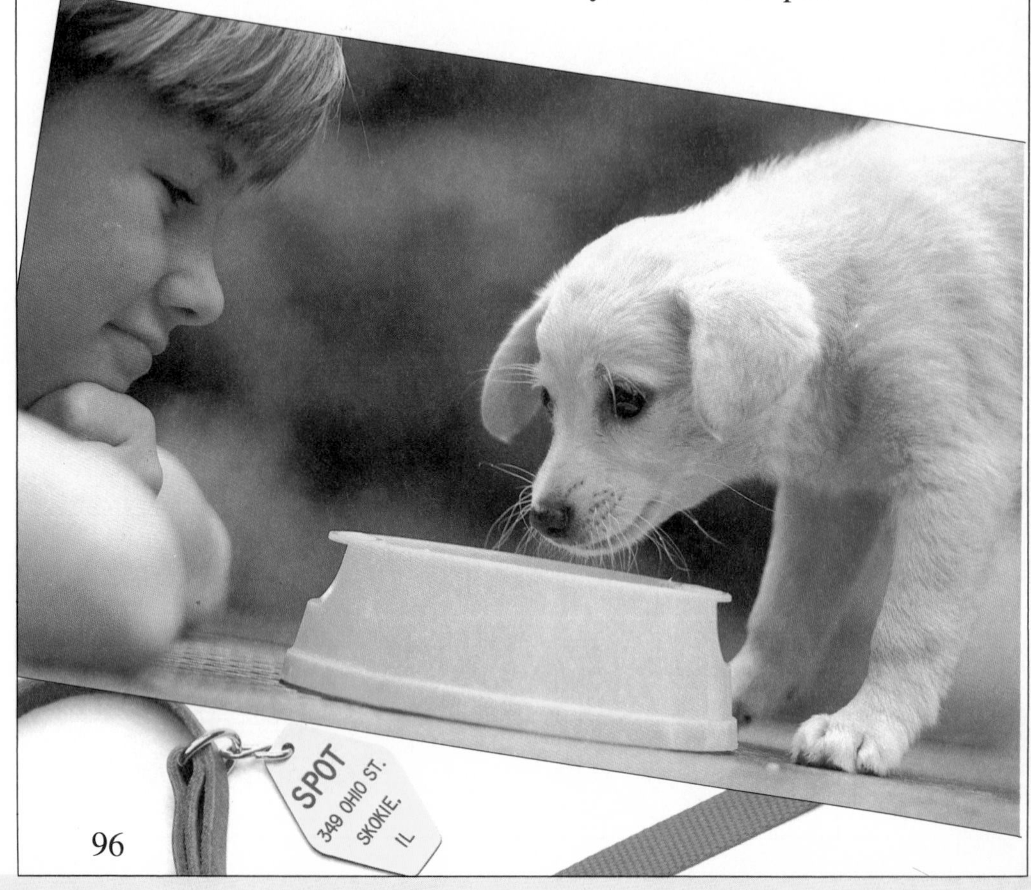

96

Teaching Options

SCIENCE BACKGROUND

Pets are animals that can become accustomed to life with humans. Generally, a pet is also expected to become tame, or manageable. When an animal is domesticated, it begins to rely on its owner for most of its care. Attempts to domesticate such animals as lions, alligators, and monkeys are usually unsuccessful because of the animals' genetic patterns of behavior. Attempts to domesticate such animals have often proved to be hazardous to the animals and their owners. Even domestic animals can be dangerous at times. Care should be taken around animals that are sick, hurt, hungry, or excitable.

Reinforcement

Encourage students with learning disabilities to relate their experiences with pets. Include them in an activity in which you write the names of several types of animals on the chalkboard and ask the students to determine which of the animals would make good pets and which would not. Have them tell what type of home each pet might need.

♦ ***Suitable as a language development activity***

[1] dog, cat, rabbit
[2] Answers should indicate a safe, appropriate shelter.

Cats, dogs, and fish are good pets.

People enjoy having them.

What pets do you see here?[1]

What kinds of homes do they need?[2]

Lesson Review

1. What do pets need?
2. What animals are good pets?

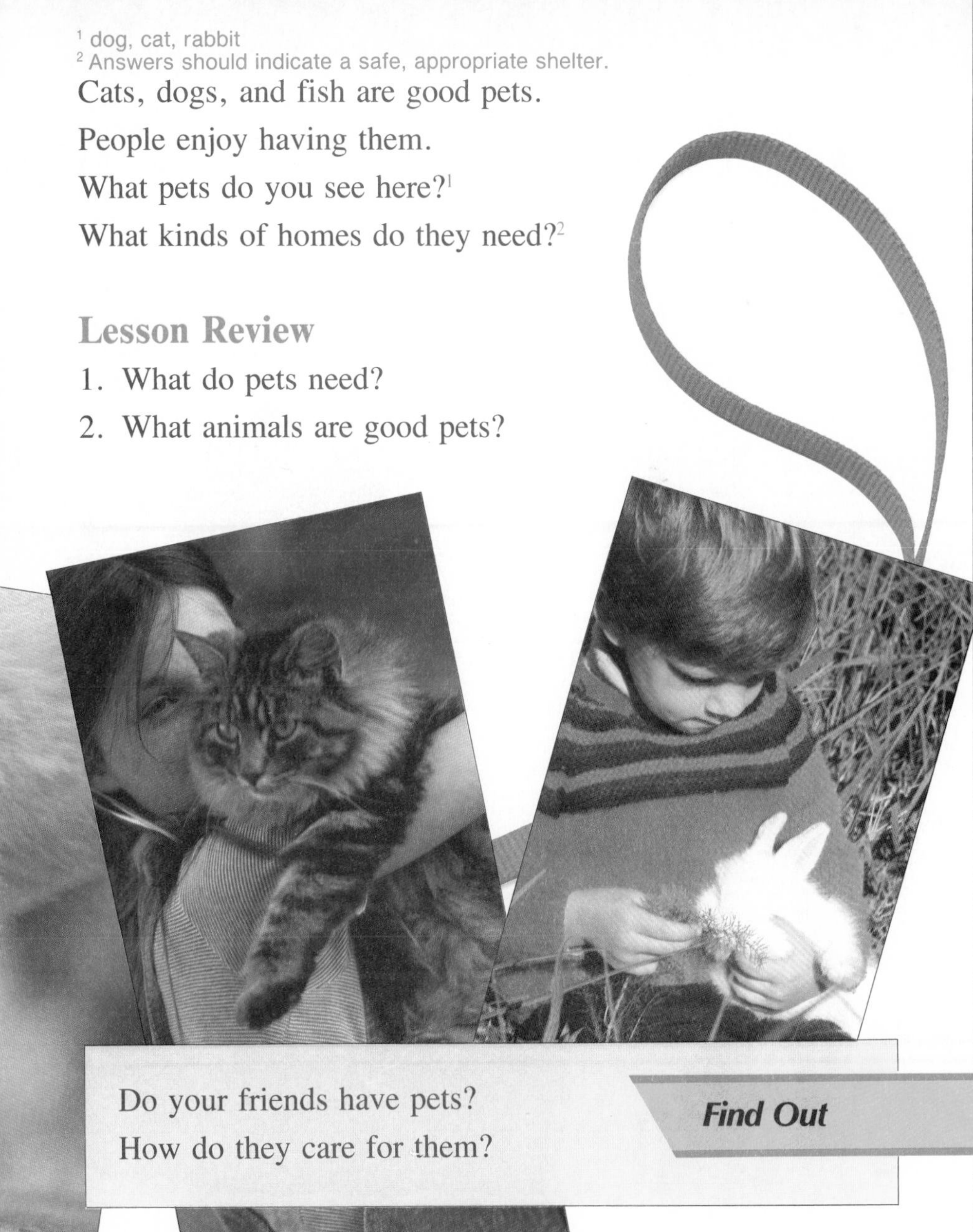

Find Out

Do your friends have pets?

How do they care for them?

2 TEACH

Teaching Tips

- Have students read page 96. Have students tell what they like about dogs.
- Ask students to read page 97. Have student *identify* the animals in the picture and tell why they make good pets. Question: **What types of animals would not make good pets?** (Students should *name* animals that are not tame.)
- **Possible Misconception:** Be aware that children sometimes think pets have the same needs as people do.

3 ASSESS

Lesson Review

1. Pets need food, water, and a place to live.
2. Answers should include cats, dogs, and fish.

Challenge! Question: **What is one animal that you think should stay in the wild and not become a pet? Tell why.** (Answers will vary, but should include animals who would be hard to take care of and animals that might be dangerous to humans.) **Thinking Skill:** *Inferring*

Find Out

Students could make a list of the different kinds of pets owned by their friends, and the ways the pets are cared for. **Thinking Skill:** *Restating or explaining ideas*

Workbook page 30 *

Name ______ Chapter 5
Use with Lesson 4: pages 96-97
Vocabulary Puzzle

Animals Wordsearch

Read the words in the word bank.
Write the words on the lines.
Then find each word in the puzzle below.

Word Bank: coverings, insect, pet, protect, snake

coverings

Circle the animal words.
Five are hiding in the puzzle.
One is done for you.

d w z c o v e r i n g s v
i a i n s e c t d q a z x
y p r o t e c t w s e d c
t f v s n a k e u h n t e
t r o g v v v p e t v v v

30

Reteaching Suggestion ♦

Remind students that pets need food, water, and a place to live. Make arrangements to keep a pet, such as a fish or hamster, at school. Allow the students to help you plan what the animal will eat, what type of home it will need, and who will be responsible for its care each day (on a rotating schedule). *CAUTION:* Investigate any allergies your students may have before planning to house a classroom pet. Make certain that any water spilled on the floor is wiped up immediately. Direct students to wash their hands after handling the animal.

* ***Answers to masters on pages 84E–84F***

TEACHING PLAN

SKILLS FOR SOLVING PROBLEMS
pages 98–99

Purpose
To *compare* animal sizes by making and interpreting a chart.

Materials
For each student: paper, pencil

1 MOTIVATE

Discussion
Ask students if they consider a kitten to be large or small. Then ask the same question about a fly. Discuss the relative nature of such terms as large, small, tall, short, young, old, weak, and strong. The same thing may be considered tall and small depending on what it is compared to. Ask students to compare their heights to the heights of things around them, such as desks, books, shelves, or cabinets.

Skills for Solving Problems

Making Charts About Animals

What can a chart show about animals?

1. Look at the pictures.
   Notice the size of each animal.
   Is the bird taller than the bear?
   Is the dog taller than the bird?
   Is the dog taller than the bear?

98

Teaching Options

SCIENCE BACKGROUND

The tallest animal in the world is the giraffe. It is more than 1-1/2 m (5 ft) tall at birth. A giraffe nearly doubles its height in the first year. An adult may be as tall as a 2-story building. The largest animal is the blue whale, with some specimens over 33 m (110 ft) long.

2. Use your own paper.
Make a chart like this.
Write words or draw pictures.
Number the animals from short to tall.

1	bird	shortest
2	dog	taller
3	bear	tallest

3. What does your chart show?
Which animal is tallest?
Which animal is shortest?

99

2 TEACH

Teaching Tips

- After students have *observed* the height of the animals in the picture, have them record their findings on a chart. Students should record the shortest to tallest animals, numbering them from 1 to 3.
- Students might want to *compare* the heights of other animals.

3 ASSESS

Students' charts should show that the bird is the shortest, the dog is taller, and the bear is tallest.

Resource Book page 39 *

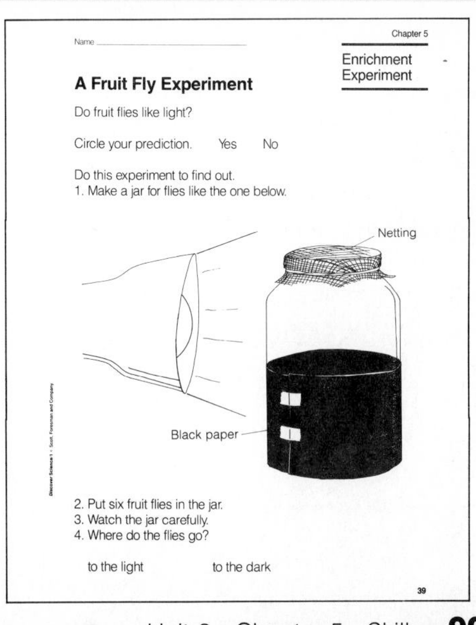
Chapter 5
Enrichment Experiment

Name

A Fruit Fly Experiment

Do fruit flies like light?

Circle your prediction. Yes No

Do this experiment to find out.
1. Make a jar for flies like the one below.

2. Put six fruit flies in the jar.
3. Watch the jar carefully.
4. Where do the flies go?

to the light to the dark

39

*** Answers to masters on pages 84E–84F**

REVIEW PLAN

CHAPTER 5 REVIEW
pages 100–101

Review Chapter Ideas

1. Some differences in animals are size, shape, color, and ways of growing.
2. Children might demonstrate how animals can swim, crawl, hop, jump, or fly.
3. The calf and the cow look alike; the caterpillar and the butterfly do not look alike.
4. Answers could include any baby mammals or birds.
5. People use animals for food, clothing, work, protection, and recreation or entertainment.
6. The pets need food, water, and a place to live.

For further review, use Study Guide page 233.

Chapter 5 Review

Review Chapter Ideas

1. Tell about differences in animals.
2. Show ways animals can move.
3. Look at these baby animals.
   Tell which look like their parents.

a.

b.

c.

d.

4. Name baby animals that need care.
5. Tell how people use animals.
6. Look at these pictures of pets.
   Tell what care they need.

a.

b.

c.

100

Review Options

Cooperative Learning ♦

STAD Format (See page T23.)
Assign students to work in four- to five-member teams to study Chapter 5 Review. Students should work together to make sure that they and their teammates know the material in the chapter. After students have had enough time to study together, give them a test to complete individually (Chapter 5 Test A or B in the *Test Book*). Award Superteam certificates to teams whose average test scores exceed 90% and Greatteam certificates to teams whose average test scores exceed 80%.

Test Book page 19 *

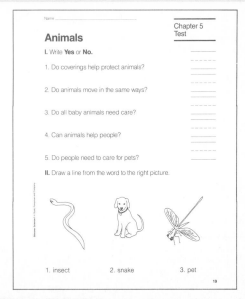

Name ______

Chapter 5 Test

Animals

I. Write **Yes** or **No.**

1. Do coverings help protect animals?
2. Do animals move in the same ways?
3. Do all baby animals need care?
4. Can animals help people?
5. Do people need to care for pets?

II. Draw a line from the word to the right picture.

1. insect 2. snake 3. pet

19

♦ ***Suitable as a language development activity***

Review Science Words

Match the words and the pictures.

1. insect
2. pet
3. snake

a. 

b. 

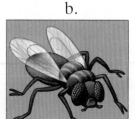

c. 

Tell what the words mean.

4. coverings
5. protect

Use Science Ideas

Tell what happens first, next, and last.

a.

b. 

c. 

Review Science Words

Match the words and the pictures.

1. b
2. c
3. a

Tell what the words mean.
Thinking Skill: *Restating or explaining ideas*
4. coverings—the various surfaces of animals
5. protect—to take care of something

Use What You Learned

First, the frog is a tadpole (c). Next, the frog changes shape and loses its tail as it grows legs (b). Last, the frog becomes an adult and has no tail (a). **Thinking Skill:** *Applying information to new situations*

* ***Answers to masters on pages 84E–84F***

TEACHING PLAN

CAREERS

Purpose

In this feature, students will learn how a pet shop worker contributes to the well being of animals. Anyone who loves animals can be a pet shop worker. The main qualification needed is an interest in animals and a willingness to help keep the animals comfortable, fed, and clean.

Teaching Tips

- Questions: **How many of you would like to work with animals when you are older? Why?** (Answers will vary.) Encourage students to think of jobs they could have which would involve working with animals.
- Instruct the class to study the illustration on page 102. Ask the students which of the animals in the picture they have seen in pet stores. (Answers will vary depending on students' background.)

Careers

Pet Store Worker

Some stores sell pets.
Workers take care of the pets.
The pets stay in cages or tanks.
Workers clean the cages and tanks.
They feed the animals.
The workers know about many animals.
They tell people about the pets.

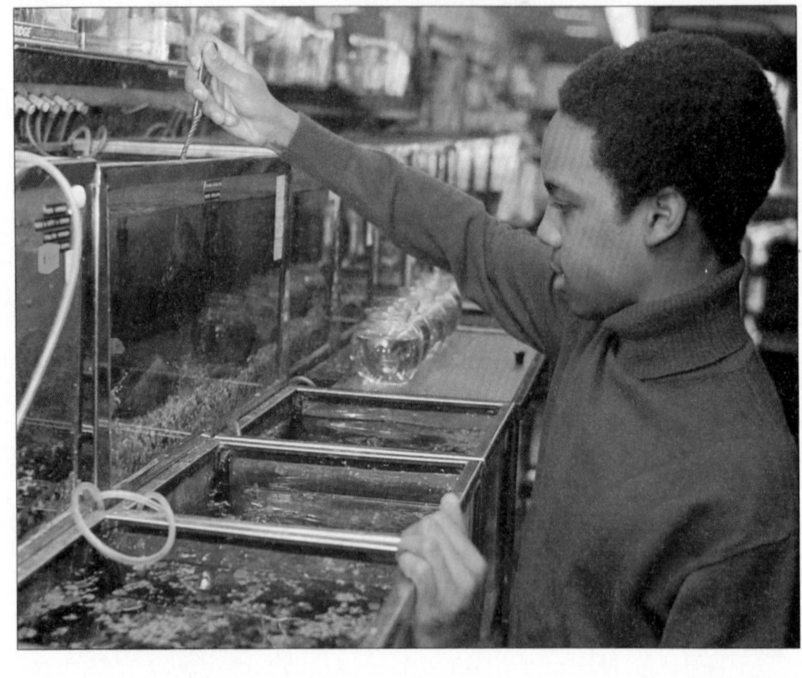

Teaching Options

Enrichment

Encourage interested students to find out which breeds of dogs are usually sold at pet stores. Instruct the students to find out how the dogs are groomed, and what types of personalities the different breeds have.

Where to Write

For additional information about this career contact:
National Retail Pet Store and Groomers' Association, PO Box 1337, 711 Mission Street, Suite B., South Pasadena, California 91030

How It Works

Fireflies

Why does a firefly seem to light up?
A firefly's body makes special juices.
These juices mix with air.
Then the firefly lights up.
Why does a firefly make this light?
Scientists are not sure.
It might want to attract other fireflies.

103

HOW IT WORKS

Teaching Tips

- If possible capture some fireflies and display them for the class. Question: **Have you ever seen these insects before?** Encourage the students to *describe* their experiences with fireflies.
- Point out to the students that people have used captured fireflies to light their path in a night jungle or woods. Question: **What do people usually use to light their paths in the night woods?** (flashlights or lanterns)
- Explain to the students that the light of a firefly is cold and does not burn like a fire would.
- Question: **Why are fireflies sometimes called lightning bugs?** (Answers will vary. Lead the students to *conclude* that the bug gives off flashes of light like lightning does.

SCIENCE BACKGROUND

Many fireflies belong to the *Lampyridae* family of beetles. However, unlike other beetles they do not have a hard shell. Fireflies produce light as a result of a chemical reaction between an enzyme, luciferase, and a fatty compound, luciferin. The primary function of the bioluminescence in fireflies appears to be that of attracting individuals of the opposite sex. Studies show that specific light patterns emitted by males of particular species are recognized by and responded to by females of the same species.

UNIT 2 REVIEW

Answer the Questions
1. living thing: B, D; nonliving: A, C, E
2. Most plants have roots, stems, and leaves; some have flowers.
3. Plants can grow from seeds, or can grow from their parts.
4. Animals are different in size, shape, and in the ways they move.
5. Baby animals grow larger; some change in shape and color.
6. Animals help people because people can use them for food, clothing, work, and entertainment. People need plants for food and other products.

Study the Picture
The plant (A) in the dark needs light; the dry plant (B) needs water. **Thinking Skill:** *Inferring*

Unit 2 Review

Answer the Questions

1. Which are living things?
   Which are nonliving things?

a.

b.

c.

d.

e.

2. What parts do most plants have?
3. What are two ways a plant can start?
4. What are differences in animals?
5. How do baby animals grow and change?
6. How do plants and animals help people?

Study the Picture

What do these plants need?

a.

b.
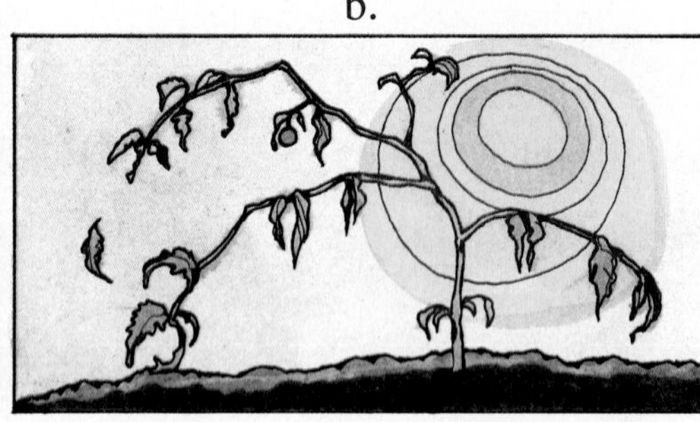

104

Review Options

Test Book page 21

Name ______________

Life Science — Unit Test

I. Write **Yes** or **No**.

1. Do people need air to stay alive?
2. Do coverings help protect animals?
3. Can a plant grow without any water?
4. Is a plant a living thing?
5. Do people need to care for pets?

II. Draw a line from the word to the right picture.

1. stem 2. roots 3. shelter 4. nonliving 5. leaf

21

What to Do

1. Make a model of something alive.
   You might use clay or paper.
2. Plan a garden.
   Decide what plants you want.
   Draw a picture of your garden.
3. Make a picture zoo.
   Cut out pictures of animals.
   Paste them on a poster.

UNIT PROJECTS

Teaching Tips

1. Students could model a plant or animal from clay, or could construct one from colored paper. Display students models and give students an opportunity to tell the class about their projects.
2. Students could draw or paint a picture of a garden that includes a variety of flowers, vegetables, or fruits.
3. If you prefer, make this a class project by taping a large sheet of paper to one wall. Allow the students to paste or draw pictures of animals on the paper.

Books in Spanish

Hall, Derek. Series of six books that illustrate that growing up is difficult for young animals. Knopf, 1986. (grades 1-2) *El elefante* (the elephant). *El gorila* (the gorilla). *El oso polar* (the polar bear). *El panda* The panda). *El tigre* (the tiger). *La nutria* (the otter).

Books for Students

Claridge, Marit. *Living Things: A Simple Introduction*. Random House, 1986. An introduction to plant and animal life. (grades k-3)
Rowland-Entwistle, Theodore. *Animal Homes*. Random House, 1987. Illustrates various animals' homes. (grades 2-5)

UNIT 3

Planning Guide

Unit Components			Pages
Unit Overview			106–107
Chapter 6 Grouping Things	**Lesson 1** What Ways Can You Group Things? **Lesson 2** What Takes Up Space?	**Lesson 3** What Are Solids and Liquids Like? **Lesson 4** What Are Gases Like?	108–125
Chapter 7 Light, Sound, and Heat	**Lesson 1** How Can Light Change? **Lesson 2** How Can Sound Change?	**Lesson 3** What Can You Learn About Heat?	126–143
Chapter 8 Moving and Working	**Lesson 1** What Ways Do Objects Move? **Lesson 2** What Can Move Objects?	**Lesson 3** What Work Can Machines Do?	144–161
Careers	pilot		162
How It Works	Pencil Sharpener		163
Unit Review			164
Unit Projects			165

Science Process Skills Book
The Science Process Skills Book contains worksheets that can be used to teach and then assess student mastery of the basic science process skills. In addition, other worksheets in this book teach students the manipulative skills they will need to use basic science equipment. Assign these worksheets whenever you think it fits in your curriculum.

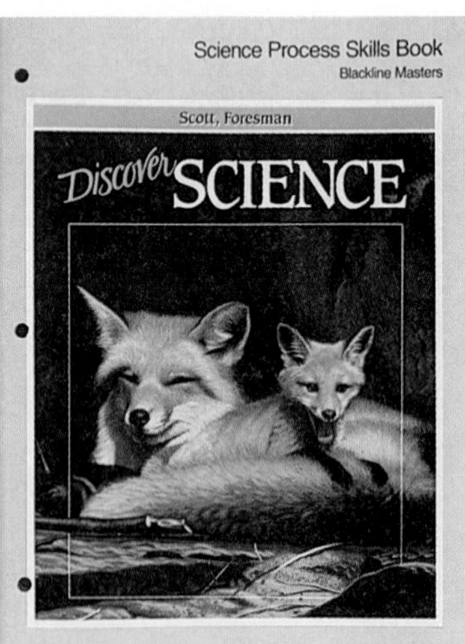

Science Resources for the Unit

Resource Books

How Things Work. National Geographic, 1983. Explains the mechanics and dynamic principles underlying 21 technological devices.

Kettlekamp, Larry. *Magic of Sound.* Morrow, 1982. Simple experiments probe aspects of resonance, frequency, echo, and sound effects.

Tocci, Salvatore. *Chemistry Around You: Experiments and Projects with Everyday Products.* Arco, 1985. Chemical experiments involving substances commonly found in the home.

Community Resources

Take students on a study trip to a grocery store. Ask the manager to explain how items are grouped. Students might look for various types of liquids and solids. Try to point out similar products in both forms, such as laundry detergent in both liquid and powder form, or oranges and orange juice.

Take the class to observe machines at work—construction site, loading dock, department store, and so on. Ask the operator of a machine to explain what kind of work the machine can do and how it works.

Audio-Visual Resources

Bending and Reflecting Light. Britannica. Film, 7 minutes. Three boys play with a magnifying glass, a water-filled jar, and a water-hose spray and begin to grasp the principles of magnification, bent images, and rainbows.

Fire: What Makes It Burn. Britannica. Film, 11 minutes. Shows what makes a fire, what a flame is, how combustion takes place, and how a fire can be extinguished.

Go. AIMS. Film or video, 10 minutes. How we rely on energy to make things go, where we get energy, why we must conserve it, and how children can help.

Learning About Sounds. Britannica. Sound filmstrip series, average 48 frames/8 minutes each. Encourages students to observe, describe, and classify familiar and unfamiliar sounds.

Learning About Water. AIMS. Film or video, 12 minutes. Children explore water and its various states. The water cycle is explained.

Movement Everywhere. Britannica. Film, 11 minutes. Defines the concept of work in terms that young students can understand.

Solid, Liquid, Gas. National Geographic. Film or video, 15 minutes. Explores three forms of matter with everyday materials.

Thermometers and How They Work. Britannica. Film, 11 minutes. Explores the three basic types of thermometers—those made with liquids, gases, and solids—and demonstrates how each type works.

Wondering About Air. Britannica. Film, 13 minutes. Three clowns pursue what cannot be seen or tasted—air.

Wondering About Sound. Britannica. Film, 10 minutes. A musical band explains vibration and sound waves.

Computer Software

Creative Contraptions. Looking Glass. Apple II, II+, IIe, IIc. Build all sorts of simple machines.

How Things Work. World Book. Apple IIc/IIe 64K. Science simulation program featuring animation of simple machines and the use of simple machines to solve problems.

Simple Machines. January Productions. Shows how simple machines help us work and explains that all machines are made up of simple machines.

INTRODUCING UNIT 3

Unit Overview
This unit is designed to stimulate students' awareness of their physical world. Students will learn basic physical concepts about matter, mechanics, and energy.

About the Photograph
The photograph shows a dramatic display of rapid chemical change. Most chemical changes, like the fire you see in the picture, release energy in the form of heat. Firefighters, to protect themselves from heat injury, wear special suits similar to the one pictured. These suits offer the advantage of reflecting heat energy away from the firefighter's body.

106

Teaching Options

Chapter 6 Preview

Grouping Things
This chapter focuses on classifying and on the physical states of matter. Students will be introduced to the process of grouping or classifying by placing various objects in water and forming groups of objects that float and sink. Students will learn that objects can be grouped by other characteristics such as shape, color, length, mass, and texture. Students will learn the characteristics which distinguish three forms of matter.

Chapter 7 Preview

Light, Sound, and Heat
In this chapter, students will discover that light comes from many sources and that some things block light and produce shadows while other things reflect light. The students will also learn about sources of sound and that sound travels in all directions and can vary in intensity. The students will investigate how sound is transmitted. In addition, students will learn that heat comes from various sources and can be measured through the use of a thermometer.

Unit 3

Physical Science

These firefighters wear special clothes.
How do they help the firefighters?
The clothes cover the firefighters.
They protect the firefighters from heat.

Pretend you are a firefighter.
What might you wear for protection?
Draw a picture of your special clothes.

107

Teaching Tips

- After studying the photograph, have the students *make inferences* about the suit's fabric and the function of the suit. (The suit is nonflammable, and it protects the firefighter from heat.)
- Relate the heat of the fire to the students' experiences. Ask the students how they felt when they were close to a fire. Encourage the students to imagine what it would be like standing very close to a big fire.
- After the class discussion, have the students write a story about a firefighter.

Chapter 8 Preview

Moving and Working

This chapter explores movement, work, and how machines use motion and force to do work. The students will make a paper airplane and watch it move to discover that motion varies and objects take different positions as they move. The students will also learn that pushing, pulling, or lifting move objects. Gravity and magnets also cause objects to move. In addition, students will *identify* the work of different machines.

Teaching Plan

Chapter Components	Skills	Materials
Chapter Opener/*TRY THIS:* Grouping by Floating or Sinking pp. 108-109	***TRY THIS*** p. 109 **Science Process Skills** *Predicting, Classifying*	***TRY THIS*** p. 109 (groups of 2) 15 metal baking pans, 60 assorted objects that float, 60 assorted objects that sink, water
Lesson 1: What Ways Can You Group Things? pp. 110-112	**Thinking Skills** Challenge!: *Suggesting alternatives* Find Out: *Applying information to new situations*	**Demonstration** p. 110 1 large sheet red construction paper, 1 large sheet green construction paper, variety of round objects, variety of objects that are not round
Activity: Grouping in Different Ways p. 113	**Science Process Skills** *Observing, Communicating*	(individual) 300 assorted metal nuts 300 assorted metal screws 300 assorted metal washers 300 assorted metal bolts
Lesson 2: What Takes Up Space? pp. 114-115	**Thinking Skills** Challenge!: *Making inferences* Find Out: *Applying information to new situations*	**Demonstration** p. 114 pan, drinking glass, paper, water
Lesson 3: What Are Solids and Liquids Like? pp. 116-117	**Thinking Skills** Challenge!: *Applying information to new situations* Find Out: *Observing, Communicating*	**Demonstration** p. 116 containers of various shapes, cup, water
Lesson 4: What Are Gases Like? pp. 118-119	**Thinking Skills** Challenge!: *Drawing conclusions* Find Out: *Observing, Communicating*	**Demonstration** p. 118 balloon
Activity: Blowing Up a Balloon p. 120	**Science Process Skills** *Observing, Communicating, Inferring*	(groups of 2) 15 clear bottles, 1 bottle white vinegar, 1 box baking soda, 15 balloons, 15 small funnels
Science and People: Dr. Isabella Karle p. 121	**Thinking Skill** *Making generalizations*	
Skills for Solving Problems: Measuring solid objects pp. 122-123	**Problem Solving Skills** *Making decisions/Identifying and solving problems, Interpreting charts, maps, and graphs*	(individual) paper clips, toothpicks, paper, ruler
Chapter Review pp. 124-125	**Thinking Skills** *Restating or explaining ideas, Predicting*	

Teaching Options

Strategies	Extensions		Resource Masters
			Family Letter: *Resource Book* p. 43 Vocabulary Preview: *Workbook* pp. 31-32
	Reinforcement p. 110 Special Education p. 111 Enrichment p. 111	Game Suggestion p. 111 Reteaching Suggestion p. 112	Science and Language Arts: *Workbook* p. 33
	Enrichment Activity p. 113		
	Reinforcement p. 114 Special Education p. 115 Reteaching Suggestion p. 115		Science Activity: *Workbook* p. 34
	Enrichment p. 116 Special Education p. 117 Reteaching Suggestion p. 117		Science Skills: *Workbook* p. 35
	Reinforcement p. 118 Special Education p. 119 Reteaching Suggestion p. 119		Vocabulary Puzzle: *Workbook* p. 36
	Enrichment Activity p. 120		
			Enrichment Activity: *Resource Book* p. 47
Cooperative Learning p. 124 (Also see p. T23)			Chapter Test: *Test Book* p. 23

Preteaching Suggestions

For Advance Preparation

TRY THIS, page 109
Collect a variety of objects, including those that will float and those that will not. Fill a sink or plastic tub with water.

Activity, page 113
Obtain a large collection of nails, screws, and bolts. Be sure the collection includes a variety of shapes, lengths, thicknesses, and so on. You might ask students to bring these items from home. Divide the collection into several, making one collection for each 4–6 students so that they are able to work in small groups.

Activity, page 120
For each group obtain newspapers, one 8-oz. plastic bottle with a small neck (clean soda bottles, dish detergent bottles, glue bottles will work well), a balloon about 10 inches in diameter, a tablespoon or a 1/4-cup measure, a small funnel, vinegar, and baking soda. Use the small funnel to pour 1 tablespoon baking soda into each balloon.

For Vocabulary Review

Use the following sentences with your students to review the meanings of the underlined words.

1. Things that float stay on the surface of water.
2. Cars, bicycles, and computers are kinds of machines.
3. To see or learn something for the first time is to make a discovery.
4. A ruler is used to measure length.

For High-Potential Students

Ask students to compile a list of liquids which become solids when the temperature is lowered, such as water, milk, juice, and others. Students should also make a list of liquids which become solid as a result of increased temperature, such as eggs and most batters. In order to compile the lists, students might want to do some experimenting with adult supervision. They might also ask other people for suggestions to add to the list. You could extend the experience by asking students to identify the changes which can be easily reversed, such as gelatin (a semi-solid) returning to a liquid state.

For Mainstreamed Students

Visually Impaired
Provide opportunities for students with visual impairments to sort specific objects that can be sorted using tactile and auditory senses. When students are to sort objects classified by their visual characteristics, give students verbal descriptions of the objects and let them touch the objects.

Hearing Impaired
Point out to students with hearing impairments that things can be sorted by sound as well as by sight. Recordings can be sorted by those with voice and those with music (vocal vs. orchestral); music can be played loudly or softly; music can be made with a piano or a trumpet; and so on. When sorting sounds, allow hearing-impaired students to place their hands on solid objects to feel the vibrations. Give them visual cues and gestures, in conjunction with sign, to aid the student in sorting sounds.

For Science Fair Projects

Encourage interested students to do one of the following projects:

1. Make a display showing the same amount of liquid in containers of various sizes. Describe the differences in appearance.
2. Collect a variety of objects and group them by several different categories. Make drawings which show the various groupings devised.

Classroom Resources

Bulletin Board
Encourage students to name some ways that things are grouped in their own homes.

HOW CAN THESE THINGS BE GROUPED?

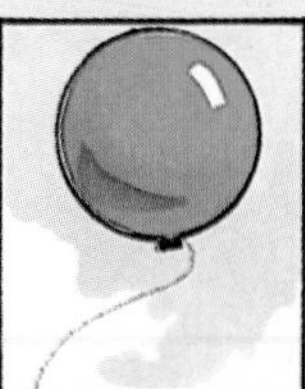

Chapter 6 Poster

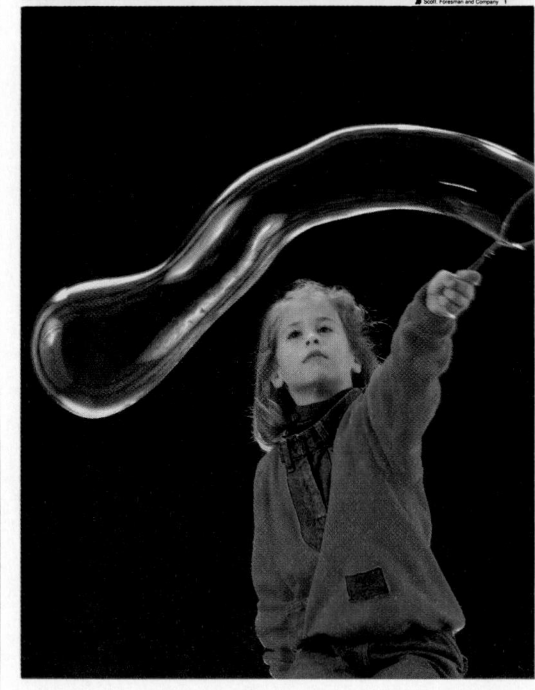
What is inside the bubble?

Science Discovery Center
Use pages from Chapter 6 in the *Science Discovery Center Book*. Place these worksheets in the appropriate pockets in the Science Discovery Center.

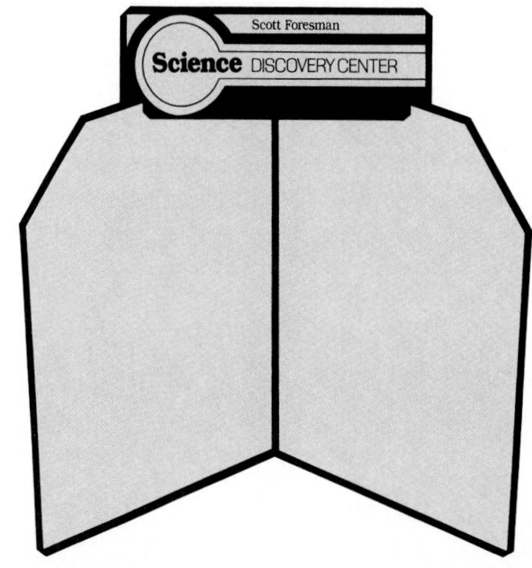
Scott Foresman
Science DISCOVERY CENTER

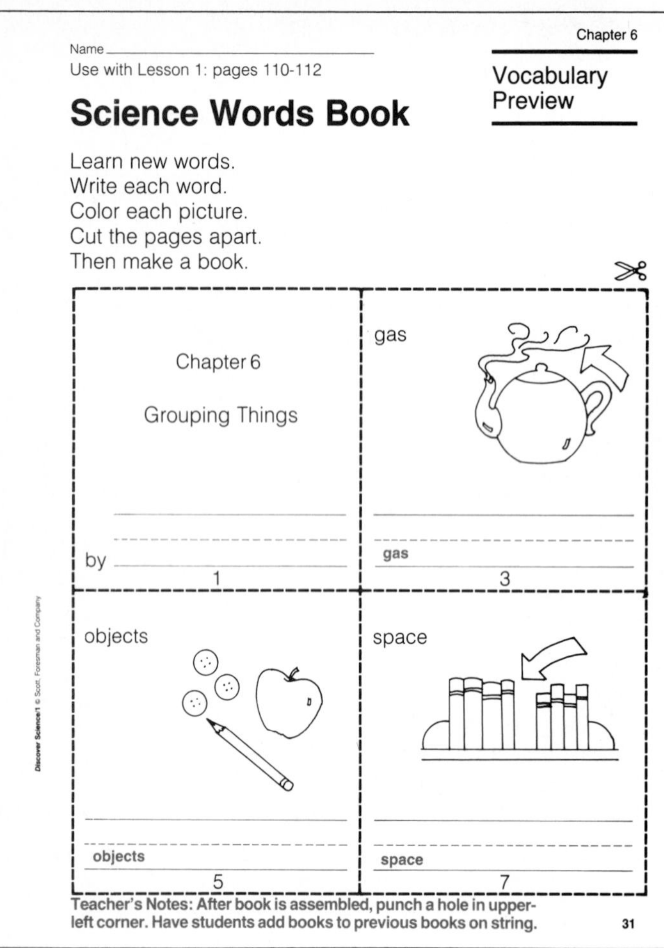

Name ______________

Use with Lesson 1: pages 110-112

Chapter 6

Vocabulary Preview

Science Words Book

Learn new words.
Write each word.
Color each picture.
Cut the pages apart.
Then make a book.

Teacher's Notes: After book is assembled, punch a hole in upper-left corner. Have students add books to previous books on string.

31

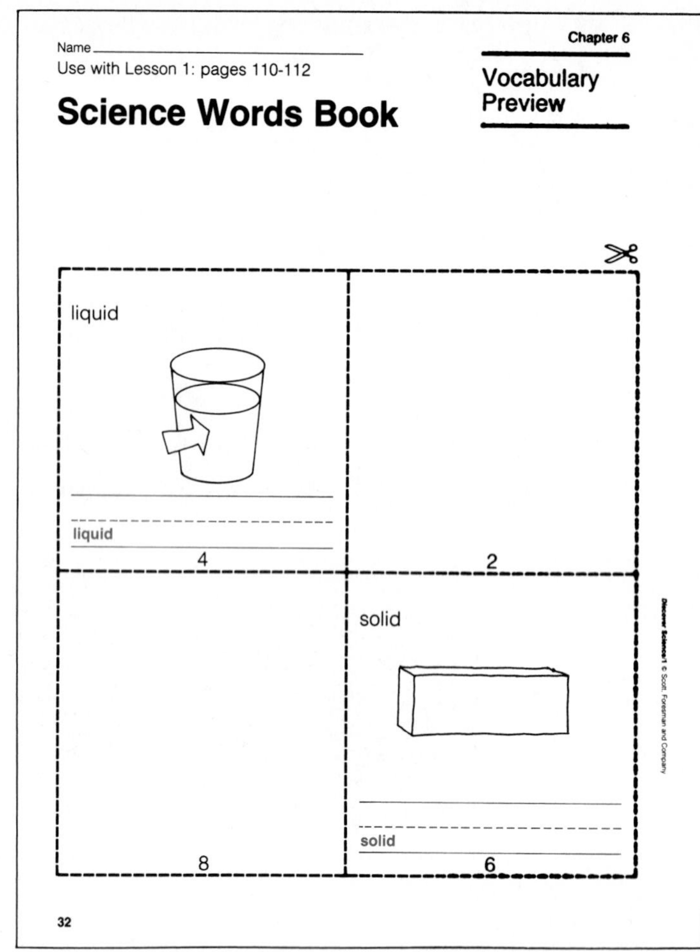

Name ______________

Use with Lesson 1: pages 110-112

Chapter 6

Vocabulary Preview

Science Words Book

32

Name ______________

Use with Lesson 1: pages 110-112

Chapter 6

Science and Language Arts

Using Words to Describe

Look at each picture.
Circle the word that describes it.
Then write the word on the line.
One is done for you.

As soft as a sheep.
hard (soft) blue
As tall as a dinosaur.
tiny red (tall)
As tiny as a mouse.
(tiny) big rough
As green as grass.
round white (green)

Teacher's Notes: Ask the students to read their similes. Invite students to write similes about things in their environment.

33

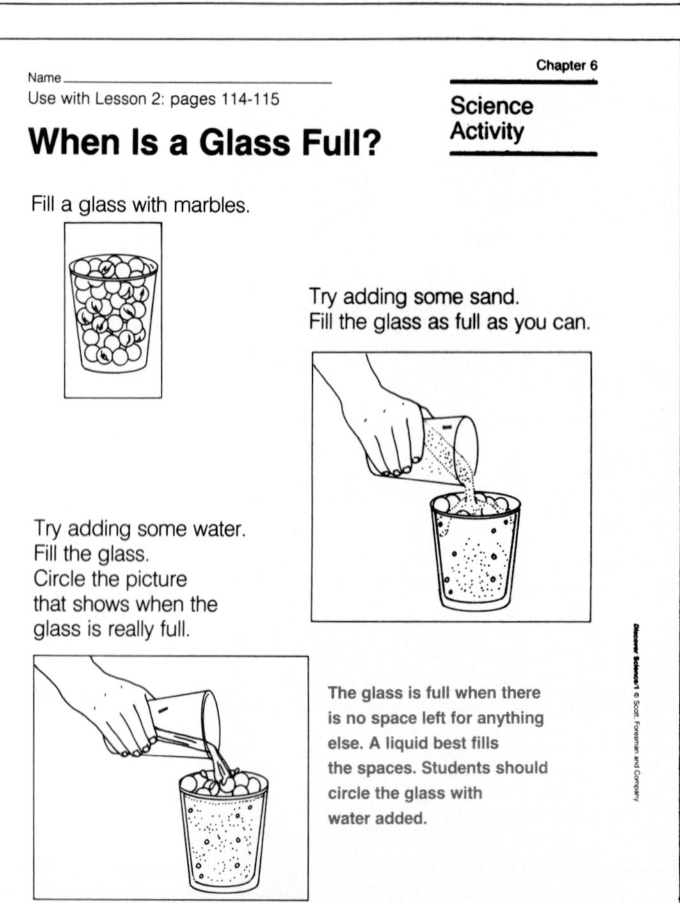

Name ______________

Use with Lesson 2: pages 114-115

Chapter 6

Science Activity

When Is a Glass Full?

Fill a glass with marbles.

Try adding some sand.
Fill the glass as full as you can.

Try adding some water.
Fill the glass.
Circle the picture that shows when the glass is really full.

The glass is full when there is no space left for anything else. A liquid best fills the spaces. Students should circle the glass with water added.

Teacher's Notes: After the activity ask, "Why could liquid be added to the sand and marbles?" (space between sand and marbles)

34

Name ____________________

Use with Lesson 3: pages 116-117

Chapter 6

Science Skills

Classifying Objects

Write the word *solid* under the solid things.
Write the word *liquid* under the liquid things.
Color all the objects.

solid

liquid

solid

solid

liquid

solid

Teacher's Notes: Take students on a walking tour to classify objects in your environment as solids, liquids, or gases.

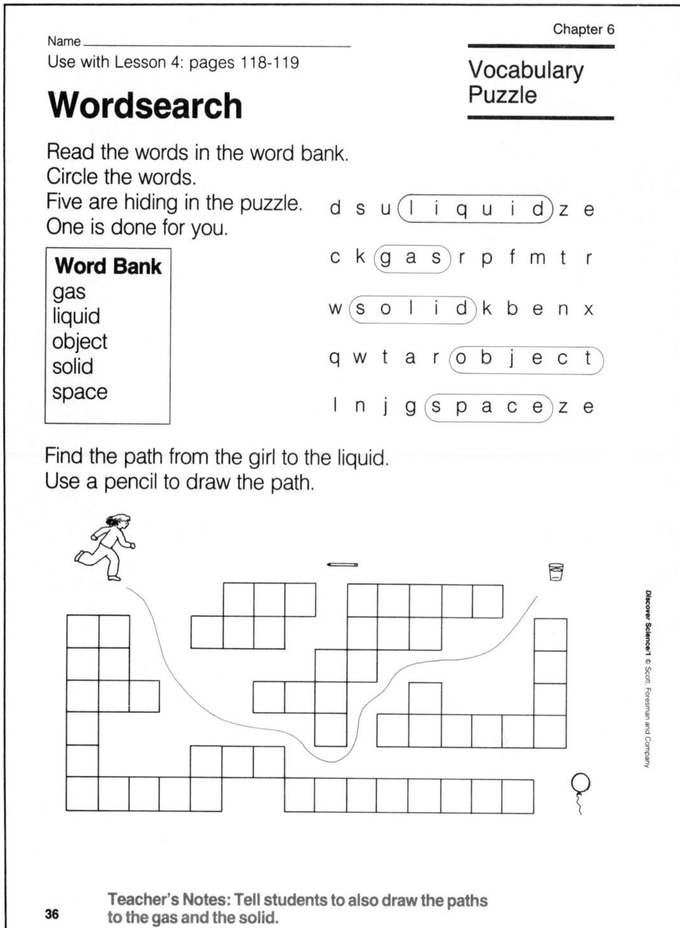

Name ____________________

Use with Lesson 4: pages 118-119

Chapter 6

Vocabulary Puzzle

Wordsearch

Read the words in the word bank.
Circle the words.
Five are hiding in the puzzle.
One is done for you.

Word Bank
gas
liquid
object
solid
space

d s u l i q u i d z e
c k g a s r p f m t r
w s o l i d k b e n x
q w t a r o b j e c t
l n j g s p a c e z e

Find the path from the girl to the liquid.
Use a pencil to draw the path.

Teacher's Notes: Tell students to also draw the paths to the gas and the solid.

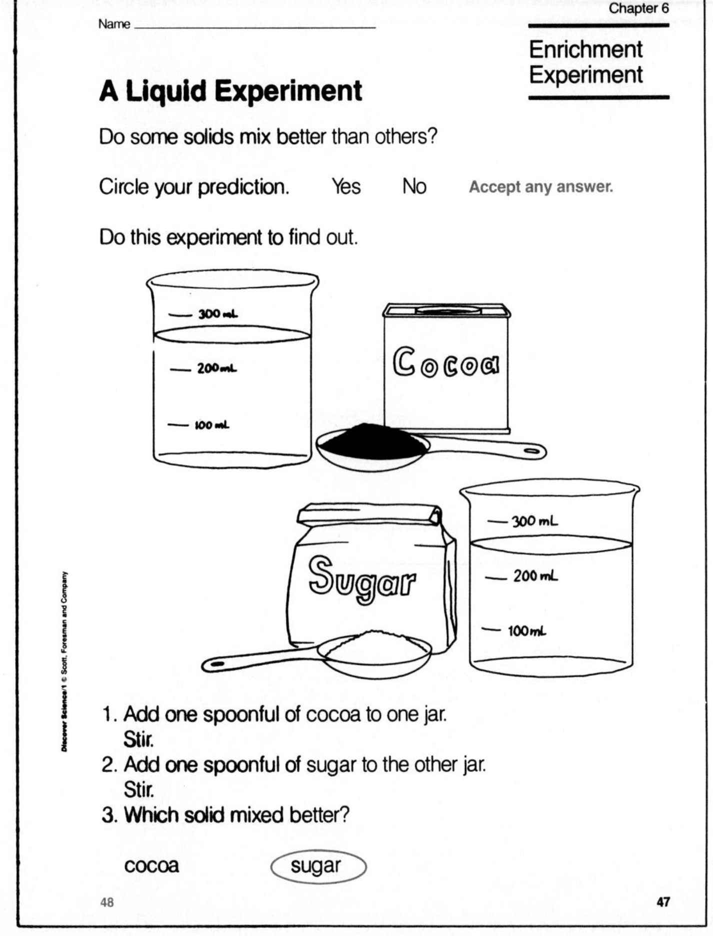

Name ____________________

Chapter 6

Enrichment Experiment

A Liquid Experiment

Do some solids mix better than others?

Circle your prediction. Yes No Accept any answer.

Do this experiment to find out.

1. Add one spoonful of cocoa to one jar.
   Stir.
2. Add one spoonful of sugar to the other jar.
   Stir.
3. Which solid mixed better?

cocoa (sugar)

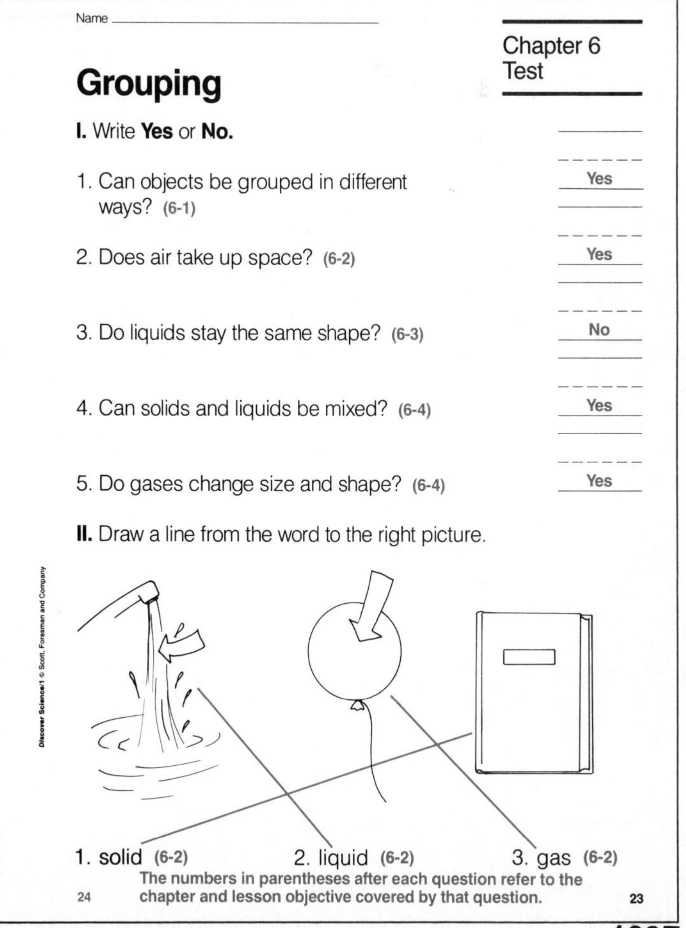

Name ____________________

Chapter 6 Test

Grouping

I. Write **Yes** or **No.**

1. Can objects be grouped in different ways? (6-1) Yes
2. Does air take up space? (6-2) Yes
3. Do liquids stay the same shape? (6-3) No
4. Can solids and liquids be mixed? (6-4) Yes
5. Do gases change size and shape? (6-4) Yes

II. Draw a line from the word to the right picture.

1. solid (6-2) 2. liquid (6-2) 3. gas (6-2)

The numbers in parentheses after each question refer to the chapter and lesson objective covered by that question.

TEACHING PLAN

INTRODUCING CHAPTER 6

Major Concepts

Lesson 1 Matter can be grouped according to its various properties.
Lesson 2 Most matter can be classified as solid, liquid, or gas, all of which take up space.
Lesson 3 Solids and liquids have similar and different characteristics.
Lesson 4 Gases have no definite size or shape.

Vocabulary

gas, liquid, object, solid, space

[1] most likely by type; by fruits and vegetables

Chapter 6

Grouping Things

Suppose you went to a market.
How might the food be grouped?[1]
How would you group the food?

108

Teaching Options

Workbook page 31 *

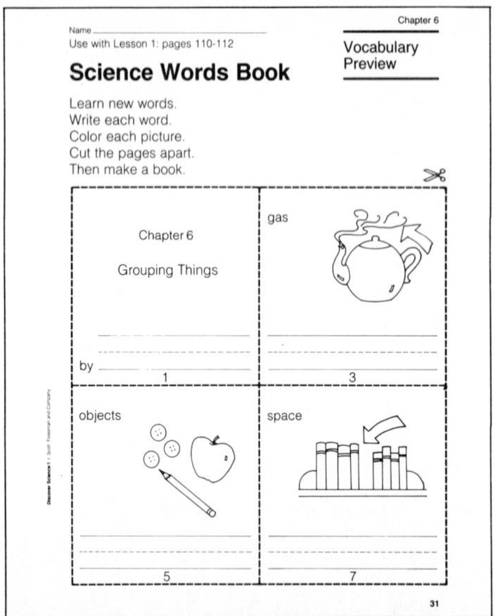

Name
Use with Lesson 1: pages 110-112

Chapter 6
Vocabulary Preview

Science Words Book

Learn new words.
Write each word.
Color each picture.
Cut the pages apart.
Then make a book.

Chapter 6 Grouping Things by 1	gas 3
objects 5	space 7

31

Workbook page 32 *

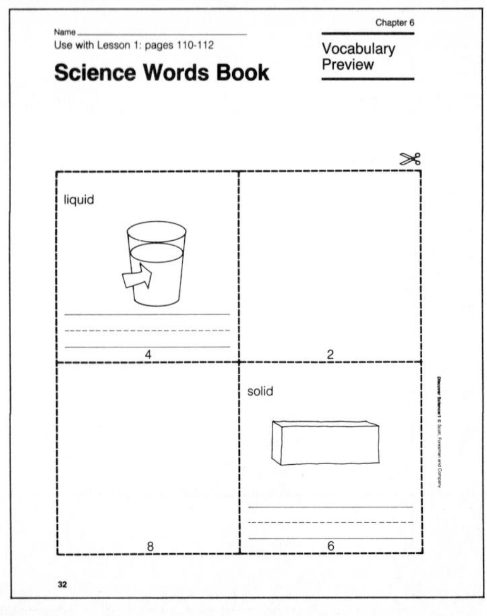

Name
Use with Lesson 1: pages 110-112

Chapter 6
Vocabulary Preview

Science Words Book

liquid 4	2
8	solid 6

32

◆ ***Suitable as a language development activity***

Starting the Chapter

What things can you put in groups?
You can group things that float.
You can group things that sink.
Then read about more ways of grouping.

TRY THIS

Grouping by Floating or Sinking

Put things like these in water.
See if they float or sink.
Make groups that float or sink.
What is in each group?

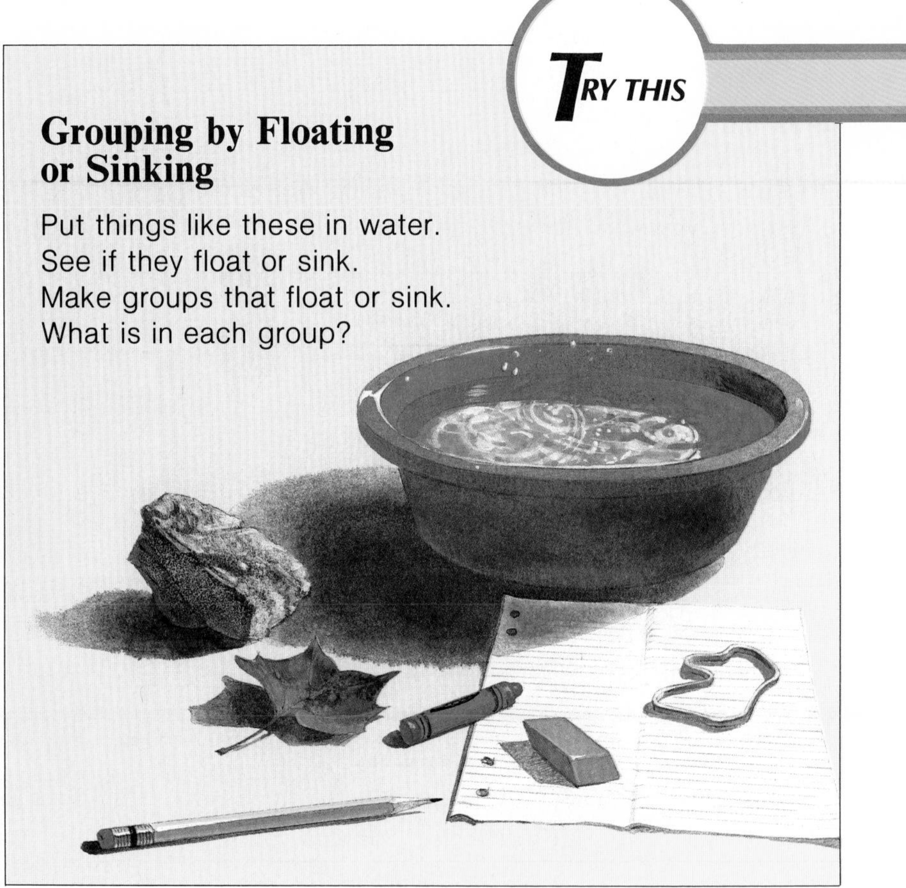

TRY THIS

Objective ♦
This optional *TRY THIS* activity will help students explore and build background information about the concept that objects can be grouped. Later in the chapter, students will be able to draw on this experience to help them assimilate the new content.

Science Process Skills
Predicting, Classifying

Materials
For each pair of students: metal baking pan, 4 objects that float, 4 objects that sink, water

Safety Tip (See page T27.)
- Instruct students to immediately wipe up any water that spills on the floor to prevent slipping accidents.

Teaching Tip
- Direct students to draw and write the name of each item to be tested on a sheet of paper. Ask students to ***predict*** whether each item will sink or float and ***record*** their predictions beside each item. Have students ***experiment*** to determine whether their predictions were correct.

Answer
Answers will vary depending on the items chosen.

Resource Book page 43

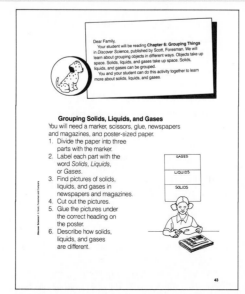

Dear Family,
Your student will be reading **Chapter 6: Grouping Things** in *Discover Science*, published by Scott, Foresman. We will learn about grouping objects in different ways. Objects take up space. Solids, liquids, and gases take up space. Solids, liquids, and gases can be grouped.
You and your student can do this activity together to learn more about solids, liquids, and gases.

Grouping Solids, Liquids, and Gases
You will need a marker, scissors, glue, newspapers and magazines, and poster-sized paper.
1. Divide the paper into three parts with the marker.
2. Label each part with the word *Solids, Liquids,* or *Gases.*
3. Find pictures of solids, liquids, and gases in newspapers and magazines.
4. Cut out the pictures.
5. Glue the pictures under the correct heading on the poster.
6. Describe how solids, liquids, and gases are different.

43

SCIENCE BACKGROUND

One material floats in another because of the differences in their densities. Density is a measure of how closely molecules are packed together and of the mass of the molecules. A denser material has more mass than a less dense material of the same size. Therefore, gravity pulls more on the denser one, making it heavier, and it sinks.

* **Answers to masters on pages 108E-108F**

TEACHING PLAN

LESSON 1
pages 110–112

Lesson Objective
- *State* that objects can be grouped by shape, size, color, weight, length, and texture.

Lesson Vocabulary
object

1 MOTIVATE

Demonstration Activity ♦
Gather students into a circle on the floor. Place two large sheets of construction paper, one red and one green, in the center of the circle. As students watch, pull objects, one at a time, out of a sack and group them on the large construction paper, placing round objects on the red paper and objects that are not round on the green paper. After you have grouped several objects, hold up an object and ask students to indicate which group it belongs in.

Discussion
Encourage students to discuss the way in which the objects were grouped, as well as other ways in which the objects might have been grouped.

[1] by grouping identical buttons
[2] by size, color, shape, number of buttonholes

Lesson 1 What Ways Can You Group Things?

Objects are things you can see or touch.
You can group objects by shape.
You can group them by color.
How are these buttons grouped?[1]
What other groups could you make?[2]

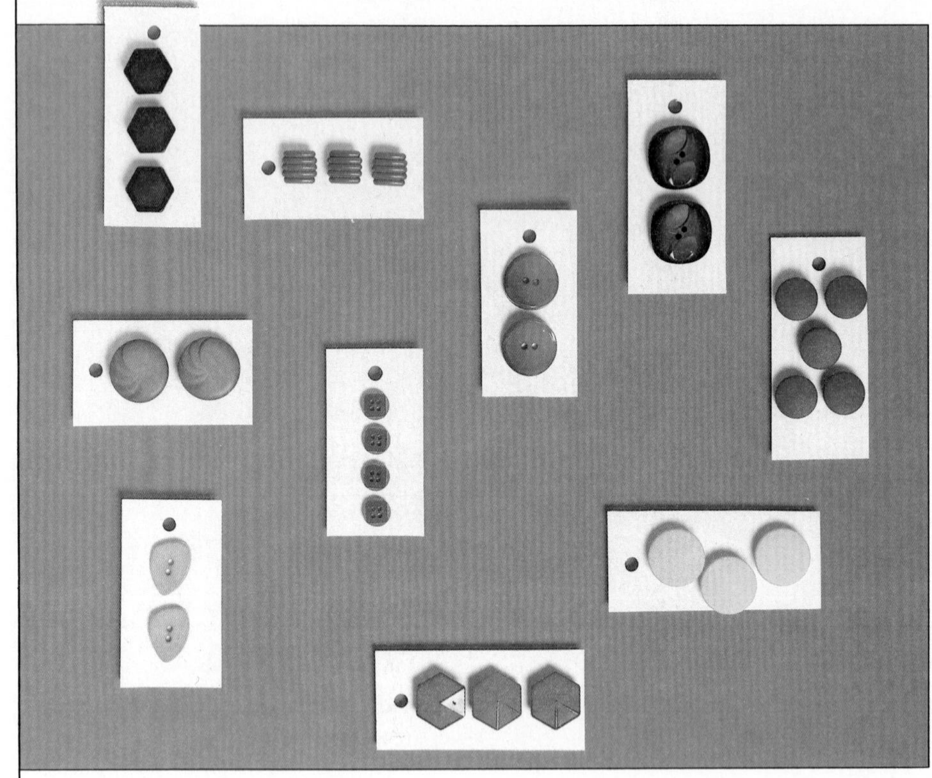

110

Teaching Options

SCIENCE BACKGROUND

Classification schemes are basic to the structures of science. Elements of the universe are grouped in a periodic table; organisms are classified on the basis of their evolutionary relationships; all forms of radiant energy are classified in a spectrum against properties of wave length and frequency. In everyday life, classification is essential to bring order and understanding to a world that moves continuously into disorder by natural law. Encouraging students to recognize and identify similar and different properties of entities helps them to apply the skills of classification more readily.

Reinforcement

Collect a variety of small objects of different lengths. Show students how to find the 6 cm (2.36 in.) mark on a ruler, and have them divide the objects into two groups: those shorter than 6 cm and those longer than 6 cm.

♦ ***Suitable as a language development activity***

[1] by color and length
[2] by weight

You can group objects other ways.

One way is by how long the objects are.

Another way is by how heavy they are.

How are the pens grouped?[1]

How are the apples grouped?[2]

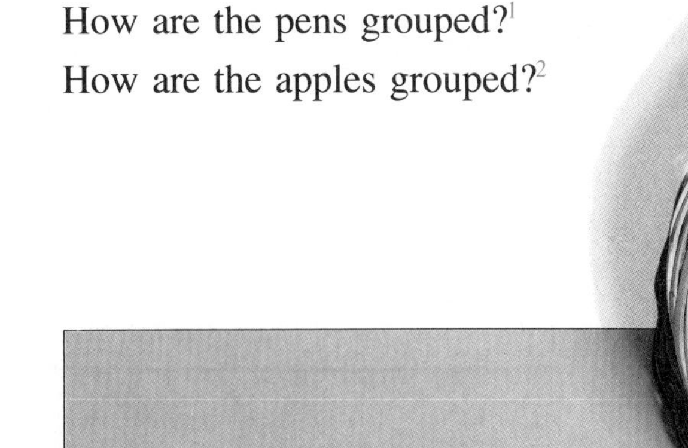

2 TEACH

Teaching Tips

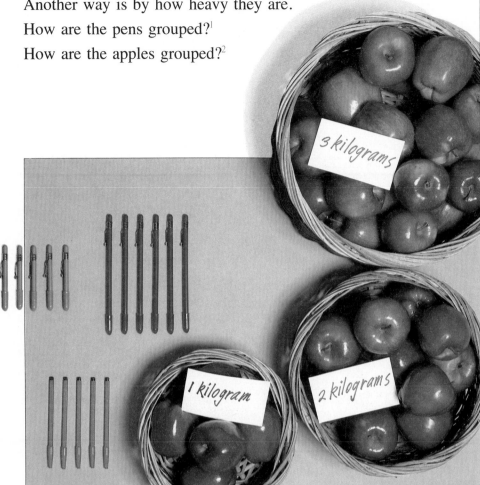

- Remind students of the *TRY THIS* on page 109, where they learned that objects can be grouped according to whether or not they float. Read pages 110–111 with the students and discuss other ways in which objects can be grouped (by shape, by color, by how long they are, by how heavy they are, and so on).
- Point out the picture of the buttons on page 110, and encourage students to discuss how they are grouped and other ways in which they could be grouped.
- Point out the picture of the pens and apples on page 111 and ask students to *describe* how they are grouped. Questions: **What objects have you seen that are grouped in the same way as the pens?** (Students might *name* drinking straws, toothpicks.) **What objects have you seen grouped like the apples?** (other fruits and vegetables)
- **Possible Misconception:** Some students might think that there are right and wrong classification schemes. Emphasize that there are many ways to group items, and that none are inherently right or wrong.

Special Education

Provide a large group of buttons for students with learning disabilities to sort. Include a variety of shapes, sizes, and colors. Have the students sort the buttons by color, by shape, by size, and by unusual characteristics. *CAUTION:* Remind students not to put buttons into their noses, ears, or mouths. When each student has demonstrated the ability to do simple sorting, have him/her sort objects by two characteristics, such as color and shape.

Enrichment

Extend the process of grouping by showing students that some objects can belong in more than one group. Collect objects of different shapes and colors. Place two hula hoops or jumpropes formed into circles on the floor. Overlap the circles. Begin by having the students place all of the objects that are round in one circle and all of the objects that are blue in the other circle. Direct students to place objects that are both round and blue in the area where the circles overlap.

Game Suggestion ♦

Play "In or Out of the Group." Begin by calling the students up one at a time and grouping them by a predetermined characteristic such as wearing shoes that tie or shirts with stripes. Do not tell the students the characteristic. Those who have the characteristic are "in the group"; those who do not are "out of the group." After several students have been grouped, encourage students to guess the characteristic that determined the grouping. Let students take turns thinking of a characteristic and naming the classmates who are "in" or "out" of the group. Encourage classmates to guess the characteristic.

TEACHING PLAN

Teaching Tip

• Direct the students' attention to the illustration on page 112. Encourage them to *describe* how the objects pictured might feel. Under the heading "Ways We Can Group Objects," list on the chalkboard the students' suggestions for grouping the objects.

3 ASSESS

Lesson Review

1. Answers might include shape, color, size, length, weight, or how things feel.
2. Answers could include by size, color, texture, or weight.
Challenge! Question: **What are three different ways you could group bicycles?** (color, size, make, shape of seat, and so on) **Thinking Skill:** *Suggesting alternatives*

Find Out

Students might answer that stores group clothing by item, color, style, size, or type. **Thinking Skill:** *Applying information to new situations*

[1] by size, shape, color, weight
[2] soft and hard; rough and smooth
[3] groups of soft objects and hard objects

How could you group these objects?[1]
Pretend you could touch them.
How would they feel?[2]
What groups could you make?[3]

Lesson Review

1. What are four ways to group things?
2. What are five ways to group rocks?

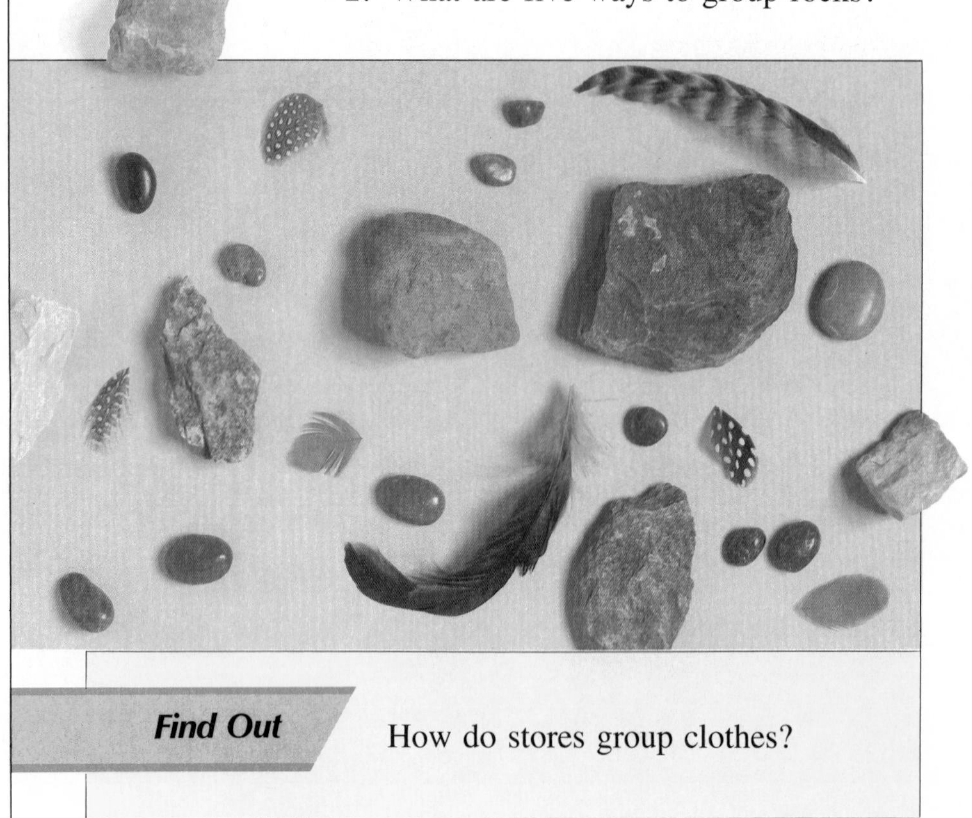

Find Out How do stores group clothes?

Teaching Options

SCIENCE ANECDOTE

Grouping is one of the roots of science. A scientist must be able to organize information into a useful form, and grouping allows him/her to do this. Great scientists, such as Newton and Einstein, were able to make new discoveries by recognizing relationships that others had overlooked.

Reteaching Suggestion ♦

Remind students that having things organized in groups is very important in everyday life. Take a walking tour of the school to find out how grouping is used at school. Include the library, cafeteria, nurse's office, textbook storage room, and principal's office on the tour. After returning to the classroom, have the students discuss the kinds of groupings they observed.

Workbook page 33 *

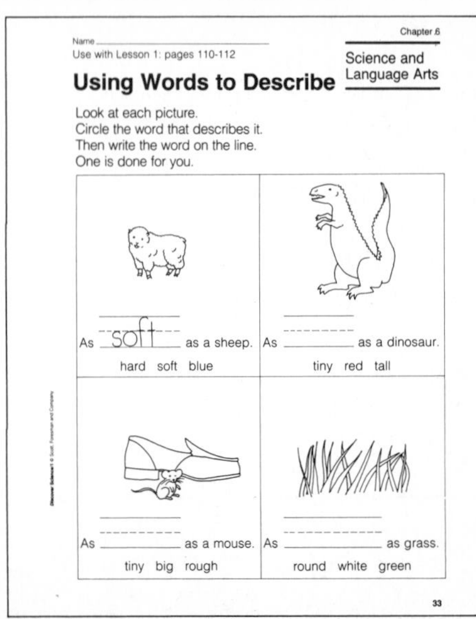

Name ______ Chapter 6
Use with Lesson 1: pages 110-112
Science and Language Arts

Using Words to Describe

Look at each picture.
Circle the word that describes it.
Then write the word on the line.
One is done for you.

As soft as a sheep. — hard soft blue
As ______ as a dinosaur. — tiny red tall
As ______ as a mouse. — tiny big rough
As ______ as grass. — round white green

33

♦ *Suitable as a language development activity*

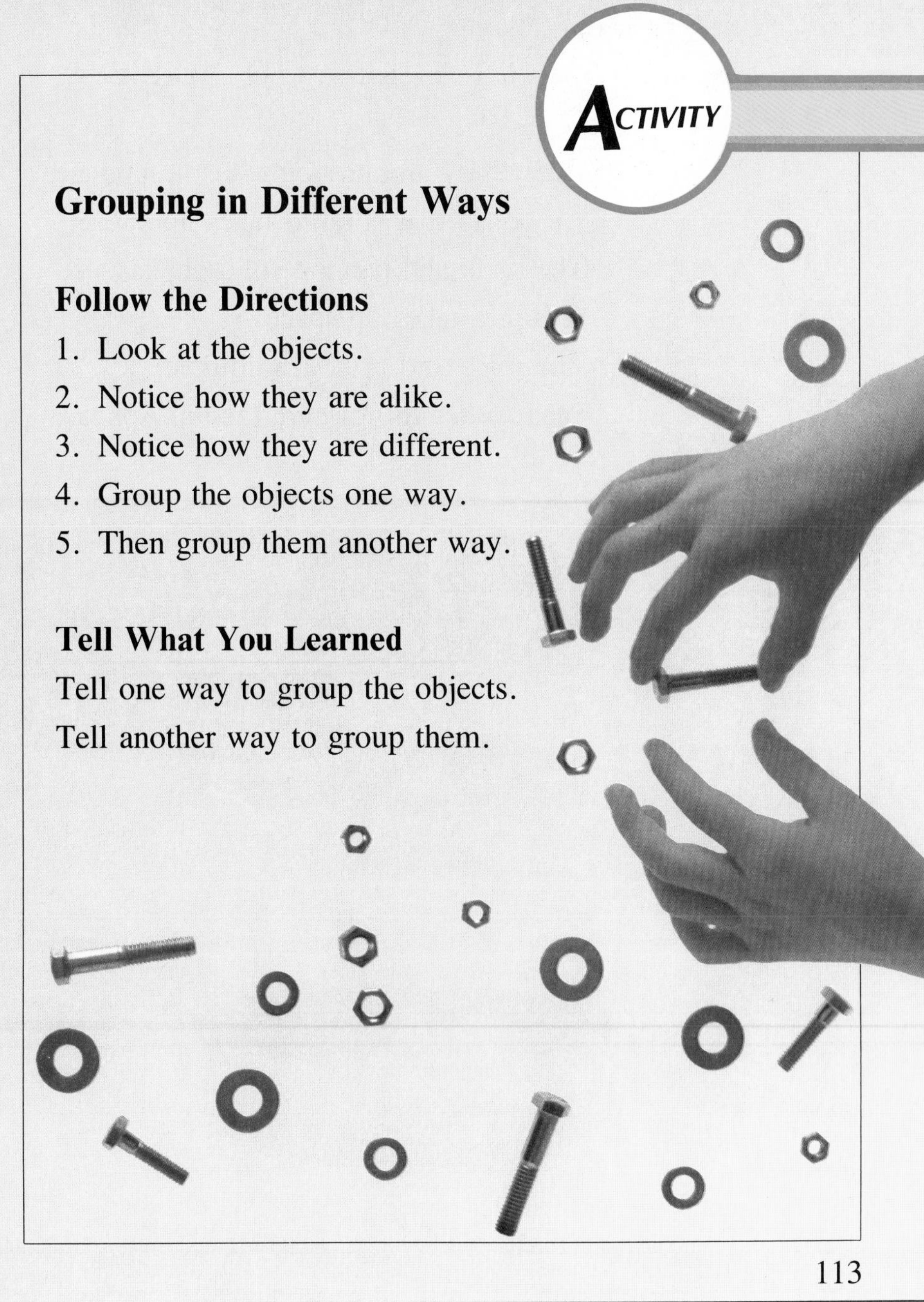

ACTIVITY
Grouping in Different Ways
Follow the Directions
1. Look at the objects.
2. Notice how they are alike.
3. Notice how they are different.
4. Group the objects one way.
5. Then group them another way.
Tell What You Learned
Tell one way to group the objects.
Tell another way to group them.
113

ACTIVITY PLAN

Concept
Objects with similar properties can be grouped together.

Objectives/Process Skills
- *Observe* a variety of objects.
- *Compare* and *contrast* the objects.
- *Classify* objects according to their properties.
- *Describe* how the objects were classified.

Time Allotment
Allow 15 minutes.

Materials
For each student: 10 assorted metal nuts, 10 assorted metal washers, 10 assorted metal bolts, 10 assorted metal screws

Safety Tip (See page T27.)
- Instruct students to handle sharp items such as nails and screws very carefully to avoid punctures or scrapes.

Teaching Tips
- Show students a collection of objects with similar properties (plastic, metal, wood). Discuss the similarities and differences. Explain to the students that there are many ways to sort the objects and that no one way is correct.
- Help students read the activity and follow the directions.
- Encourage students to explore a variety of ways to classify their objects such as size, length, shape, and so on.

Answers
Tell What You Learned.
For the first statement, students should explain one way that they grouped their collection (all nails together, all screws together, all bolts together, by length, by shape, by color, and so on). For the second statement, students should explain another way to group the collection.
Thinking Skill: *Restating or explaining ideas*

Enrichment Activity
Have students bring collections of objects from home to share with the class. These might be existing collections or ones that the students might collect and classify as a special project.

Activity Results
The nuts and bolts could be grouped in several ways. Possible groupings include: by size, by shape, by length, and by mass.

*** Answers to masters on pages 108E–108F**

TEACHING PLAN

LESSON 2
pages 114–115

Lesson Objective
- *State* that solids, liquids, and gases take up space and give one example of each.

Lesson Vocabulary
gas, liquid, space, solid

1 MOTIVATE

Demonstration Activity ♦
Place crumpled paper in the bottom of a drinking glass. Invert the glass, and push it straight down into a pan of water. Pull it straight out of the water and show the students the dry paper. Place the glass in the water again, tipping it to allow water to enter it.

Discussion
Point out that it is more difficult to see a gas taking up space than it is to see a solid or liquid. Question: **How can you tell that the glass was filled with air?** (Guide students to *conclude* that the air stayed inside the glass and the paper remained dry when the glass was placed straight down into the water; the air escaped, and was visible in the form of bubbles, when the glass was tipped.)

[1] all other pictured objects and containers

Lesson 2 What Takes Up Space?

Everything around you takes up **space.**
An object that is **solid** takes up space.
The book and pan are solid objects.
A **liquid** takes up space.
The juice and milk are liquids.
What other things here take up space?

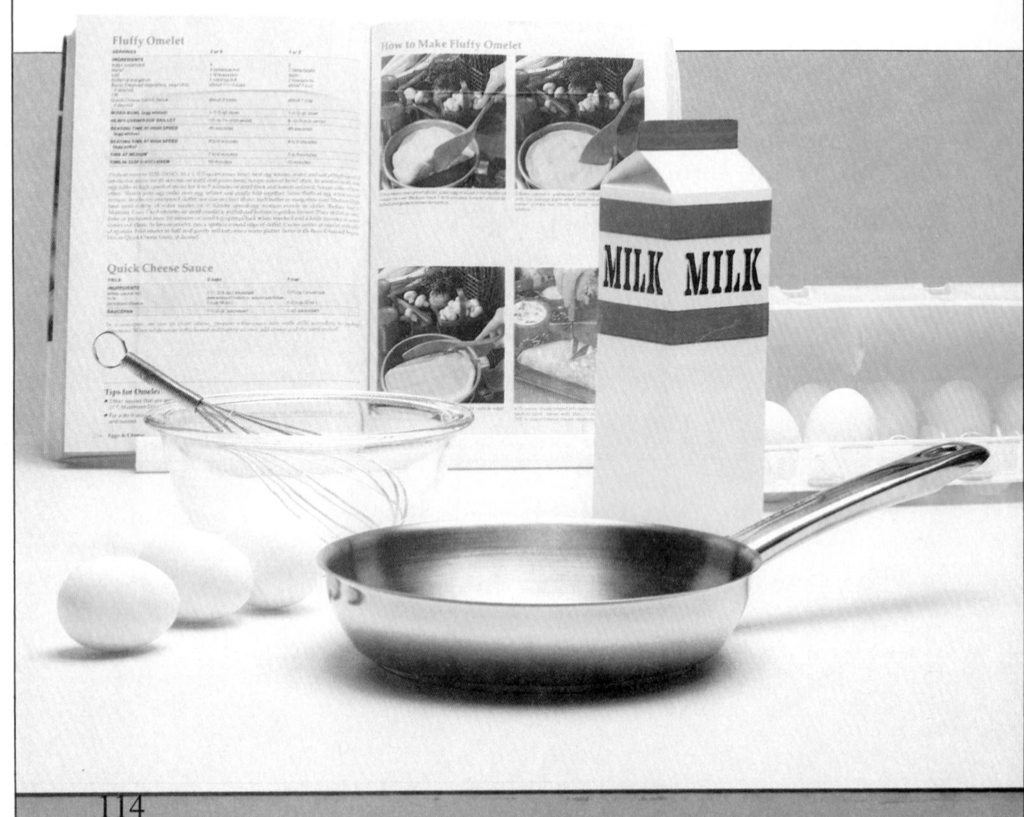

114

Teaching Options

SCIENCE BACKGROUND
The state of a substance depends on how strongly its particles are held together. In a solid, the particles are held together closely and strongly. As a result, a solid keeps a definite shape and volume. In a liquid, the particles are not held together as tightly as they are in a solid. The particles are held loosely and slide past one another. As a result, a liquid can flow. Thus, even though a liquid has a definite volume, it takes on the shape of its container. In a gas, the particles can move quickly in all directions. As a result, gases do not have a definite shape or volume. Instead, the container determines both their volume and shape.

Reinforcement
Give each student a clipboard made from a piece of heavy cardboard with a thick rubber band to hold paper and a pencil in place. Have the students divide their papers into three columns and to label the columns *Solids*, *Liquids*, and *Gases*. Take a walk around the school building and grounds to *observe* various forms of solids, liquids, and gases. Ask the students to list the items that they observed in the appropriate categories on their papers. After returning to the classroom, have the students *compare* and discuss their lists.

♦ ***Suitable as a language development activity***

What else takes up space?

A **gas** takes up space.

Air is made of gases.

Gases take up the space in this ball.

Lesson Review

1. What things take up space?
2. Name a solid, a liquid, and a gas.

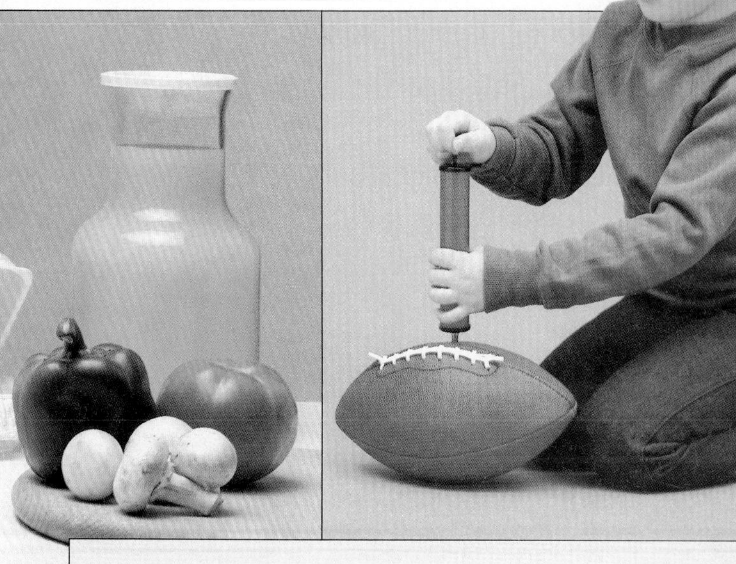

Find Out

What takes up the space in a shoe?
Is it a solid, liquid, or gas?

115

2 TEACH

Teaching Tips

- After reading pages 114 and 115, ask the students to *list* other examples of gases taking up space. (Answers may include the air in the classroom, helium in a balloon, and so on.)
- **Possible Misconception:** Many students think that the term "gas" refers only to the liquid fuel that is used to run an automobile. Remind them that a gas is a substance that is not a solid or a liquid.

3 ASSESS

Lesson Review

1. solids, liquids, gases
2. Answers will vary.

Challenge! Question: **What makes the water in a bath rise when you enter it?** (Space the body takes pushes the water up.) **Thinking Skill:** *Making inferences*

Find Out

A foot takes up the space in a shoe. The foot is solid. **Thinking Skill:** *Applying information to new situations*

Workbook page 34 *

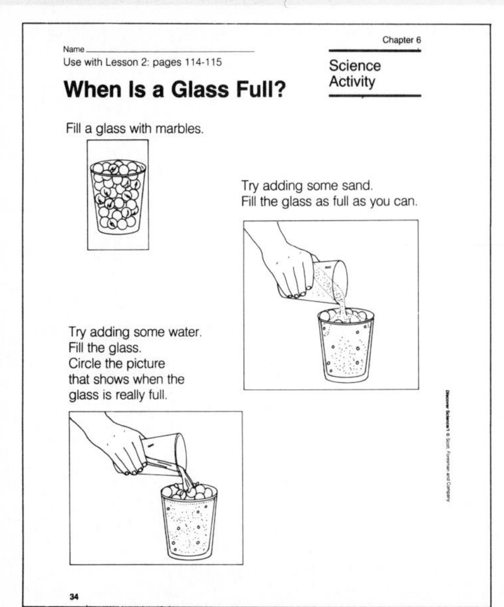

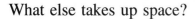

Name ______ Chapter 6
Use with Lesson 2: pages 114-115
Science Activity

When Is a Glass Full?

Fill a glass with marbles.

Try adding some sand.
Fill the glass as full as you can.

Try adding some water.
Fill the glass.
Circle the picture that shows when the glass is really full.

34

Special Education

For students with learning disabilities, provide a variety of experiences that introduce the properties of gases, liquids, and solids within a natural environment. For example, to illustrate the properties of water in its three states, demonstrate the progression of water from solid (ice cube) to liquid (water/melted ice) to gas (steam). Observe the student's reactions and discuss the properties. *CAUTION:* Immediately wipe up any water that spills on the floor. When heating water, use a Pyrex container. Do not allow students to approach water as it is heated or handle the container until it is completely cooled.

Reteaching Suggestion ♦

Tell students that solids, liquids, and gases all take up space and give an example of each. If the classroom has an aquarium, have the students observe it. Question: **What takes up space?** Students should identify solids (fish, plants, rocks), liquids (water), and gases (bubbles in the water, air at the top of the water).

***** *Answers to masters on pages 108E–108F***

TEACHING PLAN

LESSON 3
pages 116–117

Lesson Objectives
- *Describe* the size and shape of liquids and solids.
- *State* that solids and liquids can be mixed together.

Lesson Vocabulary
liquid, solid

1 MOTIVATE

Demonstration Activity ♦
Have the students *observe* as you place a small object, such as an inch cube, into containers of various shapes. Then have them *observe* as you pour a cup of water into each of the containers.

Discussion
Questions: **What happened to the solid when it was moved from container to container?** (Accept reasonable responses.) **Did it change size?** (No.) **Shape?** (No.) Help the students understand that a solid has a definite shape. Have the students *describe* what happened to the water. Be sure they understand that the amount of water stayed the same, but its shape changed.

[1] Solids are round and oblong.
[2] Liquids are shaped by their containers.

Lesson 3 What Are Solids and Liquids Like?

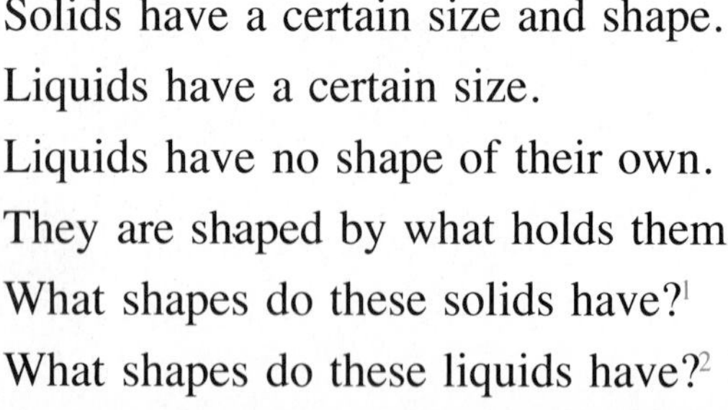

Solids have a certain size and shape.
Liquids have a certain size.
Liquids have no shape of their own.
They are shaped by what holds them.
What shapes do these solids have?[1]
What shapes do these liquids have?[2]

116

Teaching Options

SCIENCE BACKGROUND

Heating breaks the bonds that hold molecules of a solid or a liquid together. This results in the material changing from one physical state to another. For example, the main raw material in the manufacture of glass is sand. In any form of glass manufacturing, the first step is the melting together of the sand and other raw materials. Heat helps glass blowers shape a variety of objects, such as bottles, laboratory flasks, tubes for neon signs, and glass art objects.

Enrichment

Obtain several clear plastic containers with lids. Into each of half of the containers, place a small solid, using sand or a powder for one of the solids. Into each of the other containers, pour a different liquid. *CAUTION*: Do not select liquids that might be harmful or irritating if students should spill them. Immediately wipe up any liquid that spills on the floor to prevent slipping accidents. Tightly close the containers, and pass them around the classroom, encouraging students to tip them slowly to *observe* what happens. Discuss the contents of the jars and have students group them according to whether the contents are solids or liquids.

♦ ***Suitable as a language development activity***

[1] Liquids will take on the shapes of their new containers.

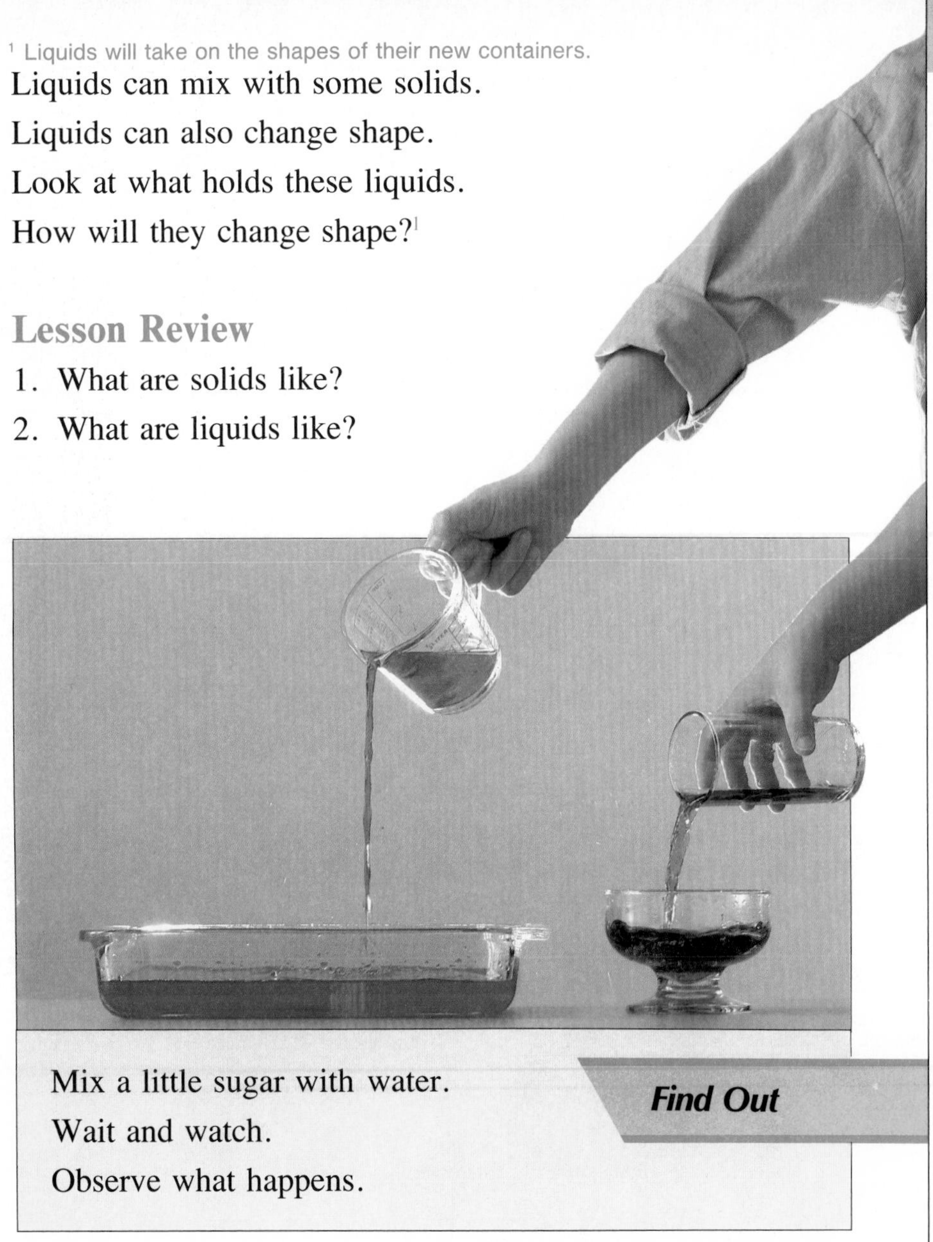

Liquids can mix with some solids.

Liquids can also change shape.

Look at what holds these liquids.

How will they change shape?[1]

Lesson Review

1. What are solids like?
2. What are liquids like?

Find Out

Mix a little sugar with water.

Wait and watch.

Observe what happens.

2 TEACH

Teaching Tip

• **Possible Misconception:** Students might think that the state of matter cannot change. To reinforce the fact that the state of matter does change, remind them of an ice cube, which becomes liquid water if melted and water vapor when boiled.

3 ASSESS

Lesson Review

1. Solids have a certain size and shape.
2. Liquids change shape to fit their container, have a certain size, and can mix with some solids.

Challenge! Question: **How can you change liquid water to a solid?** (freeze it) **Thinking Skill:** *Applying information to new situations*

Find Out

Sugar mixes with the water. **Thinking Skills:** *Observing, Communicating*

Workbook page 35 *

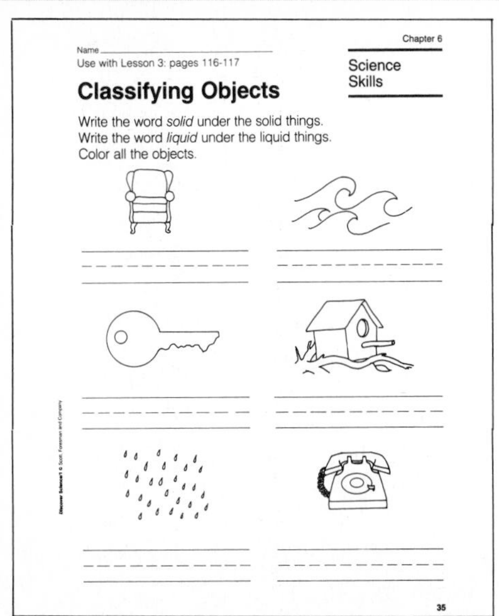

Name ____________ Chapter 6
Use with Lesson 3: pages 116-117
Science Skills

Classifying Objects

Write the word *solid* under the solid things.
Write the word *liquid* under the liquid things.
Color all the objects.

35

*** Answers to masters on pages 108E-108F**

Special Education

The mixing of sugar and water might confuse some students: a teaspoon of sugar may seem like a liquid because it is pourable and takes on the shape of the spoon like a liquid. Therefore, it is important to point out that a teaspoon of sugar is not one solid, but hundreds of sugar granules. Isolate one granule of sugar to show students with learning disabilities. Point out that the quantity and shape of the granule do not change when placed in a container alone.

Reteaching Suggestion ♦

Have students pour water into a variety of containers to observe how its shape changes. *CAUTION:* Immediately wipe up any water that spills to prevent slipping accidents. Provide small objects for the students to manipulate. Discuss the characteristics of the solids and the liquids.

LESSON 4
pages 118–119

Lesson Objective
- *State* that gases have no definite size or shape, and can change size and shape.

1 MOTIVATE

Demonstration Activity ♦
As students watch, blow up a balloon. Slowly release some of the air from the balloon and let the students feel the air movement. *CAUTION:* Cover goggles should be worn.

Discussion
Discuss with the students what filled the balloon (gases) and have them describe the shape. Questions: **What happened when the gases were released from the balloon?** (The balloon's size and shape changed.) **Could you see anything?** (the size and shape of the balloon changing) **Did you feel anything?** (the movement of air as it escaped the balloon) **Did you hear anything?** (the sound of air escaping the balloon)

[1] The balloons inflated to various sizes and shapes.

Lesson 4 What Are Gases Like?

A gas has no special size.
A gas has no special shape.
A gas can change size and shape.
Gases filled these balloons.
How did the balloons change?[1]

Teaching Options

SCIENCE BACKGROUND

Air is a mixture of such gases as nitrogen, oxygen, carbon dioxide, and water vapor. As air is cooled the gas molecules slow down and move closer together. First, the water vapor condenses into liquid water. Next, at lower temperatures, the carbon dioxide changes into solid dry ice without becoming a liquid. At very low temperatures, the nitrogen and oxygen change to liquids. Molecules of some gases are lighter or heavier than air. Balloons filled with helium float in the air, and a submarine can be made to float in water by regulating the amount of air (gases) in its tanks.

Reinforcement

Instruct the students to "capture' air (gases) in small self-sealing plastic bags. *CAUTION:* Use only bags that are too small to present a suffocation hazard. Help students learn about safety by discussing the rules associated with using larger plastic bags. (Never place a plastic bag over anyone's head.) Direct students to blow into their bags and to seal them (provide assistance with sealing if necessary).Point out that gases take up space, are the shape of the container (bag) and cannot be seen. If the bags are not too full, have the students squeeze them gently to *observe* the changes in shape.

♦ ***Suitable as a language development activity***

[1] gases (air) moving as wind

You cannot see most gases.
You can smell many gases.
You can feel a moving gas.
What would you feel here?[1]

Lesson Review

1. What size and shape do gases have?
2. How can a gas change?

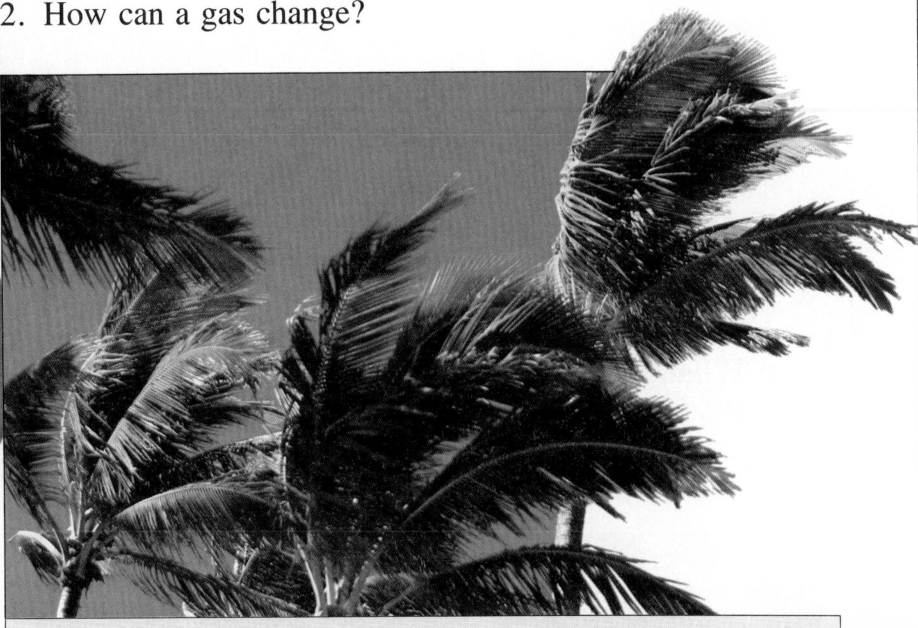

Find Out

Put a paper clip on your desk.
Blow through a straw.
Make the paper clip move.

2 TEACH

Teaching Tips

- **Possible Misconception:** Some students might think gases do not exist since most gases are invisible. Remind them of the demonstration activity, where they felt the movement of gases and saw evidence of it taking up space.
- Read pages 118 and 119 with the students to learn about the characteristics of gases. Discuss the different shapes gases will become when filling the balloons in the illustration on page 118.

3 ASSESS

Lesson Review

1. no certain size or shape
2. can change its size and shape

Challenge! Question: **How does gas make a sailboat move?** (Air is a gas. Wind is moving air, and air makes a sailboat move.) **Thinking Skill:** *Drawing conclusions*

Find Out

Students should note that gas bubbles are usually round. **Thinking Skills:** *Observing, Communicating*

Workbook page 36 *

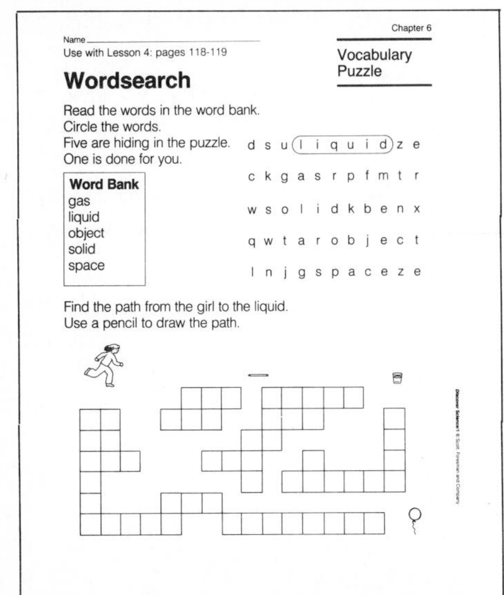

Name
Use with Lesson 4: pages 118-119

Chapter 6
Vocabulary Puzzle

Wordsearch

Read the words in the word bank.
Circle the words.
Five are hiding in the puzzle.
One is done for you.

Word Bank
gas
liquid
object
solid
space

d s u l i q u i d z e
c k g a s r p f m t r
w s o l i d k b e n x
q w t a r o b j e c t
l n j g s p a c e z e

Find the path from the girl to the liquid.
Use a pencil to draw the path.

36

* *Answers to masters on pages 108E-108F*

Special Education

For students who have learning disabilities, provide a dish containing 1/4 cup vinegar and 1 tablespoon of baking soda. Direct them to add a pinch of the baking soda to the vinegar, and to *observe* the reaction of mixing these two substances. Then, have them add the remainder of the baking soda. Encourage students to discuss and *describe* what they saw, felt, and heard. The students should recognize and state that they were mixing a liquid and a solid to make a gas. *CAUTION:* Have students wear cover goggles. Immediately wipe up any vinegar that spills on the floor to prevent accidents.

Reteaching Suggestion ♦

Provide the students with balloons of different shapes and sizes and instruct them to blow them up. Lead a discussion about what takes up space in the balloons and note what happens. Encourage the students to summarize the experience by naming the characteristics of gases. *CAUTION:* Make certain that students wear cover goggles during this activity.

ACTIVITY PLAN

Concept
Mixing a solid and a liquid can make a gas that will inflate a balloon.

Objectives/Process Skills
- *Observe* what happens when vinegar and baking soda are mixed.
- *Describe* how the balloon changed.
- *Infer* what caused the balloon to inflate.

Time Allotment
Allow 15 minutes.

Materials
For each pair of students: 1 small mouth, plastic bottle; white vinegar, baking soda, 1 large balloon, 1 small funnel, measuring cup

Safety Tips (See page T27.)
- Remind students to immediately wipe up any liquid that spills on the floor to prevent slipping accidents.
- Instruct students to wear cover goggles at all times during this activity.

Teaching Tips
- **Helpful Hint:** Have students cover their desks with newspapers to aid cleanup.
- Instruct students not to tip the baking soda into the bottle until the balloon is securely over the neck of the bottle.
- Show students an empty balloon and an empty bottle. Question: **If you place the balloon on the bottle, how can you inflate it?** Explain that they are going to mix a liquid and a solid together to see if they can make the balloon inflate when it is on the bottle.
- Have one student hold the bottle while the other works with the balloon.

Answers
Tell What You Learned
For the first statement, students should state that the balloon inflated. For the second statement, answers will vary, but should refer to a change resulting from the liquid and solid mixing to form a gas that inflated the balloon. **Thinking Skill:** *Inferring*

Wear cover goggles for this activity.

Blowing Up a Balloon

Follow the Directions
1. Measure the liquid.
2. Pour it into the plastic bottle.
3. Put the powder in the balloon.
4. Put the balloon on the bottle.
5. Tip the powder into the bottle.
6. Observe the balloon.

Tell What You Learned
Tell how the balloon changed.
Tell what you think filled it up

1.

2.

3.

4.

120

Activity Results
The baking soda-and-vinegar mixture produces a gas that inflates the balloon.

Enrichment Activity
Pour the liquid from one bottle into a hallow dish. Place the dish in a sunny location (if available). After the water evaporates, the students should notice a white powder in the dish. Explain that the white powder was dissolved in the liquid. After the liquid evaporated, the white powder remained in the dish.

Dr. Isabella Karle

Isabella Karle built a machine.

It showed parts of things too tiny to see.

Dr. Karle used the machine to learn.

She studied tiny parts of gases.

She studied solids and liquids.

Dr. Karle made important discoveries.

What Do You Think?

How can studying help with discoveries?

121

TEACHING PLAN

SCIENCE AND PEOPLE

Discussion

Remind students of the importance of observation in science. Explain that scientists use special equipment to help with their observations. Question: **What objects do scientists use to help them learn?** (microscope, hand lenses, telescope, X-ray machine, and so on) Discuss how each object helps the scientist.

Teaching Tips

- Write "Dr. Isabella Karle" on the chalkboard and help the students to pronounce and read the name. Tell them that Dr. Karle is a scientist who invented a special machine.
- Read page 121 with the students to find out about the machine she invented. Question: **What would you like to observe in the machine that Dr. Karle invented?** (Answers might include: motor, size, shape, number of parts, and so on.)

Answers

What do you think?

Students might say that you learn more, which can lead to making new discoveries. **Thinking Skill:** *Making generalizations*

Teaching Options

Books to Read

Noble, Iris. *Contemporary Women Scientists of America*. Messner, 1979. (for the teacher)

SCIENCE BACKGROUND

Isabella Lugoski Karle was born in Detroit, Michigan. She received her B.S. in physical chemistry there in 1944. She and her husband, Jerome Karle, worked with Lawrence Brudeway, a professor at the University of Michigan, in experiments using gases. As a result of their work, Isabella designed and built with her own hands an electron diffraction apparatus—a huge, costly, and sophisticated machine. Working at the Naval Research Laboratory, she used the machine to identify and analyze a substance in wood that chemists were then able to produce synthetically. A similar product she identified was found to be an excellent dip for wood, making it resistant to wood borers.

TEACHING PLAN

SKILLS FOR SOLVING PROBLEMS
pages 122–123

Purpose
To develop the skills of collecting and organizing information using rulers to solve problems.

Materials
For each student: paper clips, toothpicks, paper, ruler

1 MOTIVATE

Discussion
Discuss with students the importance of measurement in everyday life. Ask them to *describe* situations in which they observed the use of measurement, and to *explain* why the measurements were important. (doctor's office—to determine whether appropriate growth is occurring; in sewing—to ensure properly sized and proportioned garments; in carpentry—to ensure properly sized items; and so on)

Skills for Solving Problems

Measuring Solid Objects

What ways can you measure solids?

1. Measure how long each solid object is. Measure with a ruler.

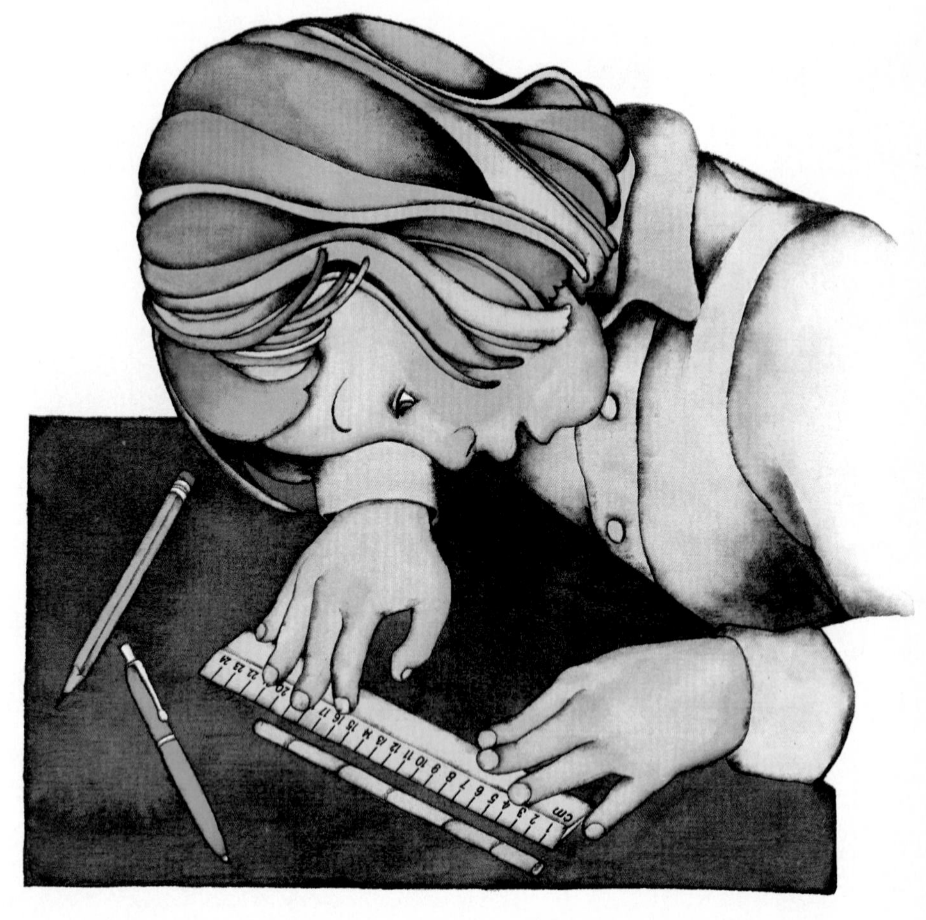

Teaching Options

SCIENCE BACKGROUND

The length of anything can be described in drinking straw lengths, paper clip lengths, or toothpick lengths. Each of these objects is considered an arbitrary (or capricious) unit of measure. Arbitrary units serve a useful function as long as similar units are being used by others. Thus, when the need to communicate or translate data becomes necessary, the two parties will understand one another. If one person measures something in a unit that no one else is familiar with, no communication can take place. We each need to know something about the arbitrary unit being used. For example, a person may be seven soda straws tall. Having seen a soda straw, one can visualize his/her height.

2. Use your own paper.
   Draw each solid object.
   How long is each solid object?
   Write the numbers.

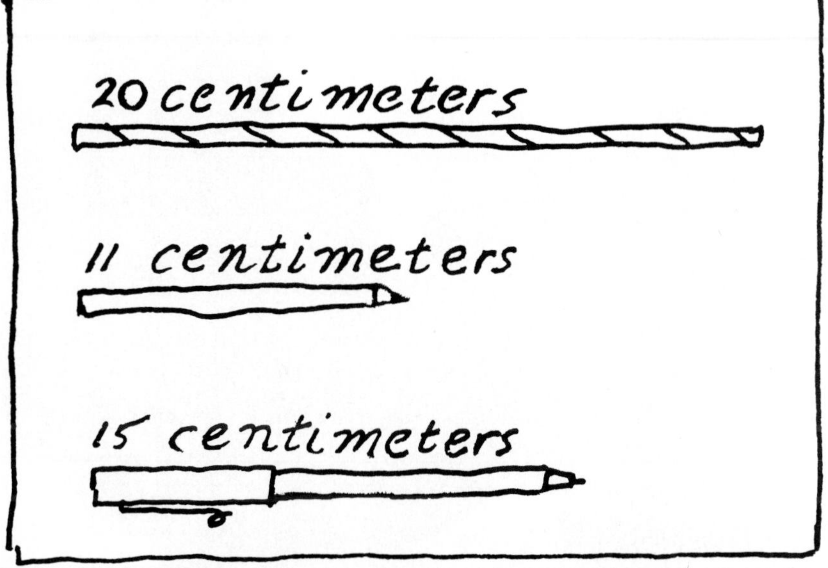

3. Look at the numbers.
   Which object is the longest?
   Which object is the shortest?

123

2 TEACH

Teaching Tips

- Direct students to carefully align the ruler with the end of the object being measured.
- To extend the activity, encourage students to measure each object with paper clips. Instruct the students to place the end of a paper clip next to one end of the object being measured. Have the students continue laying the paper clips end to end. Then have the students count the total number of paper clips to find the total length of the object. Instruct the students to record the two measurements for each object and to *compare* the paper clip and ruler measurements for each item. Point out that, although different measurements were obtained with different methods of measuring, the items measured are the same size.

3 ASSESS

Answer will vary depending on the objects measured.

Resource Book page 47 *

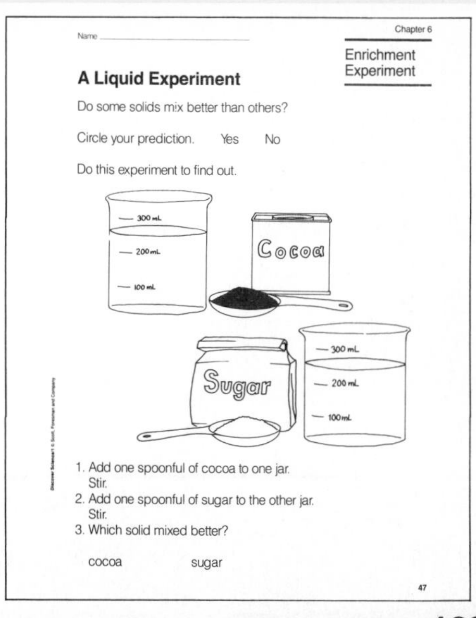
Name ____________ Chapter 6

Enrichment Experiment

A Liquid Experiment

Do some solids mix better than others?

Circle your prediction. Yes No

Do this experiment to find out.

1. Add one spoonful of cocoa to one jar. Stir.
2. Add one spoonful of sugar to the other jar. Stir.
3. Which solid mixed better?

cocoa sugar

47

*** Answers to masters on pages 108E–108F**

REVIEW PLAN

CHAPTER 6 REVIEW
pages 124–125

Review Chapter Ideas
1. Answers should include size, shape, and color.
2. Solids, liquids, and gases take up space.
3. Gases take up space and are shaped by their container. Air is made of gases you cannot see.
4. Solids take up space and have their own shape.
5. Liquids take up space and change in shape to fit a container.

For further review, use Study Guide page 233.

Chapter 6 Review

Review Chapter Ideas
1. Look at the picture of blocks. Name three ways to group them.
2. Tell what takes up space.
3. Describe a gas.
4. Describe a solid.
5. Describe a liquid.

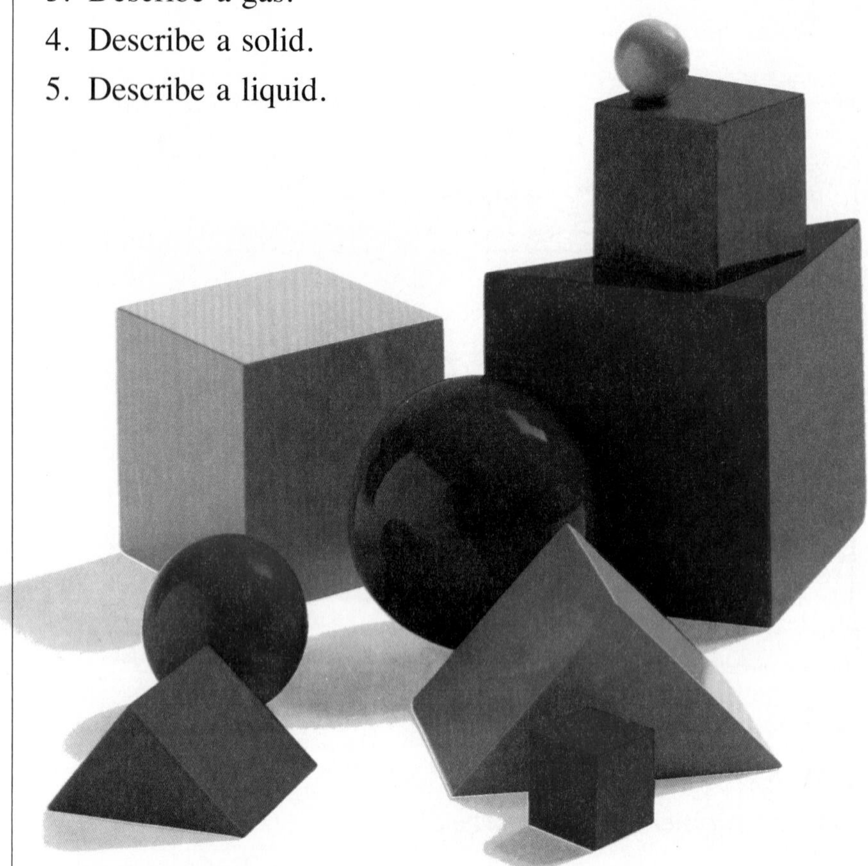

124

Review Options

Cooperative Learning ♦

STAD Format (see page T23.)
Assign students to work in four- to five-member teams to study Chapter 6 Review. Students should work together to make sure that they and their teammates know the material in the chapter. After students have had enough time to study together, give them a test to complete individually (Chapter 6 Test in the *Test Book*). Award Superteam certificates to teams whose average test scores exceed 90% and Greatteam certificates to teams whose average test scores exceed 80%.

♦ ***Suitable as a language development activity***

Review Science Words

Match the words and the pictures.

1. solid
2. liquid
3. gas

a. 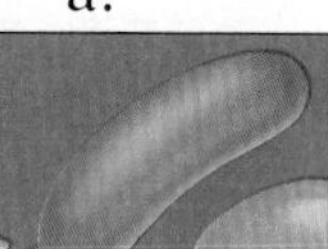

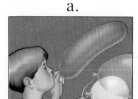

b. 

c. 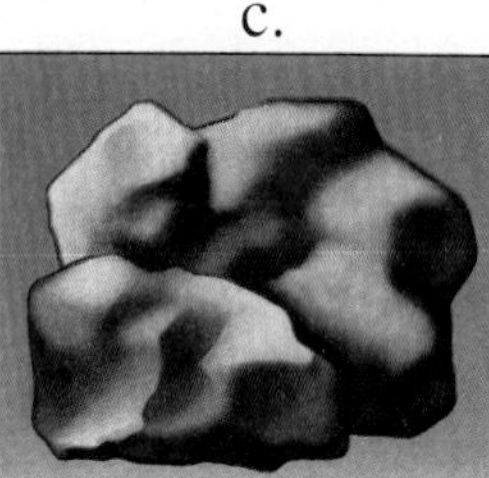

Tell what the words mean.

4. objects
5. space

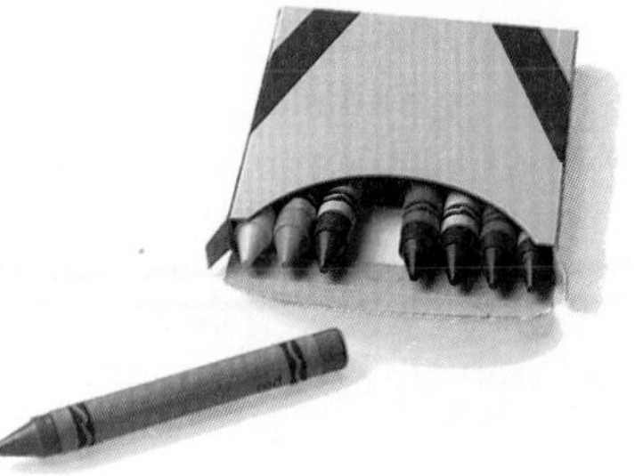

Use Science Ideas

Tell how this solid will change.

Review Science Words

Match the words and the pictures.

1. c
2. b
3. a

Tell what the words mean.
Thinking Skill: *Restating or explaining ideas*
4. Object—something that can be seen or touched.
5. Space—the amount of room something takes up.

Use Science Ideas

The solid will take up the space in the box between the two crayons. **Thinking Skill:** *Predicting*

Test Book page 23 *

Name

Chapter 6 Test

Grouping

I. Write **Yes** or **No.**

1. Can objects be grouped in different ways?
2. Does air take up space?
3. Do liquids stay the same shape?
4. Can solids and liquids be mixed?
5. Do gases change size and shape?

II. Draw a line from the word to the right picture.

1. solid 2. liquid 3. gas

23

*** Answers to masters on pages 108E-108F**

Teaching Plan

Chapter Components	Skills	Materials
Chapter Opener/*TRY THIS:* Using Different Light pp. 126-127	***TRY THIS*** p. 127 **Science Process Skills** *Measuring, Observing*	***TRY THIS*** p. 127 (group of 30) 30 books, 3 lamps of varying light intensities
Lesson 1: How Can Light Change? pp. 128-130	**Thinking Skills** Challenge!: *Drawing Conclusions* Find Out: *Restating or explaining ideas*	**Demonstration** p. 128 flashlight
Activity: Making Shadows p. 131	**Science Process Skills** *Observing, Inferring*	(groups of 10) 3 slide projectors, 1 roll masking tape, 9 sheets cardboard (1 meter square) 3 large sheets white tissue paper
Lesson 2: How Can Sound Change? pp. 132-134	**Thinking Skills** Challenge!: *Applying information to new situations* Find Out: *Recognizing relevant information and data*	**Demonstration** p. 132 no materials needed
Activity: Listening to Sound p. 135	**Science Process Skills** *Communicating, Observing*	(individual) 30 stainless steel spoons, 30 meters string
Lesson 3: What Can You Learn About Heat? pp. 136-138	**Thinking Skills** Challenge!: *Comparing, Contrasting* Find Out: *Applying information to new situations*	**Demonstration** p. 136 ball of modeling clay for each student
Science in Your Life: Using a Different Thermometer p. 139	**Thinking Skills** *Making generalizations*	
Skills for Solving Problems: Using a Thermometer pp. 140-141	**Problem Solving Skills** *Making decisions/Identifying and solving problems, Interpreting charts, maps, and graphs*	
Chapter Review pp. 142-143	**Thinking Skills** *Restating or explaining ideas, Making inferences*	

Teaching Options

Strategies	Extensions		Resource Masters
			Family Letter: *Resource Book* p. 51 Vocabulary Preview: *Workbook* pp. 37-38
	Enrichment p. 128 Game Suggestion p. 129 Science and Math p. 129	Special Education p. 130 Reteaching Suggestion p. 130	Science Activity: *Workbook* p. 39
	Enrichment Activity p. 131		
	Reinforcement p. 132 Enrichment p. 133 Special Education p. 133	Science and Art p. 133 Reteaching Suggestion p. 134	Science Skill: *Workbook* p. 40
	Enrichment Activity p. 131		
	Special Education p. 136 Enrichment p. 137 Science and Social Studies p. 137 Reteaching Suggestion p. 138		Science and Reading: *Workbook* p. 41 Vocabulary Puzzle: *Workbook* p. 42
			Enrichment Experiment: *Resource Book* p. 55
Cooperative Learning p. 142 (Also see p. T23.)			Chapter Test: *Test Book* p. 25

Preteaching Suggestions

For Advance Preparation

TRY THIS, page 127
For each group of students, provide a flashlight, a light with a small bulb, and a light with a large bulb.

Demonstration, page 128
You will need a flashlight for this demonstration. You might use a flashlight from the Try This activity on page 127.

Activity, page 131
Obtain a filmstrip or slide projector, white cloth or paper, and a variety of objects that block light.

Activity, page 135
Provide a spoon and a piece of string one yard long for each student.

Demonstration, page 136
Provide a ball of modeling clay for each student.

For Vocabulary Review

Use the following sentences with your students to review the meanings of the underlined words.

1. The air is made of many gases you cannot see.
2. Water, milk, juices, and other things that pour are liquids.
3. Books, bread, furniture, and other things that feel hard are solids.

For High-Potential Students

Ask high-potential students to cut out pictures in magazines that illustrate the roles light, sound, and heat play in our everyday lives. Let students arrange these pictures to create a bulletin board display with a section on each of the three topics.

For Mainstreamed Students

Visually Impaired
Provide students with a sound-effects tape that recreates certain sounds. Have the students listen to the tape and name the sounds and their origins.

Help blind students understand the concepts of brightness and dimness by comparing brightness to turning the volume of a radio up and dimness to turning the volume down.

Hearing Impaired
Have students look at the text illustrations on pages 132–134. Point to one object at a time and indicate whether or not the object makes any sound. Provide students with examples of objects that make sound when struck together (cymbals, two blocks, a triangle and wand). Give students examples of items in nature that make sound when they come in contact with each other, such as the wind that blows tree leaves, water in a brook splashing over pebbles, and a crickets' legs rubbing against each other. Point out that students can feel the vibrations from some sounds, such as heavy footsteps or music from radio or stereo speakers.

For Science Fair Projects

Encourage interested students to do one of the following projects:

1. Collect a variety of objects and test them to determine whether they block or transmit light. Make a display showing the results.
2. Investigate differences in pitch. Fill ten or more identical bottles with different amounts of water. Use a spoon to tap the sides of the bottles and listen to the differences in pitch. Use the bottles to play familiar tunes or write new ones. Transcribe the tunes by numbering the bottles and writing down the numbers in the sequence in which the bottles should be tapped.

Classroom Resources

Bulletin Board
Encourage students to bring in pictures to add to the bulletin board that show people using light, heat, and sound.

HOW DO YOU USE LIGHT, HEAT, AND SOUND?

Chapter 7 Poster

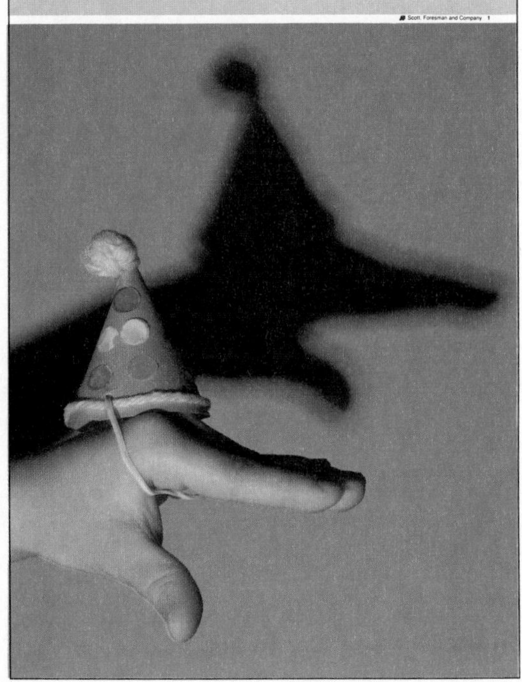

How can you make shadows?

Science Discovery Center
Use pages from Chapter 7 in the *Science Discovery Center Book*. Place these worksheets in the appropriate pockets in the Science Discovery Center.

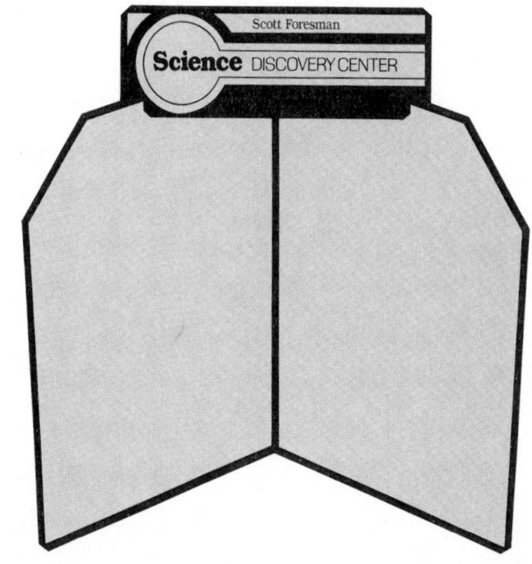

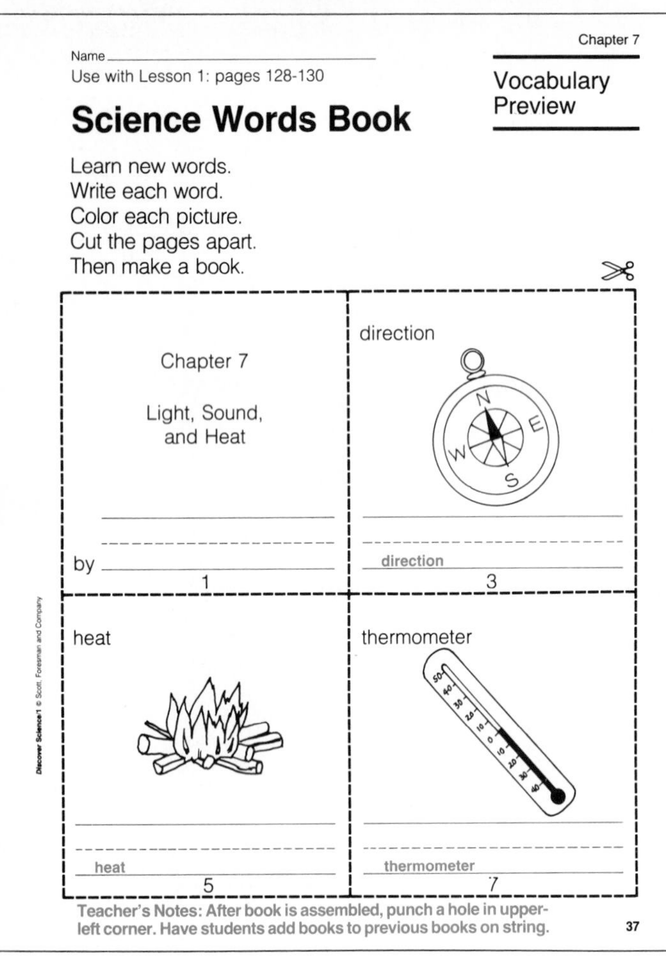

Chapter 7

Name ______________________

Use with Lesson 1: pages 128-130

Vocabulary Preview

Science Words Book

Learn new words.
Write each word.
Color each picture.
Cut the pages apart.
Then make a book.

Teacher's Notes: After book is assembled, punch a hole in upper-left corner. Have students add books to previous books on string.

37

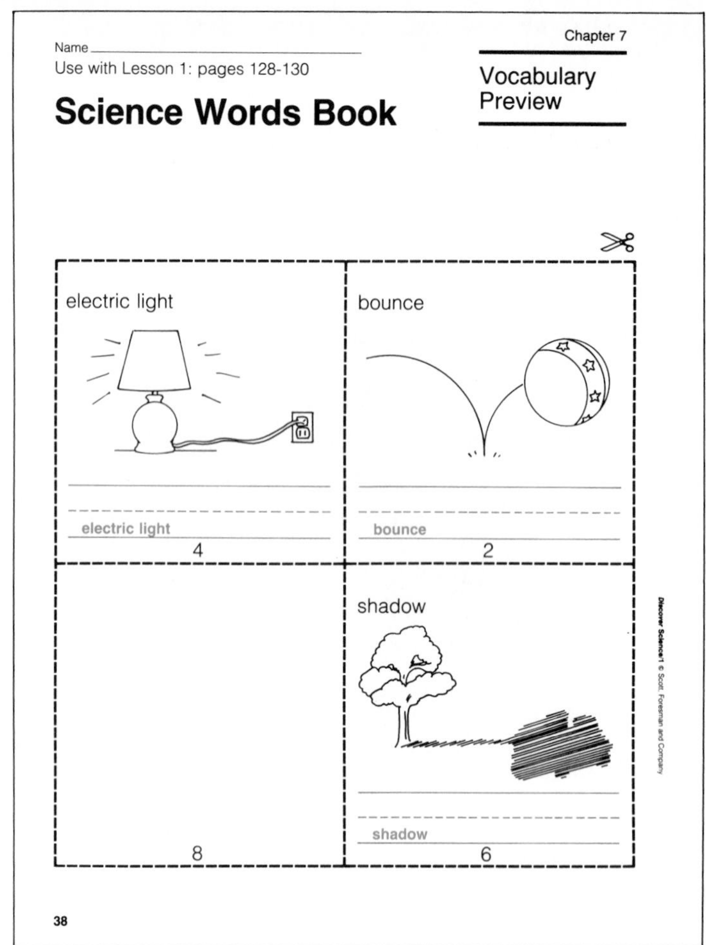

Chapter 7

Name ______________________

Use with Lesson 1: pages 128-130

Vocabulary Preview

Science Words Book

38

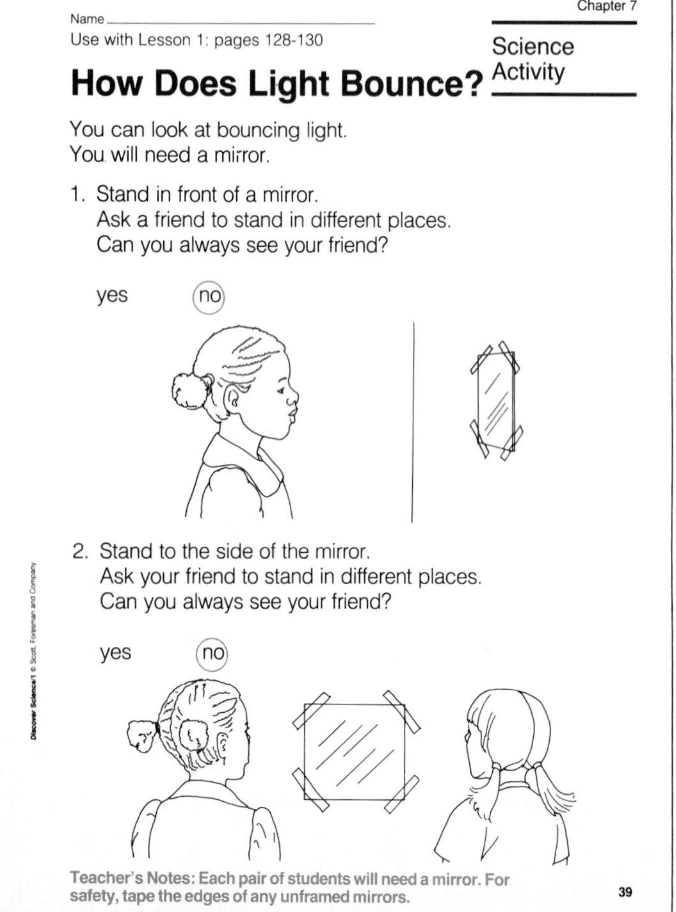

Chapter 7

Name ______________________

Use with Lesson 1: pages 128-130

Science Activity

How Does Light Bounce?

You can look at bouncing light.
You will need a mirror.

1. Stand in front of a mirror.
   Ask a friend to stand in different places.
   Can you always see your friend?

   yes (no)

2. Stand to the side of the mirror.
   Ask your friend to stand in different places.
   Can you always see your friend?

   yes (no)

Teacher's Notes: Each pair of students will need a mirror. For safety, tape the edges of any unframed mirrors.

39

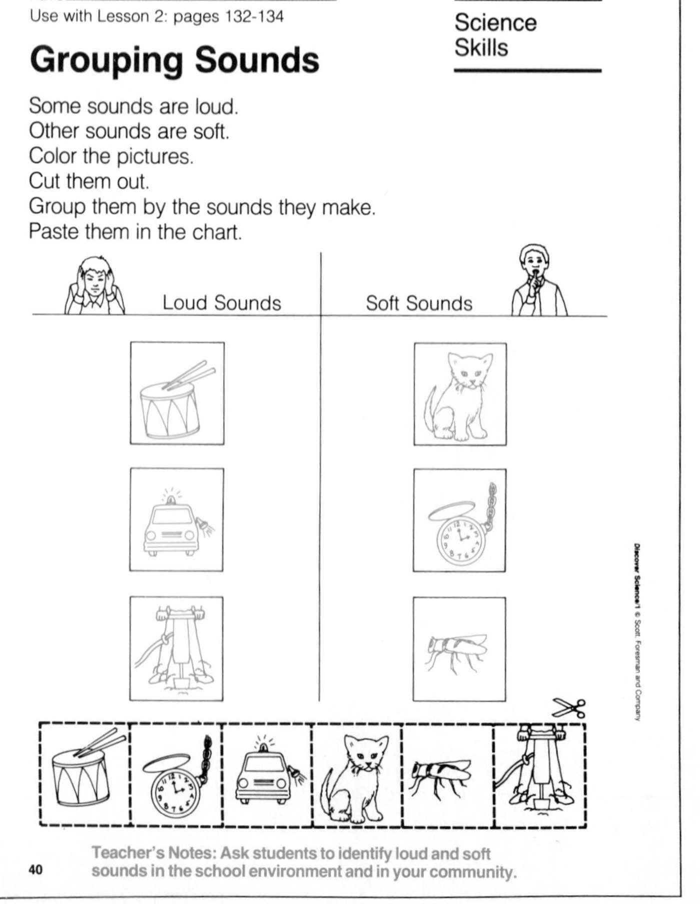

Chapter 7

Name ______________________

Use with Lesson 2: pages 132-134

Science Skills

Grouping Sounds

Some sounds are loud.
Other sounds are soft.
Color the pictures.
Cut them out.
Group them by the sounds they make.
Paste them in the chart.

Teacher's Notes: Ask students to identify loud and soft sounds in the school environment and in your community.

40

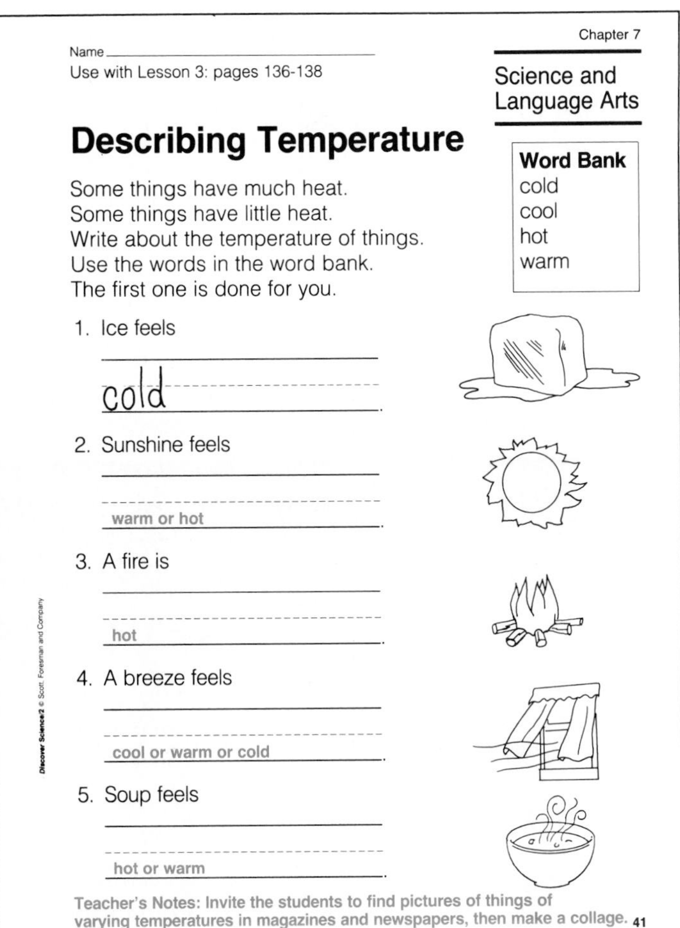

Name ____________
Use with Lesson 3: pages 136-138

Chapter 7

Science and Language Arts

Describing Temperature

Word Bank
cold
cool
hot
warm

Some things have much heat.
Some things have little heat.
Write about the temperature of things.
Use the words in the word bank.
The first one is done for you.

1. Ice feels
   cold.
2. Sunshine feels
   warm or hot.
3. A fire is
   hot.
4. A breeze feels
   cool or warm or cold.
5. Soup feels
   hot or warm.

Teacher's Notes: Invite the students to find pictures of things of varying temperatures in magazines and newspapers, then make a collage. 41

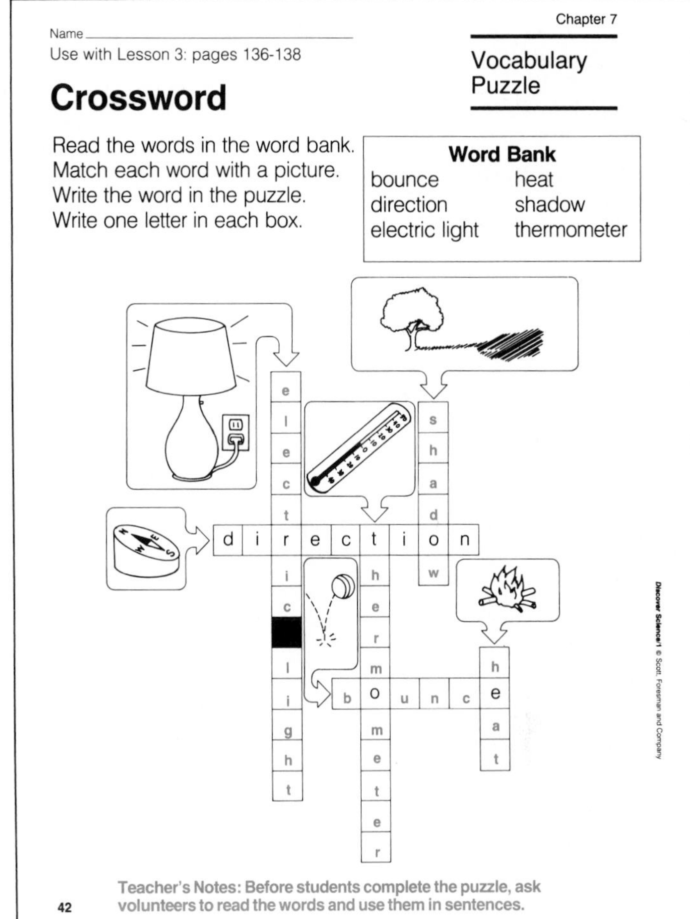

Name ____________
Use with Lesson 3: pages 136-138

Chapter 7

Vocabulary Puzzle

Crossword

Read the words in the word bank.
Match each word with a picture.
Write the word in the puzzle.
Write one letter in each box.

Word Bank	
bounce	heat
direction	shadow
electric light	thermometer

42 **Teacher's Notes:** Before students complete the puzzle, ask volunteers to read the words and use them in sentences.

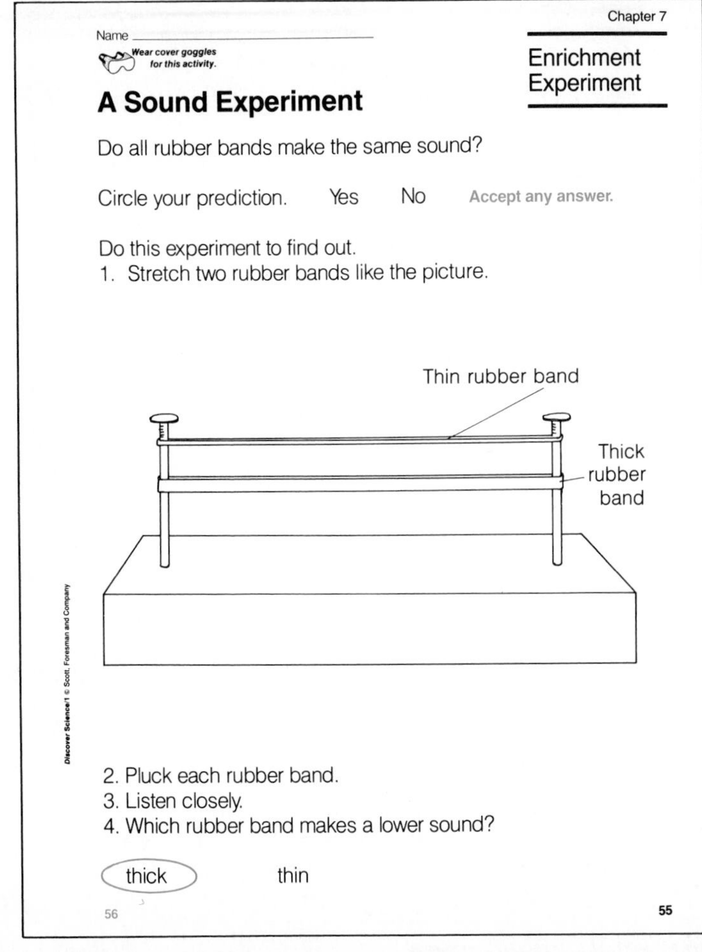

Name ____________
Wear cover goggles for this activity.

Chapter 7

Enrichment Experiment

A Sound Experiment

Do all rubber bands make the same sound?

Circle your prediction. Yes No **Accept any answer.**

Do this experiment to find out.
1. Stretch two rubber bands like the picture.

2. Pluck each rubber band.
3. Listen closely.
4. Which rubber band makes a lower sound?

(thick) thin

56 55

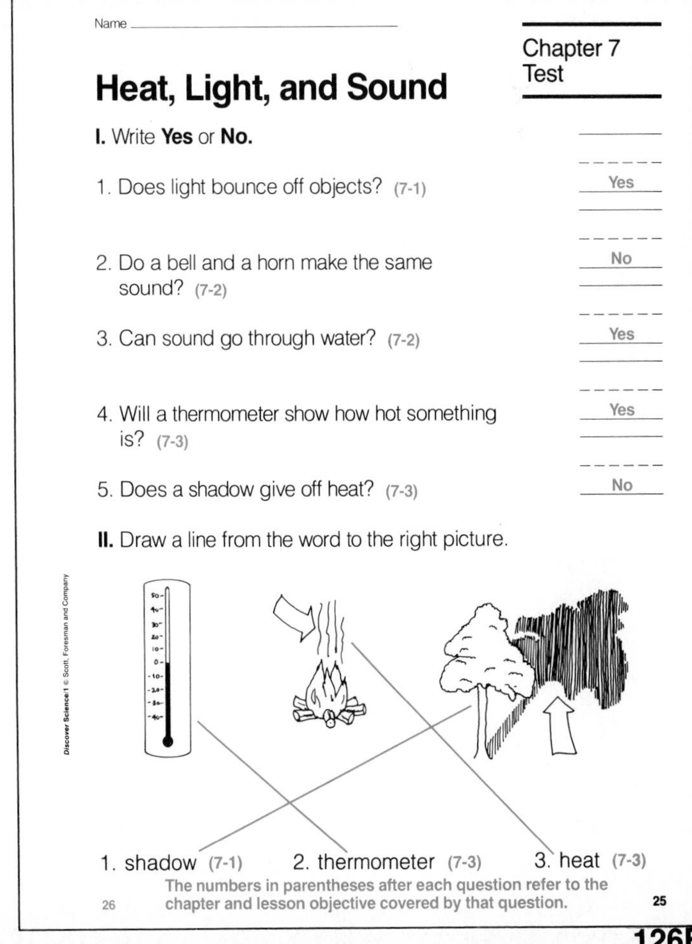

Name ____________

Chapter 7 Test

Heat, Light, and Sound

I. Write **Yes** or **No.**

1. Does light bounce off objects? (7-1) Yes
2. Do a bell and a horn make the same sound? (7-2) No
3. Can sound go through water? (7-2) Yes
4. Will a thermometer show how hot something is? (7-3) Yes
5. Does a shadow give off heat? (7-3) No

II. Draw a line from the word to the right picture.

1. shadow (7-1) 2. thermometer (7-3) 3. heat (7-3)

The numbers in parentheses after each question refer to the chapter and lesson objective covered by that question.

26 25

TEACHING PLAN

INTRODUCING CHAPTER 7

Major Concepts

Lesson 1 Light comes from various sources, can vary in intensity, and can be blocked or bounced back from certain objects.
Lesson 2 Sound comes from various sources, can vary in intensity, and is transmitted in various ways.
Lesson 3 Heat comes from various sources and has special characteristics; temperature can be measured.

Vocabulary

bounce, direction, electric light, heat, shadow, thermometer

[1] Answers might include birds singing, sun shining.

Chapter 7

Light, Sound, and Heat

Think about a warm, sunny morning.
You might see and hear many things.
What might you see and hear?[1]

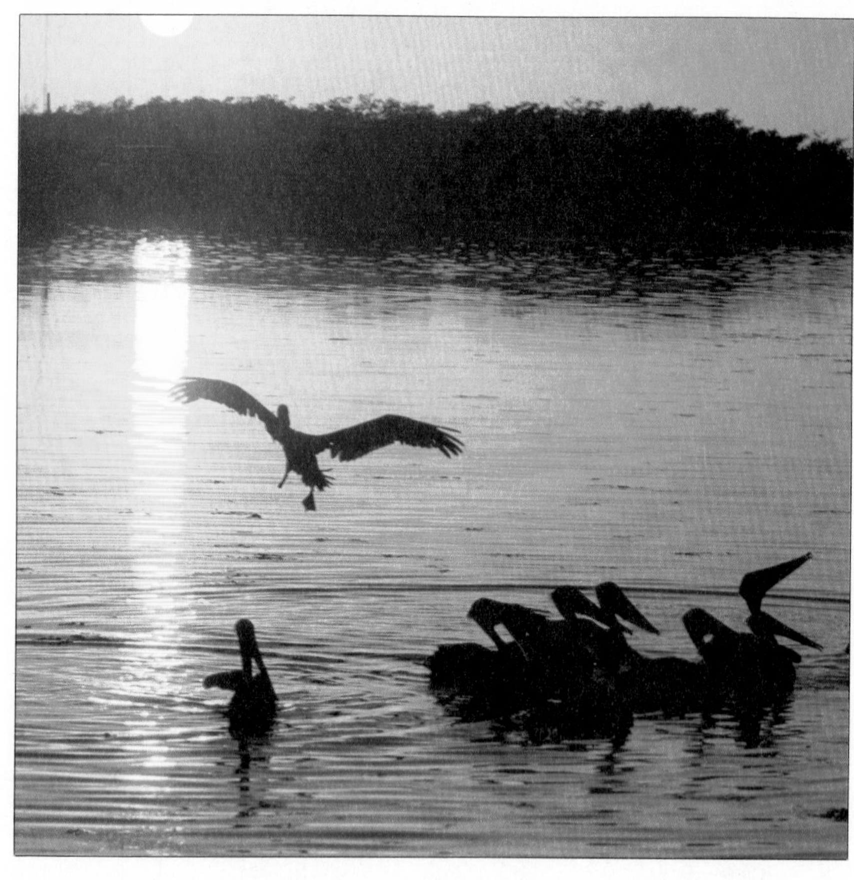

126

Teaching Options

Workbook page 37 *

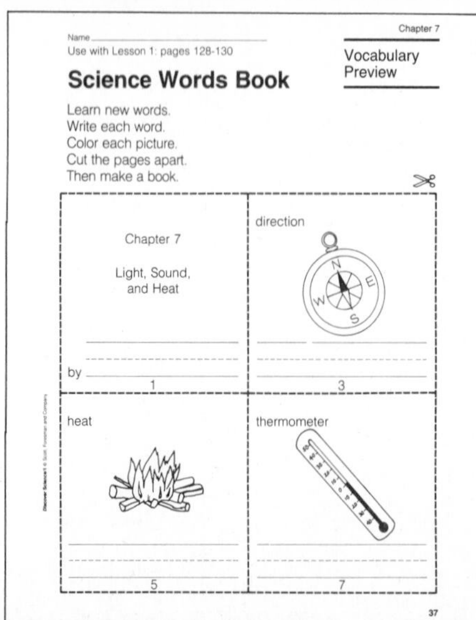

Name ______
Use with Lesson 1: pages 128-130

Chapter 7
Vocabulary Preview

Science Words Book

Learn new words.
Write each word.
Color each picture.
Cut the pages apart.
Then make a book.

Chapter 7 Light, Sound, and Heat by ______ 1	direction 3
heat 5	thermometer 7

37

Workbook page 38 *

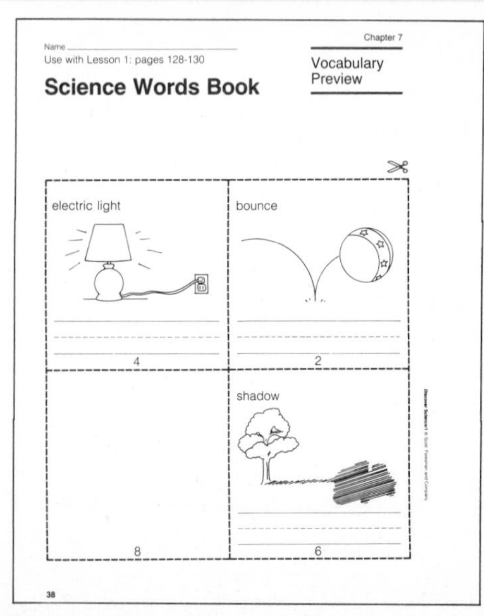

Name ______
Use with Lesson 1: pages 128-130

Chapter 7
Vocabulary Preview

Science Words Book

electric light 4	bounce 2
8	shadow 6

38

◆ ***Suitable as a language development activity***

[1] artificial light (light bulbs) or natural light (sunlight)

Starting the Chapter

What light do you use to read?[1]
Try reading with more and less light.
Light helps you see better.
Then read to learn more about light.

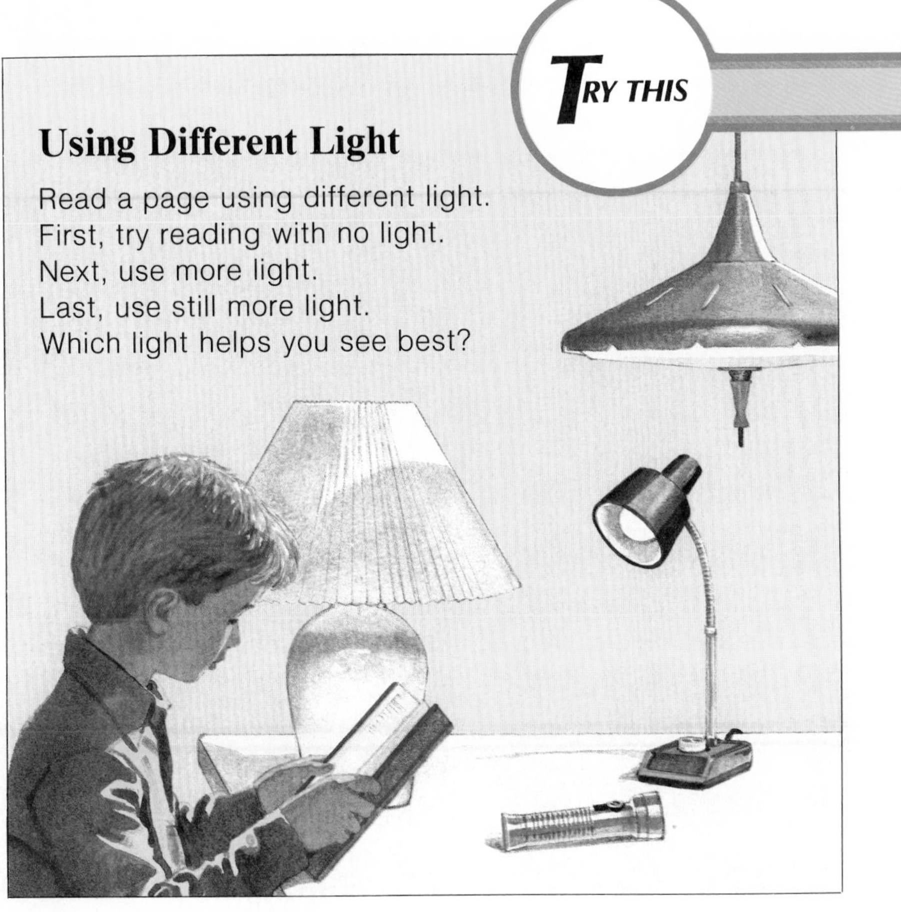

TRY THIS

Using Different Light

Read a page using different light.
First, try reading with no light.
Next, use more light.
Last, use still more light.
Which light helps you see best?

TRY THIS

Objective ♦
This optional *TRY THIS* activity will help students explore and build background information about the concept of using bright light for reading. Later in the chapter students will be able to draw on this experience to help them assimilate the new content.

Science Process Skills
Measuring, Observing

Materials
For each student: book, flashlight, lamp with small bulb, lamp with large bulb

Safety Tip (See page T27.)
- Warn students who are handling lights to not shine them at other students.

Teaching Tip
- This activity can also be done by adjusting the curtains in the room to let in more or less light. Have students ***compare*** the ease with which they read in different intensities of light. Under each light source, students should write a comparative term such as *good, better,* or *best.*

Answer
Answers will depend on the light sources that the students used. Some students might not agree that the brightest light made it easiest to read.

Resource Book page 51

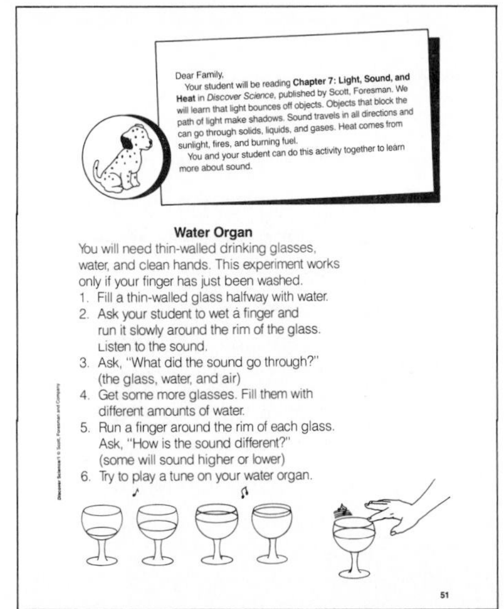

Dear Family,
Your student will be reading **Chapter 7: Light, Sound, and Heat** in *Discover Science*, published by Scott, Foresman. We will learn that light bounces off objects. Objects that block the path of light make shadows. Sound travels in all directions and can go through solids, liquids, and gases. Heat comes from sunlight, fires, and burning fuel.
You and your student can do this activity together to learn more about sound.

Water Organ

You will need thin-walled drinking glasses, water, and clean hands. This experiment works only if your finger has just been washed.

1. Fill a thin-walled glass halfway with water.
2. Ask your student to wet a finger and run it slowly around the rim of the glass. Listen to the sound.
3. Ask, "What did the sound go through?" (the glass, water, and air)
4. Get some more glasses. Fill them with different amounts of water.
5. Run a finger around the rim of each glass. Ask, "How is the sound different?" (some will sound higher or lower)
6. Try to play a tune on your water organ.

51

SCIENCE BACKGROUND

Light spreads out from its source in straight lines called rays. As the distance from a light source to an area increases, less light reaches the area. (The farther away a source is from an area, the less light the area receives.) The amount of light that reaches an area is refered to as the light's *intensity*.

* ***Answers to masters on pages 126E–126F***

TEACHING PLAN

LESSON 1
pages 128–130

Lesson Objectives
- *Explain* how light can change.
- *Describe* ways that light can bounce off objects.
- *Describe* how objects block light.

Lesson Vocabulary
bounce, electric light, shadow

1 MOTIVATE

Demonstration Activity ♦
Have the students observe their classroom under the following lighting conditions: lights off and blinds open; lights off, blinds closed, and a flashlight lit; lights off, flashlight lit, and blinds open; lights on.

Discussion
Have the students *identify* the various sources of light in the classroom. (light, flashlight, sunlight) Then have students discuss which of the lighting conditions made it easiest for them to see, and which light source was brightest. Write *electric lights* on the chalkboard and have the students *identify* the classroom lights as electric lights.

[1] relatively bright since it is dark outside

Lesson 1 How Can Light Change?

Light comes from the sun and fires.
It also comes from an **electric light.**
Light can change.
Sometimes light is not very bright.
Light can be brighter.
How bright are these lights?[1]

Teaching Options

SCIENCE BACKGROUND

Laser light is different from other kinds of light. Because the waves of a laser light are the same length, travel in one direction, and all line up, a beam of laser light can be very powerful. Laser beams can drill holes in metal. A lens is used to focus the beam of laser light in the place where the hole is to be drilled. Laser beams are also being used for many other functions, including surgery. The beams can make precise incisions that usually heal quickly, partiallly because tissue around the incision is not harmed. For this reason, surgical lasers are sometimes referred to as "bloodless scalpels."

Enrichment

Have students find out what people used for light before the discovery of electricity. If available, obtain and read to students a book or story about how Abe Lincoln was able to read books at night.

♦ ***Suitable as a language development activity***

[1] to the top of the table

Light can change its path.
It can **bounce** off objects.
Sunlight comes in this window.
The light reaches the mirror.
Then it bounces off the mirror.
Where does the light go next?[1]

2 TEACH

Teaching Tips

- Review the role of the senses. Questions: **What part of the body uses light? How do we see?**
- Ask students to think of different sources of light. (flashlight, lamp, sunlight, and so on) List students' suggestion on the chalkboard. Question: **Which of the light sources listed is brightest?** (Students should *compare* the sources and *draw conclusions* about which of the sources is the brightest.)
- **Possible Misconception:** Children usually think that the moon is a source of light. Explain that the moon is bright because light from the sun bounces off the moon.
- Use a rubber ball and show students how it can bounce off different surfaces. (the wall, the floor, and so on) Explain that light can bounce off some surfaces too.
- Provide a small, metal mirror and let the students investigate bouncing light.

Workbook page 39 *

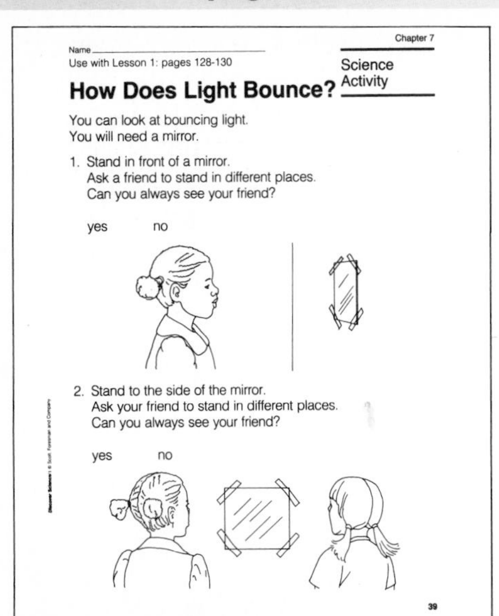

Chapter 7

Name ____________________

Use with Lesson 1: pages 128-130

Science Activity

How Does Light Bounce?

You can look at bouncing light.
You will need a mirror.

1. Stand in front of a mirror.
Ask a friend to stand in different places.
Can you always see your friend?

yes no

2. Stand to the side of the mirror.
Ask your friend to stand in different places.
Can you always see your friend?

yes no

39

* ***Answers to masters on pages 126E–126F***

Game Suggestion ♦

Take students outside and let them play shadow tag. Whoever is "It" must step on the shadow of another person to get that person "out."

Science and Math

Have the students use meter sticks to measure each other's shadows at various times of the day. Ask students to record the results.

TEACHING PLAN

Teaching Tip

• Write the word *shadows* on the chalkboard. Question: **How are shadows made?** (Guide the students to *infer* that shadows are made by objects that block light. Set aside time for students to experiment with making shadows.

3 ASSESS

Lesson Review

1. Light can change from bright to not very bright, and can change its path or bounce off objects.

2. Objects that light cannot pass through can block light.

Challenge! Question: **Why might a tree make a very small shadow or no shadow at noon, and a long shadow late in the afternoon?** (The sun is high in the sky at noon, and light from the sun is not blocked much by the tree. In late afternoon the sun is ready to set, and the tree blocks the light from the sun.) **Thinking Skill:** *Drawing conclusions*

Find Out

Students might draw pictures of electric lights, fireplaces, battery-operated lights, or candles. **Thinking Skill:** *Restating or explaining ideas*

What can block the path of light?
Objects like these block light.
Light cannot pass through them.
Objects like these make **shadows.**

Lesson Review

1. What ways can light change?
2. What can block light?

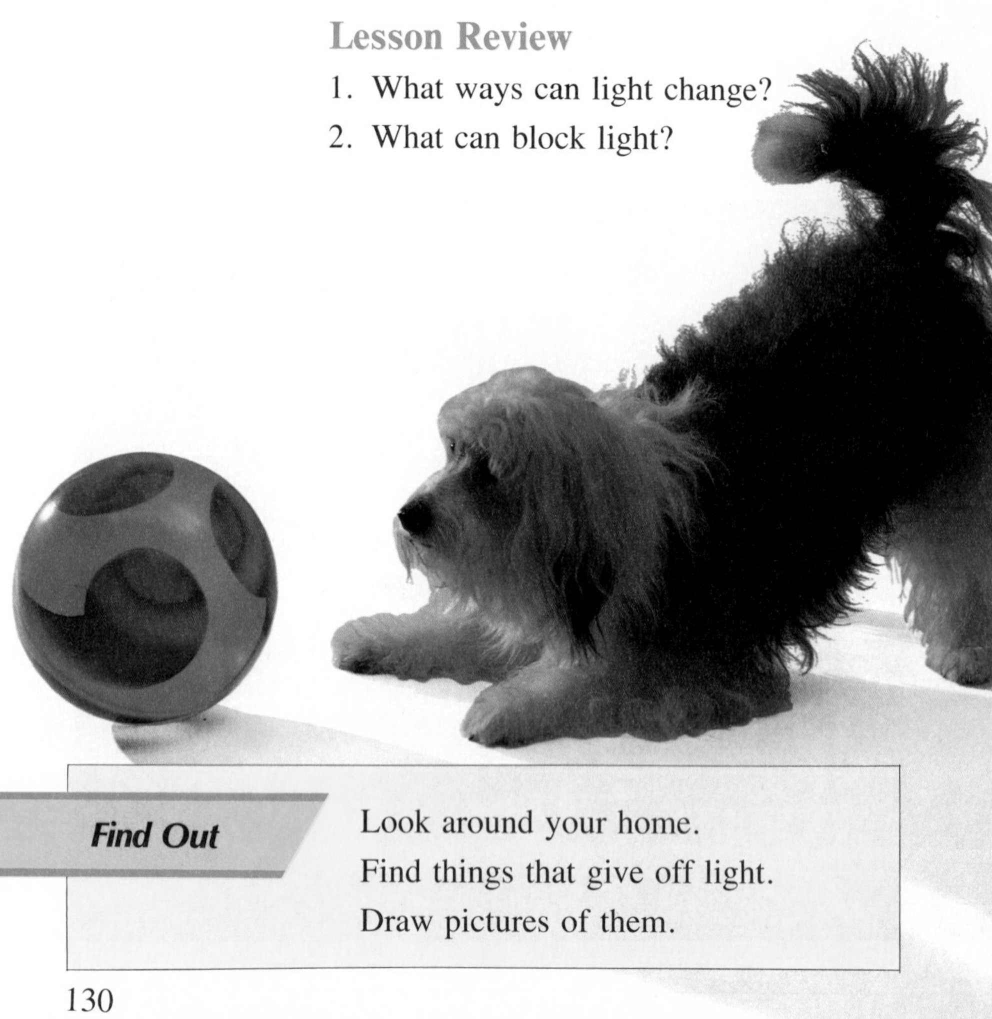

Find Out

Look around your home.
Find things that give off light.
Draw pictures of them.

130

Teaching Options

SCIENCE ANECDOTE

Sunlight takes more than eight minutes to reach the earth. Other stars are so far away that their light travels for years before reaching the earth. In fact, some stars might have burned out by the time we see their light.

Reteaching Suggestion ♦

Place a picture book in the bottom of a box that is lined with black paper or is painted black on the inside. Ask a volunteer to descibe the pictures in the book. Then, turn off the classroom lights and darken the room. When the student is no longer able to describe the pictures, guide the class to discuss the importance of light. Ask students to close their eyes for a few moments. Question: **What would life be like without light?**

Special Education

For students with learning disabilities, provide a variety of objects—some that are opaque, some that are translucent, and some that are transparent. Have students group the objects according to those they can see through, those they cannot see through, and those they can see through partially. Instruct students to use a flashlight to test each group to determine which objects make shadows, which let most light through, and which let some light through.

♦ ***Suitable as a language development activity***

ACTIVITY

Making Shadows

Follow the Directions

1. Make shadows of objects this way.
2. Ask others to guess your objects.
3. Ask them to make shadows.
4. Guess what objects they use.

Tell What You Learned

Tell what objects made the shadows.
Tell another way to make shadows.

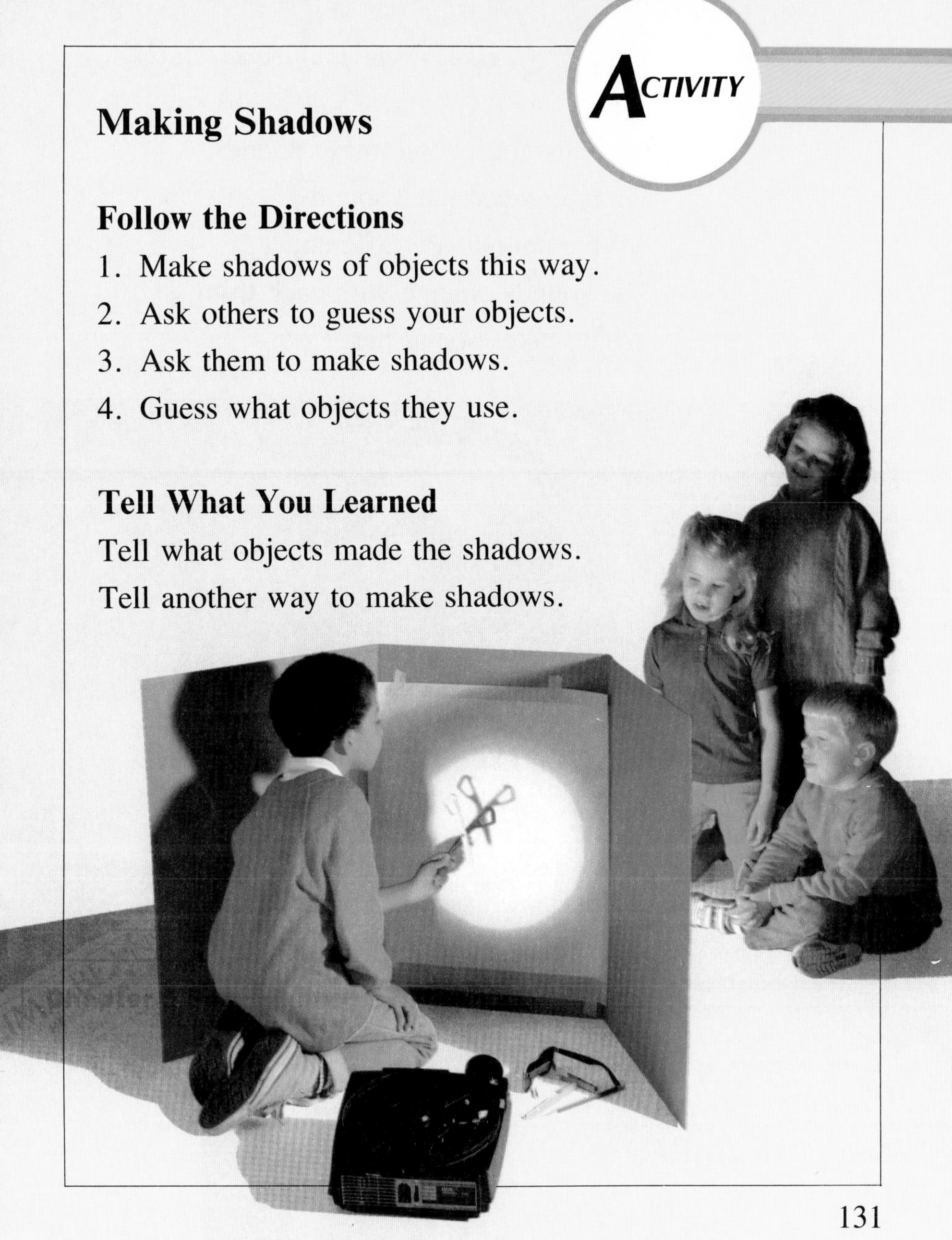

131

Enrichment Activity

Allow students to make shadow puppets. Students might also want to write a play for the puppets about how they spend their early mornings when the sun is bright, and what they do at night.

Activity Results

Students should discover that objects with different shapes make shadows that are similar to their shapes, because the objects block the light according to their shape. Students should be able to tell what object is being used to block light by looking at the shape of the shadow that is made.

Concept

Light can be blocked, which causes a shadow.

Objectives/Process Skills

- *Observe* shadows.
- *Infer* the objects that caused the shadows.
- *Identify* objects that can block light and cause a shadow.

Time Allotment

Allow 20 minutes.

Materials

For each group of 10: slide or filmstrip projector, masking tape, 3 sheets of cardboard, 1 large sheet of white tissue paper

Safety Tip (See page T27.)

- Warn students to not look directly into the beam of light from the projector.

Teaching Tip

- Explain to the students that they will work in groups to try to guess what objects are being used to make shadows. Turn off the classroom lights. Have a student hold an object up between the projector light and a piece of white cloth or paper hanging on a wall, or over a hole cut out from a side of a carton from which the opposite side has been removed. Instruct the student to rotate the object so that the class can see if the shadow changes shape. (A coffee mug will give different shadows when the handle is placed in different positions.) Let the class try to guess what the object is. Then have a different student hold an object, and let the other students guess its identity. Continue until all students have had a turn.

Answers

Tell What You Learned.
Students should name the objects that were used to make the shadows. (Verify answers with the students that held each object.) Students might suggest that shadows could also be made by using a flashlight and their hands, or by standing in the sun so that their bodies make shadows by blocking the sunlight.
Thinking Skill: *Applying information to new situations*

TEACHING PLAN

LESSON 2
pages 132–134

Lesson Objectives
- *Describe* how sound can change.
- *State* what can carry sound.

Lesson Vocabulary
direction

1 MOTIVATE

Demonstration Activity ♦
Have students close their eyes and listen for different sounds. First, instruct students to listen only to environmental sounds. Then begin to make other sounds by opening and closing a desk drawer, sharpening a pencil, writing on a chalkboard, and so on. Finally, instruct students to open their eyes.

Discussion
Have the students list all of the sounds they could hear. Discuss which of the sounds were loudest and which were softest. Ask students to try to determine which direction the sounds came from.

[1] lion, doorbell, tree blowing in wind, bicycle horn, bird

Lesson 2 How Can Sound Change?

Animals and people make sounds.
Many objects make sounds.
All the sounds are different.
The sounds change with each thing.
What makes sound here?[1]

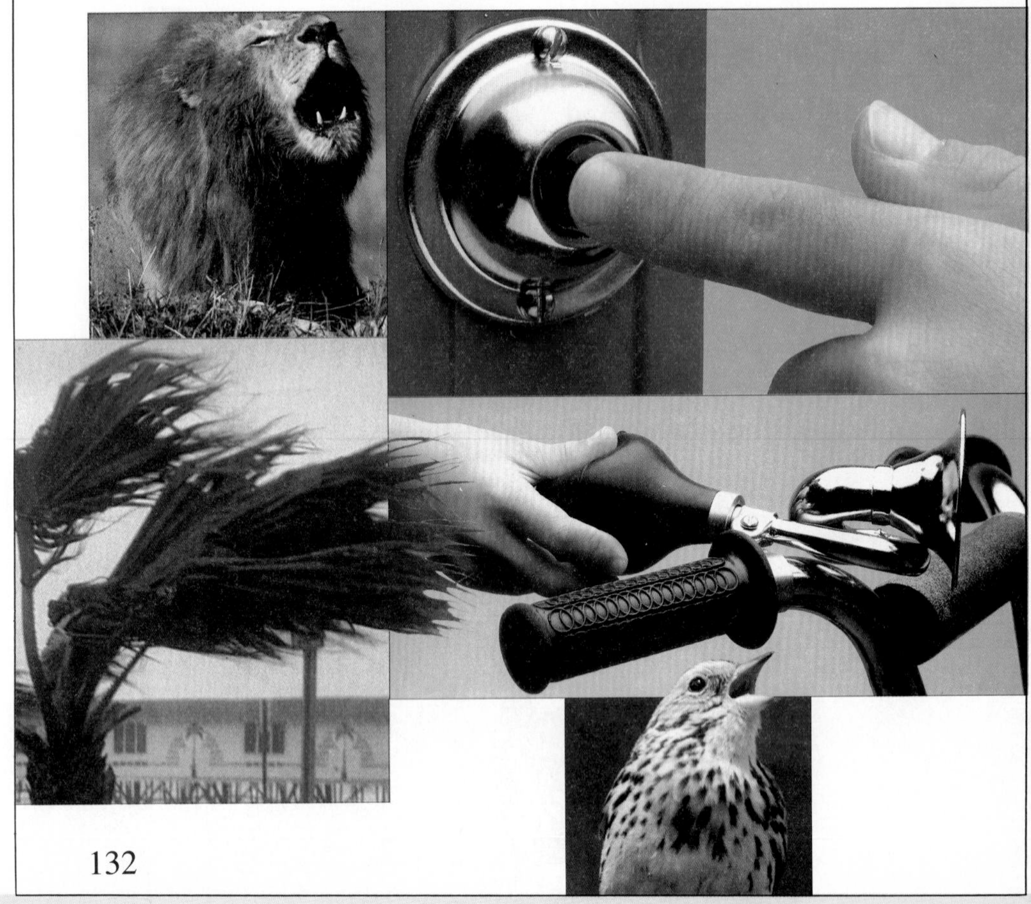

132

Teaching Options

SCIENCE BACKGROUND

Sound waves occur when matter vibrates. Vibrations are quick, back-and-forth motions of an object. When vibration is very fast, a high-pitched sound is made. When one molecule of a solid is disturbed, the disturbance is quickly transmited to many other molecules, because molecules on a solid are close together. In a liquid this process is slower. In gas it is even slower. Sounds travel fastest through solids and slowest through gases. Sound cannot travel through a vacuum, because a vacuum has no matter to transmit the sound waves. Sound waves bend around objects more easily than light waves. Because of this, it is possible to hear around corners even though it is impossible to see around them.

Reinforcement

Tape record several different types of sounds (made by animals, objects, or people). Have the students try to identify who or what made the sound, and whether the sound is loud or soft.

♦ ***Suitable as a language development activity***

[1] The music can become softer or louder.

Sound can change from loud to soft.
This person plays music.
How might the sounds change?[1]
Sound can also change **direction.**
It can go many different ways.

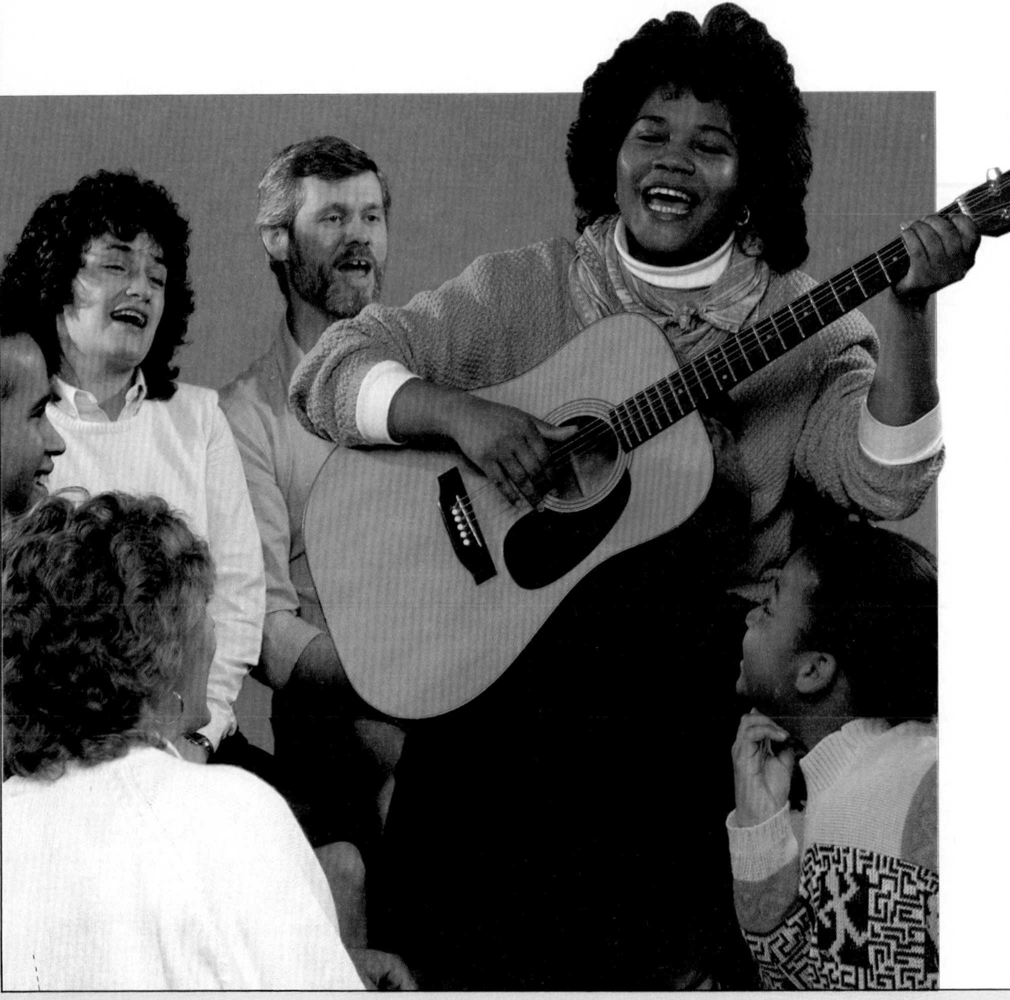

2 TEACH

Teaching Tips

- Refer to the pictures on page 132 and 133. Question: **What are these objects, and what sounds do they make?** (Students should name the objects and *describe* the sounds they make.) Have the students make different sounds, using classroom objects.
- Questions: **What things can make very loud sounds?** (Students might *name* things such as fireworks, sirens, or drums.) **What can make soft sounds?** (Students might *name* handbells, fans or air conditioners, pages being turned, and so on.) Have students *identify* sounds that they hear during a normal school day as being loud or soft. (For example, the class bell is loud.)
- **Possible Misconception:** Students might think that sound travels from an object directly to their ears. Explain that sound travels in waves that pass through the object and through air.

Enrichment

Explain that sound is produced by vibrations. Let students experiment with musical instruments to see what parts vibrate and if the sound stops when the vibration stops. (Provide at least one stringed instrument, a triangle, and a drum.) You might also want to give students large rubber bands and have them experiment to see what sounds they can make. Also, have students hum and feel the vibration in their throats. *CAUTION:* Students should wear cover goggles during this activity.

Special Education

For students with learning disabilities, play a tape of a person reading a story, but place the tape recorder outside the classroom, keeping the door closed. Set the volume so that students can hear the tape, but cannot discern what is being said. Next, bring the machine into the room, put it in a box of newspapers, and turn the volume up slightly. Finally, place the tape recorder near the students and turn the volume up so that students can hear the tape. Help students determine what made it difficult for them to hear the tape at times. (The sound was travelling across different distances and through various materials.)

Science and Art

Divide the class into groups and have them create murals about sound. Assign to each group a topic such as: noisy animals, quiet animals, warning sounds, or musical sounds.

TEACHING PLAN

Teaching Tip

• Refer to the picture on page 134. Questions: **Who is making the sound?** (the child who is talking through the window) **Where does the sound travel?** (through the window to the other side, where the other child can hear it) Explain that the sound had to travel through a solid (the window) and a gas (air) before the other child could hear it.

3 ASSESS

Lesson Review

1. Sound changes according to what makes the sound, by getting louder or softer, and in the direction it travels.
2. Sound can pass through gas, liquids, and solids.
Challenge! Question: **In what ways can the sound of a person's voice change?** (A person's voice can get softer or louder, and higher or lower.) **Thinking Skill:** *Applying information to new situations*

Find Out

A piano's keys are connected to small hammers. When a key is touched, a hammer strikes strings in the piano. When the strings are struck, they vibrate, and the vibrations create sounds. **Thinking Skill:** *Recognizing relevant information and data*

[1] the closed window

What can sound go through?
Sound can go through gas and liquid.
Sound also can go through solids.
What does sound go through here?[1]

Lesson Review

1. What ways does sound change?
2. What can sound go through?

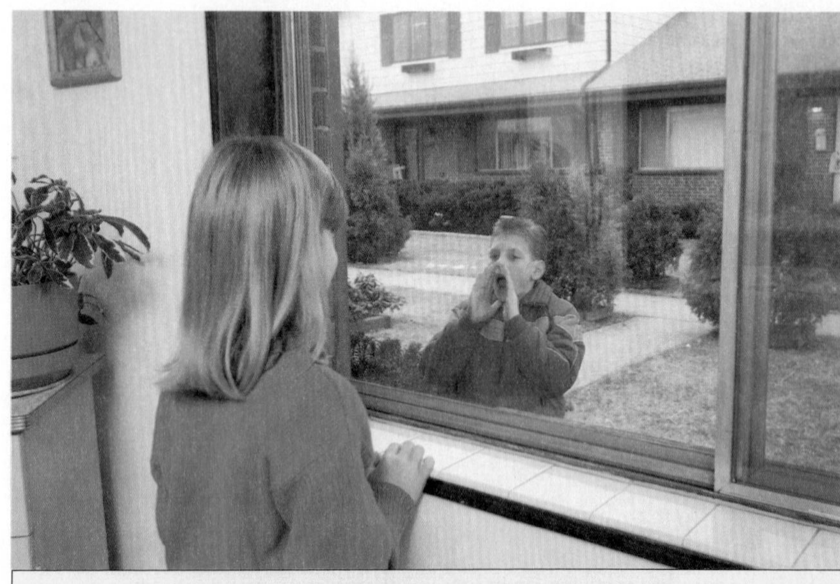

Find Out

A piano has strings.
How do the strings make sound?

Teaching Options

SCIENCE ANECDOTE

People can hear sound waves that vibrate as fast as 20,000 times per second. Dogs can hear sounds resulting from even faster vibrations.

Reteaching Suggestion ♦

Have the students be "sound detectives." Give each student a piece of sturdy cardboard "clipboard," paper, and a pencil. Take a walk through the school and have the students list the sounds they hear. Return to the classroom and discuss the sounds students have listed. Ask the students whether the sounds were loud or soft, and what materials the sound might have traveled through to reach the students.

Workbook page 40 *

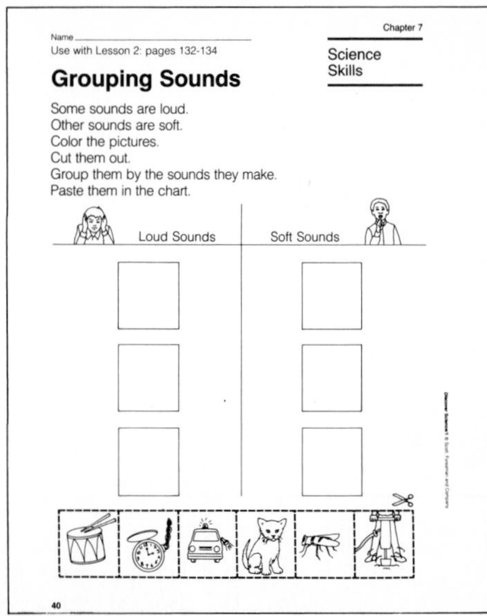

Name ______
Use with Lesson 2: pages 132-134

Chapter 7
Science Skills

Grouping Sounds

Some sounds are loud.
Other sounds are soft.
Color the pictures.
Cut them out.
Group them by the sounds they make.
Paste them in the chart.

Loud Sounds	Soft Sounds

40

♦ *Suitable as a language development activity*

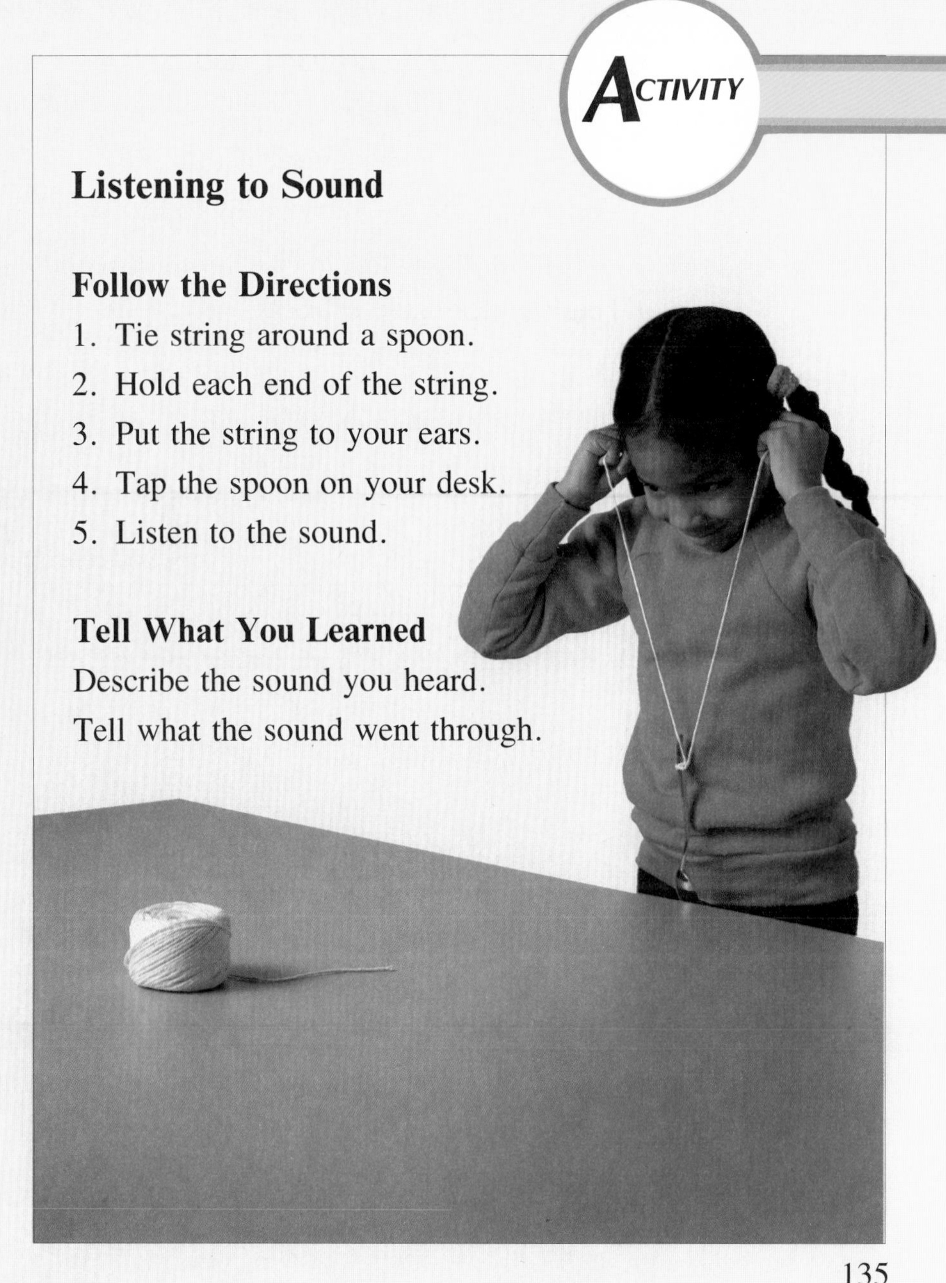

ACTIVITY

Listening to Sound

Follow the Directions

1. Tie string around a spoon.
2. Hold each end of the string.
3. Put the string to your ears.
4. Tap the spoon on your desk.
5. Listen to the sound.

Tell What You Learned

Describe the sound you heard.

Tell what the sound went through.

135

ACTIVITY PLAN

Concept

Sound goes through solid objects.

Objectives/Process Skills

- *Observe* that sound goes through a solid object.
- *Describe* some solid objects sound passes through.

Materials

For each student: metal spoon, string

Safety Tip (See page T27.)

- Warn students to not put the string *in* their ears or mouth.

Teaching Tips

- Question: **Can sound travel along a string?** (Students should *formulate hypotheses* about whether or not string can carry sound.) Demonstrate how to tie a simple knot around the handle of a spoon. Point out that the spoon should be tied in the middle of the string so there is enough string remaining to hold to each ear.
- Allow students to experiment with a variety of spoon sizes, and with other metal objects. You might also let them try the activity using plastic or wooden spoons.

Answers

Tell What You Learned

Students should state that they heard a ringing sound similar to the sound of a bell. They should state that the sound went from the spoon, along the string, to their ears. **Thinking Skill:** *Inferring*

Enrichment Activity

Allow students to make and use paper cup telephones. You will need 2 paper cups, 2 toothpicks, and a piece of string 2 meters (about 2 yards) long for each telephone set. Make a hole in the bottom of each cup. Pass one end of the string through each hole. Tie a toothpick to each end of the string to keep it from pulling out of the cup. Pull the string taut and let students take turns talking and listening. *CAUTION:* Instruct students to handle toothpicks with care, and to not poke themselves or other students with them.

Activity Results

Students should be able to hear a ringing or chiming sound through the string when they do the activity using a metal spoon. Students should realize that the string carried sound.

*** Answers to masters on pages 126E–126F**

TEACHING PLAN

LESSON 3
pages 136–138

Lesson Objectives
- *Name* sources of heat.
- *Describe* how heat can change the temperature of objects.
- Tell what a thermometer does.

Lesson Vocabulary
heat, thermometer

1 MOTIVATE

Demonstration Activity ♦
Give each student a ball of modeling clay to play with. After several minutes of play, collect the clay.

Discussion
Questions: **What was the modeling clay like when you first began to play with it?** (Students should *describe* how the clay felt and looked.) **How did it change as you played with it?** (Guide students to *infer* that the clay became softer as the heat from the students' hands warmed the clay.) Tell students that Lesson 3 will explain more about heat.

[1] possible responses: furnace, oven, car, lights, hot water

Lesson 3 What Can You Learn About Heat?

The light from the sun carries **heat.**
Fires give off heat.
These objects give off heat.
What else makes heat?[1]

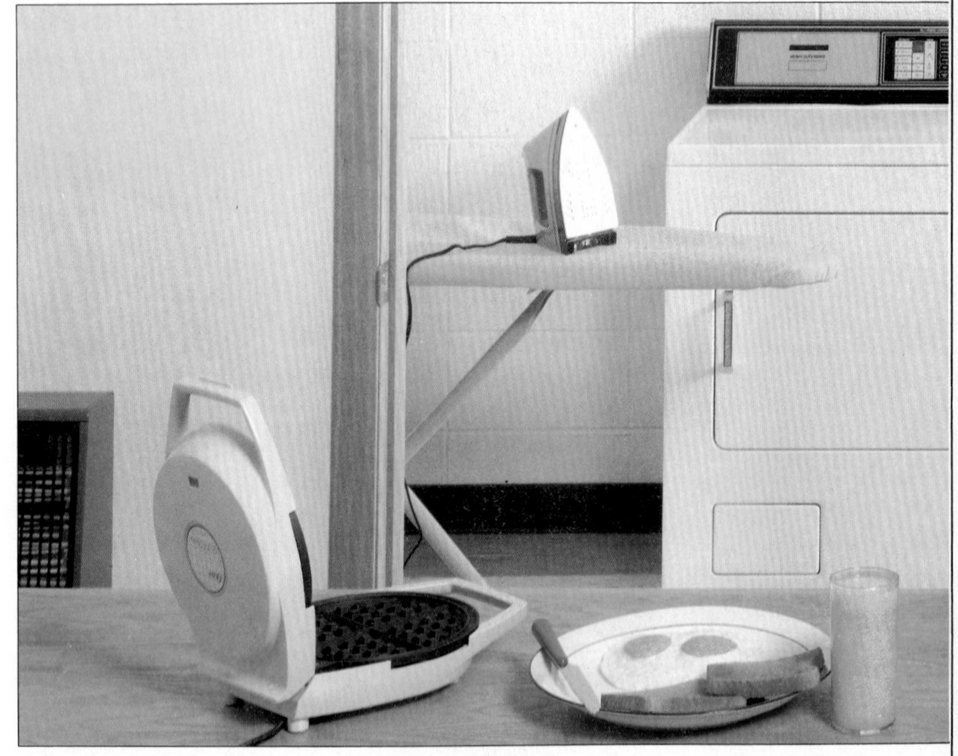

136

Teaching Options

SCIENCE BACKGROUND

Energy travels to the earth from the sun as radiation. We see some of this energy as light. Radiation from the sun also heats us and warms the earth. When matter absorbs radiation, the molecules in the matter move. The more energy the matter is holding, the faster the molecules move. Heat flows from places of higher temperature to places of lower temperature. A heat source is an object that has a higher temperature than its surroundings. The human body is a heat source for objects near it that have a temperature of less than 37°C (98.6°F). Human sensory receptors for heat are distributed throughout the body along with sensors for pain and touch.

Special Education

Leave a thermometer outside all day. Help students with learning disabilities read the temperature at various times of the day. Ask them to tell whether the temperature was higher or lower at different times. Discuss why the temperature changed.

♦ *Suitable as a language development activity*

This pot is very hot.

What happens after the fire goes out?

The pot will not be as hot.

Soon the pot will only be warm.

Later, the pot will be cool.

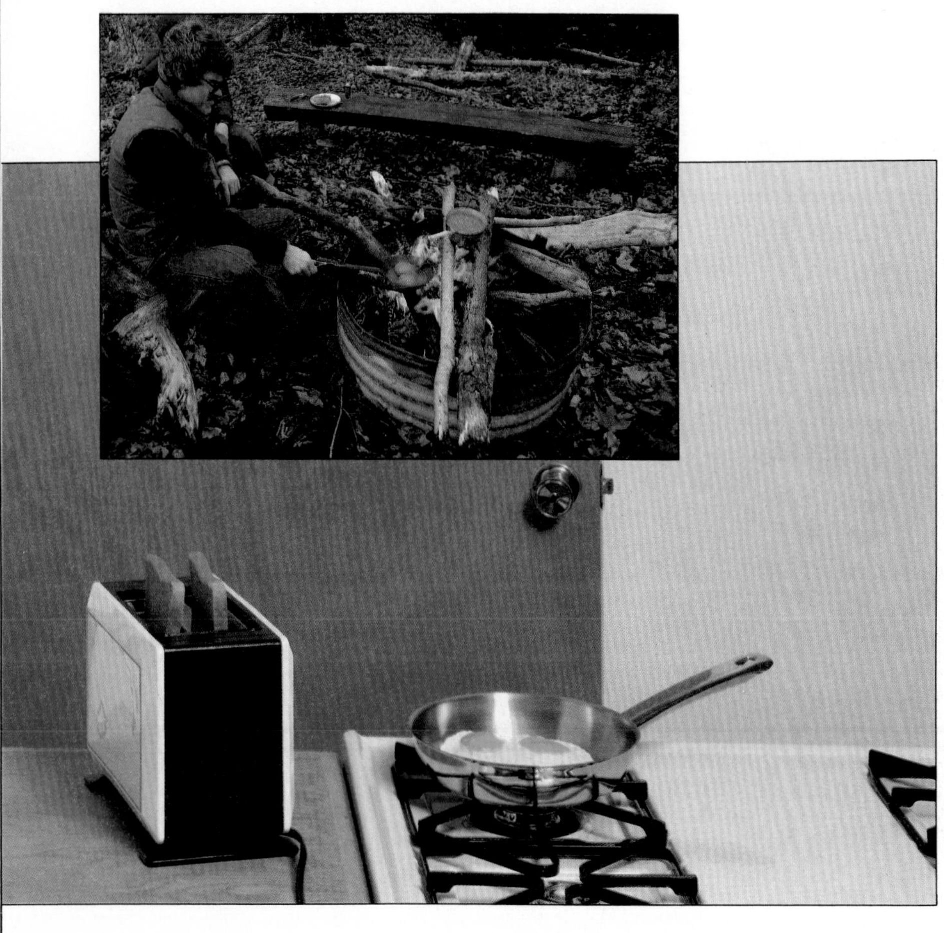

2 TEACH

Teaching Tips

- Question: **How can you tell that the sun gives off heat?** (Students might mention that the sun's heat melts things that are frozen, feels warm on their skin, and can sometimes burn their skin.)
- Ask students to look at the picture and *identify* the items that give off heat.
- **Possible Misconception:** Children often think that sweaters and non-electric blankets give off heat because people can get warmer by putting these items on. Explain that the items only hold in a person's body heat—they do not produce any heat of their own.
- Questions: **What happens if you leave your dinner on the table when it is hot and come back to eat it later?** (Students should realize that the food will become colder.) **Why does food that is left on a table cool off?** (Guide students to *infer* that the air in a room is cooler than the food, and that the heat in the food goes into the air.) **How can you tell that an oven gives off heat even without touching it?** (The kitchen gets warmer when the oven is being used.)
- Warn students to not touch a pot on a stove, even if the fire is out.

Workbook page 41 *

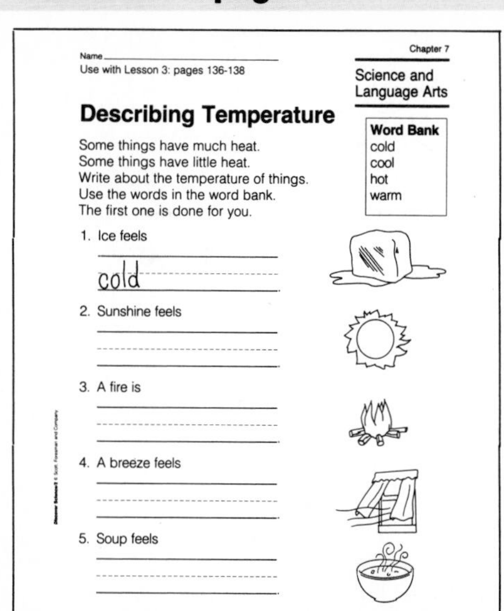

Name __________

Use with Lesson 3: pages 136-138

Chapter 7

Science and Language Arts

Describing Temperature

Some things have much heat.
Some things have little heat.
Write about the temperature of things.
Use the words in the word bank.
The first one is done for you.

Word Bank
cold
cool
hot
warm

1. Ice feels cold
2. Sunshine feels
3. A fire is
4. A breeze feels
5. Soup feels

41

* **Answers to masters on pages 126E–126F**

Enrichment

Provide experiences for students to observe how heat changes matter. For example, let them watch ice cubes melt (solid to liquid), or have them cook pancakes (liquid to solid).

Science and Social Studies

Help students find out which countries or areas of the world have hot climates and what these areas have in common. (Explain that areas along the Equator are usually hot because the sun's rays hit the earth more directly at the Equator than at other parts of the earth.)

TEACHING PLAN

3 ASSESS

Lesson Review

1. Answers can include the sun, fire, and electrical appliances such as ovens, toasters, or space heaters.

2. A thermometer shows how hot things are.

Challenge! Question: **How are your hand and a thermometer alike and how are they different?** (They are alike because they both detect heat; they are different because a thermometer can measure exactly how hot something is.)

Thinking Skills: *Comparing, Contrasting*

Find Out

Answers will vary but could include one or more of the following heat sources: gas or oil furnace, wood-burning stove, fireplace, electric heater, solar heat.

Thinking Skill: *Applying information to new situations*

[1] indoor and outdoor temperatures; turkey temperature
[2] temperature of liquids and solids

What does a **thermometer** show?

It shows how hot something is.

What do these thermometers show?[1]

What do other thermometers show?[2]

Lesson Review

1. What gives off heat?
2. What shows how hot things are?

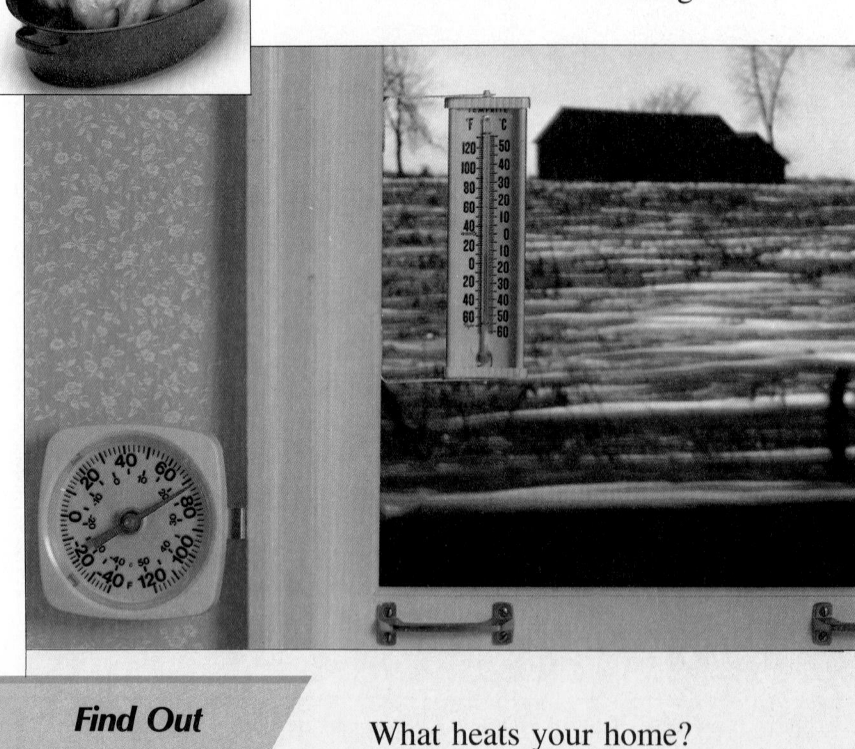

Find Out What heats your home?

138

Teaching Options

SCIENCE ANECDOTE

A very cold ice cube might stick to your hand. The heat from your hand melts the ice cube's surface. The surface refreezes quickly because the ice draws the heat away from the melted water, causing the ice cube to freeze and stick to your hand.

Reteaching Suggestion ♦

Make a chart of the different types of rooms in a house. Have the students draw pictures of objects that produce heat. Instruct students to cut out their pictures and attach them to the appropriate room on the chart.

Workbook page 42 *

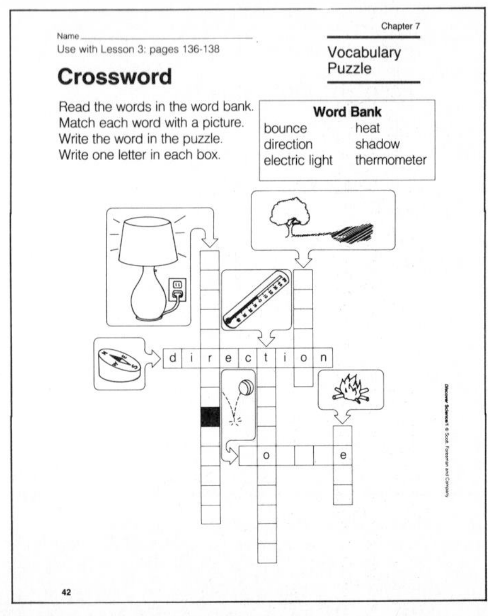

Name ____
Use with Lesson 3: pages 136-138

Chapter 7
Vocabulary Puzzle

Crossword

Read the words in the word bank.
Match each word with a picture.
Write the word in the puzzle.
Write one letter in each box.

Word Bank

bounce	heat
direction	shadow
electric light	thermometer

d i r e c t i o n

o e

42

♦ ***Suitable as a language development activity***

Using a Different Thermometer

Why is this thermometer different?

You do not put it in your mouth.

You put it on your forehead.

It measures how hot your skin is.

Notice the colors on the thermometer.

Heat makes the colors change.

What Do You Think?

Why is this thermometer useful?

SCIENCE IN YOUR LIFE

Discussion

Ask students to remember the last time they had their temperature taken. Question: **What type of thermometer was used?** (Students should tell whether the thermometer was glass, digital, or a fever strip.) Tell students that they will learn about a liquid crystal fever strip, which makes taking temperature easier.

Teaching Tips

- Questions: **Have any of you ever used a thermometer like the one in the picture? Why might this thermometer be easier or safer to use than another kind?** (Guide students to *infer* that many thermometers are made of glass and could break, and many are uncomfortable to hold in the mouth for a long time.)
- Question: **How does the thermometer in the picture show that a person has a temperature?** (Students should *describe* the color change when a person's temperature is above normal.)

Answers

What Do You Think?

Students' answers might include the following ideas: the thermometer will not break if it is dropped, works fast, is easy to use, and can be left on the forehead to determine whether a temperature is going up or down. **Thinking Skill:** *Making generalizations*

SCIENCE BACKGROUND

Fever thermometers that can measure temperature on the forehead contain liquid crystals that are calibrated to specific temperature values. These thermometers measure skin surface temperature (on the forehead) as an indication of body core temperature. Liquid crystals respond to heat instantaneously and continuously, allowing easy, noninvasive temperature monitoring. Liquid-crystal thermometers are useful for continuously monitoring the progress of a fever.

* ***Answers to masters on pages 126E–126F***

TEACHING PLAN

SKILLS FOR SOLVING PROBLEMS
pages 140–141

Purpose
These pages provide students with the opportunity to read temperature indications on a thermometer and to record their findings on a chart.

Materials
For each student: centigrade alcohol thermometer, jar of ice water, jar of warm water, crayons, paper

1 MOTIVATE

Discussion
Display a model of a thermometer that you have made of a long piece of cardboard with a red strip that can move up and down. Allow students to move the strip to indicate how they think a thermometer's liquid will move to indicate the temperature of a warm object and of a cold object.

2 TEACH

Safety Tips
- Warn students about the hazards of the liquid in the thermometers.
- Wipe up any water spills.

Skills for Solving Problems

Using a Thermometer

What does a thermometer show?

1. Observe the thermometer.
   Notice the colors on this thermometer.
2. Put a thermometer on your desk.
   Put it in warm water.
   Put it in ice water.
   See what color it reaches each time.

140

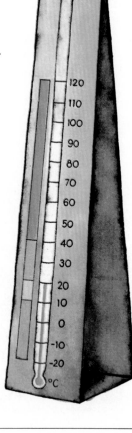

Teaching Options

SCIENCE BACKGROUND

All thermometers have two reference points, one hot and one cold. The usual reference points are the temperature at which water freezes and the temperature at which water boils. A certain number of equal steps, usually called degrees, occur between the two reference points. On the Celsius temperature scale, ice melts at 0 degrees and water boils at 100 degrees. On the Fahrenheit temperature scale, the degree steps are smaller than on the Celsius scale. The freezing point of water on the Fahrenheit scale is 32 degrees, and the boiling point is 212 degrees.

3. Use your own paper.
Make a chart like this one.
Show the colors.

4. Look at your chart.
What does it show about thermometers?

Teaching Tips

- Students should place the thermometer on a flat, safe area of the desk. Allow time for the thermometer to settle at a temperature level, and have students compare the level with the color range indicated on the page. Students might not read a specific number, but will observe a color area (orange).
- Have students submerge only the bulbous part of the thermometer in the warm water, with your supervision. Avoid very hot water. Water temperature of about 30°C is advised. Students should report that the temperature is in the red area.
- Have students submerge the bulb of the thermometer in ice water. The liquid level in the thermometer should lower. Students should report that the temperature is in the blue area.

3 ASSESS

Students' charts should show that on the desk the temperature is in the orange group, in the warm water the temperature is in the red group, and in the ice water the temperature is in the blue group. Students should answer that thermometers have different areas that show different temperatures.

Resource Book page 55 *

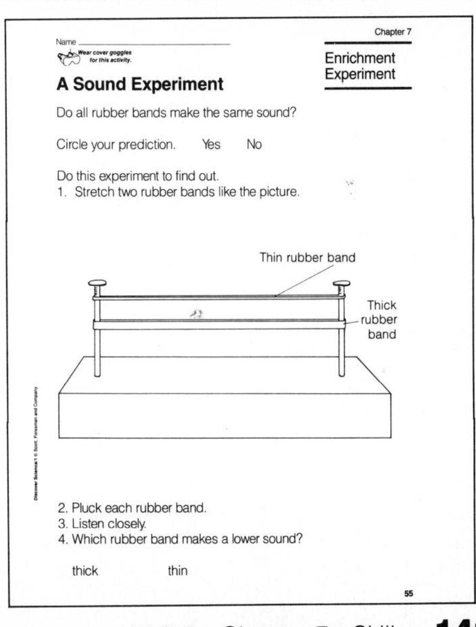

Name

Wear cover goggles for this activity.

Chapter 7

Enrichment Experiment

A Sound Experiment

Do all rubber bands make the same sound?

Circle your prediction. Yes No

Do this experiment to find out.
1. Stretch two rubber bands like the picture.

2. Pluck each rubber band.
3. Listen closely.
4. Which rubber band makes a lower sound?

thick thin

55

* Answers to masters on pages 126E–126F

CHAPTER 7 REVIEW
pages 142–143

Review Chapter Ideas
1. Light changes in brightness and in the direction it travels.
2. Objects that light cannot pass through make shadows.
3. Sound changes according to what makes it, it changes in loudness or softness, and it changes direction.
4. Sound can pass through air (gas), water (liquids), and solids.
5. The sun, fire, toaster, and space heater give off heat
6. A thermometer shows how hot something is.

For further review, use Study Guide page 234.

Chapter 7 Review

Review Chapter Ideas

1. Tell how light changes.
2. Tell what objects make shadows.
3. Tell how sound changes.
4. Tell what sound passes through.
5. Look at the pictures.
   Tell which things give off heat.
6. Explain what a thermometer does.

a. b. c.

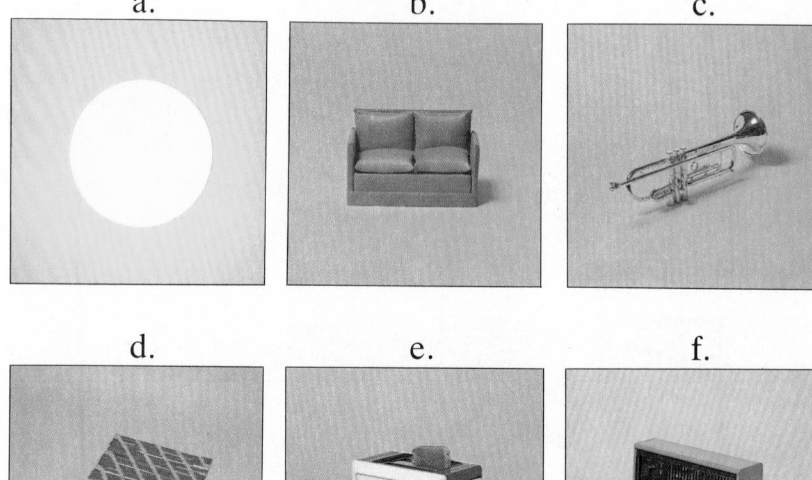

d. e. f.

Review Options

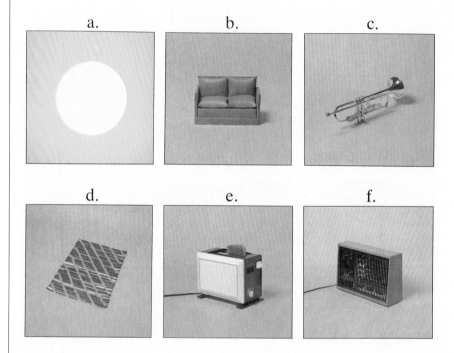

Cooperative Learning ♦

STAD Format (See page T23.)
Assign students to work in four- to five-member teams to study Chapter 7 Review. Students should work together to make sure that they and their teammates know the material in the chapter. After students have had enough time to study together, give them a test to complete individually (Chapter 7 Test in the *Test Book*). Award Superteam certificates to teams whose average test scores exceed 90%, and Greatteam certificates to teams whose average test scores exceed 80%.

♦ ***Suitable as a language development activity***

Review Science Words

Match the words and the pictures.

1. electric light
2. shadow
3. thermometer
4. heat

a. 

b. 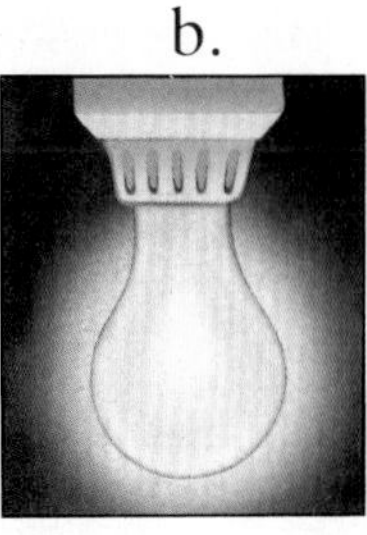

c. 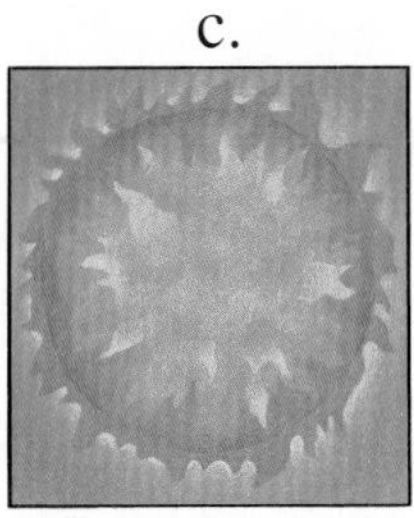

d. 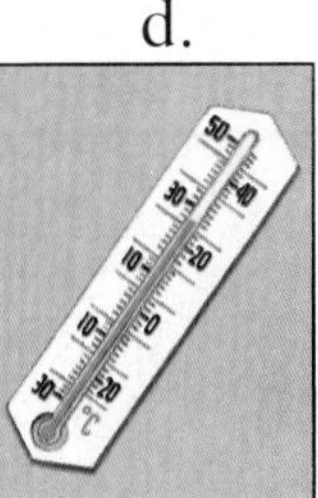

Tell what the words mean.

5. bounce
6. direction

a. 

Use Science Ideas

Tell which car is in brighter light.

143

Review Science Words

Match the words and pictures.

1. b
2. a
3. d
4. c

Tell what the words mean.

Thinking Skill: *Restating or explaining ideas*

5. bounce: to hit something and come back from it

6. direction: the way that something can move or travel

Use Science Ideas

The car in the sun is in the brighter light.

Thinking Skill: *Making inferences*

Test Book page 25 *

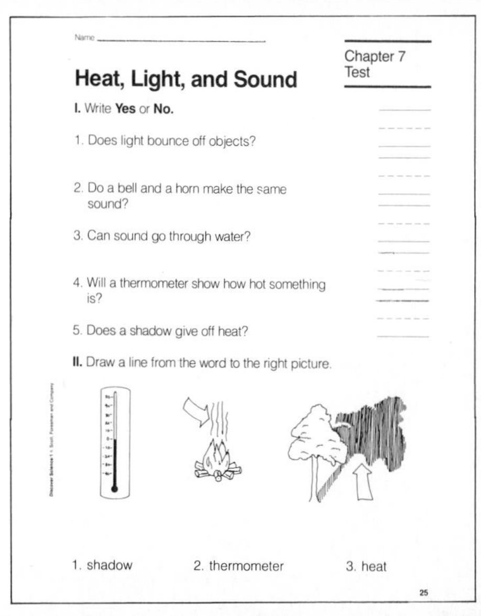

Name ____________

Chapter 7 Test

Heat, Light, and Sound

I. Write **Yes** or **No.**

1. Does light bounce off objects?
2. Do a bell and a horn make the same sound?
3. Can sound go through water?
4. Will a thermometer show how hot something is?
5. Does a shadow give off heat?

II. Draw a line from the word to the right picture.

1. shadow 2. thermometer 3. heat

25

* ***Answers to masters on pages 126E–126F***

CHAPTER 8

Teaching Plan

Chapter Components	**Skills**	**Materials**
Chapter Opener/*TRY THIS:* Observing an Airplane Move pp. 144-145	***TRY THIS*** p. 145 **Science Process Skills** *Making models, Observing*	***TRY THIS*** p. 145 (individual) 30 sheets assorted construction paper
Lesson 1: What Ways Do Objects Move? pp. 146-148	**Thinking Skills** Challenge!: *Making analogies* Find Out: *Restating or explaining ideas*	**Demonstration** p. 146 wind-up toy
Science in Your Life: Using Robots for Work p. 149	**Thinking Skill** *Making inferences*	
Lesson 2: What Can Move Objects? pp. 150-152	**Thinking Skills** Challenge!: *Predicting* Find Out: *Recognizing cause and effect*	**Demonstration** p. 150 toy car
Activity: Using a Magnet p. 153	**Science Process Skills** *Observing, Inferring*	(individual) 30 magnets (bar), 30 paper plates, 30 paper clips, 30 scissors, 1 roll transparent tape, 15 pieces assorted construction paper (3 cm square)
Lesson 3: What Work Can Machines Do? pp. 154-156	**Thinking Skills** Challenge!: *Drawing conclusions* Find Out: *Collecting data*	**Demonstration** p. 154 screwdriver, can with a lipped lid, bag
Activity: Moving a Rock p. 157	**Science Process Skills** *Making models, Inferring, Communicating*	(groups of 2) 15 wooden spoons, 30 meters string, 15 pencils, 15 small rocks
Skills for Solving Problems: Using a Machine pp. 158-159	**Problem Solving Skills** *Making decisions/Identifying and solving problems, interpreting charts, maps, and graphs*	(individual) metric ruler, book, pencil
Chapter Review pp. 160-161	**Thinking Skills** *Restating or explaining ideas, Predicting*	

Teaching Options

Strategies	Extensions		Resource Masters
			Family Letter: *Resource Book* p. 59 Vocabulary Preview: *Workbook* pp. 43-44
	Reinforcement p. 146 Special Education p. 147 Enrichment p. 147	Game Suggestion p. 147 Reteaching Suggestion p. 148	Science Skills: *Workbook* p. 45
	Reinforcement p. 150 Special Education p. 151	Enrichment p. 151 Reteaching Suggestion p. 152	Science Activity: *Workbook* p. 46
	Enrichment activity p. 153		
	Reinforcement p. 154 Special Education p. 155	Enrichment p. 155 Reteaching Suggestion p. 156	Science and Reading: *Workbook* p. 47 Vocabulary Puzzle: *Workbook* p. 48
	Enrichment Activity p. 157		
			Enrichment Activity: *Resource Book* p. 63
Cooperative Learning p. 160 (Also see p. T23)			Chapter Test: *Test Book* p. 27

Preteaching Suggestions

For Advance Preparation

Demonstration, page 146
Bring a wind-up toy to class.

Demonstration, page 150
Obtain a toy car for this demonstration.

Activity, page 153
Provide a magnet and a paper plate for each group.

Demonstration, page 154
Bring a screwdriver and a can with a lipped lid, such as a paint can, to class for this demonstration.

Activity, page 157
Provide each group with an empty thread spool, a pencil or piece of dowling that will fit through the spool hole, about 18 inches of string, and small rocks.

For Vocabulary Review

Use the following sentences with your students to review the meanings of the underlined words.

1. Objects are things you can see or touch.
2. The line something moves along is its direction.
3. When you move something by pushing or pulling, you do work.

For High-Potential Students

As a brainstorming activity, have students make lists of ways they might use magnets to help do everyday tasks. Next, ask students to select a particular chore or activity such as making the bed, picking up or organizing toys, feeding a pet, brushing one's teeth, waking up in the morning, and so on, and invent a method which uses magnets to help complete the task. For example, a student might glue a magnetic strip to the inside of a notebook and stick thumbtacks into pencils thereby inventing a method of carrying pencils to school which also helps avoid losing them. Encourage students' creativity even if the new methods seem somewhat impractical and outrageous.

For Mainstreamed Students

Orthopedically Handicapped
Discuss with students with orthopedic handicaps the difference between those objects that they can move themselves and those that help them move. Ask volunteers to show the class how a wheelchair or braces helps them move. Respect students' feelings if they do not wish to volunteer.

Visually Impaired
Let students prepare the paper airplane as described in the TRY THIS activity on page 145 but place sharp creases in the paper, allowing students with visual impairments to do the actual folding. If the student has enough vision, use a wide line marker and draw the folding lines on the paper, allowing the student to fold the airplane with direction as needed. Have a sighted partner describe the flight of the plane.

For Science Fair Projects

Encourage interested students to do one of the following projects:

1. Build a machine that can carry objects across water in a bathtub or plastic wash basin. Investigate how many objects the machine can hold and still float.
2. Build a machine that has wheels and investigate how it moves across a variety of surfaces.

Classroom Resources

Bulletin Board
Ask students to act out a scene of themselves moving and working in some way. Have the class guess what each student is showing.

Chapter 8 Poster

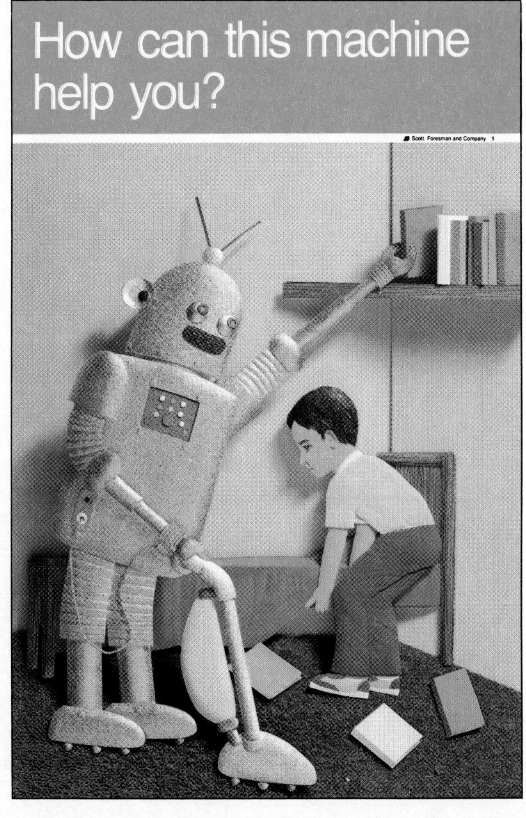

Science Discovery Center
Use pages from Chapter 8 in the *Science Discovery Center Book*. Place these worksheets in the appropriate pockets in the Science Discovery Center.

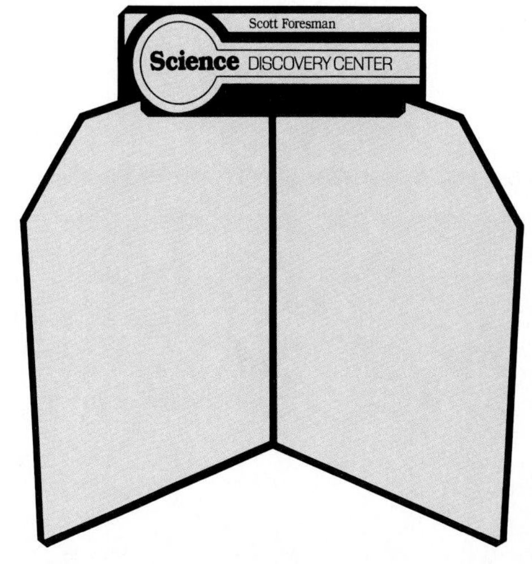

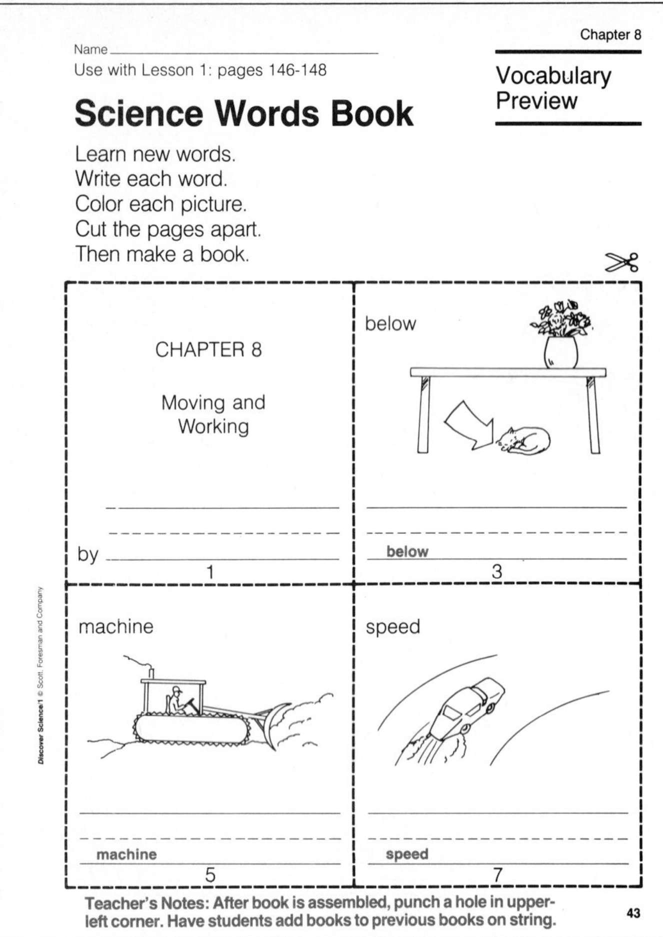

Name ____________________

Use with Lesson 1: pages 146-148

Chapter 8

Vocabulary Preview

Science Words Book

Learn new words.
Write each word.
Color each picture.
Cut the pages apart.
Then make a book.

Teacher's Notes: After book is assembled, punch a hole in upper-left corner. Have students add books to previous books on string.

43

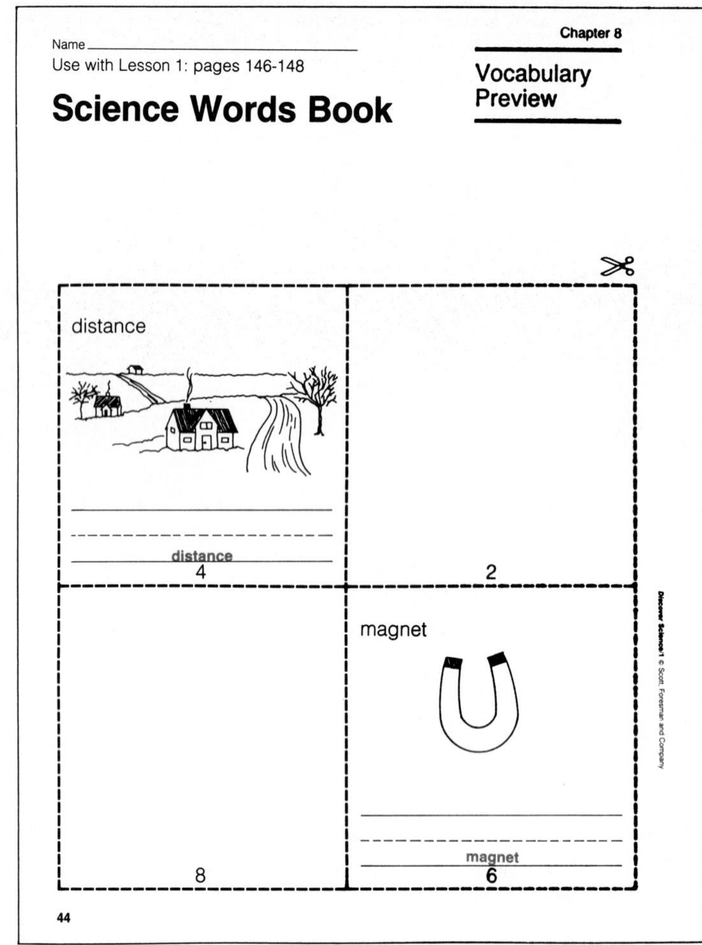

Name ____________________

Use with Lesson 1: pages 146-148

Chapter 8

Vocabulary Preview

Science Words Book

44

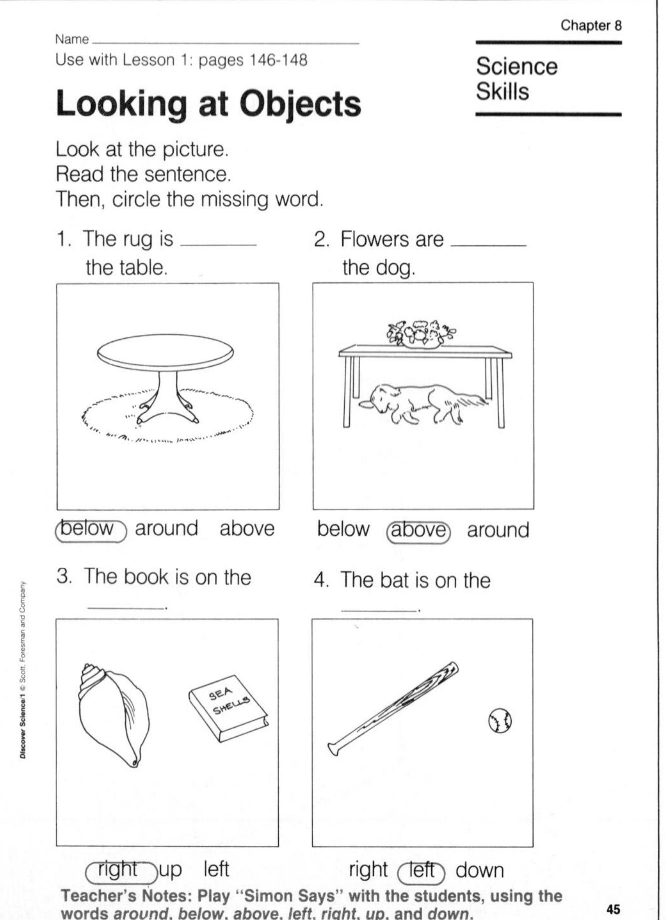

Name ____________________

Use with Lesson 1: pages 146-148

Chapter 8

Science Skills

Looking at Objects

Look at the picture.
Read the sentence.
Then, circle the missing word.

1. The rug is ________ the table.

(below) around above

2. Flowers are ________ the dog.

below (above) around

3. The book is on the ________.

(right) up left

4. The bat is on the ________.

right (left) down

Teacher's Notes: Play "Simon Says" with the students, using the words *around*, *below*, *above*, *left*, *right*, *up*, and *down*.

45

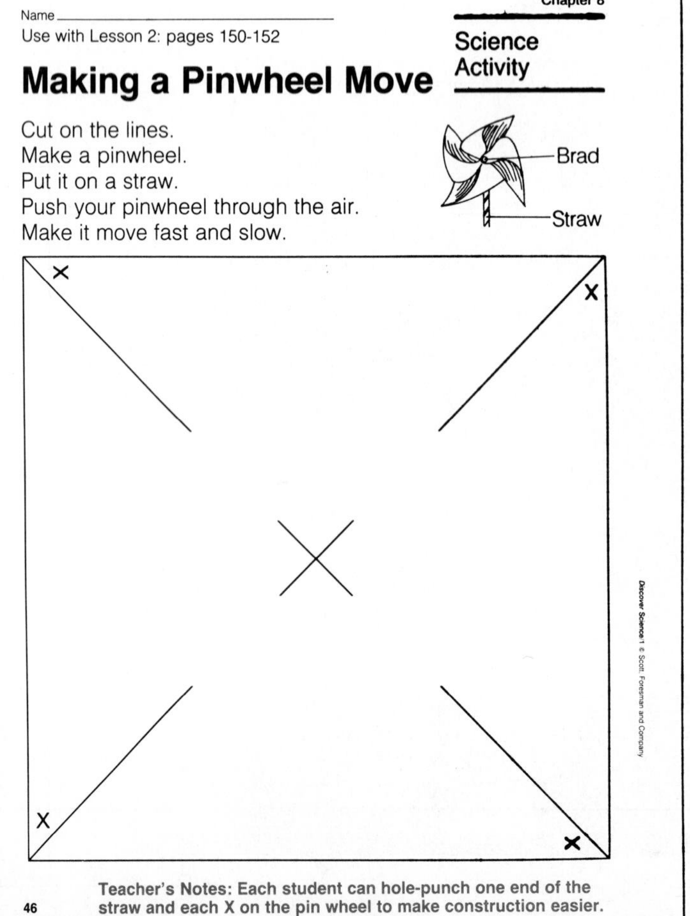

Name ____________________

Use with Lesson 2: pages 150-152

Chapter 8

Science Activity

Making a Pinwheel Move

Cut on the lines.
Make a pinwheel.
Put it on a straw.
Push your pinwheel through the air.
Make it move fast and slow.

46

Teacher's Notes: Each student can hole-punch one end of the straw and each X on the pin wheel to make construction easier.

Name ______________________

Use with Lesson 3: pages 154-156

Chapter 8

Science and Reading

Sandy and Her Wagon

Read the story.

The Wagon

Sandy has a wagon.
She pulls the wagon.
She pushes the wagon.
The wagon moves.

The wagon has wheels.
The wheels turn.
They help Sandy move the wagon.

Now read each question.
Circle the best answer.
The first one is done for you.

1. What does Sandy have?

a car   a dog   (a wagon)

2. What does the wagon have?

(wheels)   a house   a car

3. What do the wheels do?

push   (turn)   pull

4. What happens when Sandy pushes the wagon?

(It moves.)   It sits.   She falls.

Teacher's Notes: Have students push and pull things with wheels and things without wheels. Ask "Which is easier?"

Name ______________________

Use with Lesson 3: pages 154-156

Chapter 8

Vocabulary Puzzle

Code

Each number in the code stands for a letter.
Match each number below to a letter in the code.
Write the word.
One is done for you.

1	2	3	4	5	6	7	8	9	10	11	12	13
a	b	c	d	e	f	g	h	i	j	k	l	m

14	15	16	17	18	19	20	21	22	23	24	25	26
n	o	p	q	r	s	t	u	v	w	x	y	z

1. b e l o w
   2 5 12 15 23

2. 

   4 9 19 20 1 14 3 5

3. 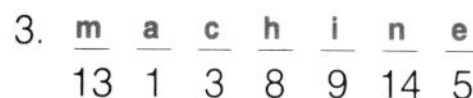

   13 1 3 8 9 14 5

4. 

   13 1 7 14 5 20

5. 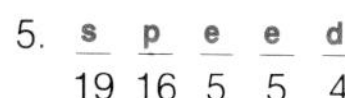

   19 16 5 5 4

Teacher's Notes: Help students decode the following numbers: a) 16, 21, 19, 8 (push); b) 16, 21, 12, 12 (pull).

Name ______________________

Chapter 8

Enrichment Experiment

A Magnet Experiment

Are two magnets stronger than one magnet?

Circle your prediction.   Yes   No   Accept any answer.

Do this experiment to find out.

1. Collect the objects below.

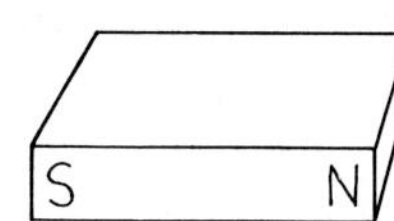

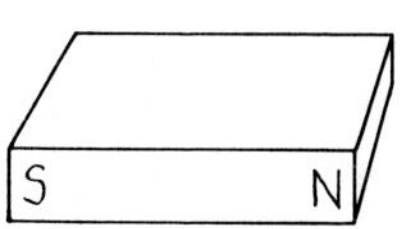

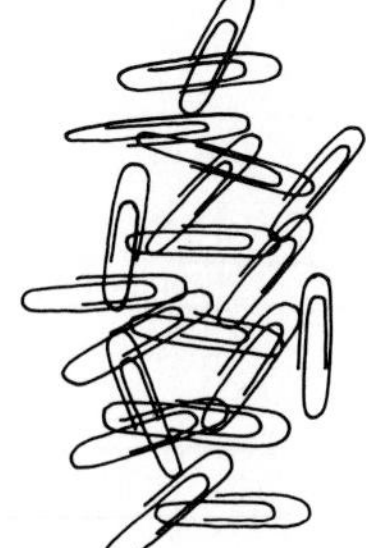

2. Use one magnet to pick up paper clips.
   Count how many you pick up with one.
3. Use two magnets together to pick up paper clips.
   Count how many you pick up with two.
4. Circle which picked up more paper clips.

1 magnet   (2 magnets)

Name ______________________

Chapter 8 Test

Moving and Working

I. Write **Yes** or **No**.

1. Do objects move only one way? (8-1) No
2. Can objects move at different speeds? (8-1) Yes
3. Can magnets pull some objects? (8-2) Yes
4. Do some machines push and pull objects? (8-3) Yes
5. Do some machines help people work? (8-3) Yes

II. Draw a line from the word to the right picture.

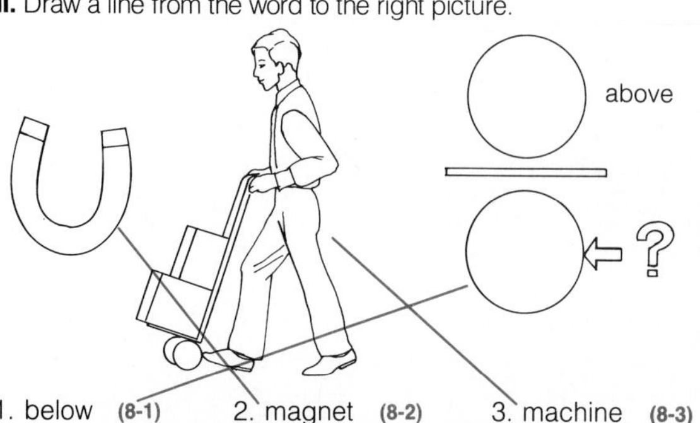

1. below (8-1)   2. magnet (8-2)   3. machine (8-3)

The numbers in parentheses after each question refer to the chapter and lesson objective covered by that question.

TEACHING PLAN

INTRODUCING CHAPTER 8

Major Concepts

Lesson 1 Motion can vary.

Lesson 2 Various forces can move objects.

Lesson 3 Various machines use motion combined with force to produce different kinds of work.

Vocabulary

below, distance, machine, magnet, speed

[1] Airplanes can transport people and goods.

Chapter 8

Moving and Working

Airplanes move in the sky.
What work can airplanes do?[1]

144

Teaching Options

Workbook page 43 *

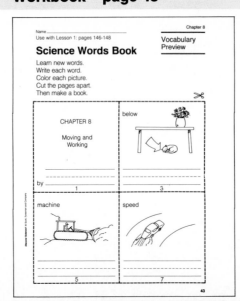

Name
Use with Lesson 1: pages 146-148

Chapter 8
Vocabulary Preview

Science Words Book

Learn new words.
Write each word.
Color each picture.
Cut the pages apart.
Then make a book.

CHAPTER 8
Moving and Working
by
1

below
3

machine
5

speed
7

43

Workbook page 44 *

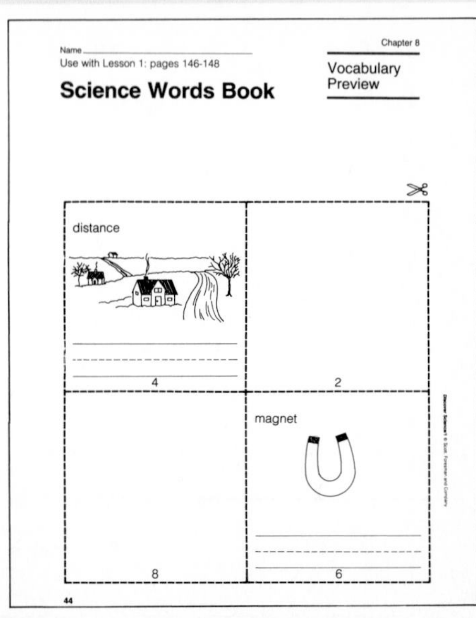
Name
Use with Lesson 1: pages 146-148

Chapter 8
Vocabulary Preview

Science Words Book

distance
4

2

8

magnet
6

44

♦ ***Suitable as a language development activity***

Starting the Chapter

What objects can you move at home?
What objects can you move at school?
You can make a paper airplane move.
Read more about ways things move.

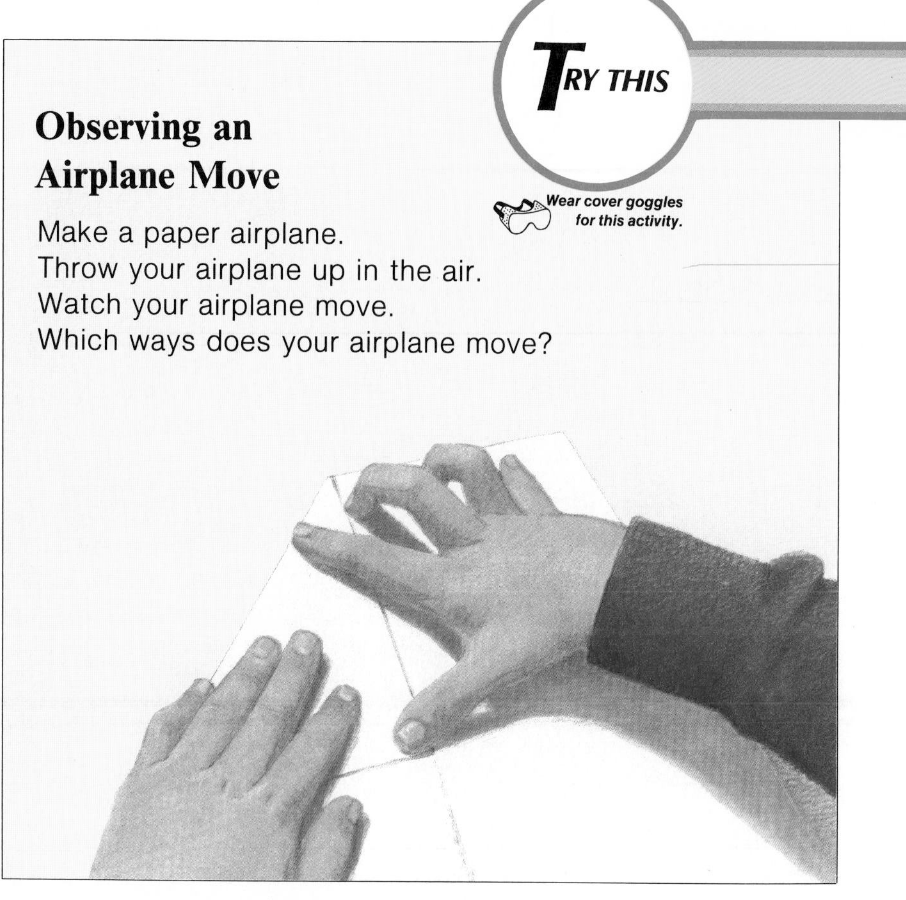

TRY THIS
Wear cover goggles for this activity.

Observing an Airplane Move

Make a paper airplane.
Throw your airplane up in the air.
Watch your airplane move.
Which ways does your airplane move?

145

TRY THIS

Objective ♦
This optional *TRY THIS* activity will help students explore and build background information about the concept that motion can vary. Later in the chapter, students will be able to draw on this experience to help them assimilate the new content.

Science Process Skills
Making models, Observing

Materials
For each student: 1 sheet construction paper

Safety Tip (See page T27.)
- Instruct students not to aim their paper airplanes in the direction of their classmates.

Teaching Tips
- Help students follow directions for making a paper airplane.
- Students should have plenty of room to test and *observe* the ways their airplanes fly. Be sure they understand that this is not a test of how far it will fly or how good they are at making paper airplanes.

Answer
Students should *describe* the ways the airplane moves, such as up, down, around, side-to-side, and so on.

Resource Book page 59

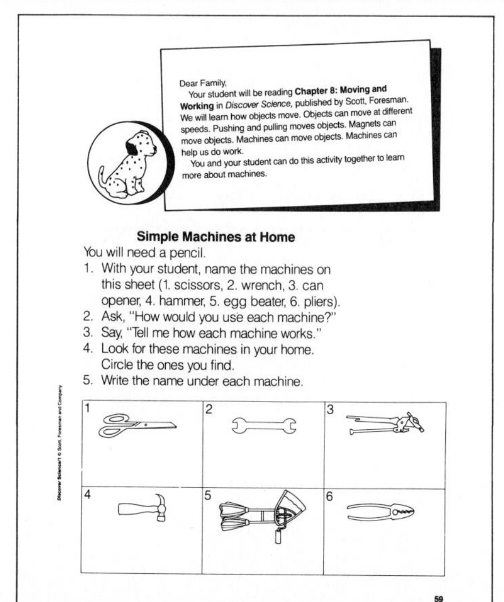

Dear Family,
Your student will be reading **Chapter 8: Moving and Working** in *Discover Science*, published by Scott, Foresman. We will learn how objects move. Objects can move at different speeds. Pushing and pulling moves objects. Magnets can move objects. Machines can move objects. Machines can help us do work.
You and your student can do this activity together to learn more about machines.

Simple Machines at Home

You will need a pencil.
1. With your student, name the machines on this sheet (1. scissors, 2. wrench, 3. can opener, 4. hammer, 5. egg beater, 6. pliers).
2. Ask, "How would you use each machine?"
3. Say, "Tell me how each machine works."
4. Look for these machines in your home. Circle the ones you find.
5. Write the name under each machine.

1	2	3
4	5	6

59

SCIENCE BACKGROUND

Because motion must be measured or observed relative to a fixed object, called a reference point, the term *relative motion* is more accurate than the term *motion*. An object is in motion when it changes position relative to the reference point.

* **Answers to masters on pages 144E–144F**

TEACHING PLAN

LESSON 1
pages 146–148

Lesson Objectives
- *Name* different positions objects take when they move.
- *Explain* that objects can change distance and speed.

Lesson Vocabulary
below, distance, speed

1 MOTIVATE

Demonstration Activity ♦
Bring a wind-up toy to class and have students *observe* its motion.

Discussion
Discuss the movement of the wind-up toy. Encourage students to use positional terms to *describe* the movement of the toy.

[1] Objects that can move independently can usually move up, down, left, and right.

Lesson 1 What Ways Do Objects Move?

Objects move in different ways.
The butterfly can move around the branches.
It can move up and down.
The butterfly can move left and right.
It can move above and **below** the branches.
What other objects can move in these ways?[1]

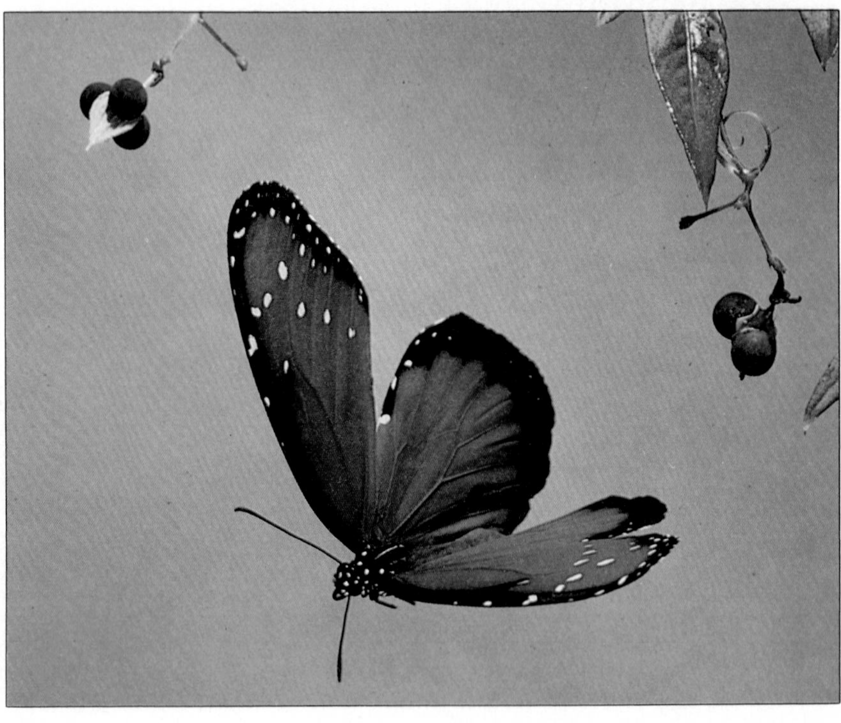

146

Teaching Options

SCIENCE BACKGROUND

The way a person views the position and motion of an object depends on the person's frame of reference. An object that is near, above, to the left, and in front occupies that position relative to the observer. To another observer, the same object may be far away, below, to the right, and behind. Similarly, the directions and speeds of moving objects are relative to the observer.

Reinforcement

Provide students with magazines to look through for pictures of people, animals, or objects in motion. Have students cut out and paste pictures on paper and write sentences to *describe* the motion. Make a list of motion words for the students to use in their sentences (fly, gallop, crawl, wriggle, slither, and so on).

♦ ***Suitable as a language development activity***

Objects can move near or far away.
Objects and people can change **distance.**
These people move near the elephants.
Next, the people will move away.
They will be far from the elephants.
Then they will move near the birds.

2 TEACH

Teaching Tips

- Read the text aloud with the students and have them think of other objects that can move up and down, left and right, and above and below. Have the students take small objects from their desks and move them to various positions in relation to themselves.
- Read page 147 with the students. Have several volunteers ***identify*** objects in the classroom that are near to them and far away from them.
- To help students visualize how moving far away can change one's perceptions, choose two children who are the same size and have one move to a designated spot on the other side of the room or playground while the other student stays with the class. Point out that the student far away appears to be smaller.

Special Education

Provide students who have learning disabilities with a large ball of yarn wound around a wooden spool. Tell them that they are going to "Tie Up the Classroom." With one student holding the wooden spool, have another student take the end of the yarn and start to "tie up" the room, ***describing*** where he or she is going, such as "under the desk," "around the chairs," or "above the chalk ledge." Next, have the student who has the yarn end take directions from the teacher such as "Walk to the teacher's desk," " Turn right," "Get down on your knees," "Go under the desk," and so on. Then have students "untie" the classroom, describing their positions.

Enrichment

Display several objects on a table. Direct students to close their eyes. When they do so, move one object to a new position. Have students open their eyes. Ask them which object moved and how they can tell. Repeat the game, allowing students to take turns moving the objects.

Game Suggestion ♦

Play "Simon Says" with the students, allowing students to take turns providing instructions for various body movements to their classmates.

3 ASSESS

Lesson Review
1. Answers could include that objects move up, down, left, right, around, above, below, near, and far.
2. Objects can move fast and slowly.
Challenge! Question: **How are an elevator and an airplane alike?** (They both change direction, distance, and speed. Or, they both go up and down, fast and slow, near and far.) **Thinking Skill:** *Making analogies*

Find Out
Answers will depend on individual observations. **Thinking Skill:** *Restating or explaining ideas*

[1] The girl on the left moves fastest.

Objects move at different **speeds.**
They can move fast or slow.
Which child moves fastest?[1]

Lesson Review

1. What ways can objects move?
2. At what speeds do objects move?

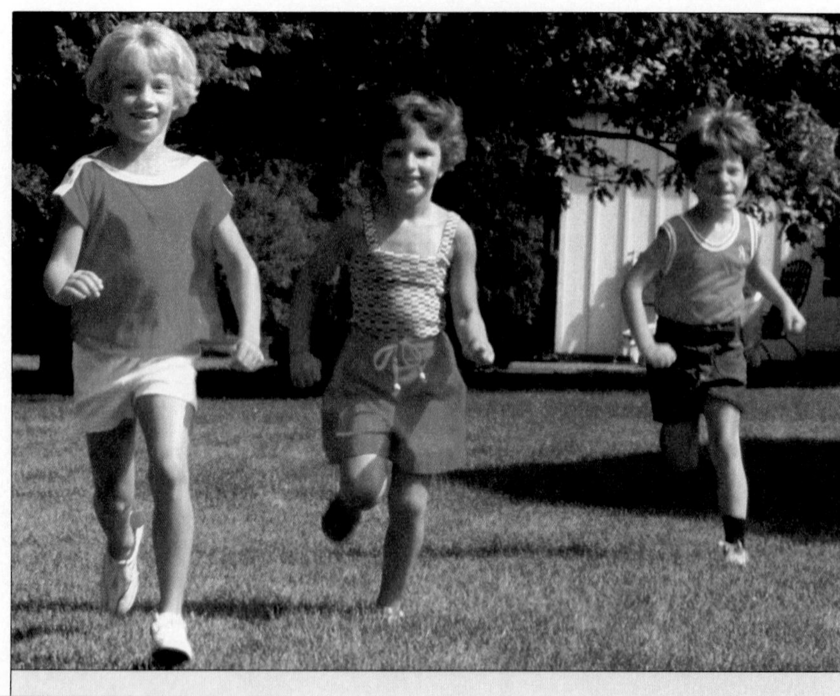

Find Out Watch friends on the playground. Notice the ways people move.

148

Teaching Options

SCIENCE ANECDOTE

A motion picture is a series of still pictures flashed on a screen in succession. The pictures are so vivid we do not notice that the screen is dark more than 50 percent of the time during a movie.

Reteaching Suggestion ♦

Take the class out to the playground and give directions for them to move in a variety of ways (to the left and right, near the slide, far from the monkey bars, fast, slow, and so on)

Workbook page 45 *

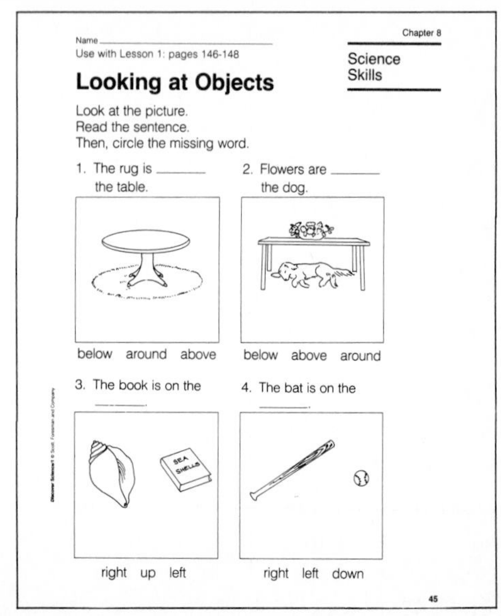
Name ____
Use with Lesson 1: pages 146-148

Chapter 8
Science Skills

Looking at Objects

Look at the picture.
Read the sentence.
Then, circle the missing word.

1. The rug is ____ the table.
below around above

2. Flowers are ____ the dog.
below above around

3. The book is on the ____
right up left

4. The bat is on the ____
right left down

45

♦ ***Suitable as a language development activity***

Using Robots for Work

People build robots that can move.
Robots move in different directions.
They can do work for people.
Robots can bring food to people.
They can help put cars together.
Someday a robot might do work for you!

What Do You Think?

What could a robot do best?

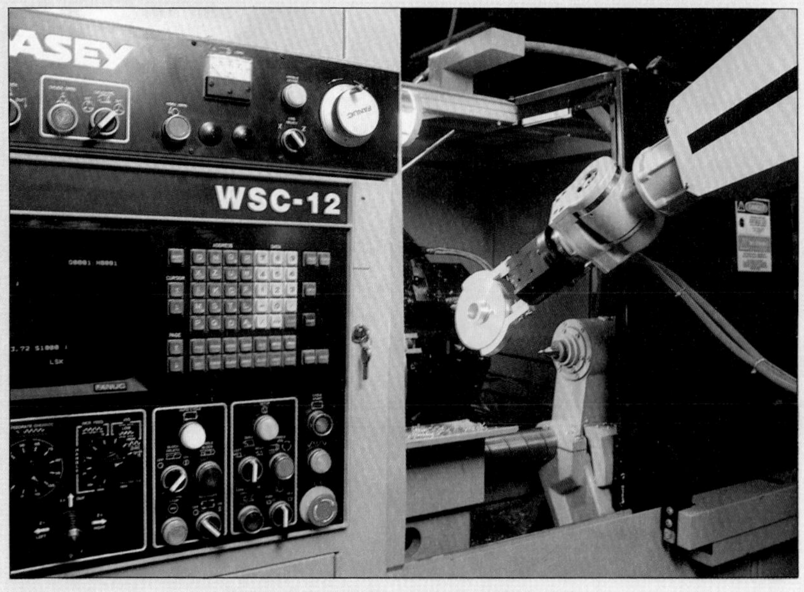

SCIENCE IN YOUR LIFE

Discussion

Discuss what students already know about robots. Help students to understand that robots do not think for themselves, but must be programmed to perform certain tasks. Let the students pretend to be robots and move according to certain directions (their program).

Teaching Tips

- Call the students' attention to the robot in the illustration. Discuss what it is doing and how the robot "knows" what to do.
- Have students read page 149 to discover some of the tasks that robots can perform. Have the students tell what they would like to have a robot do for them.

Answers

What Do You Think?
Robots could do best those jobs too boring or too dangerous for people to do.
Thinking Skill: *Making inferences*

Books to Read

McComb, Gordon. *The Robot Builder's Bonanza: 99 Inexpensive Robotics Projects*. Tab, 1987. (for the teacher)

SCIENCE BACKGROUND

Some robots respond to voice commands and some have sensors that allow them to move according to environmental stimuli. Some robots move on motorized wheels. Newer ones are designed with joints or springs allowing them to move up hills or to climb stairs. In industry, robots do some monotonous tasks such as assembly line work. They also handle explosives and traveling in space.

* ***Answers to masters on pages 144E–144F***

TEACHING PLAN

LESSON 2
pages 150–152

Lesson Objective
- *Identify* what can move objects, including pushing, pulling, lifting, and magnets

Lesson Vocabulary
magnet

1 MOTIVATE

Demonstration Activity ♦
Display a toy car. Ask students to *name* some ways the car could be moved. As each method is suggested, have a student demonstrate by moving the toy in the suggested manner.

Discussion
Write the words *push*, *pull*, and *lift* on the chalkboard and have students read them. Questions: **How could you move the toy if you were behind it?** (push) **How could you use a string to move the toy?** (pull) **How could you get the toy from the table to the top shelf of the bookcase?** (lift)

[1] The heavily-loaded wagon is harder to move.

Lesson 2 What Can Move Objects?

Pushing moves objects.
Pulling moves objects.
Pushing and pulling can move a wagon.
Heavy objects are harder to move.
You must push or pull harder.
Which wagon is harder to move?[1]

150

Teaching Options

SCIENCE BACKGROUND

A force is a push or pull that can change the motion of an object. Force can start an object moving, slow it down, or stop it. Once the object is moving, it will continue until another force acts upon it. Humans and other organisms can exert forces to change the motion of an object. Such machines as auto engines, electric motors, and rockets also can push and pull.

Reinforcement

Encourage students to bring push or pull toys to school. (Many baby toys are of this type.) Allow time for students to show their toys, demonstrate how they are moved, and *identify* the force as pushing or pulling.

♦ ***Suitable as a language development activity***

[1] The child is lifting magazines. The magazines move up. If they fall, they would move down.

Lifting can move objects.

Objects also move when they fall.

Objects fall down toward the ground.

What is this child moving by lifting?[1]

What direction do the objects move?

What direction will they go if they fall?

151

2 TEACH

Teaching Tips

- **Possible Misconception:** Students might not think of most forces they are familiar with as being forms of push or pull. Point out that stop, bat, kick, open, close, and so on are all push/pull forces.
- Call the students' attention to the illustration on page 150. Have students ***identify*** the ways the wagon is being moved. After reading the page, have the students discuss which wagon would be easiest to pull and which would be hardest to pull.
- Have students read page 151 and ***identify*** lifting and falling as two ways objects can move. Write *lift* and *fall* on the board. Have students identify the direction for each of these two ways to move.

Special Education

Provide students with learning disabilities with an empty wagon. Tell them to use the handle to move the wagon from one point to another. Ask them to ***describe*** what they did to move the wagon. Next, tell them to move the wagon from one point to another without using the handle. If they pull it, ask them if they can find another way to move it. (pushing) After students have demonstrated pushing and pulling, ask one student to get into the wagon. Talk about the weight difference in relation to the amount of push and pull needed. Add another student and again discuss the differences.

Enrichment

Have students keep a list of things they push, pull, or lift. Allow time for students to share and ***compare*** their lists with those of their classmates.

TEACHING PLAN

Teaching Tips

- Place a magnet and a variety of small objects in a box. Let the students take turns using the magnet to find out which objects it will pull.
- Tell students that magnets can pull other magnets toward them, or they can push magnets away. Put several magnets in a box and let students investigate this by placing like and unlike poles together.

3 ASSESS

Lesson Review

1. Pushing, pulling, lifting, and carrying can all move objects.
2. Objects fall to the ground.
Challenge! Ask students **What could you toss up that would not immediately come back down?** (Answer might include insects or some balloons. You might ask students if they think helium balloons ever come back down.) **Thinking Skill:** *Predicting*

Find Out

Answer will depend on objects student tries to move with magnet. **Thinking Skill:** *Recognizing cause and effect*

[1] Magnet attracts metal paper clips.
[2] Magnet is horseshoe shaped.

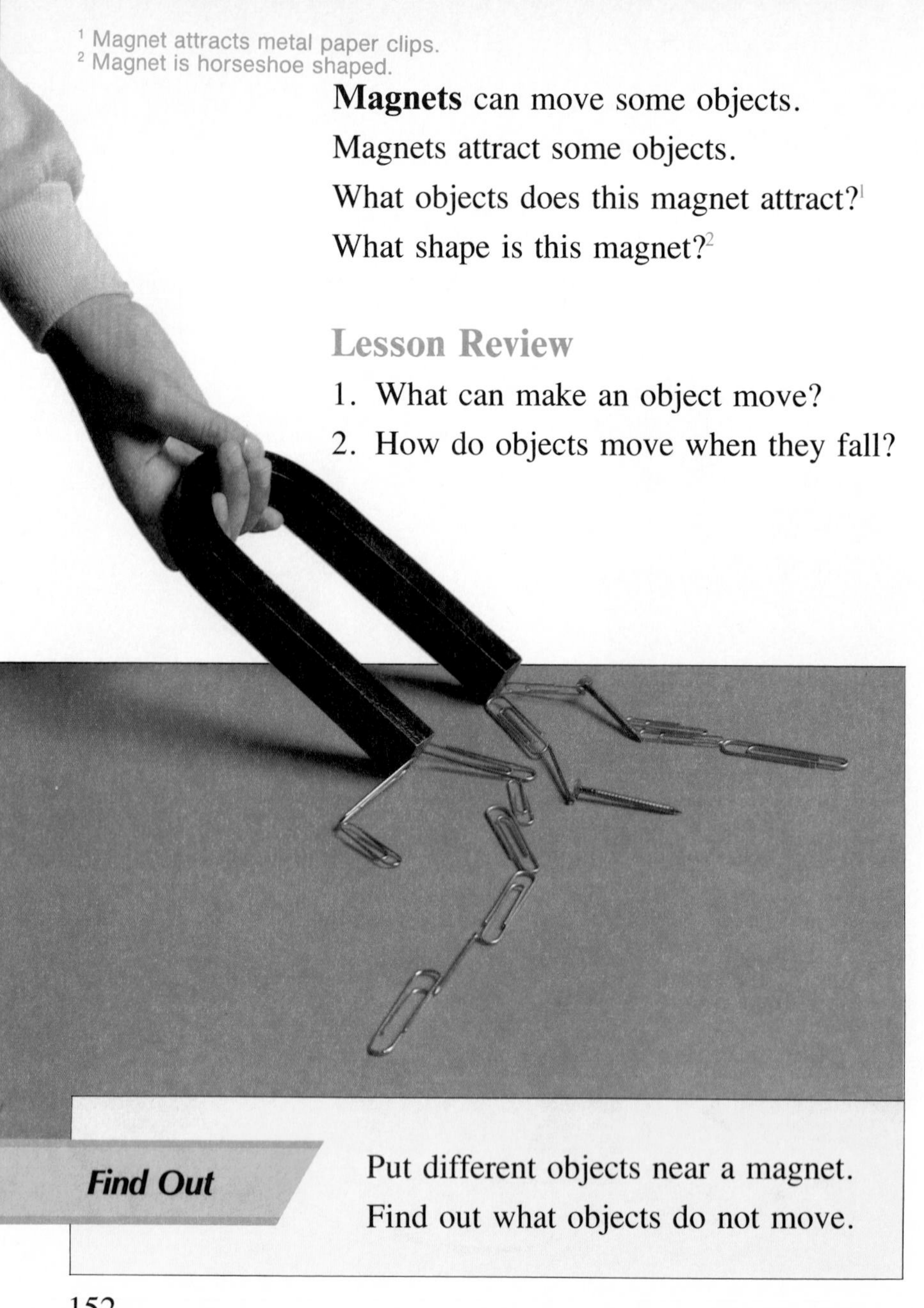

Magnets can move some objects.
Magnets attract some objects.
What objects does this magnet attract?[1]
What shape is this magnet?[2]

Lesson Review

1. What can make an object move?
2. How do objects move when they fall?

Find Out

Put different objects near a magnet.
Find out what objects do not move.

152

Teaching Options

SCIENCE ANECDOTE

Weight-lifting is an Olympic sport in which people of larger and larger sizes lift heavier and heavier weights. In the largest class, people can lift over 200 kilograms (440 pounds).

Reteaching Suggestion ♦

Have students act out pushing and pulling. Also, have them lift and drop a small object and *identify* lifting as an upward movement and falling as a downward movement.

Workbook page 46 *

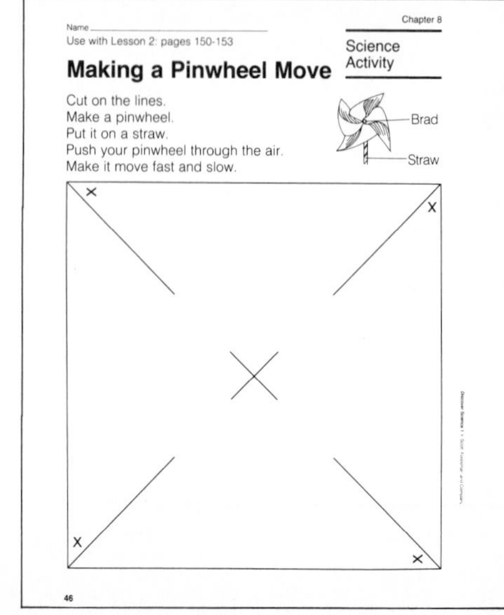

Name ___
Use with Lesson 2: pages 150-153
Chapter 8
Science Activity

Making a Pinwheel Move

Cut on the lines.
Make a pinwheel.
Put it on a straw.
Push your pinwheel through the air.
Make it move fast and slow.

46

♦ ***Suitable as a language development activity***

ACTIVITY

Using a Magnet

Follow the Directions

1. Cut out a small paper circle.
2. Tape a paper clip to the circle.
3. Put the circle on a paper plate.
4. Keep the paper clip next to the plate.
5. Move a magnet under the plate.
6. Observe what the circle does.

Tell What You Learned

Tell what you used a magnet to do.
Tell another way to use a magnet.

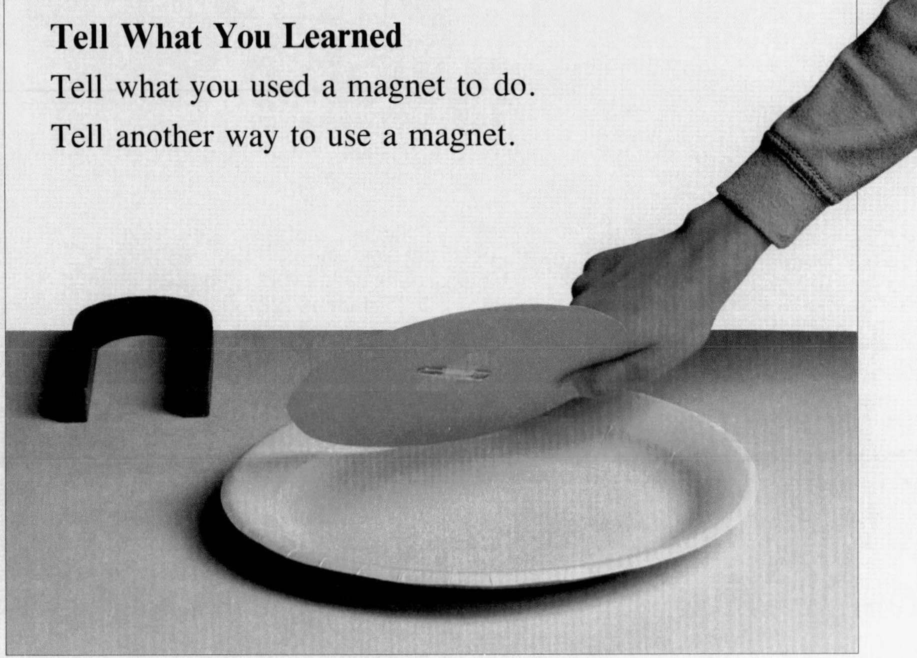

153

Enrichment Activity

Allow students to try moving other objects in the room, such as paper, cloth, and erasers, to discover what the magnet can move.

Activity Results

The paper circle moves as a result of the paper clip being attracted by the magnet.

ACTIVITY PLAN

Concept
A magnet can attract certain objects.

Objectives/Process Skills
- *Observe* the movement of a paper circle.
- *Infer* that the magnet causes the movement observed.

Time Allotment
Allow 20 minutes.

Materials
For each student: bar magnet, paper plate, paper clip, scissors, tape, sheet construction paper (3 cm square)

Safety Tip (See page T27.)
- Use only round-tipped scissors for this activity. Remind students to use scissors carefully to prevent cuts.

Teaching Tips
- Help students read the activity and follow the directions.
- Distribute materials. Ask students to each cut out a paper circle large enough to cover the clip.

Answers
Tell What You Learned
For the first statement, students should state that they used the magnet to make the clip under the paper move. For the second statement, students should *name* a way that a magnet could be used, such as to clip notes to the refrigerator, hold metal lids when opening cans, and so on. **Thinking Skills:** *Inferring, Applying Information to new situations*

*** *Answers to masters on pages 144E–144F***

TEACHING PLAN

LESSON 3
pages 154–156

Lesson Objectives
- *Describe* what work different machines do.
- *Describe* how people use machines.

Lesson Vocabulary
machines

1 MOTIVATE

Demonstration Activity ♦
Bring a screwdriver and a can with a lipped lid to class in a bag. Tell the students that you have brought a machine to school to do some work for you. Have students watch you remove the lid of the can.

Discussion
Have the students *describe* the force you used to move the screwdriver (push) and the force it used to move the lid (push, lift). Explain that a screwdriver is a machine because it can be used along with force to do work.

[1] The bulldozer pushes.

Lesson 3 What Work Can Machines Do?

What is work?

Work is using a push to move objects.

It is using a pull to move objects, too.

Machines that move objects do work.

Which machine here pushes?[1]

154

Teaching Options

SCIENCE BACKGROUND

Although all machines have less than 100 percent efficiency, the amount of work one puts into a machine is theoretically equal to the amount of work one gets out of the machine. Most machines make tasks easier by increasing the forces people apply to a machine. For example, a person exerts a relatively small force as he/she moves the handle of a car jack a relatively large distance. In return, the jack exerts a relatively large force as it lifts the car a relatively short distance. The car jack sacrifices distance for force.

Reinforcement

Suggest that students look for machines at home and make a book about them. Have them draw a picture on each page and write a sentence indicating what the machine does and who uses it.

♦ *Suitable as a language development activity*

[1] The bulldozer pushes; the truck pulls; another machine moves milk containers.

Look at these different machines.

They help people.

The machines are used to lift and carry.

What work does each machine do?[1]

When do you use machines?

155

2 TEACH

Teaching Tips

- **Possible Misconception:** Students might think that the word *work* has only one meaning, as in schoolwork, homework, or a job. Have them read page 154 to find out another use of the word *work*, such as lifting, pushing, pulling, or carrying. Have students ***identify*** the machines in the picture and the work being done by each.
- Read page 155 with the students and help them ***identify*** the machines shown on pages 154–155 that lift and carry and the work that they do. Ask students to tell where they have seen machines such as the ones in the illustration.
- Have students generate a list of machines and ***identify*** the work they do. Help students group the machines that do the same kind of work together, listing them on the chalkboard.

Special Education

Show students with learning disabilities the pulley on a curtain. Point out that the action of pulling on the cord of the pulley makes it work so that the curtain opens and closes. Next, show the students a simple hand can opener (the kind that punctures cans leaving a triangular opening). Demonstrate that when it is placed against the edge of the can with the sharp end on the lid and the blunt end lifted, the can opener, a lever, works. Next, present a library cart. Show students that as it is pushed or pulled, the wheels move and work.

Enrichment

Encourage students to look for pictures of simple machines in magazines. Have them group the pictures according to whether they are wheels and axles, pulleys, levers, inclined planes, wedges, or screws.

Workbook page 47 *

Name

Use with Lesson 3: pages 154-156

Chapter 8

Science and Reading

Sandy and Her Wagon

Read the story.

The Wagon

Sandy has a wagon.
She pulls the wagon.
She pushes the wagon.
The wagon moves.

The wagon has wheels.
The wheels turn.
They help Sandy move the wagon.

Now read each question.
Circle the best answer.
The first one is done for you.

1. What does Sandy have?

a car a dog (a wagon)

2. What does the wagon have?

wheels a house a car

3. What do the wheels do?

push turn pull

4. What happens when Sandy pushes the wagon?

It moves. It sits. She falls.

47

*** Answers to masters on pages 144E-144F***

TEACHING PLAN

Teaching Tip

• Call the students' attention to the illustration on page 156. Have them *identify* the work being done by the train (carrying people) and the machine in the factory. Encourage the students to think of ways people use machines for farming, building, and for work in homes.

3 ASSESS

Lesson Review

1. Machines lift, carry, push, and pull.
2. Machines help people build, farm, and do housework.
Challenge! Tell students that a doll does not move objects. Question: **Does it work?** (No.) **Thinking Skill:** *Drawing conclusions*

Find Out

Answers might include car, typewriter, food processor, pencil sharpener, doorknob, light switch, water faucet, and various tools. **Thinking Skill:** *Collecting data*

[1] People use machines to count money and for transportation.

People use machines for farming.
They use machines for building.
People use machines in homes.
How do people use machines here?[1]

Lesson Review

1. What kinds of work can machines do?
2. How do machines help people?

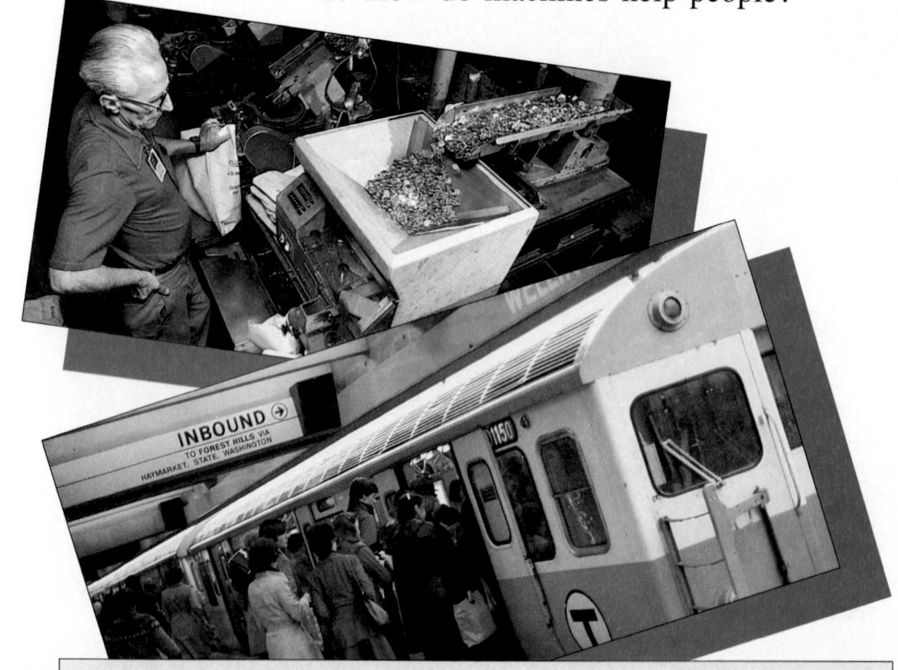

Find Out Look around your home or school. Find machines used to move things.

Teaching Options

SCIENCE ANECDOTE

Early machines imitated parts of the human body. A flint is like a fingernail. An axe is like an arm. A hammer is like a fist.

Reteaching Suggestion ♦

Take a tour of the school to look for machines that help people move things. Look for carts for moving computers or audiovisual equipment, dollies, trash carts, and so on. Make a list of the machines the students see during their walk.

Workbook page 48 *

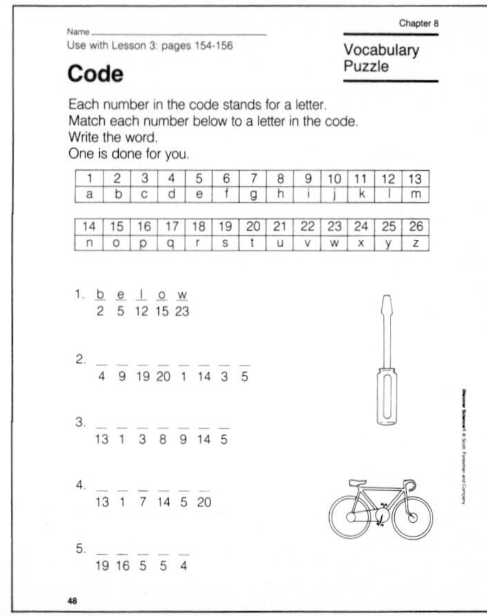

Name ______
Use with Lesson 3: pages 154-156

Chapter 8
Vocabulary Puzzle

Code

Each number in the code stands for a letter.
Match each number below to a letter in the code.
Write the word.
One is done for you.

1	2	3	4	5	6	7	8	9	10	11	12	13
a	b	c	d	e	f	g	h	i	j	k	l	m

14	15	16	17	18	19	20	21	22	23	24	25	26
n	o	p	q	r	s	t	u	v	w	x	y	z

1. b e l o w
   2 5 12 15 23
2. _ _ _ _ _ _ _ _
   4 9 19 20 1 14 3 5
3. _ _ _ _ _ _ _
   13 1 3 8 9 14 5
4. _ _ _ _ _ _
   13 1 7 14 5 20
5. _ _ _ _ _
   19 16 5 5 4

48

Discover Science® 1 © Scott, Foresman and Company

♦ ***Suitable as a language development activity***

Moving a Rock

Follow the Directions

1. Put together a machine like this.
2. Work with a partner.
3. Move a rock using the machine.
4. Notice what direction you pull the string.
5. Notice what direction the rock moves.

Tell What You Learned

Tell what work the machine did.

Tell another way to use this machine.

157

Enrichment Activity

Have students look for magazine pictures showing different ways pulleys are used.

Activity Results

The rock moves up as the string is pulled down.

ACTIVITY PLAN

Concept

Lifting an object with a fixed pulley changes the direction of the force.

Objectives/Process Skills

- ***Make and use*** a ***model*** of a pulley.
- ***Infer*** that a pulley does work.
- ***Describe*** another way to use a pulley.

Time Allotment

Allow 15 minutes.

Materials

For each pair of students: 1 wooden spool, 2 meters string, pencil, 1 small rock

Safety Tip (See page T27.)

- Have students use unsharpened pencils for this activity.

Teaching Tips

- Ask students to work with their partners to assemble a machine (pulley) using a pencil and spool. Distribute materials to each group.
- Help students read the activity and follow the directions.
- As the students are working with the pulley, encourage them to test it by using it to lift several different objects of different weights.
- Students should discover that by using a pulley, when they pull the string down, the rock goes up.

Answers

Tell What You Learned

For the first statement, students should state that the machine helped lift the rock. For the second statement, answers may include to lift heavy loads, to get something up to the top of a pole, and so on. **Thinking Skills:** ***Inferring, Applying information to new situations***

**** Answers to masters on pages 144E–144F***

SKILLS FOR SOLVING PROBLEMS
pages 158–159

Purpose
To develop the skills of collecting and organizing information using levers and charts to solve problems.

Materials
For each student: metric ruler, a book, and a pencil

1 MOTIVATE

Discussion
Ask students to *describe* what a lever is. (a simple machine used to make work easier) Discuss with them examples of levers, such as hand can openers, crowbars, and a hammer pulling a nail. Guide students to *conclude* that life would be very difficult without the use of levers.

Skills for Solving Problems

Using a Machine

What work can a machine do?

1. Use the objects in the picture. Keep them the same way you see here. They make up a machine.
2. Keep the pencil far from the book. Push down on the ruler. Move the pencil closer to the book. Push down on the ruler again. Notice how the book moves each time.

158

Teaching Options

SCIENCE BACKGROUND

Every lever has three important parts: the fulcrum (the support on which a lever turns), the force applied, and the weight or resistance. In this activity, the pencil is the fulcrum on which the lever turns, the book is the resistance, and the pressure used by the students is the force. By definition, work is done only when an object is moved. Work is the result of force moving through a distance. Pushing and pulling without movement results in no work being done.

3. Use your own paper.
Copy what you see here.
Circle how the book moved.

first time	second time
easy	easy
hard	hard

4. What did the machine lift?

2 TEACH

Teaching Tips

- Ask the students to arrange the ruler, a book, and a pencil as shown in the picture. With the pencil near the 2.5 cm (1 in.) mark, ask the students to push down on the ruler. In response to this force, the book will barely be moved. This action is dependent upon the weight of the book and the amount of the force applied.
- Ask the students to shift the pencil closer to the book and to push down on the ruler again.
- For the chart, students should circle *hard* for the first time and *easy* for the second time.
- On the playground, demonstrate how a see-saw works. Tell students that it is a machine, and help them to ***identify*** it as a lever. Point out that two students of the same weight sitting the same distance from the center cause the see-saw to balance. Also show that if there are two students of different weights, the lighter student must sit farther from the center for the see-saw to balance.

3 ASSESS

The machine lifted the book.

Resource Book page 63 *

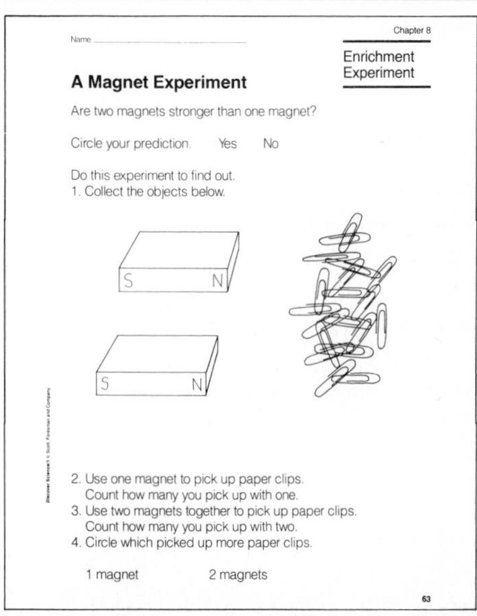
Name ______________

Chapter 8

Enrichment Experiment

A Magnet Experiment

Are two magnets stronger than one magnet?

Circle your prediction. Yes No

Do this experiment to find out.
1. Collect the objects below.

2. Use one magnet to pick up paper clips. Count how many you pick up with one.
3. Use two magnets together to pick up paper clips. Count how many you pick up with two.
4. Circle which picked up more paper clips.

1 magnet 2 magnets

63

* *Answers to masters on pages 144E-144F*

REVIEW PLAN

CHAPTER 8 REVIEW
pages 160–161

Review Chapter Ideas
1. Things move up, down, to the left, and to the right; things move in many directions.
2. Objects can change speed from fast to slow to fast.
3. Pushing and pulling moves objects.
4. A magnet can pull a metal object toward itself.
5. cart—machine carries groceries; tractor—machine pulls heavy load; hammer—machine pushes a nail

For further review, use Study Guide pages 234-235.

Chapter 8 Review

Review Chapter Ideas
1. Tell some ways things can move.
2. Tell how objects change speed.
3. Tell what can move objects.
4. Describe what a magnet can do.
5. Look at the pictures.
   Tell how machines help people.

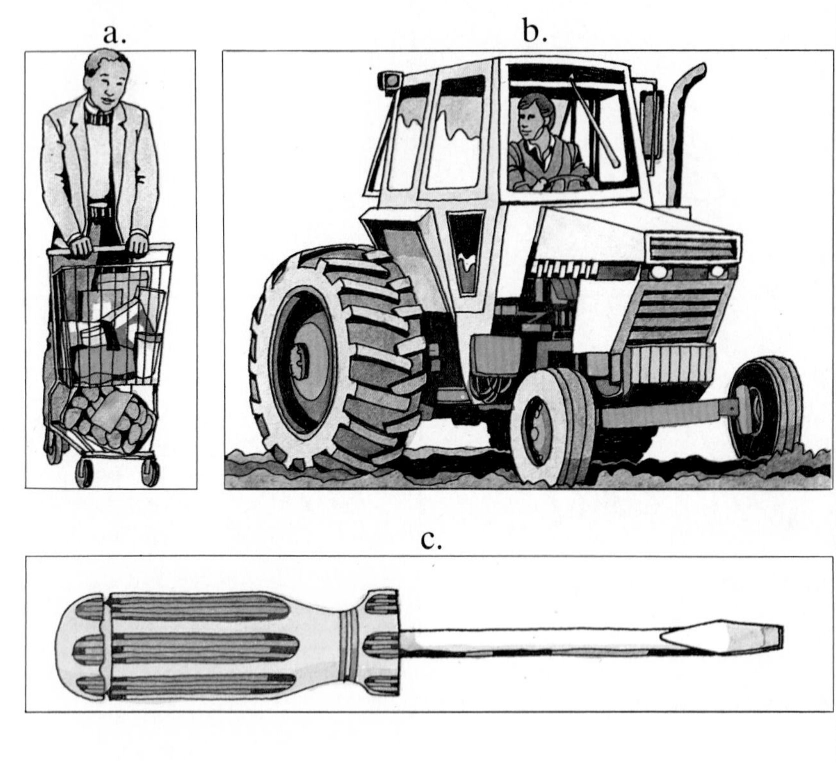

160

Review Options

Cooperative Learning ♦

STAD Format (See page T23.)
Assign students to work in four- to five-member teams to study Chapter 8 Review. Students should work together to make sure that they and their teammates know the material in the chapter. After students have had enough time to study together, give them a test to complete individually (Chapter 8 Test in the *Test Book*). Award Superteam certificates to teams whose average test scores exceed 90%, and Greatteam certificates to teams whose average test scores exceed 80%.

♦ ***Suitable as a language development activity***

Review Science Words

Match the words and the pictures.

1. magnet
2. machine
3. below

a.

b.

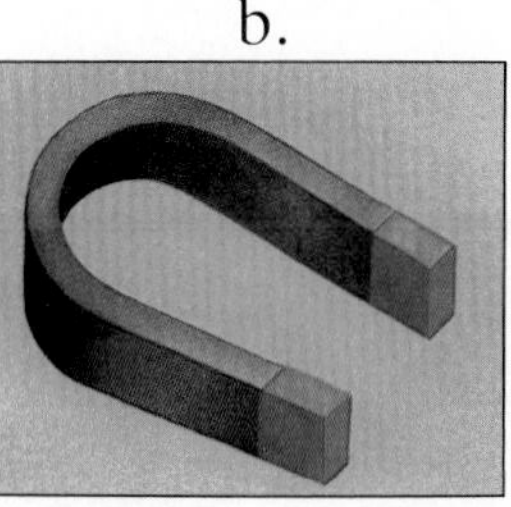

c.

Tell what each word means.

4. distance
5. speed

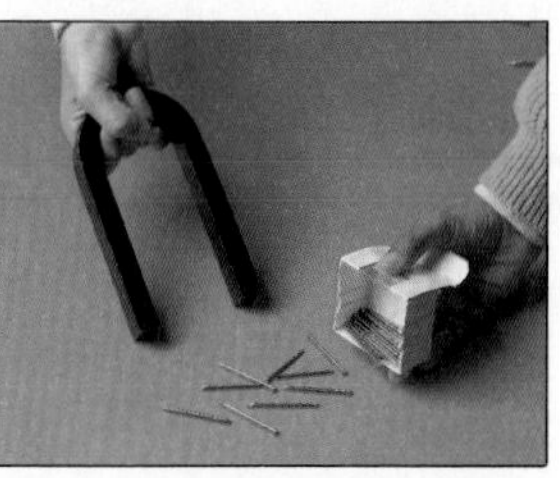

Use Science Ideas

Tell what you think will happen next.

Review Science Words

Match the words and the pictures.

1. b
2. a
3. c

Tell what words mean.
Thinking Skill: *Restating or explaining ideas*
4. Distance—how far from or how near to an object or person another object or person is
5. Speed—how fast things move.

Use Science Ideas

The person will use the magnet to pick up the pins. **Thinking Skill:** *Predicting*

Test Book page 27 *

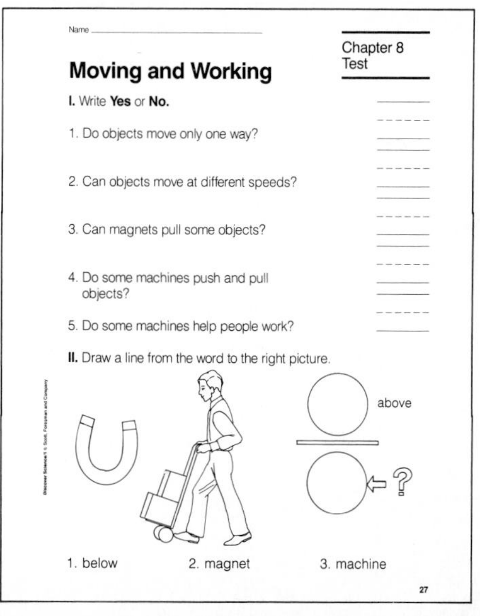

Name ____________

Chapter 8 Test

Moving and Working

I. Write **Yes** or **No.**

1. Do objects move only one way?
2. Can objects move at different speeds?
3. Can magnets pull some objects?
4. Do some machines push and pull objects?
5. Do some machines help people work?

II. Draw a line from the word to the right picture.

above

1. below 2. magnet 3. machine

Discover Science/1 © Scott, Foresman and Company

27

** Answers to masters on pages 144E-144F*

TEACHING PLAN

CAREERS

Purpose
This feature familiarizes children with the role of a pilot. In the U.S. there are four types of licensed pilots—private pilots, who cannot charge for services; commerical pilots, who may charge to carry passengers or cargo; instructor pilots, who train other pilots; and airline pilots.

Teaching Tips
- Question: **Have you ever flown?** (Students' answers will vary. Encourage those students who have flown to *describe* their experiences for the class.)
- Explain that pilots have a great responsibility. A pilot prepares flight plans before each flight that takes into account the weather along the route, the planned speed and altitude, and the amount of fuel needed.
- Encourage the students to draw a picture of an airplane or pilot.

Careers

Pilot
Airplanes are big machines.
They are used to move people and objects.
Pilots fly many kinds of airplanes.
Pilots must know how air moves.
They check airplanes for safety.
Pilots make airplanes move many ways.

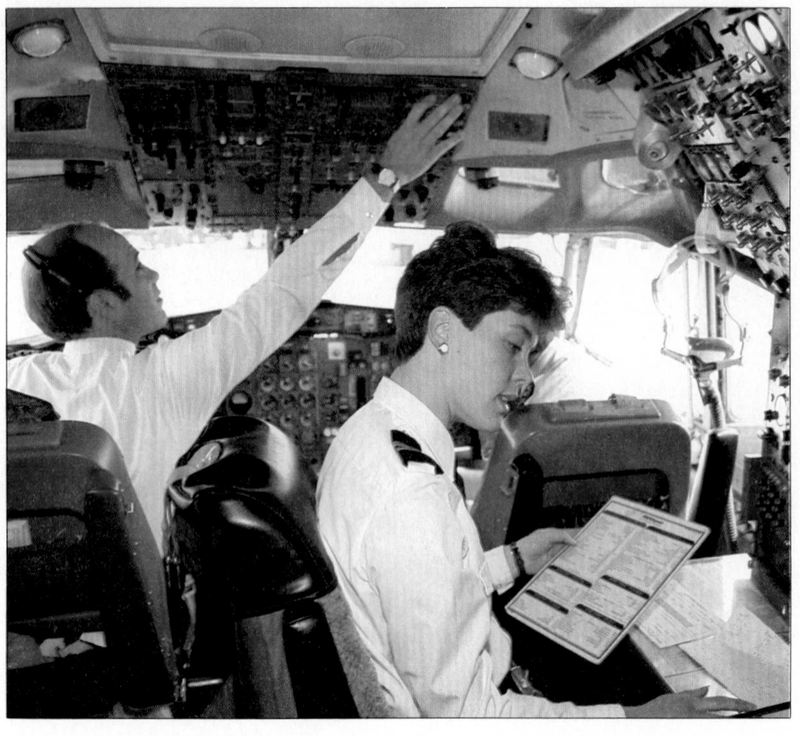

162

Teaching Options

Enrichment
Invite a pilot to speak to the class about his training and responsibilities.

Where to Write
Air Taxi and Commerical Pilots' Association, 7940-2 Airpack Drive, Gaithersburg, Maryland, 20879.
Airline Pilots Association, International, 1625 Massachusetts Avenue N.W., Washington, D.C. 20036.

How It Works

Pencil Sharpener

A pencil sharpener has two rollers.
The rollers have sharp edges.
A pencil fits between the rollers.
The space is wide at one end.
It comes to a point at the other end.
The rollers spin when you turn the crank.
The rollers shape your pencil.
Then your pencil has a point.

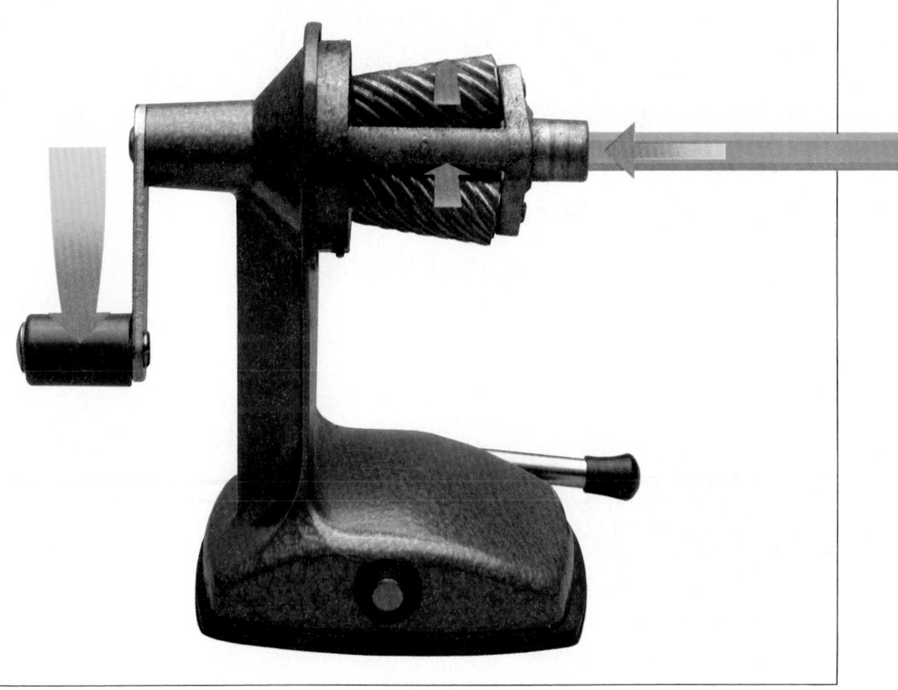

HOW IT WORKS

Teaching Tips

- Remove the cover from the class pencil sharpener and demonstrate how the sharpener works. Question: **What are the things falling from the sharpener?** (pieces of wood from the pencil) Guide the students to ***infer*** that the wood of the pencil is being shaved off by the sharp edges of the two cylinders.
- Explain to the students that a pencil sharpener is a machine. Question: **How could you sharpen a pencil without a sharpener?** (Accept any reasonable answers.) Point out to the students that machines, like the pencil sharpener, make our lives easier.

SCIENCE BACKGROUND

There are six simple machines: lever, wheel and axle, inclined plane, screw, wedge, and pulley. All other machines are composed of various combinations of these. A pencil sharpener is an example of a compound machine. The crank is a wheel and axle. The two cylinders inside are screws with wedges along the threads. Between the cylinders and handle is a set of gears. Gears are a special form of a wheel and axle.

REVIEW PLAN

UNIT 3 REVIEW

Answer the Questions

1. (A) A solid takes up space and has a certain size and shape. (B) A gas takes up space and changes shape to fill what it is in. (C) A liquid takes up space, is a certain size, but changes shape to fit what it is in.
2. Light can change from bright to not so bright. It can go in different directions.
3. Heat comes from the sun, from fires, from electric heaters, and from ovens.
4. Sound can change from loud to soft, and can change according to what object makes the sound.
5. Things move left, right, up, down, around, near, far, above, and below.
6. Objects move when there is a push or a pull.

Study the Picture

The can opener, because it is a simple machine. The other two are made of several machines put together. **Thinking Skill:** *Recognizing inconsistencies*

Unit 3 Review

Answer the Questions

1. What is each thing like?

a.

b.

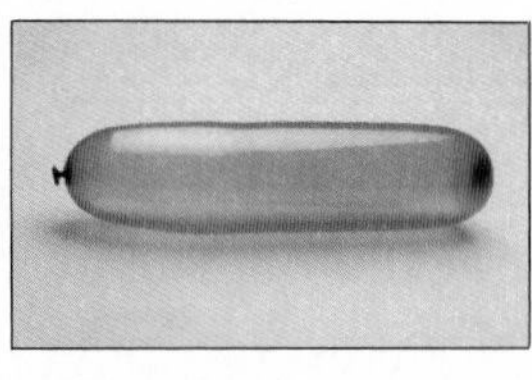

c.

2. What ways can light change?
3. Where does heat come from?
4. What ways can sound change?
5. What ways can objects move?
6. What makes objects move?

Study the Pictures

Tell what machine does not belong.
Why does it not belong?

a.

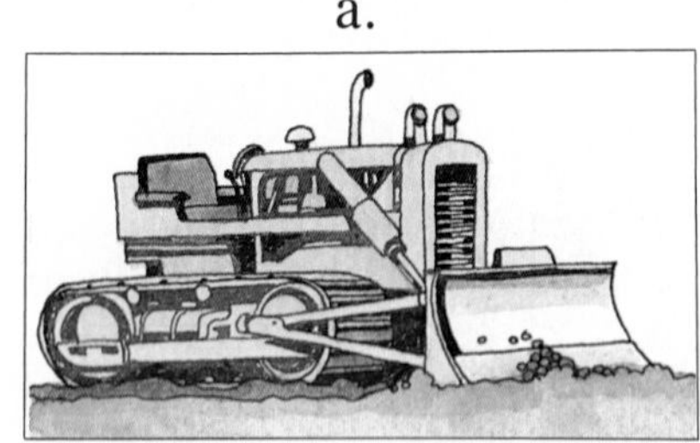

b.

c.

164

Review Options

Test Book page 29

Name ____________

Unit Test

Physical Science

I. Write **Yes** or **No.**

1. Does air take up space? ______
2. Does light bounce off objects? ______
3. Can sound go through water? ______
4. Can magnets move objects? ______
5. Do machines help people work? ______

II. Draw a line from the word to the right picture.

1. thermometer 2. liquid 3. gas 4. solid 5. heat

29

What to Do

1. Make liquid for blowing bubbles.
   Use water and liquid soap.
   Blow bubbles.
   Try to keep them in the air.

2. Keep your fingers as you see here.
   Make different sounds.
   Hum. Sing.
   Find out what you can feel.

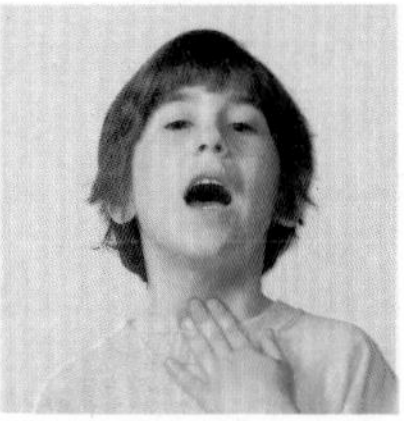

3. Pretend you have no machines.
   Tell a story.
   Tell about a day with no machines.

UNIT PROJECTS

Teaching Tips

1. Encourage students to use pipe cleaners bent into various shapes or plastic rings from beverage cans to produce different-sized bubbles. Point out that all bubbles are spherical.

2. Demonstrate placing fingers on the vocal cords so vibrations can be felt. Tell students to hum and to feel the vibrations in their throats. Let students make different sounds and feel the vibrations. Ask them to ***compare*** the vibrations made when singing high and low notes in a song.

3. Students could make a list of all the machines they use in one day to help them in telling the story.

Books in Spanish

Parramon, J.M. *El fuego*. (fire) Barron, 1985. (grades ps-1)

Robles Boza, Eduardo. *Chispa de luz*. Trillas, 1984. Electricity escapes from a cord and flies around the world making friends. (grades 2-4)

Books for Students

Bains, Rae. *Simple Machines*. Troll Association, 1985. Describes and discusses the six simple machines. (grades k-6)

Knight, David. *All about Sound*. Troll Association, 1983. Illustrates how sound travels through different materials. (grades 2-5)

Santrey, Laurence. *Heat*. Troll Association, 1985. Discusses the aspects of heat such as temperature, conduction, and convection. (grades 3-6)

Whyman, Kathryn. *Light and Lasers*. Gloucester Press, 1986. Discusses the principles of light. (grades 3-4)

Planning Guide

Science Process Skills Book
The Science Process Skills Book contains worksheets that can be used to teach and then assess student mastery of the basic science process skills. In addition, other worksheets in this book teach students the manipulative skills they will need to use basic science equipment. Assign these worksheets whenever you think it fits in your curriculum.

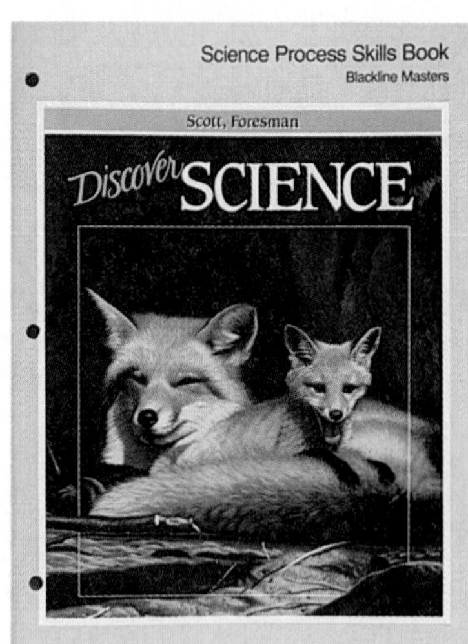

Science Resources for the Unit

Resource Books

Audouze, Jean and Israel, Guy, eds. *The Cambridge Atlas of Astronomy*. Cambridge Univ. Pr. 1985. Summarizes current knowledge about the stars and galaxies.

Facklam, Margery. *Changes in the Wind: Earth's Shifting Climate*. Harcourt, 1986. A study of major changes in earth's climate, addresses the greenhouse effect, ice ages, shifts in oceanic currents, and acid rain.

Gallant, Roy A. *Our Restless Earth*. Watts, 1986. Discusses the beginnings of the planets, revealing causes of earthquakes and volcanoes.

Kerrod, Robin. *Stars and Planets*. Arco, 1984. Includes star maps and movements, Apollo missions, and background information on the moon and planets.

O'Donnell, James J. *Earthly Matters: A Study of Our Planet*. Messner, 1982. Examines Earth's geography, geology, and climate.

Ronan, Colin A., ed. *The Skywatcher's Handbook: Night and Day What To Look for in the Heavens Above*. Crown, 1985. Gathers information about weather, the sun, and stars and tells how to set up a weather station.

Community Resources

Invite a travel agent or someone who has traveled widely to visit the classroom and show slides of different parts of the world. Emphasize the variety of landscapes on the earth.

Invite a weather forecaster from a local TV or radio station to talk to the class about his or her job.

Invite people with a variety of jobs (farmer, pilot, construction worker) to explain how weather affects his or her job.

Audio-Visual Resources

Hot, Warm, Cold. Macmillan. Film, 8 minutes. Uses animation to show how distance from the equator, altitude, and nearness to bodies of water affect temperature.

My World . . . Earth. Churchill. Film, 11 minutes. Children touch, taste, feel, play, paint, and sing about soil.

Our Planet Earth. National Geographic. Wonders of Learning Kit (30 booklets, teacher's guide and activity sheets, cassette). Shows the features of the earth, as well as the variety of life in air, water, and on land.

Rainshower. Churchill. Film, 14 1/2 minutes. The sights and sounds of rain coming to plants and animals.

Weather for Beginners. Coronet. Film, 11 minutes. Demonstrates concepts of weather, such as why air above land gets warmer than air above water and what causes winds and rain.

What Makes Weather? Cenco. Film, 12 minutes. Explains basic reasons behind changes in weather.

Why Does It Rain? National Geographic. Wonders of Learning Kit (30 booklets, teacher's guide and activity sheets, cassette). Teaches where rain comes from and where it goes.

Wind and What It Does. Britannica. Film, 10 minutes. Introduces the important aspects of wind: what it is, what it can do, and how it affects people and their surroundings.

Computer Software

Active Reader: World of Nature Series. Orange Cherry Media. Apple/TRS80/Commodore/IBM/Pet/Atari. Animals, earthquakes, volcanoes, and planets.

Stars and Planets. Intellectual Software. Apple II, IIe. Interactive tutorial introduces children to astronomy.

The Weather. Intellectual Software. Apple II+, IIe, 64K. Tutorial and drill on weather.

TEACHING PLAN

INTRODUCING UNIT 4

Unit Overview
This unit is designed to stimulate the students' awareness of the earth. The unit also discusses the uses and the conservations of land, water, and wind. Later in this unit the students will explore the changes in weather, and the reason for day and night. The students will also learn about the moon, sun, and other stars.

About the Photograph
This beautiful picture of the earth taken from the moon illustrates the dramatic contrast between the earth and the moon. The lunar surface is barren, and the clarity of the earth's features emphasizes the fact that the moon has no atmosphere.

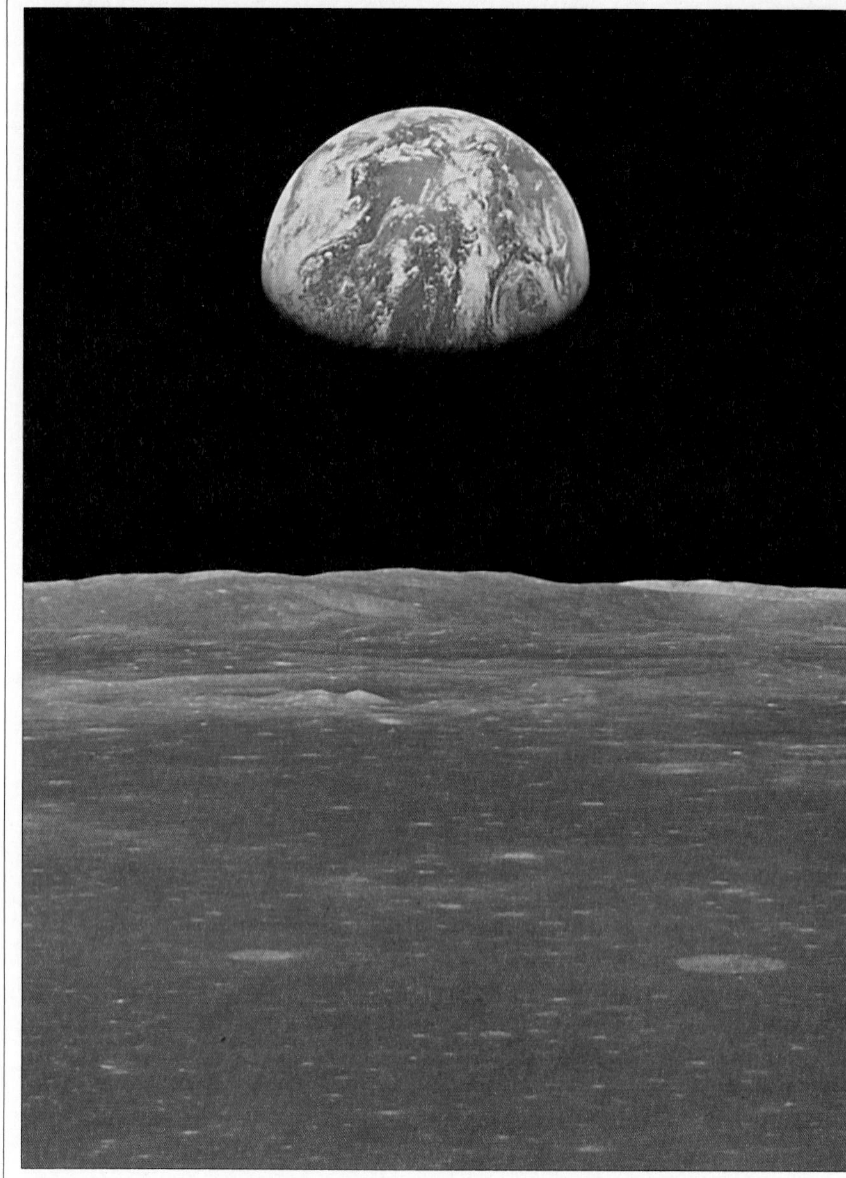

166

Teaching Options

Chapter 9 Preview

The Earth
The students will describe the earth in general, and focus on the characteristics of water, air, and land. Water on the earth is found in the ocean, and in streams, lakes, rivers, and frozen in ice. People need to have fresh water for drinking. Land is essential for building homes and raising crops. Land also supplies materials that people use as fuels and minerals. The blanket of air that surrounds the earth, our atmosphere, provides gases that living things require. People need to keep land, water, and air resources clean and need to conserve the materials that come from them.

Chapter 10 Preview

Weather
In this chapter, the students will learn that weather is whatever it is like outdoors, and they will identify five different kinds of weather. The students will learn about the four seasons and describe the weather changes from season to season. In addition, the students will explore the concept that weather affects people in a variety of ways—what they do in work and play, and how they dress.

[1] Answers will vary.

Unit 4

Earth Science

Pretend you live on the moon.
You could see the earth.
It might look like this.

You live on the earth.
You can see land, water, and sky.
How does the sky look today?[1]

Teaching Tips

- Write *earth* on the chalkboard and ask the children what the word *earth* makes them think of. Encourage the students to give their own descriptions of earth.
- Draw the students' attention to the photograph on page 166. Point out the area of darkness. Question: **What time of day do you think it is there?** (night)
- Have the students describe the photograph. Write their responses on the chalkboard. Encourage the students to look for details such as land formations, rivers, clouds, oceans,and so on.

Chapter 11 Preview

The Sky
This chapter focuses on what is visible in the sky. Students will be asked to name the sun, moon, and stars as visible in the sky, and they will compare the relative sizes of each. They will learn that the sun gives off heat and light. They will discover the reason for day and night. They will also learn that the moon reflects light from the sun and appears to have different shapes at different times. In addition, students will learn that stars give off their own light and make patterns in the sky.

Teaching Plan

Chapter Components	Skills	Materials
Chapter Opener/*TRY THIS*: Observing Land and Water pp. 168-169	***TRY THIS*** p. 169 **Science Process Skills** *Comparing, Observing*	***TRY THIS*** p. 169 (groups of 6) 5 globes
Lesson 1: What Does the Earth Have? pp. 170-172	**Thinking Skills** Challenge!: *Drawing conclusions* Find Out: *Restating or explaining ideas*	**Demonstration** p. 170 globe
Activity: Grouping Rocks p. 173	**Science Process Skills** *Observing, Classifying, Communicating*	(individual) 300 assorted rocks
Lesson 2: Where Is the Water on Earth? pp. 174-175	**Thinking Skills** Challenge!: *Applying information to new situations* Find Out: *Restating or explaining ideas, Interpreting maps*	**Demonstration** p. 174 ice cubes or pictures of ice melting, salty water
Lesson 3: How Is Air Useful? pp. 176-178	**Thinking Skills** Challenge!: *Drawing conclusions* Find Out: *Applying information to new situations*	**Demonstration** p. 176 no materials needed
Activity: Using Air to Move Boats p. 179	**Science Process Skills** *Making models, Observing, Communicating, Inferring*	(individual) 30 plastic-foam trays, water, 10 large roasting pans, 30 pieces white construction paper (10 cm square), 1 box toothpicks
Lesson 4: How Do People Use Land and Water? pp. 180-182	**Thinking Skills** Challenge!: *Making generalizations* Find Out: *Applying information to new situations*	**Demonstration** p. 180 pictures of ways people use land and water
Science and People: Rachel Carson p. 183	**Thinking Skill** *Making inferences*	
Skills for Solving Problems: Using a Map pp. 184-185	**Problem Solving Skills** *Making decisions/Identifying and solving problems, Interpreting charts, maps, and graphs*	
Chapter Review pp. 186-187	**Thinking Skills** *Restating or explaining ideas, Applying information to new situations*	

Teaching Options

Strategies	Extensions		Resource Masters
			Family Letter: *Resource Book* p. 67 Vocabulary Preview: *Workbook* pp. 49-50
	Science and Art p. 170 Special Education p. 171 Enrichment p. 171	Reteaching Suggestion p. 172 Game Suggestion p. 172	Science Activity: *Workbook* p. 51
	Enrichment Activity p. 173		
	Enrichment p. 175 Reteaching Suggestion p. 175		Science Skills: *Workbook* p. 52
	Science and Language Arts p. 177 Special Education p. 177	Enrichment p. 177 Reteaching Suggestion p. 178	Science and Social Studies: *Workbook* p. 53
	Enrichment Activity p. 179		
	Special Education p. 181 Reinforcement p. 181	Enrichment p. 181 Reteaching Suggestion p. 182	Vocabulary Puzzle: *Workbook* p. 54
			Enrichment Activity: *Resource Book* p. 71
Cooperative Learning p. 186 (Also see p. T23)			Chapter Test: *Test Book* p. 31

Preteaching Suggestions

For Advance Preparation

TRY THIS, page 169
Provide a globe for each group of students.

Demonstration, page 170
You will need a globe for this demonstration.

Activity, page 173
Ask students to collect rocks and bring them to school. You might need to supply additional rocks to have enough specimens for this activity. Make sure to have at least four dozen rocks of various colors, textures, and types.

Demonstration, page 174
You will need ice cubes or pictures of ice.

Activity, page 179
Collect plastic-foam meat trays, clean them, and cut them into squares, about 7.5 cm (3 inches) on a side. Also cut paper rectangles for sails. Each rectangle should measure 7.5 cm by 5 cm (3 inches by 2 inches). For this activity provide each group with a plastic-foam square, a rectangular piece of paper for a sail, a toothpick, and a cake pan or pie pan for sailing their boats.

Demonstration, page 180
Collect pictures showing ways people use land and water.

For Vocabulary Review

Use the following sentences with your students to review the meanings of the underlined words.

1. The name of the planet we live on is Earth.
2. You feel air moving when the wind blows.
3. Ice melts quickly on a hot day.
4. Fresh water is not salty.
5. A pump can bring water up from deep underground.

For High-Potential Students

Encourage students to investigate and compare canoes and outrigger canoes. You might suggest that students look for information concerning the following: sizes and shapes, purposes for which they were used, materials from which the vessels were constructed, the group of people who originally used the vessels, the type of water (river, lake, ocean) for which the vessels were designed. When students have finished their research, ask them to make lists comparing outriggers and canoes. Students might illustrate their lists.

For Mainstreamed Students

Emotionally Handicapped
Have students bring in photographs of landscapes and seascapes. Ask emotionally handicapped students to sort through the pictures, placing the landscape and seascape pictures into one pile and the rest into another. Let them show the pictures and explain their classification to the class.

Visually Impaired
Provide a raised relief globe or map. Permit students to feel the surface of the map or globe and describe differences in the surface. Point out that bumpy areas represent mountains, and flat areas represent plains or water.

For Science Fair Projects

Encourage interested students to do one of the following projects:

1. Collect a variety of rocks and make a display of them, with labels identifying each type.
2. Construct a boat that will carry small objects across water.
3. Construct a variety of paper airplanes. Test them for speed, distance, and ability to stay airborne.

Classroom Resources

Bulletin Board
Encourage students to describe the most beautiful things they have seen in terms of land, water, and sky.

OUR BEAUTIFUL EARTH

LAND

WATER

AIR

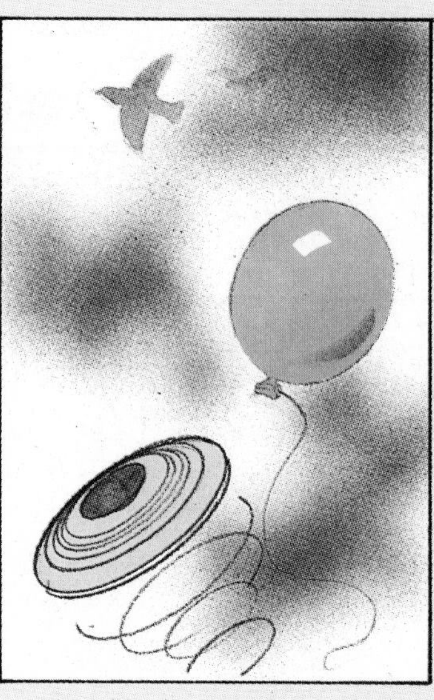

Chapter 9 Poster

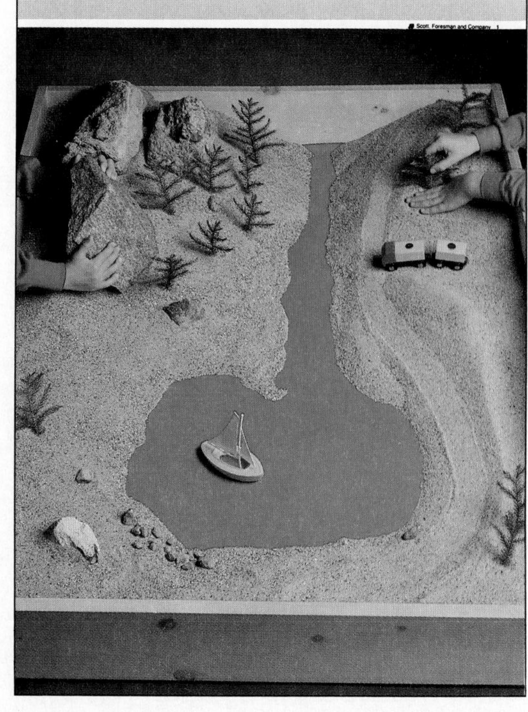

Science Discovery Center
Use pages from Chapter 9 in the *Science Discovery Center Book*. Place these worksheets in the appropriate pockets in the Science Discovery Center.

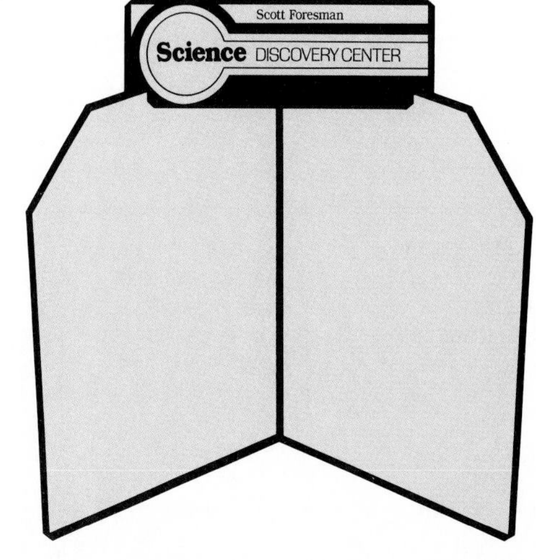

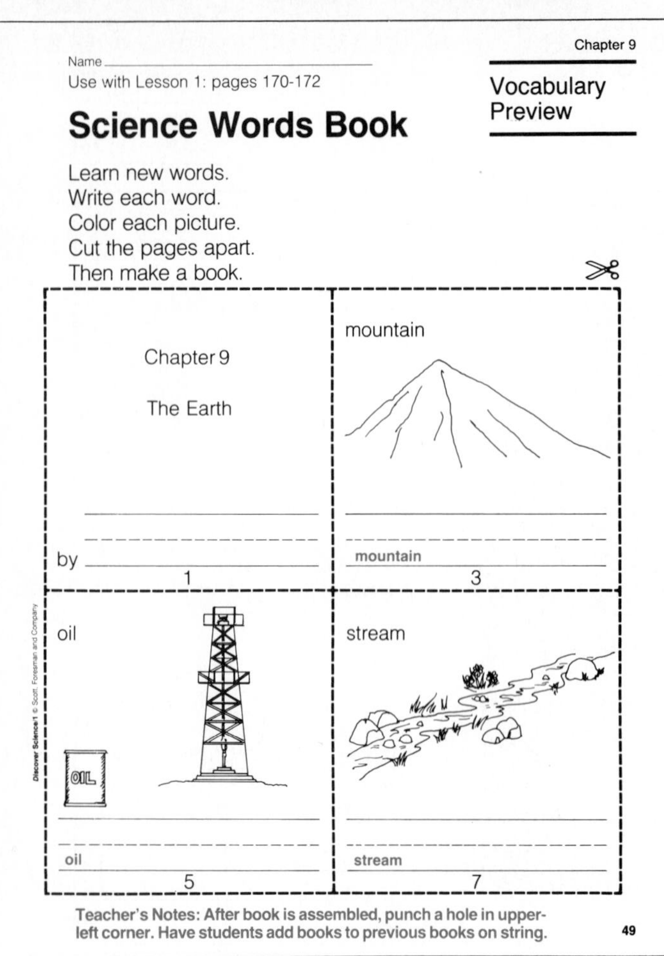
Name
Use with Lesson 1: pages 170-172
Chapter 9
Vocabulary Preview
Science Words Book
Learn new words.
Write each word.
Color each picture.
Cut the pages apart.
Then make a book.
Chapter 9
The Earth
by
1
mountain
mountain
3
oil
OIL
oil
5
stream
stream
7
Teacher's Notes: After book is assembled, punch a hole in upper-left corner. Have students add books to previous books on string.
49

Name
Use with Lesson 1: pages 170-172
Chapter 9
Vocabulary Preview
Science Words Book
ocean
ocean
4
coal
coal
2
valley
valley
8
soil
soil
6
50

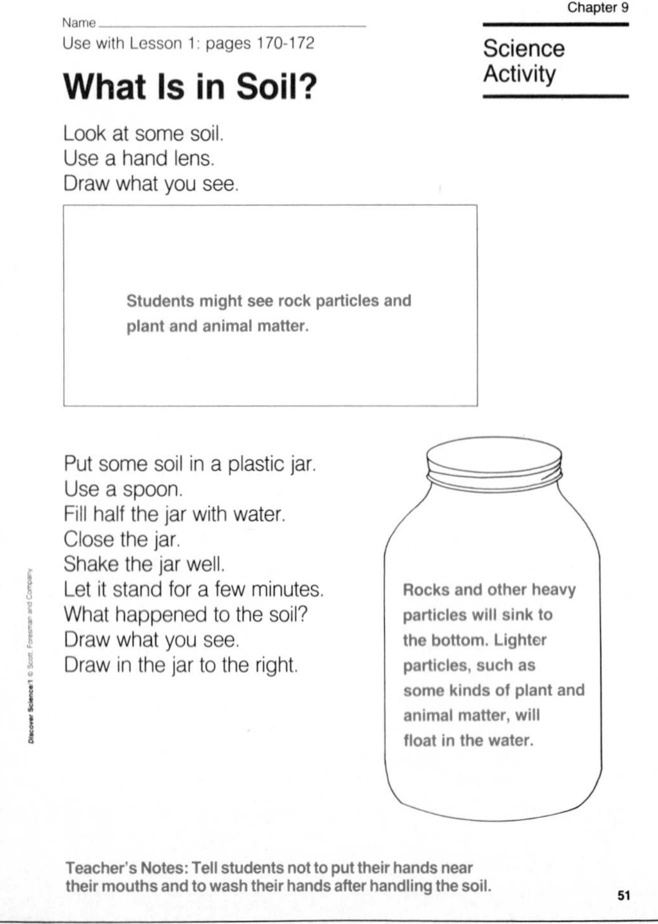
Name
Use with Lesson 1: pages 170-172
Chapter 9
Science Activity
What Is in Soil?
Look at some soil.
Use a hand lens.
Draw what you see.
Students might see rock particles and plant and animal matter.
Put some soil in a plastic jar.
Use a spoon.
Fill half the jar with water.
Close the jar.
Shake the jar well.
Let it stand for a few minutes.
What happened to the soil?
Draw what you see.
Draw in the jar to the right.
Rocks and other heavy particles will sink to the bottom. Lighter particles, such as some kinds of plant and animal matter, will float in the water.
Teacher's Notes: Tell students not to put their hands near their mouths and to wash their hands after handling the soil.
51

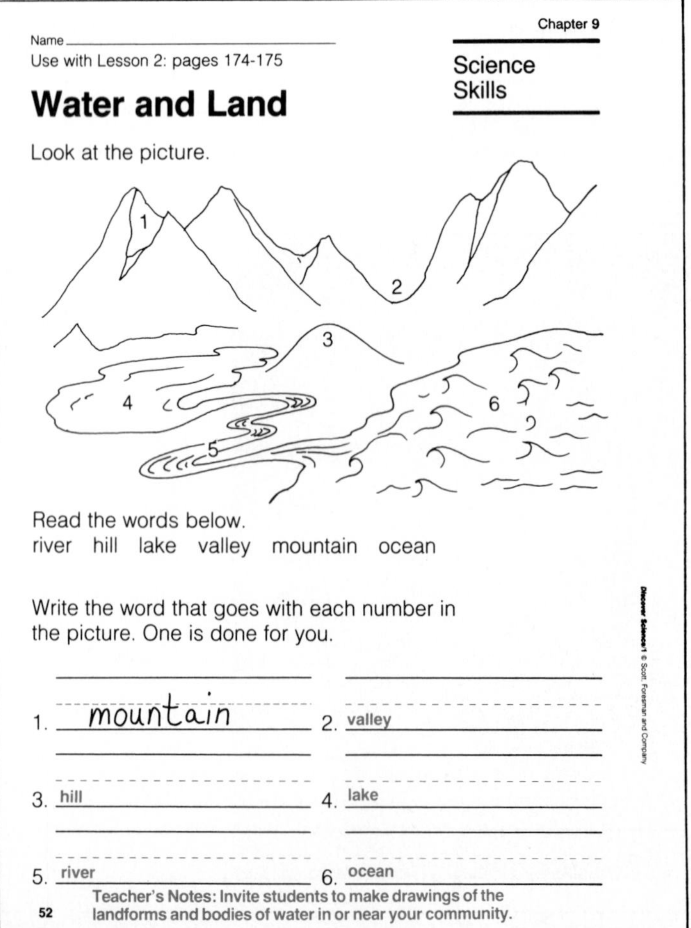
Name
Use with Lesson 2: pages 174-175
Chapter 9
Science Skills
Water and Land
Look at the picture.
1
2
3
4
5
6
Read the words below.
river hill lake valley mountain ocean
Write the word that goes with each number in the picture. One is done for you.
1. mountain
2. valley
3. hill
4. lake
5. river
6. ocean
Teacher's Notes: Invite students to make drawings of the landforms and bodies of water in or near your community.
52

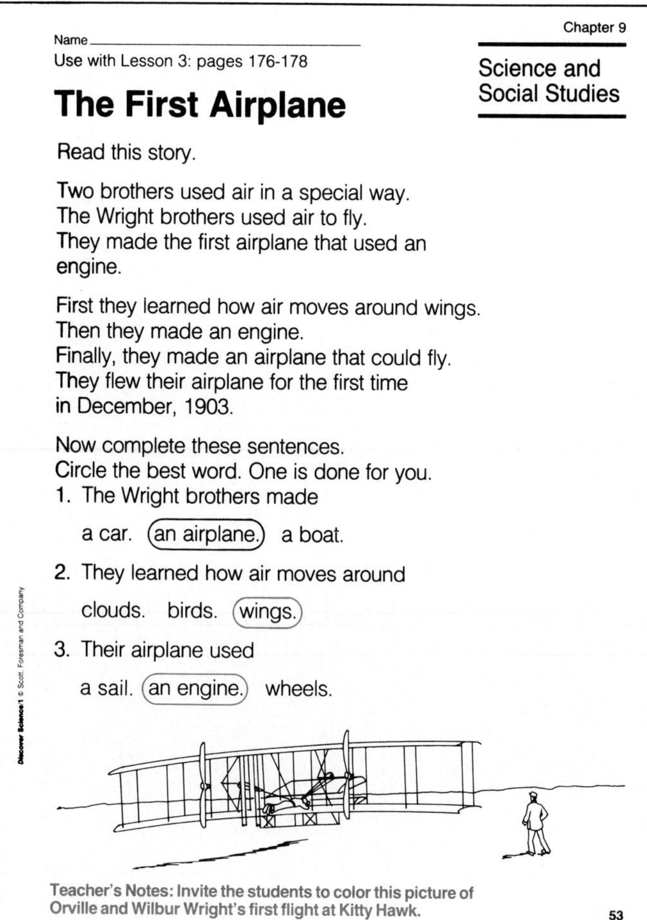

Name ______________________

Use with Lesson 3: pages 176-178

Chapter 9

Science and Social Studies

The First Airplane

Read this story.

Two brothers used air in a special way.
The Wright brothers used air to fly.
They made the first airplane that used an engine.

First they learned how air moves around wings.
Then they made an engine.
Finally, they made an airplane that could fly.
They flew their airplane for the first time in December, 1903.

Now complete these sentences.
Circle the best word. One is done for you.

1. The Wright brothers made
   a car. (an airplane.) a boat.
2. They learned how air moves around
   clouds. birds. (wings.)
3. Their airplane used
   a sail. (an engine.) wheels.

Teacher's Notes: Invite the students to color this picture of Orville and Wilbur Wright's first flight at Kitty Hawk.

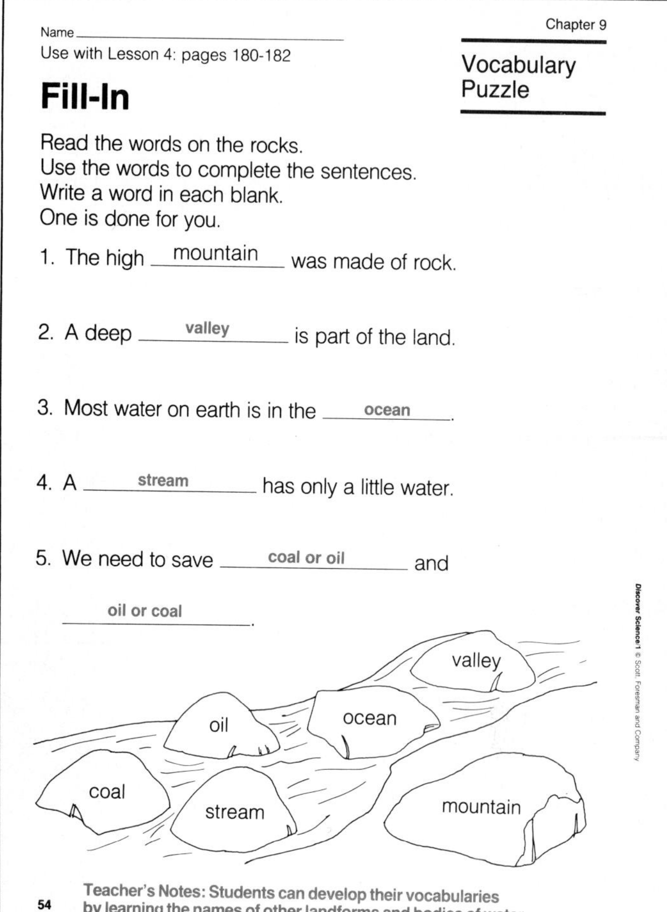

Name ______________________

Use with Lesson 4: pages 180-182

Chapter 9

Vocabulary Puzzle

Fill-In

Read the words on the rocks.
Use the words to complete the sentences.
Write a word in each blank.
One is done for you.

1. The high __mountain__ was made of rock.
2. A deep __valley__ is part of the land.
3. Most water on earth is in the __ocean__.
4. A __stream__ has only a little water.
5. We need to save __coal or oil__ and __oil or coal__.

valley
oil
ocean
coal
stream
mountain

Teacher's Notes: Students can develop their vocabularies by learning the names of other landforms and bodies of water.

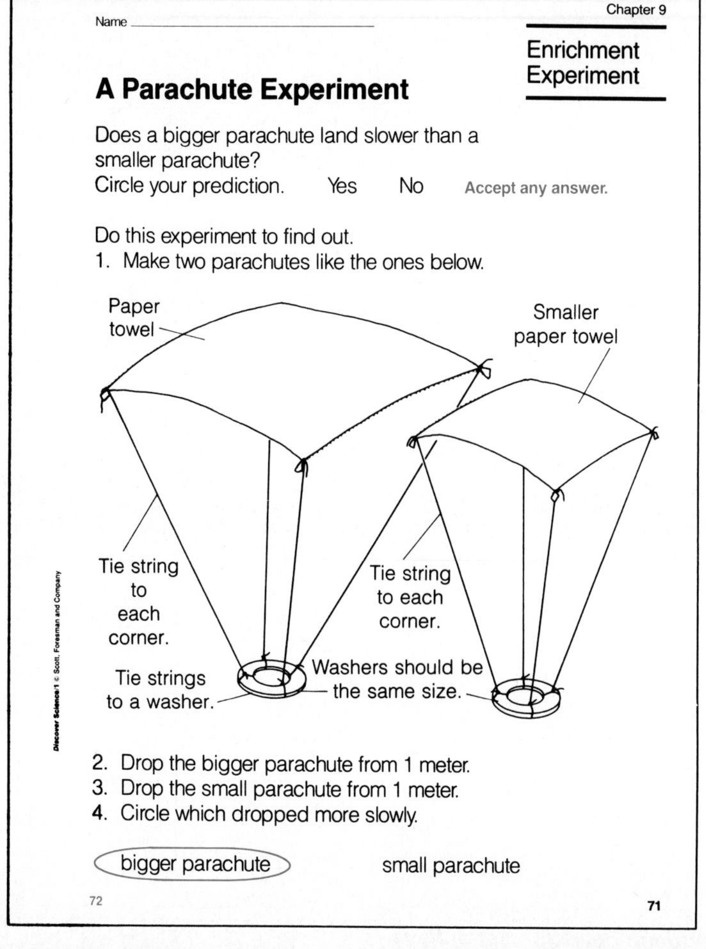

Name ______________________

Chapter 9

Enrichment Experiment

A Parachute Experiment

Does a bigger parachute land slower than a smaller parachute?
Circle your prediction. Yes No Accept any answer.

Do this experiment to find out.

1. Make two parachutes like the ones below.

Paper towel
Smaller paper towel
Tie string to each corner.
Tie string to each corner.
Tie strings to a washer.
Washers should be the same size.

2. Drop the bigger parachute from 1 meter.
3. Drop the small parachute from 1 meter.
4. Circle which dropped more slowly.

(bigger parachute) small parachute

Name ______________________

Chapter 9 Test

The Earth

I. Write **Yes** or **No.**

1. Are there land, water, and air on earth? (9-1) __Yes__
2. Is all of the land on earth flat? (9-1) __No__
3. Can you find water in a stream? (9-2) __Yes__
4. Can you see clean air? (9-3) __No__
5. Do people need clean water to stay alive? (9-4) __Yes__

II. Draw a line from the word to the right picture.

1. mountain (9-1) 2. valley (9-1) 3. stream (9-2)

The numbers in parentheses after each question refer to the chapter and lesson objective covered by that question.

TEACHING PLAN

INTRODUCING CHAPTER 9

Major Concepts

Lesson 1 The earth is surrounded by air and contains land and water; the land on earth has different forms and is made up of rock and soil.
Lesson 2 Water is found on earth in oceans, rivers, lakes, ponds, and streams, and in ice and snow.
Lesson 3 Air has certain properties, is necessary for human life, and has useful functions.
Lesson 4 People have various uses for the water and land on earth.

Vocabulary

coal, mountain, ocean, oil, soil, stream, valley

[1] mountains, lake, forest

Chapter 9

The Earth

The earth has many beautiful places.
What places does the picture show?[1]

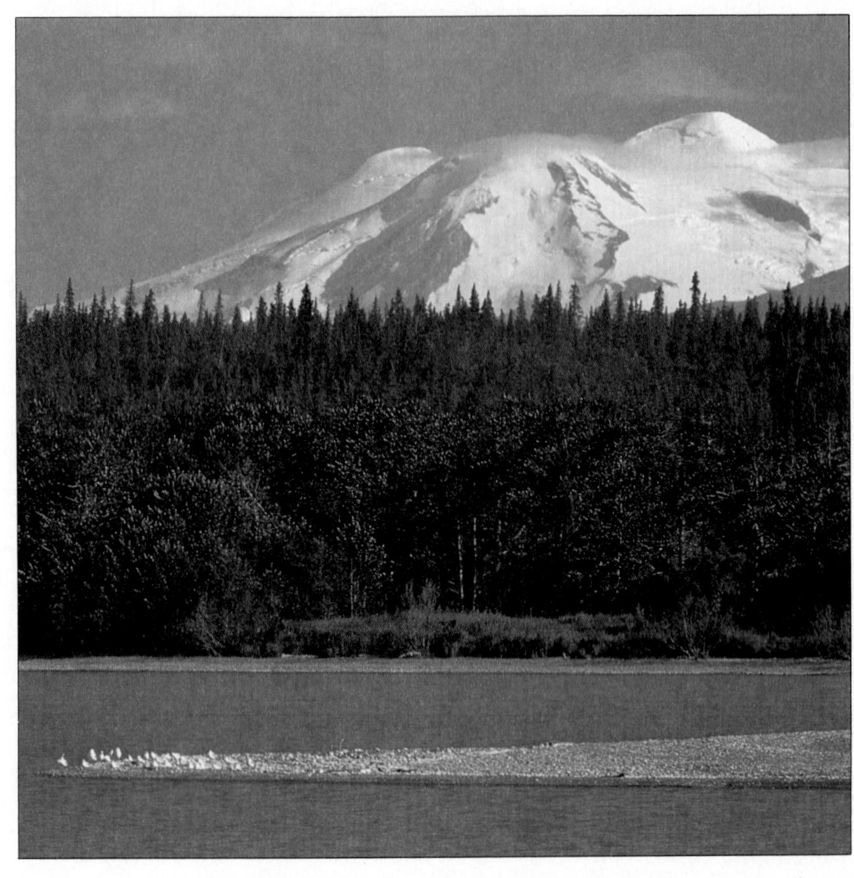

168

Teaching Options

Workbook page 49 *

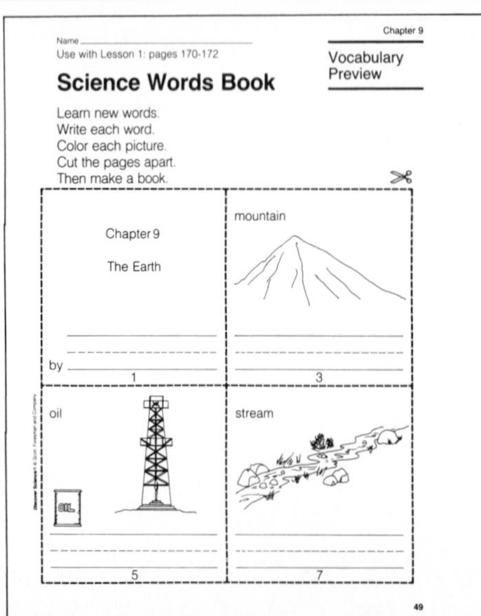

Name ________
Use with Lesson 1: pages 170-172

Chapter 9
Vocabulary Preview

Science Words Book

Learn new words.
Write each word.
Color each picture.
Cut the pages apart.
Then make a book.

Chapter 9
The Earth
by ________
1

mountain
3

oil
5

stream
7

49

Workbook page 50 *

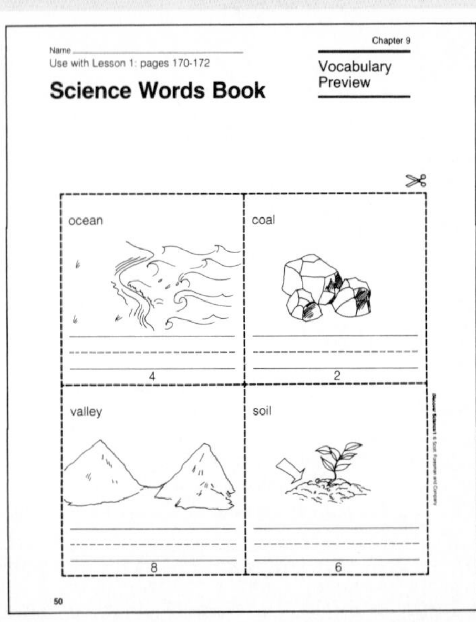

Name ________
Use with Lesson 1: pages 170-172

Chapter 9
Vocabulary Preview

Science Words Book

ocean
4

coal
2

valley
8

soil
6

50

♦ ***Suitable as a language development activity***

Starting the Chapter

The earth has land and water.
You live on the land.
See how much water the earth has.
Then read to learn more about the earth.

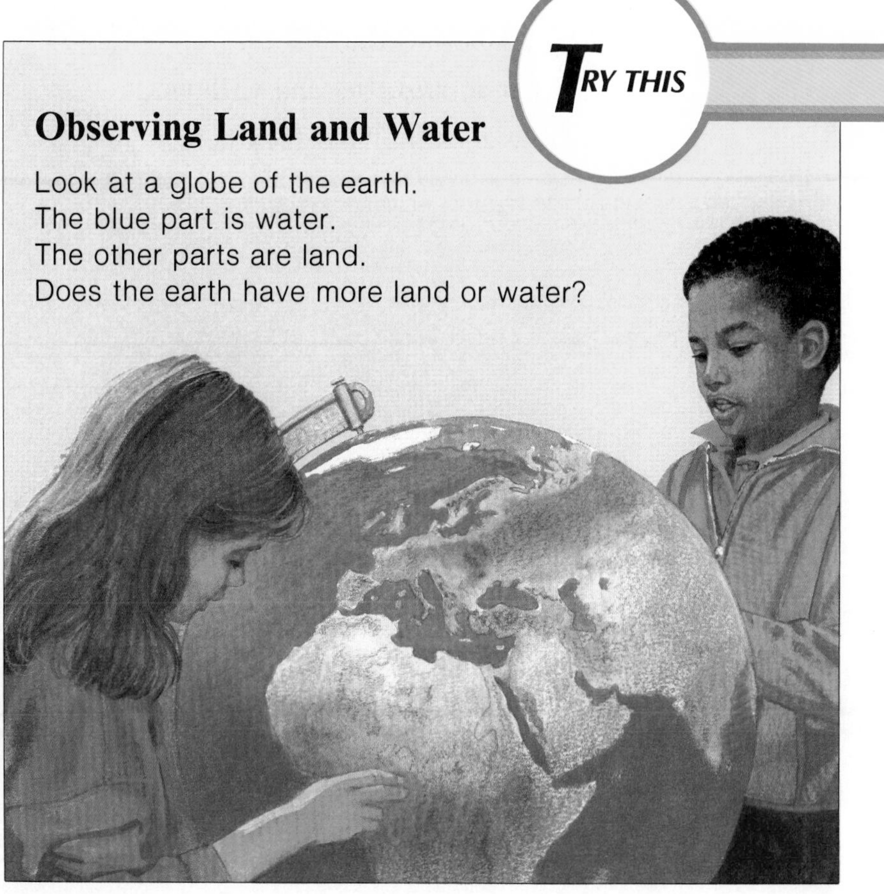

Observing Land and Water

Look at a globe of the earth.
The blue part is water.
The other parts are land.
Does the earth have more land or water?

169

TRY THIS

Objective ♦

This optional *TRY THIS* activity will help students explore and build background information about the concept of the predominance of water on Earth. Later in the chapter students will be able to draw on this experience to help them assimilate the new content.

Science Process Skills

Comparing, Observing

Materials

For each group of 6: a globe

Teaching Tips

- Write *Earth* on the chalkboard and ask students what the word makes them think of. Encourage students to give their own descriptions of Earth.
- If your area is not near a large body of water, students probably will be surprised that Earth contains so much more water than land. Ask them to imagine what it might feel like to live on a tiny island.

Answer

The earth is about 75 percent water and 25 percent land.

Resource Book page 67

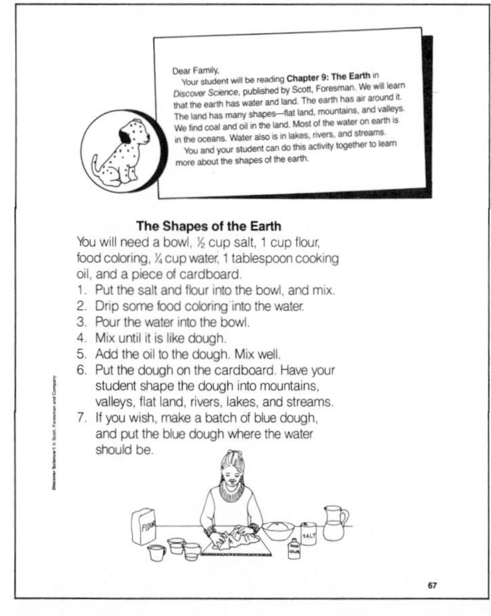

Dear Family,
Your student will be reading **Chapter 9: The Earth** in *Discover Science*, published by Scott, Foresman. We will learn that the earth has water and land. The earth has air around it. The land has many shapes—flat land, mountains, and valleys. We find coal and oil in the land. Most of the water on earth is in the oceans. Water also is in lakes, rivers, and streams.
You and your student can do this activity together to learn more about the shapes of the earth.

The Shapes of the Earth

You will need a bowl, ½ cup salt, 1 cup flour, food coloring, ¼ cup water, 1 tablespoon cooking oil, and a piece of cardboard.

1. Put the salt and flour into the bowl, and mix.
2. Drip some food coloring into the water.
3. Pour the water into the bowl.
4. Mix until it is like dough.
5. Add the oil to the dough. Mix well.
6. Put the dough on the cardboard. Have your student shape the dough into mountains, valleys, flat land, rivers, lakes, and streams.
7. If you wish, make a batch of blue dough, and put the blue dough where the water should be.

SCIENCE BACKGROUND

The oceans contain 97% of all water on Earth. Rivers, lakes, streams, and ponds hold less than 1% of Earth's water. The remaining 2% is frozen into ice in glaciers and in the polar regions. All oceans are interconnected, forming one vast world ocean. Geographers divide the ocean into separate bodies of water, such as the Pacific and Atlantic.

*** *Answers to masters on pages 168E–168F***

TEACHING PLAN

LESSON 1
pages 170–172

Lesson Objectives
- *State* that air surrounds the earth and that the earth has land, air, and water.
- *State* that land has different kinds of landforms, rocks, and soil.

Lesson Vocabulary
coal, mountain, oil, soil, valley

1 MOTIVATE

Demonstration Activity ♦
Dispay a globe. Point out the United States on the globe, and then indicate the location of the city or town in which you live. If your globe has raised areas indicating mountains, let the students feel the elevated areas. Point out land and water regions.

Discussion
Tell students that the globe is a model of the earth. Lead students to discuss what they see on the globe. Questions: **What shape is the globe? Is there much more water than land?**

[1] Land includes mountains and valley.

Lesson 1 What Does the Earth Have?

The earth is round like a ball.
The earth has air all around it.
The earth has water and land.
The land has flat places.
It has **mountains** and **valleys.**
How does the land look here?[1]

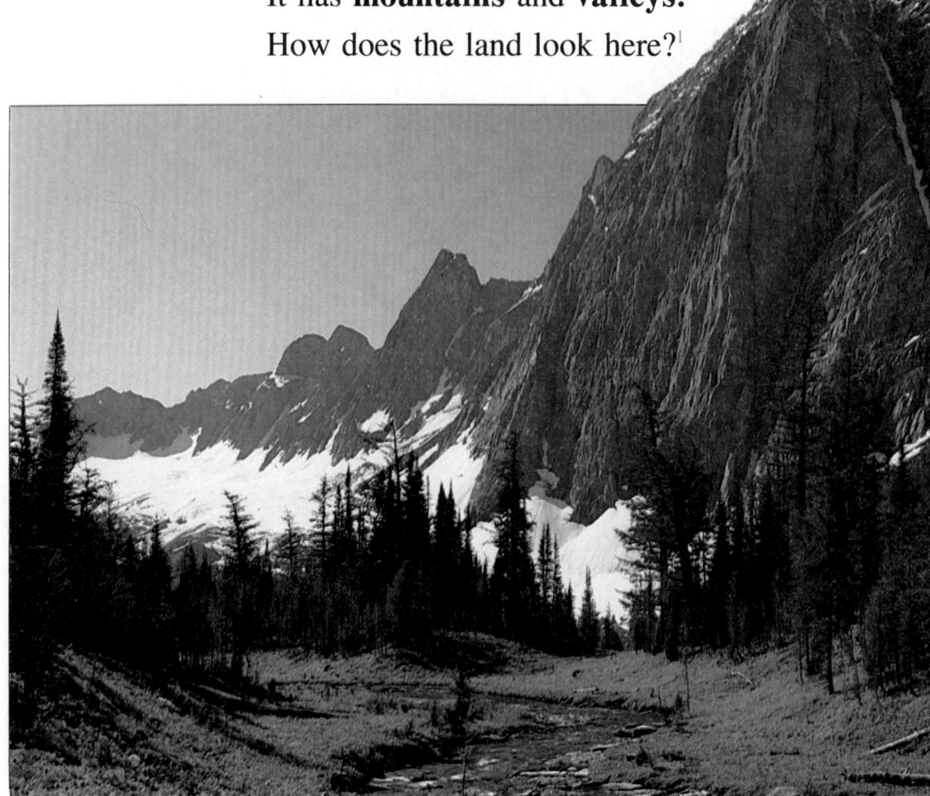

170

Teaching Options

SCIENCE BACKGROUND

Earth is comprised of three layers—the crust, mantle, and core. The crust, which is the outer layer, is made up of plates that float on the mantle. Breaks between plates or fractures of the crust are faults along which bodies of rock move. The collision of plates and the spreading apart of plates cause mountains and valleys to form and continents to move. Weathering and subsequent erosion sculpts mountains further, redistributing rocks in the form of sand and soil. The major components of soil are the grains of minerals and rocks produced by weathering and deposited by water movements and erosion.

Science and Art

Have students make globes by covering inflated, round balloons with papier-mâché. Students should sculpt mountains, valleys, and river beds. When the globes dry, students might use tempera paint to color the land and water areas. *CAUTION:* Students should wear cover goggles when working with balloons until the balloons are covered with papier-mâché.

♦ ***Suitable as a language development activity***

[1] brown, gray, white, black

Land is made of many kinds of **soil.**
Land is made of many kinds of rock.
Most mountains are made of rock.
What colors of rock do you see here?[1]

2 TEACH

Teaching Tips

- Read page 170 aloud with the students. Have students find the mountains and valleys in the illustration.
- Have students *describe* the land in your area. Question: **Do we have mountains or valleys nearby?**
- Write the word *soil* on the chalkboard. Have students identify its meaning. Question: **What are some kinds of soil?** Students might *describe* sandy soil, dark brown soil, mud, or clay-like soil.
- Ask students to *describe* the rocks in the picture. Explain that the stripes in the rocks represent layers of material that have been pressed together.
- **Possible Misconception:** Students might think that rocks are so hard that they consist of one piece and can never break. Explain that some rocks are made of separate pieces of material that are pressed together. Rocks can be broken apart, and wind and water can make rocks crumble to form soil.

Workbook page 51 *

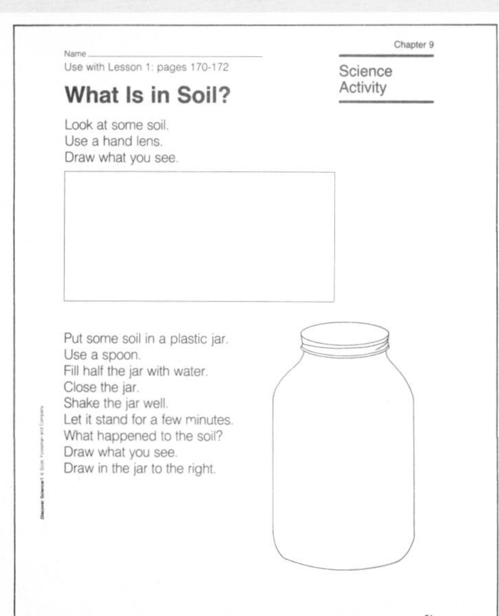

Name ____________
Use with Lesson 1: pages 170-172

Chapter 9
Science Activity

What Is in Soil?

Look at some soil.
Use a hand lens.
Draw what you see.

Put some soil in a plastic jar.
Use a spoon.
Fill half the jar with water.
Close the jar.
Shake the jar well.
Let it stand for a few minutes.
What happened to the soil?
Draw what you see.
Draw in the jar to the right.

51

*** Answers to masters on pages 168E–168F**

Special Education

Provide at least fifteen photographs showing a variety of landscapes. Have students with learning disabilities sort the pictures into these three categories: mountains, valleys, and plains. Have them describe the categories and discuss how they differ from one another. Then, have students talk about where they would like to live, given the three choices. Be prepared to discuss the various climates of the three types of landscape.

Enrichment

To illustrate that rocks change or break, place several small pieces of rock into a can of water. Cover the can. Shake the can several times each day for several days and have students observe what happens. Encourage the students to predict what eventually will happen to the pieces of rock.

TEACHING PLAN

Teaching Tips

- Write *coal* and *oil* on the chalkboard and pronounce the words for students. Tell students that people burn coal and oil to make electric power and to run machines. Coal and oil are important sources of energy that come from the earth.
- Refer students to the picture, and discuss how coal and oil are taken from the earth.

3 ASSESS

Lesson Review

1. Earth has water, land, and air.
2. We can get oil and coal from land.
Challenge! Question: **How can water on earth change the shape of the land?** (Water can flood the land and wear away soil and rock. Water can change coastlines.) **Thinking Skill:** *Drawing conclusions*

Find Out

Students should examine soil for color, shape and size of grains, composition (might contain rocks or living things, such as leaves). **Thinking Skill:** *Restating or explaining ideas*

What can people get from the land?
They can get **coal** and **oil.**
People can try to use less coal and oil.
Then coal and oil can last longer.

Lesson Review

1. What three things does earth have?
2. What things can people get from land?

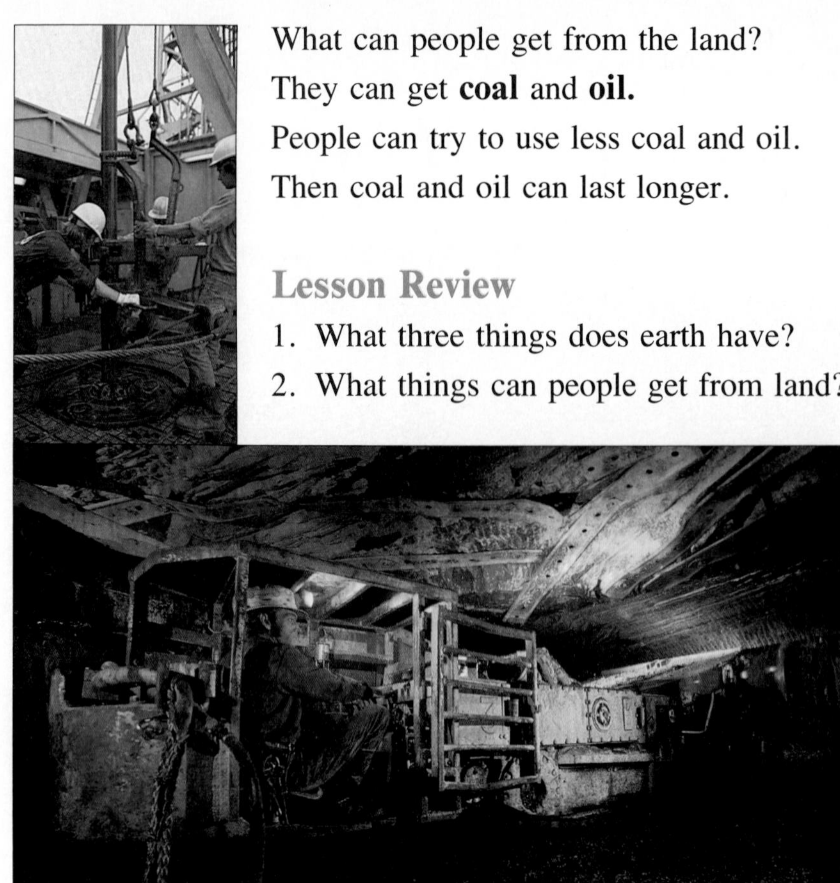

Find Out Look at soil with a hand lens.
Tell about what you see.

172

Teaching Options

SCIENCE ANECDOTE

Much of the soil in the arctic regions of northern Canada and Alaska is frozen. This hard layer of permanently frozen soil is called *permafrost.*

Reteaching Suggestion ♦

Have students identify water and land on the globe. Then, ask students to tell what surrounds the earth (air).

Game Suggestion ♦

Make sets of word and picture cards for these words: *coal, mountain, oil, soil,* and *valley.* Divide the class into small groups and give each group a set of cards. Tell students to place the cards face down in rows. One after another, each student in the group should turn over two cards and try to match a word with a picture.

♦ ***Suitable as a language development activity***

Grouping Rocks

Follow the Directions

1. Look at different kinds of rocks.
2. Notice the colors, sizes, and shapes.
3. Touch each rock.
4. Then group the rocks.
5. Group them by how they are alike.

Tell What You Learned

Tell how the rocks are alike.

Think of other ways to group the rocks.

173

Enrichment Activity

Allow students to make a rock collection and to identify the rocks.

Activity Results

Students should group the rocks based on similar characteristics. Characteristics include size, shape, color, texture, and mass.

ACTIVITY PLAN

Concept
The land has many types of rocks.

Objectives/Process Skills
- *Observe* a variety of rocks.
- *Compare* the properties of rocks.
- *Classify* rocks by common properties.
- *Describe* the common properties of each group.

Materials
For each student: 10 assorted rocks

Time Allotment
Allow 20 minutes.

Safety Tips (See page T27.)
- Instruct students to not place rocks in their mouths.
- Tell students to wash their hands after completing the activity.

Teaching Tips
- Show students two rocks that have similar properties (color, texture, layering, veins). Identify the similar properties.
- Explain that students are going to look at rocks in order to find out how they are alike.
- Allow students to observe the rocks carefully.
- Students should be able to identify rocks that are alike in one or more ways. Students also should be able to identify differences between rocks.

Answers
Tell What You Learned
For the first statement, students should explain the similarities in their rock collection. For the second statement, students should state that they can group rocks according to their differences (color, texture, presence or absence of veins, layers). **Thinking Skills:** ***Comparing, Contrasting***

TEACHING PLAN

LESSON 2
pages 174–175

Lesson Objectives
- *Identify* sources of water on Earth.
- *Contrast* fresh water with salt water.

Lesson Vocabulary
ocean, stream

1 MOTIVATE

Demonstration Activity ♦
Let the students observe ice cubes melting. (If this is impractical, display pictures of melting ice.) Also, allow students to taste small amounts of salty water. *CAUTION:* Provide individual samples for the students.

Discussion
Question: **What does ice become as it melts?** After students answer, lead them to discuss that water for drinking might come from ice melting far away in mountains. Explain that even though the ocean covers so much of the world, we cannot drink salty ocean water.

[1] water

Lesson 2 Where Is the Water on Earth?

Most water on Earth is in **oceans.**
Water is in lakes and rivers, too.
It is also in **streams** like this one.
The earth gets water when it rains.
What comes from melting ice and snow?[1]

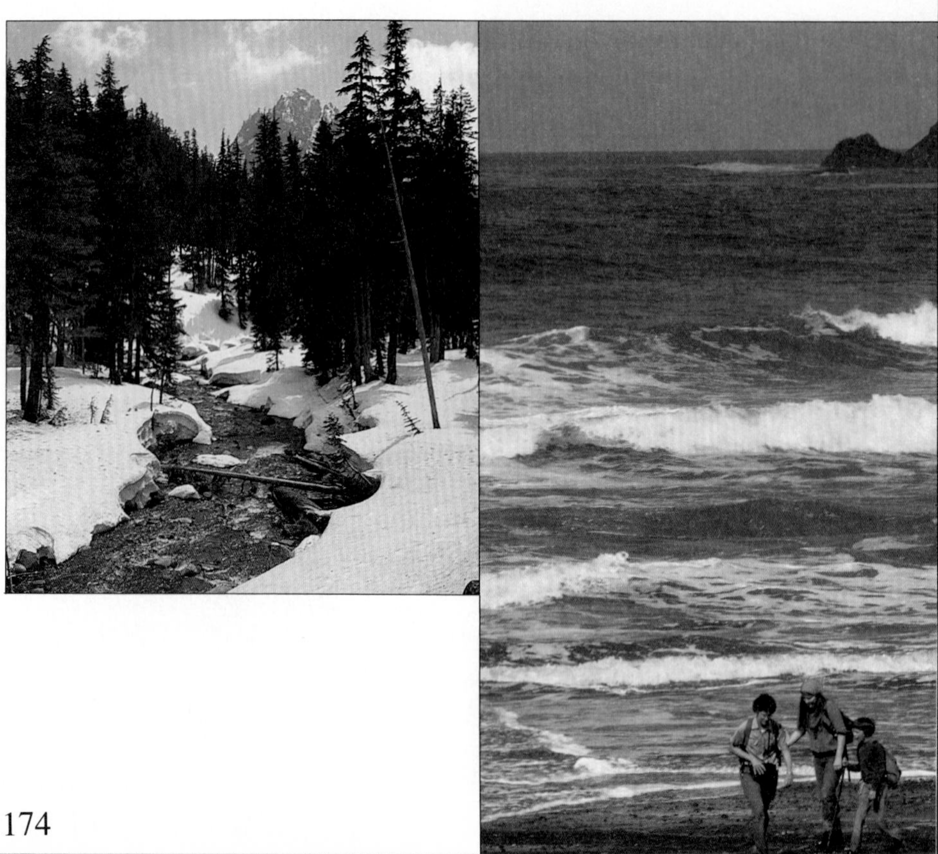

174

Teaching Options

SCIENCE BACKGROUND

Water evaporates from the ocean and lakes, entering the atmosphere as the gas, water vapor. As the water vapor rises and cools, water condenses as tiny droplets or ice crystals, forming clouds. Much of the water falls back into the ocean as rain. Rain and snow also fall on mountains. These waters gather in lakes and streams, which eventually flow back to the ocean.

People cannot drink sea water because it is saltier than body fluids. If salty water surrounds body cells, water from the cells will diffuse into the surrounding fluid. Cells and tissues then become dehydrated.

♦ *Suitable as a language development activity*

[1] from lakes, rivers, underground, and other sources

The ocean has salty water.

People cannot drink this salty water.

They can drink only fresh water.

Where do these people get fresh water?[1]

Lesson Review

1. Where do you find water on earth?
2. What kind of water do people drink?

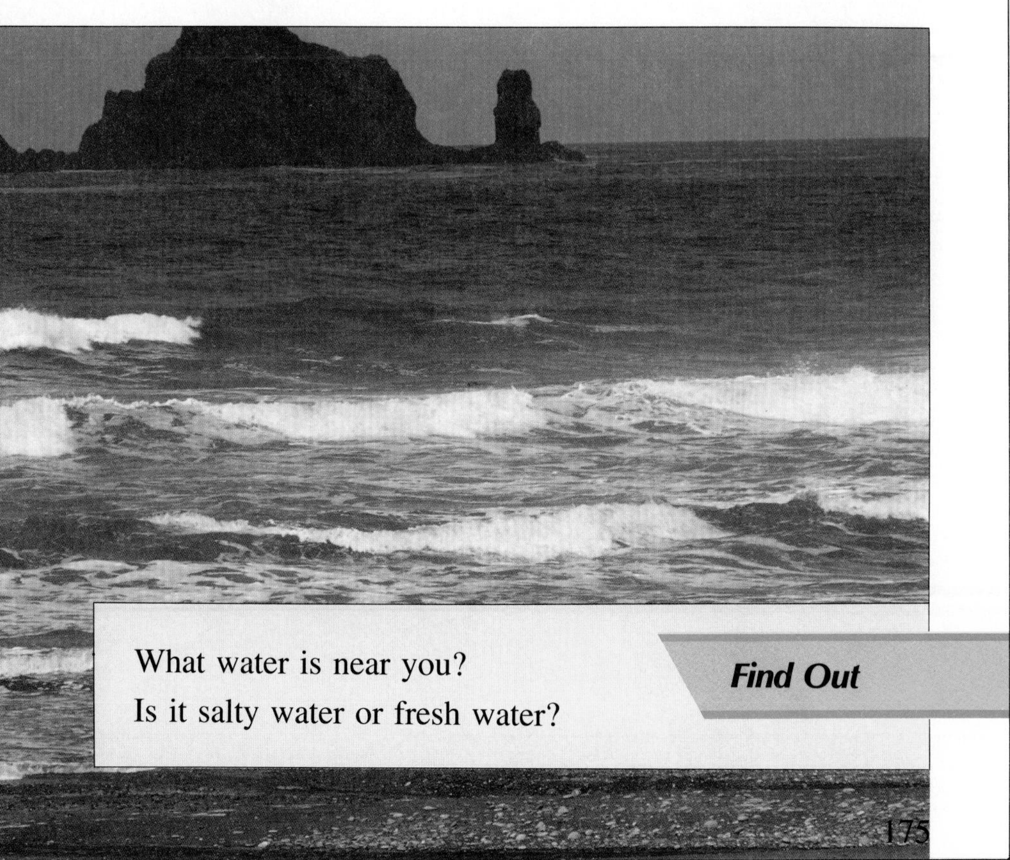

What water is near you?
Is it salty water or fresh water?

Find Out

175

2 TEACH

Teaching Tips

- Have the students discuss the illustration of the stream on page 174. Question: **Have you ever seen such a stream? Where did the water come from?** (Students might *infer* that stream water comes from mountain lakes or from underground.)
- Question: **How is ocean water different from water in most lakes and streams?** Explain that most lakes and streams have fresh water, but the ocean has salty water.

3 ASSESS

Lesson Review

1. Water is in streams, rivers, lakes, ocean.
2. People drink fresh water.
Challenge! Question: **How could a person get drinking water from mountain ice or snow?** (Melt the ice or snow.) **Thinking Skill:** *Applying information to new situations.*

Find Out

Students might recall seeing or visiting a body of water nearby. Students also might consult a map of your area to locate bodies of water, or ask an adult about nearby bodies of water. **Thinking Skills:** *Restating or explaining ideas, Interpreting maps*

Workbook page 52 *

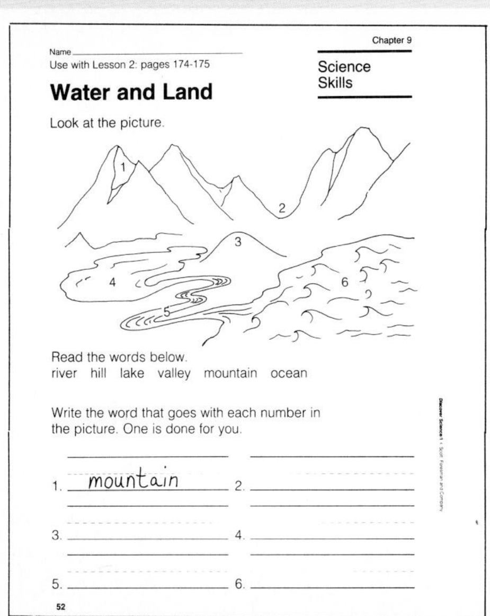
Name
Use with Lesson 2: pages 174-175
Chapter 9
Science Skills

Water and Land

Look at the picture.

Read the words below.
river hill lake valley mountain ocean

Write the word that goes with each number in the picture. One is done for you.

1. mountain 2. ______
3. ______ 4. ______
5. ______ 6. ______

52

*** Answers to masters on pages 168E–168F***

Enrichment

Provide small amounts of fresh and dehydrated food for children to observe and taste (for example: grapes and raisins, fresh and dried parsley, fresh and dried apples). Discuss the differences in appearance and taste. Explain that the dried forms are the same as the fresh objects, except that the water was removed.

Reteaching Suggestion ♦

Have students look for pictures that show sources of water such as lakes, rivers, snow, ice, oceans, and so on. Provide large sheets of paper on which students can paste their pictures. Have students label their pictures.

LESSON 3
pages 176–178

Lesson Objectives
- *Describe* some properties of air.
- *Identify* how people use air.

1 MOTIVATE

Demonstration Activity ♦
Have the students hold their breath for a few seconds. Then, have them place one hand about 5 centimeters (about 2 inches) in front of their faces as they breathe normally.

Discussion
Ask students to *describe* how they felt as they held their breath. Discuss the importance of breathing. Question: **What do we take in as we breathe?** (air). Ask students if they could see the air as they breathed in and out. Then, have them *describe* what they could feel on their hands as they breathed.

[1] Air is everywhere.

Lesson 3 How Is Air Useful?

People need air to breathe.
You cannot see clean air.
You usually cannot smell or taste air.
Where is air in this picture?[1]

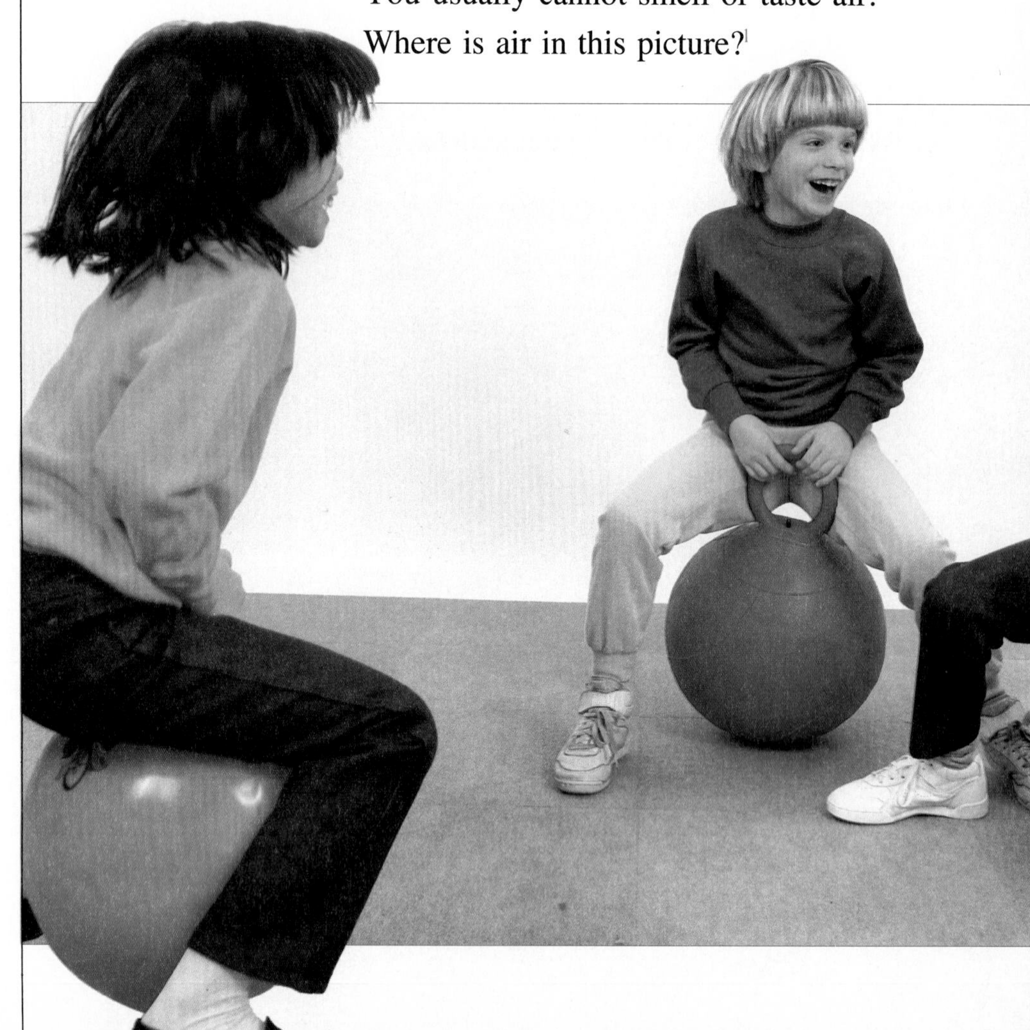

Teaching Options

SCIENCE BACKGROUND

Air is a mixture of about a dozen different gases. Nitrogen and oxygen are most abundant, but the atmosphere also contains argon, carbon dioxide, neon, helium, hydrogen, methane, water vapor, and several other gases in smaller amounts. Many complicated chemical reactions occur in the atmosphere, some of them powered by energy from the sun. The atmosphere aids life not only because it provides necessary gases, but also because it keeps the earth warm and absorbs harmful radiation from the sun, shielding living things from these rays. Pollutants produce measurable, harmful effects on living things and materials. Some common pollutants include sulfur oxides, nitrogen oxides, particulates, carbon monoxide, and hydrocarbons.

♦ ***Suitable as a language development activity***

Moving air is wind.
What can wind do?
You need wind to fly a kite.
Warm, moving wind can dry clothes.
Wind moves the top of this machine.
Wind helps the machine pump water.

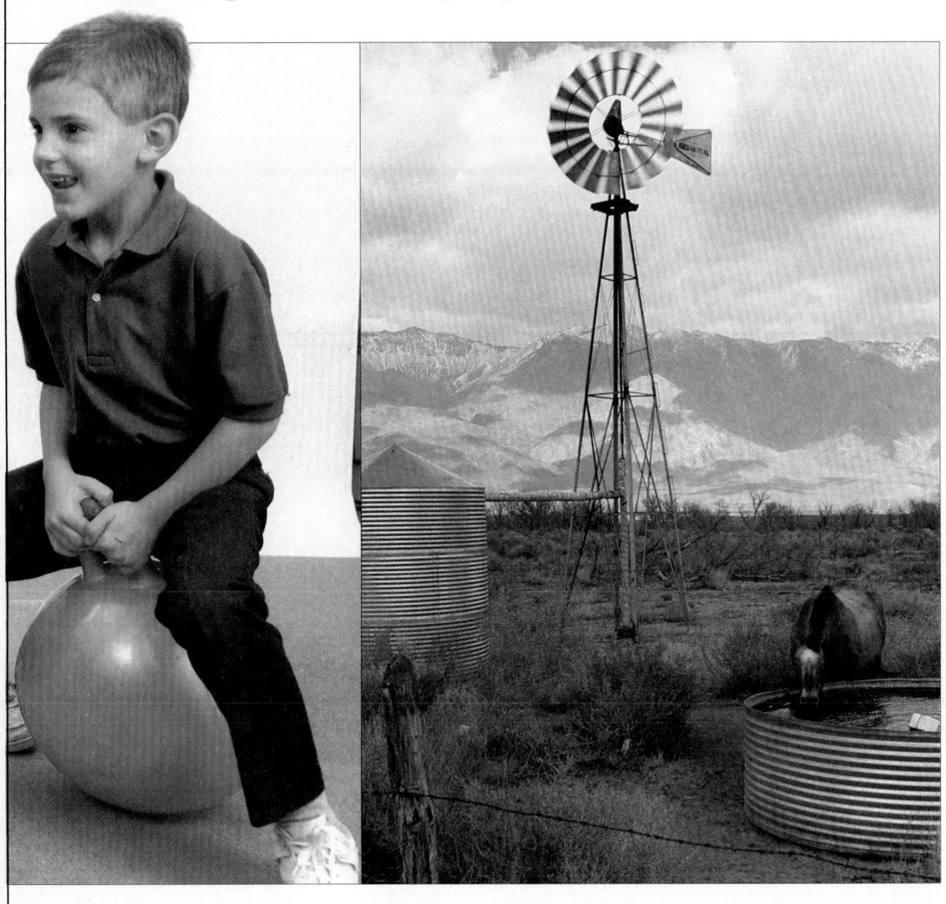

177

2 TEACH

Teaching Tips

- Refer to the illustration on page 176 and have students discuss what the children are doing. Ask students who have participated in a similar activity to ***describe*** what it was like.
- Explain that air can make things move. Read page 177 together and encourage students to give other examples of things air can move.
- **Possible Misconception:** Children usually do not think of air as part of Earth. Emphasize that life on Earth is possible only because our planet contains water and land, and is surrounded by air.

Science and Language Arts

Let students pretend they are the wind traveling all over the world. Have students make up stories about what the wind would do as it blew over land and water. Students might illustrate their stories.

Special Education

Provide one or two appliances that blow air, such as a fan or a hair dryer. While using the low setting on the fan or the cool setting on the dryer, ask students with learning disabilities to take turns placing a hand in front of the machine. *CAUTION:* Hold the appliance at least 0.3 meters (about 1 foot) from a student's hand. Have them describe what they feel. Ask if they can see the air, smell it, grab it, or hold it. Turn off the machine and repeat the questions. Relate the still air to the air we breathe. Relate the moving air to a breeze or a wind.

Enrichment

Have students observe the effects of air on falling objects. Drop a flat piece of paper horizontally. At the same time, drop a crumpled ball of paper from the same height. Lead a discussion about the difference in the way the two pieces of paper fell. Explain that air pushing on the flat paper causes it to drift down more slowly.

TEACHING PLAN

Teaching Tips

- Question: **How does polluted air look?** (Students might state that polluted air looks dirty.) Explain that sometimes polluted air looks clear, but it contains harmful things.
- Question: **What can we do to keep air clean?** Lead students to state actions that they themselves can take, such as avoiding hitting chalkboard erasers in order to reduce the amount of chalk dust in the air.

3 ASSESS

Lesson Review

1. People need to breathe air. Air dries things and moves things.
2. Using cars less is one way to help keep air clean.
Challenge! Question: **When might you be able to see or smell air?** Students might respond that they can see or smell air that is dirty, smoky, and polluted. **Thinking Skill:** *Drawing conclusions*

Find Out

Answers might include fans, air conditioners, dryers, heaters, vacuum cleaners. **Thinking Skill:** *Applying information to new situations*

[1] by using cleaner-burning fuels and conserving resources

Smoky fires put dirt into the air.
These cars put dirt into the air, too.
Using cars less helps keep the air clean.
How else can people keep the air clean?[1]

Lesson Review

1. How do people use air?
2. What helps keep air clean?

Find Out

Think about some machines.
What machines help move air?

Teaching Options

SCIENCE ANECDOTE

Vacuum cleaners produce winds that blow across a carpet into a bag in the machine. The wind picks up dust and other dirt, as do the winds of storms.

Reteaching Suggestion ♦

Write three incomplete sentences on the chalkboard, such as:
"Air is important because . . ."
"Wind can . . ."
"People can keep air clean by . . ."
Have the students choose a sentence to copy, complete, and illustrate. Allow time for each student to read his or her sentence and display the illustration.

Workbook page 53 *

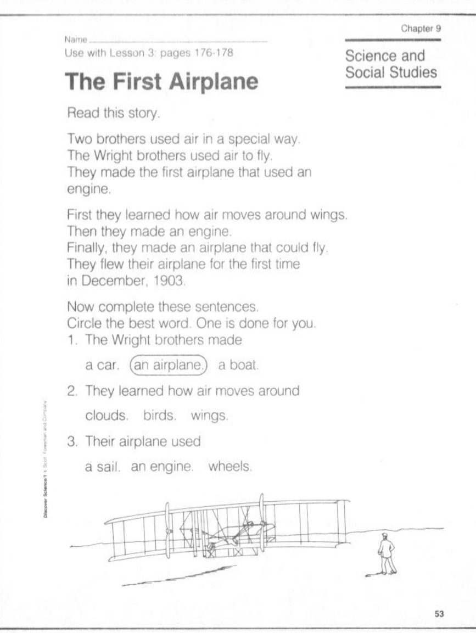
Name ______
Use with Lesson 3: pages 176-178

Chapter 9

Science and Social Studies

The First Airplane

Read this story.

Two brothers used air in a special way.
The Wright brothers used air to fly.
They made the first airplane that used an engine.

First they learned how air moves around wings.
Then they made an engine.
Finally, they made an airplane that could fly.
They flew their airplane for the first time in December, 1903.

Now complete these sentences.
Circle the best word. One is done for you.

1. The Wright brothers made
   a car. (an airplane.) a boat.
2. They learned how air moves around
   clouds. birds. wings.
3. Their airplane used
   a sail. an engine. wheels.

53

♦ *Suitable as a language development activity*

Using Air to Move Boats

Follow the Directions

1. Make a boat like the one here.
2. Put your boat in water.
3. Blow air on your boat.
4. Make it move on the water.

Tell What You Learned

Tell how the boat moved.

What other ways can we use air?

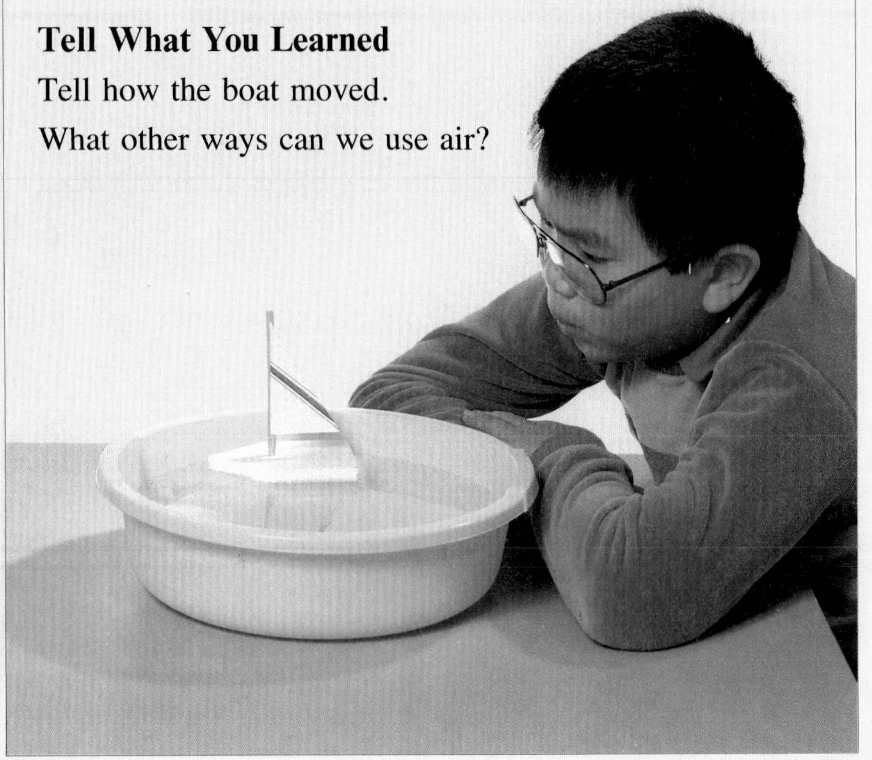

179

ACTIVITY PLAN

Concept

Air has useful functions.

Objectives/Process Skills

- *Make a model* of a boat.
- *Observe* how air can cause the boat to move.
- *Describe* how the boat moved.
- *Infer* other ways that air can be used.

Materials

For each student: plastic foam tray, tape, paper, toothpicks, shallow pan, water

Time Allotment:

Allow 20 minutes.

Safety Tips (See page T27.)

- Instruct students to handle toothpicks carefully.
- Wipe up any spilled water immediately to prevent falls.

Teaching Tips

- Ask students to name different types of boats (canoe, motorboat, sailboat, submarine, and so on). Have students explain how these boats move (motors, oars, sails).
- Explain that students are going to make toy sailboats. Distribute the materials.
- Help students read the activity and follow the directions to assemble the boats as shown in the picture. Explain that students will sail their boats in pans of water.
- When students place their boats in pans of water, let students blow on the sails to make the boats move.

Answers

Tell What You Learned

For the first statement, students should respond that air pushed on the sail and made the boat move. For the second statement, students should respond that air can dry clothes, make kites fly, turn windmills, and so on. **Thinking Skill:** *Inferring*

Enrichment Activity

Allow students to make boats from other materials, such as clay, cardboard, and wood. They also might make boats of plastic foam, but in different sizes and shapes. Allow students to display and sail their boats.

Activity Results

The boat should move across the water when the student blows air on it.

*** Answers to masters on pages 168E–168F***

TEACHING PLAN

LESSON 4
pages 180–182

Lesson Objectives
- *Describe* ways that people use land and water.
- *State* that people can use land and water carefully.

1 MOTIVATE

Demonstration Activity ♦
Display many pictures of ways people use land and water. Examples include farming showing irrigation, children playing on a playground, a strip mine, an oil rig, a fishing boat hauling in a catch, people swimming, and so on.

Discussion
Question: **In what other ways do people use land and water?** Lead students to *conclude* that land and water have countless uses, and that life depends on land and water.

[1] to grow flowers

Lesson 4 How Do People Use Land and Water?

People use plants they grow on the land.
They use coal from deep in the land.
People use oil they pump from the land.
They build homes and farms on land.
How do people use this land?[1]

Teaching Options

SCIENCE BACKGROUND

Coal, oil, and natural gas are nonrenewable resources. After they are used up, none will be available for millions of years. Conservation is important because it postpones the time when supplies of these fossil fuels run out.

Some major water pollutants are chemicals, sediments, pathogens, and heat. The improper disposal of chemical wastes has caused contamination of ground water, because buried chemicals can leak out of metal drums and enter the underground aquifers. Some major air pollutants are sulfur oxides and nitrogen oxides, carbon monoxide, hydrocarbons, and suspended particles. Most air pollutants result from burning of fossil fuels.

♦ ***Suitable as a language development activity***

[1] to transport goods

People drink water.
They use it for washing.
People swim and fish in water.
They also travel on water by boat.
What is water used for here?[1]

181

2 TEACH

Teaching Tips

- Lead students to discuss using land to grow crops, not just for people to eat, but also for feeding other animals, such as cattle and hogs.
- Point out that some crops, such as cotton, are used to make fabrics for clothing.
- Question: **How do people use coal and oil?** Students might recall that these fuels are used to heat homes and operate machines. Explain that a major use for these fuels is for making electric power.
- Recall the *TRY THIS* activity on page 169 in which students observed how much water covers the earth. Question: **How does oil get from areas where there are wells to other countries that need it?** Explain that large tanker ships carry oil across the ocean.
- Discuss the use of rivers to transport goods. Explain that cities often grew near rivers because they acted as ports for shipping and receiving goods.

Special Education

Tell students with learning disabilities that you are going to play a listening game. Whenever they hear you name something you can do with land, students should raise their hands. Whenever they hear you name something you can do with water, students should shake their heads. On the blackboard, draw a mountain with a hand next to it, and below that draw a pond with a head next to it. Activities you might mention include: swimming, walking, planting flowers, diving, fishing, mining for coal, boating, drinking, building homes, washing, riding bicycles, cleaning.

Reinforcement

Tell students that one way they can help use land and water carefully is by not littering. Take the class to the playground to look for litter. Take a plastic trash bag along, and have the class properly dispose of any trash they find. *CAUTION:* Students should wear gloves when picking up litter and should notify you if they come across broken glass.

Enrichment

Have students fill two aluminum foil pans with potting soil. Plant grass seed in one pan. After the grass has grown, tilt the pans and place a brick or block under them to maintain the slope. Have students slowly pour water over both pans and watch what happens. Explain that water causes land to erode, or wash away. Ask students to explain why more erosion occurred in one pan than in the other. Question: **How can people help keep hillsides and other areas from eroding?** (plant grass and trees)

TEACHING PLAN

Teaching Tips

- Question: **How can campers in forests and parks take good care of land and water?** (Campers should dispose of trash properly, should not cut down trees, should tend fires carefully and put out all fires before they leave a campsite.)
- **Possible Misconception:** Children might think that Earth has an unlimited supply of fresh water. Explain that we cannot drink untreated seawater, and need to conserve fresh water.

3 ASSESS

Lesson Review

1. People use land and water to live on, to grow things, to take them places, to work with, and to have fun.
2. By keeping them clean

Challenge! Question: **How does not wasting fresh water help Earth?** (It makes more fresh water available.)
Thinking Skill: *Making generalizations*

Find Out

They should not cut them down unnecessarily. **Thinking Skill:** *Applying information to new situations*

conserve resources such as oil, water, and land

These people are careful.
They keep the land and water clean.
They use the land and water wisely.
What can you do to help?[1]

Lesson Review

1. How can people use land and water?
2. What is careful use of land and water?

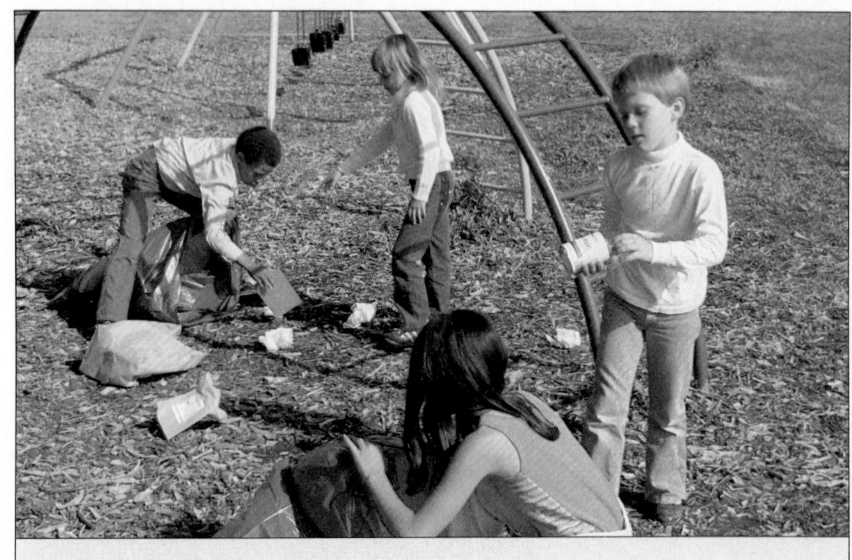

Find Out

Trees grow on land.
How can people use trees wisely?

182

Teaching Options

SCIENCE ANECDOTE

In part of the United States, power companies get energy from hot rock beneath the ground. Water is pumped through the rock, and the steam that is produced is used to turn electric generators.

Reteaching Suggestion ♦

Instruct students to fold a piece of paper in half. On one side, have them draw pictures of ways that land is used. On the other side, they should draw pictures of ways water is used. Allow time for students to show and explain their pictures.

Workbook page 54 *

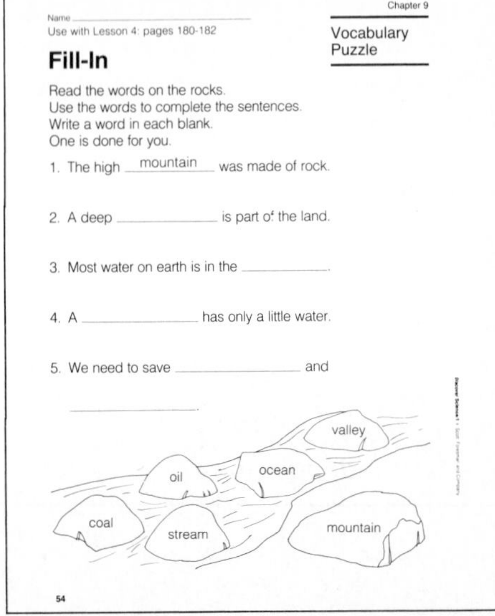

Name ______ Chapter 9
Use with Lesson 4: pages 180-182
Vocabulary Puzzle

Fill-In

Read the words on the rocks.
Use the words to complete the sentences.
Write a word in each blank.
One is done for you.

1. The high mountain was made of rock.
2. A deep ______ is part of the land.
3. Most water on earth is in the ______
4. A ______ has only a little water.
5. We need to save ______ and ______

54

♦ *Suitable as a language development activity*

Science and People

Rachel Carson

Rachel Carson cared about the earth.
She studied and learned about oceans.
She wrote books about them.
Some books told how she loved oceans.
Her books also helped many people.
They learned to care about oceans, too.

What Do You Think?

How can people care about oceans?

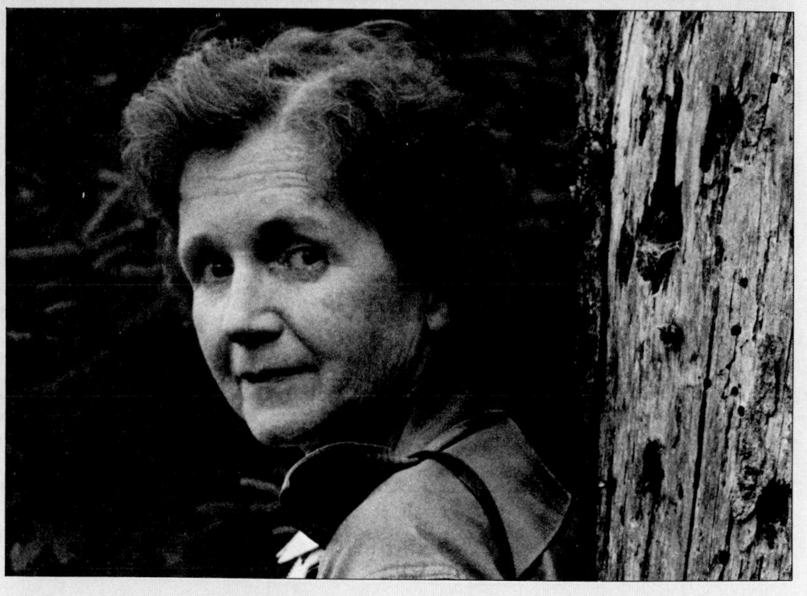

183

SCIENCE AND PEOPLE

Discussion

Question: **Why do people take care of other living things?** (Students might *infer* that all living things depend on one another. People need other living things as much as other organisms are affected by actions of people.)

Teaching Tips

- Question: **What things do we get from oceans?** (fish, shellfish, oil, salt) Explain that some people eat plants that grow in the ocean.
- Question: **Can people live in the ocean?** (Students might *infer* that they cannot because people need fresh water.) Explain that people can only live on the ocean in boats that carry fresh water. People also need air to breathe, so they cannot live under the water.

Answer

What Do You Think?
People can clean up harmful materials that accidentally spill into oceans, and not put harmful materials into oceans on purpose. **Thinking Skill:** *Making inferences*

SCIENCE BACKGROUND

Rachel Louise Carson was born in 1907 in Springfield, Pennsylvania. She died in 1964 in Silver Spring, Maryland. Her formal education included Pennsylvania College for Women (graduated, 1929), Johns Hopkins University (A.M., 1932), and graduate work at the Woods Hole Marine Biological Laboratory in Massachusetts.

Carson taught and wrote extensively on the sea. Some of her books about the sea are *The Sea Around Us, The Edge of the Sea,* and *Under the Sea-Wind.* However, Carson is best known for her book *Silent Spring*, which warns of the dangers to the earth of indiscriminate use of pesticides and other poisons.

* ***Answers to masters on pages 168E–168F***

TEACHING PLAN

SKILLS FOR SOLVING PROBLEMS
pages 184–185

Purpose
This feature provides an opportunity for students to develop skill in reading a map, and then to apply this skill by drawing a map of their own.

1 MOTIVATE

Discussion
Display a map of your community. Question: **Where on this map is our school?** Help students locate the school, major roads, and other landmarks.

2 TEACH

Teaching Tip
- Guide students in finding each item on the map on page 184.

Skills for Solving Problems

Using a Map

What can a map show?

1. Look at this map.
   Find the land.
   Point to the oceans.
   Find a river.

184

Teaching Options

SCIENCE BACKGROUND

Maps provide useful information. Maps tell how to get somewhere. They describe roads, streets, and highways. They tell which trails are best to hike, which trails are the easiest to climb or ski, and what objects might be passed along the way. Weather maps help predict the weather, and show weather patterns in other parts of the country. Airplane pilots depend on weather maps in order to fly planes safely.

2. Choose a place you have seen.
   Use your own paper.
   Draw a map like these maps.
   Write what each thing on your map is.

3. Show your map to a friend.
   Point to places on your map.

Teaching Tips

- Look at the sample maps on page 185 with the students and discuss places they may want to use for their own maps. Develop the idea that a map presents a picture as if someone were looking down on an area. Explain that a map is a drawing of a real place and real things.
- Before students draw their own maps, they should decide which items from the place they choose should be on the map. Not every item need be shown.
- Students can make maps as colorful and detailed or as simple as they like.

3 ASSESS

Answers will depend on individual students' maps, but should include information on the maps, such as items in a room, on a street, in a park.

Resource Book page 71 *

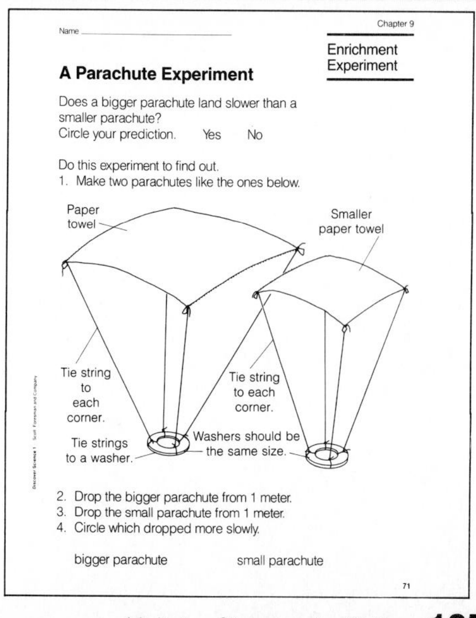
Name

Chapter 9

Enrichment Experiment

A Parachute Experiment

Does a bigger parachute land slower than a smaller parachute?
Circle your prediction. Yes No

Do this experiment to find out.
1. Make two parachutes like the ones below.

2. Drop the bigger parachute from 1 meter.
3. Drop the small parachute from 1 meter.
4. Circle which dropped more slowly.

bigger parachute small parachute

71

* *Answers to masters on pages 168E–168F*

REVIEW PLAN

CHAPTER 9 REVIEW
pages 186–187

Review Chapter Ideas
1. Earth has air, water, land.
2. Land has different kinds of rocks and soil. The land has mountains, valleys, and flat places.
3. Ocean water is salty. Earth has freshwater in rivers, in rain, ice, and snow.
4. You cannot see, taste, or smell air. You can feel moving air.
5. People need air to breathe. People use air for drying clothes and flying kites.
6. People use water for drinking, for work, and for play; people use boats on water to go places. People use land to grow things, to take things like oil and coal, to build homes.

For further review, use Study Guide page 235.

Chapter 9 Review

Review Chapter Ideas

1. Tell what the earth has.
2. Describe what the land has.
3. Look at the pictures.
   Tell about the water on earth.

a.

b.

c.

d.

e.

4. Describe what air is like.
5. Describe how people use air.
6. Tell how people use land and water.

186

Review Options

Cooperative Learning ♦

STAD Format (See page T23.)
Assign students to work in four- to five-member teams to study Chapter 9 Review. Students should work together to make sure that they and their teammates know the material in the chapter. After students have had enough time to study together, give them a test to complete individually (Chapter 9 Test in the *Test Book*). Award Superteam certificates to teams whose average test scores exceed 90%, and Greatteam certificates to teams whose average test scores exceed 80%.

♦ ***Suitable as a language development activity***

Review Science Words

Match the words and the pictures.

1. stream
2. valley
3. mountain
4. soil

a. 

b. 

c. 

d. 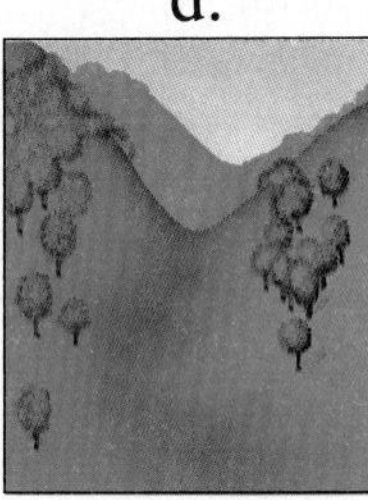

Tell what the words mean.

5. oil
6. coal
7. ocean

Use Science Ideas

Tell who is helping the earth.

Review Science Words

Match the words and pictures.

1. c **3.** a
2. d **4.** b

Tell what the words mean.
Thinking Skill: *Restating or explaining ideas*

5. Oil—pumped from the land to be used for energy. It can be all used up.
6. Coal—a kind of rock dug out from the land to be used for energy. It can be used up.
7. Ocean—contains most of the water on earth. Most of earth is ocean. Ocean water is salty, and people cannot drink it.

Use Science Ideas

The person riding the bicycle and throwing trash in a basket helps the earth.
Thinking Skill: *Applying information to new situations*

Test Book page 31 *

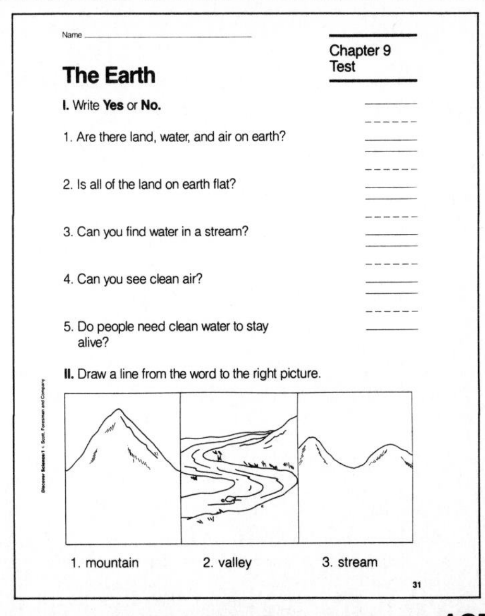

Name ____

Chapter 9 Test

The Earth

I. Write **Yes** or **No.**

1. Are there land, water, and air on earth? ____
2. Is all of the land on earth flat? ____
3. Can you find water in a stream? ____
4. Can you see clean air? ____
5. Do people need clean water to stay alive? ____

II. Draw a line from the word to the right picture.

1. mountain 2. valley 3. stream

31

*** *Answers to masters on pages 168E–168F***

Teaching Plan

Chapter Components	Skills	Materials
Chapter Opener/*TRY THIS:* Observing the Weather pp. 188-189	***TRY THIS*** p. 189 **Science Process Skill** *Observing*	***TRY THIS*** p. 189 (individual) 30 boxes crayons, 30 pencils, 30 sheets drawing paper
Lesson 1: What Are Different Kinds of Weather? pp. 190-192	**Thinking Skills** Challenge!: *Drawing conclusions* Find Out: *Collecting and communicating information*	**Demonstration** p. 190 no materials needed
Activity: Showing Air Temperature p. 193	**Science Process Skills** *Making models, Communicating*	(individual) 90 flat wooden sticks, 30 pencils, 30 boxes crayons, 30 bottles white glue, 30 sheets white construction paper, 30 scissors
Lesson 2: How Can Weather Change in Seasons? pp. 194-197	**Thinking Skills** Challenge!: *Applying information to new situations* Find Out: *Restating or explaining ideas*	**Demonstration** p. 194 pictures depicting the four seasons
Lesson 3: How Is Weather Important to People? pp. 198-199	**Thinking Skills** Challenge!: *Drawing conclusions* Find Out: *Restating ideas*	**Demonstration** p. 198 articles or pictures of clothing for different kinds of weather
Activity: Making a Weather Chart p. 200	**Science Process Skills** *Observing, Communicating, Collecting and interpreting data*	(individual) 30 sheets drawing paper, 30 boxes crayons, 30 pencils
Science in Your Life: Taking Weather Pictures p. 201	**Thinking Skill** *Drawing conclusions*	
Skills for Solving Problems: Measuring Rain pp. 202-203	**Problem Solving Skills** *Making decisions/Identifying and solving problems, Interpreting charts, maps, and graphs*	(individual) paper, crayons, or coloring pencils
Chapter Review pp. 204-205	**Thinking Skills** *Restating or explaining ideas, Recognizing relevant information and data*	

Teaching Options

Strategies	Extensions		Resource Masters
			Family Letter: *Resource Book* p. 75 Vocabulary Preview: *Workbook* pp. 55-56
	Special Education p. 191 Reinforcement p. 191	Reteaching Suggestion p. 192 Game Suggestion p. 192	Science Activity: *Workbook* p. 57
	Enrichment Activity p. 193		
	Science and Art p. 195 Special Education p. 195 Reinforcement p. 195	Enrichment p. 196 Science and Social Studies p. 196 Reteaching Suggestion p. 197	Science Skills: *Workbook* p. 58 Science and Social Studies: *Workbook* p. 59
	Special Education p. 199 Reteaching Suggestion p. 199		Vocabulary Puzzle *Workbook* p. 60
	Enrichment Activity p. 200		
			Enrichment Activity: *Resource Book* p. 79
Cooperative Learning p. 204 (Also see p. T23)			Chapter Test: *Test Book* p. 33

Preteaching Suggestions

For Advance Preparation

Activity, page 193
Collect three flat, wooden sticks, such as tongue depressors, for each group of students.

Demonstration, page 194
Find pictures of each of the four seasons for this demonstration.

Demonstration, page 198
Bring articles of clothing suitable for different kinds of weather or collect pictures of such articles.

For Vocabulary Review

Use the following sentences with your students to review the meanings of the underlined words.

1. When you look at something, you observe it.
2. Temperature is a measure of how hot or cold something is.
3. A thermometer tells the temperature.
4. A pilot flies airplanes.
5. A computer is a machine that stores information.

For High-Potential Students

Encourage students to observe and record clouds for a couple of weeks. Ask them to look at the shape, size, and color of clouds and to estimate the amount of sky covered by clouds. Students might draw pictures or take photographs of the different types of clouds they observe. After a few weeks of observing, students should make a chart indicating which types of clouds are associated with particular weather patterns: clear and dry; sunny and humid; partly cloudy; brief rain showers; continuous rain; thunder showers; snow. They can use cotton or other materials to represent the clouds.

For Mainstreamed Students

Hearing Impaired
Write on the chalkboard different terms associated with weather, such as "hot," "cold," "sunny," and "windy." Then act out each term, using dramatic actions and facial expressions. After hearing-impaired students have figured out the meaning of each word, give them a chance to mime the weather words.

Emotionally Handicapped
Prepare a simple weather board using basic weather terms such as "hot," "cold," "sunny," and "windy." Also prepare a picture of each of the four seasons to place below the weather board. Ask emotionally handicapped students to be in charge of using the weather board to report the weather. Encourage each student to give a daily weather report to the class.

For Science Fair Projects

Encourage interested students to do one of the following:

1. Make a display showing record temperatures in the United States and around the world. List the locations where the record temperatures have occurred, noting latitude, longitude, altitude, and type of environment of the region.
2. Choose a city that you would like to visit anywhere in the world. Find out what the weather is like in that city. Make a display of the special clothes and equipment you might take on a trip to that city.

Classroom Resources

Bulletin Board
Ask students to draw or bring in pictures of things that remind them of each of the four seasons.

THE FOUR SEASONS

WINTER

SPRING

SUMMER

FALL

Chapter 10 Poster

When would you wear these clothes?

Science Discovery Center
Use pages from Chapter 10 in the *Science Discovery Center Book*. Place these worksheets in the appropriate pockets in the Science Discovery Center.

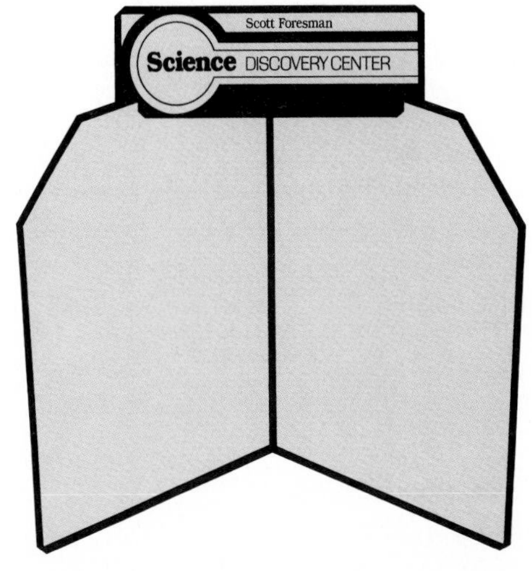

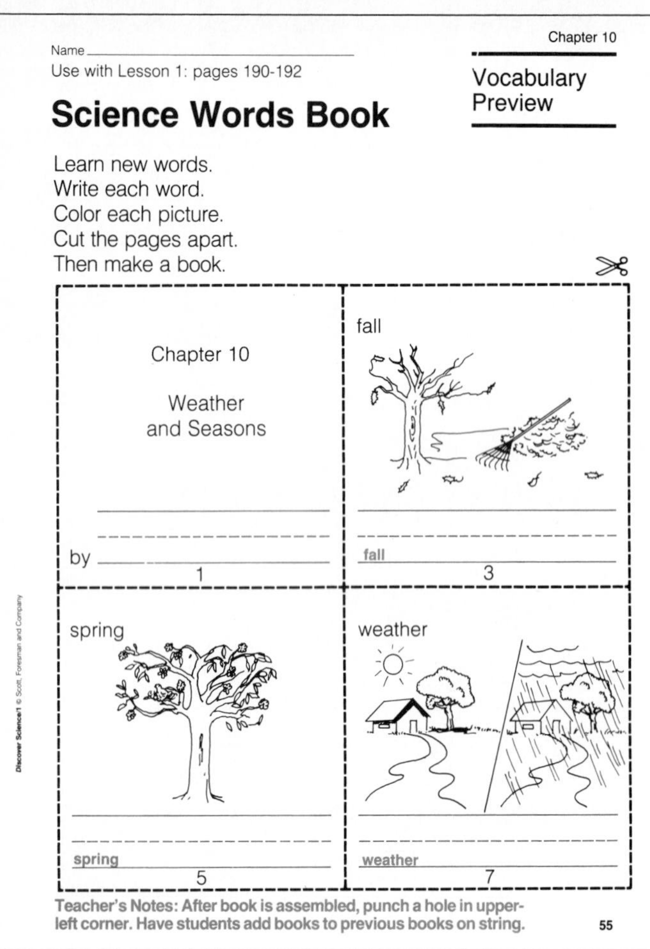

Name ____________________

Use with Lesson 1: pages 190-192

Chapter 10

Vocabulary Preview

Science Words Book

Learn new words.
Write each word.
Color each picture.
Cut the pages apart.
Then make a book.

Teacher's Notes: After book is assembled, punch a hole in upper-left corner. Have students add books to previous books on string.

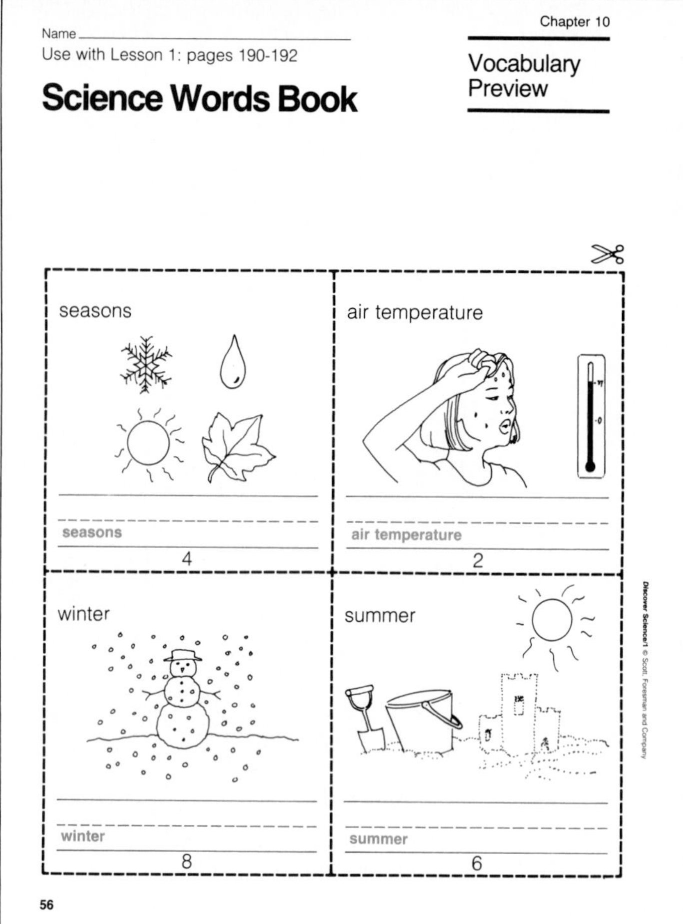

Name ____________________

Use with Lesson 1: pages 190-192

Chapter 10

Vocabulary Preview

Science Words Book

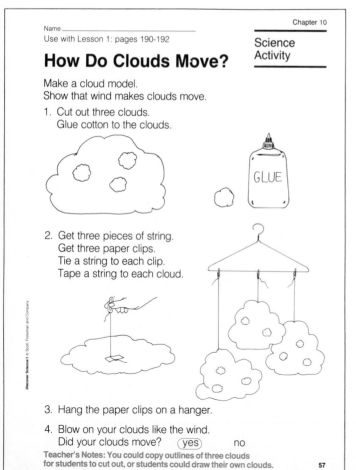

Name ____________________

Use with Lesson 1: pages 190-192

Chapter 10

Science Activity

How Do Clouds Move?

Make a cloud model.
Show that wind makes clouds move.

1. Cut out three clouds.
   Glue cotton to the clouds.

2. Get three pieces of string.
   Get three paper clips.
   Tie a string to each clip.
   Tape a string to each cloud.
3. Hang the paper clips on a hanger.
4. Blow on your clouds like the wind.
   Did your clouds move? (yes) no

Teacher's Notes: You could copy outlines of three clouds for students to cut out, or students could draw their own clouds.

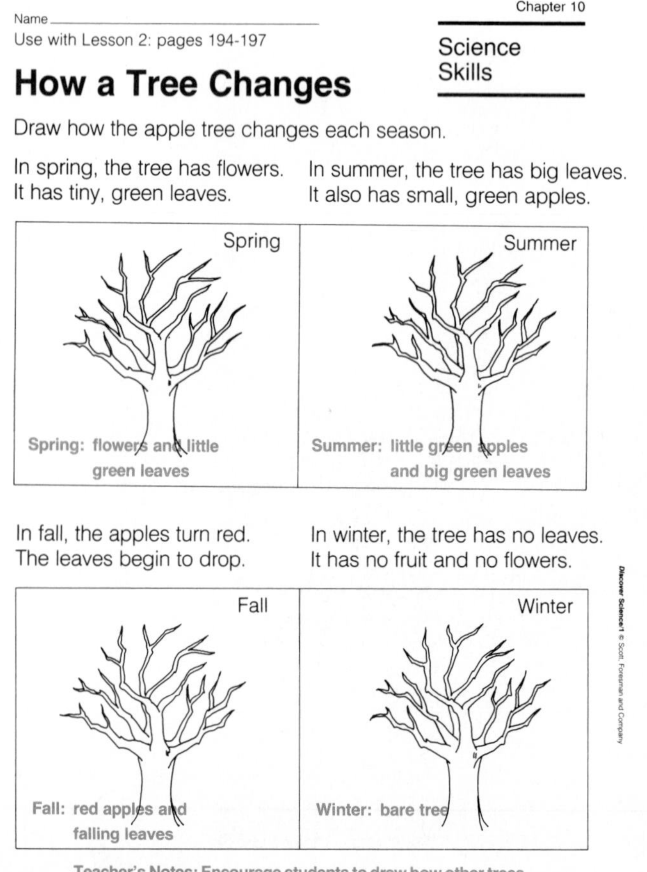

Name ____________________

Use with Lesson 2: pages 194-197

Chapter 10

Science Skills

How a Tree Changes

Draw how the apple tree changes each season.

In spring, the tree has flowers.
It has tiny, green leaves.

In summer, the tree has big leaves.
It also has small, green apples.

In fall, the apples turn red.
The leaves begin to drop.

In winter, the tree has no leaves.
It has no fruit and no flowers.

Teacher's Notes: Encourage students to draw how other trees change from season to season.

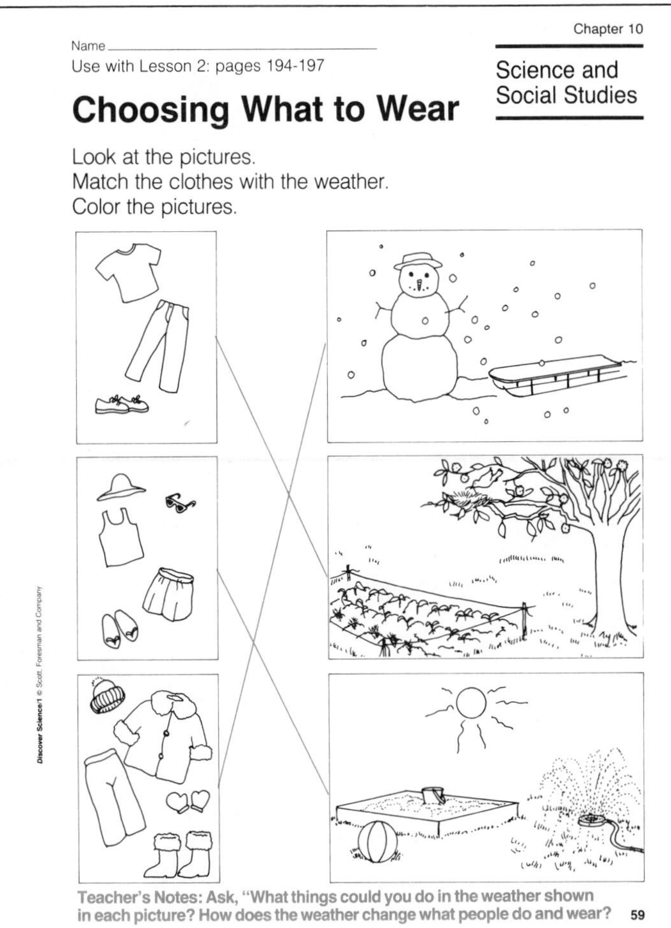

Name ____________________

Use with Lesson 2: pages 194-197

Chapter 10

Science and Social Studies

Choosing What to Wear

Look at the pictures.
Match the clothes with the weather.
Color the pictures.

Teacher's Notes: Ask, "What things could you do in the weather shown in each picture? How does the weather change what people do and wear?"

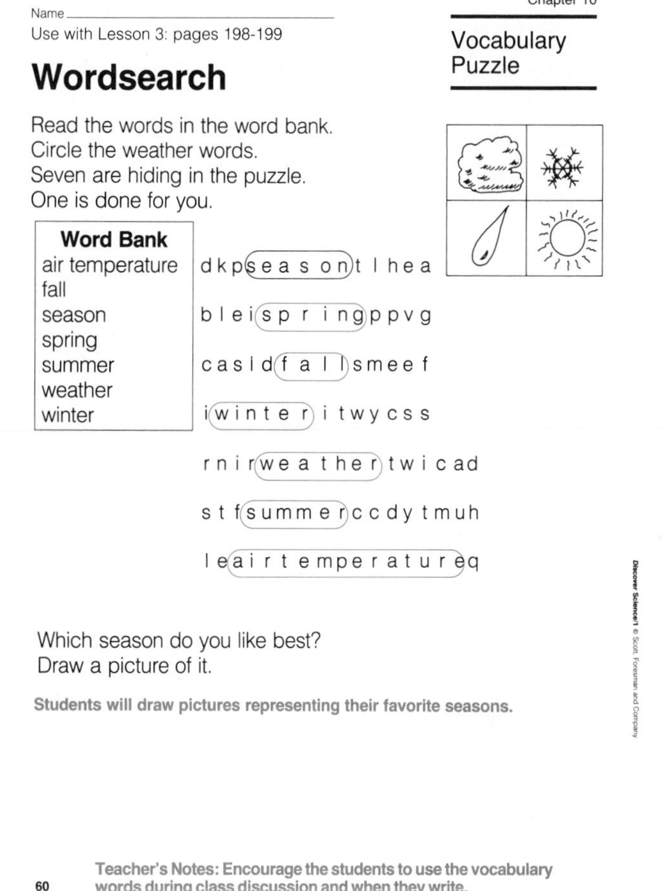

Name ____________________

Use with Lesson 3: pages 198-199

Chapter 10

Vocabulary Puzzle

Wordsearch

Read the words in the word bank.
Circle the weather words.
Seven are hiding in the puzzle.
One is done for you.

Word Bank
air temperature
fall
season
spring
summer
weather
winter

d k p s e a s o n t l h e a

b l e i s p r i n g p p v g

c a s l d f a l l s m e e f

i w i n t e r i t w y c s s

r n i r w e a t h e r t w i c a d

s t f s u m m e r c c d y t m u h

l e a i r t e m p e r a t u r e q

Which season do you like best?
Draw a picture of it.

Students will draw pictures representing their favorite seasons.

Teacher's Notes: Encourage the students to use the vocabulary words during class discussion and when they write.

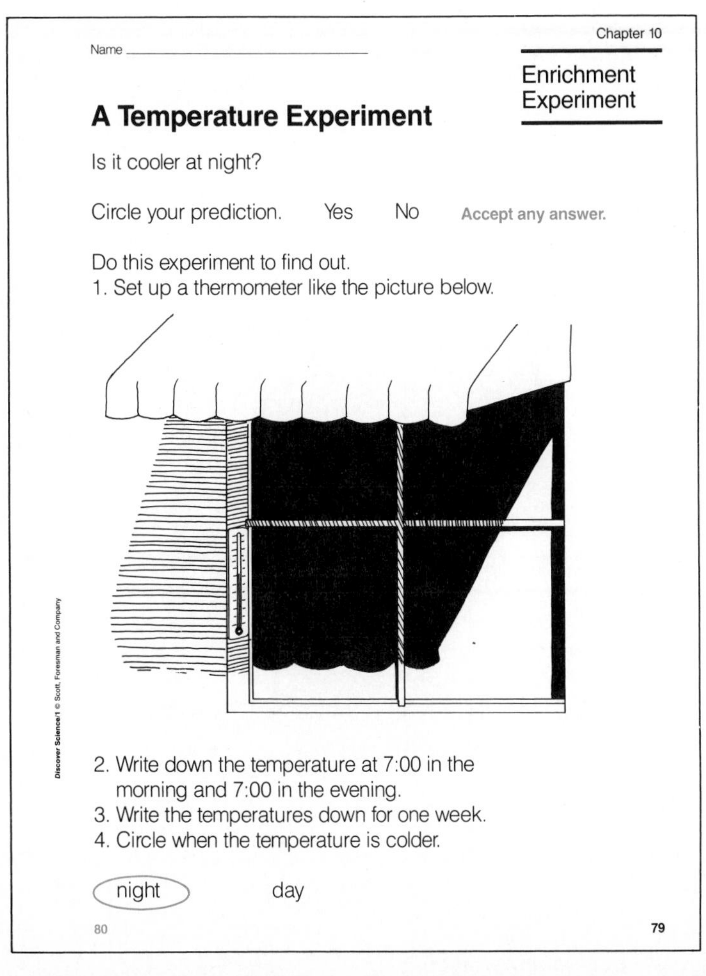

Name ____________________

Chapter 10

Enrichment Experiment

A Temperature Experiment

Is it cooler at night?

Circle your prediction. Yes No Accept any answer.

Do this experiment to find out.

1. Set up a thermometer like the picture below.
2. Write down the temperature at 7:00 in the morning and 7:00 in the evening.
3. Write the temperatures down for one week.
4. Circle when the temperature is colder.

(night) day

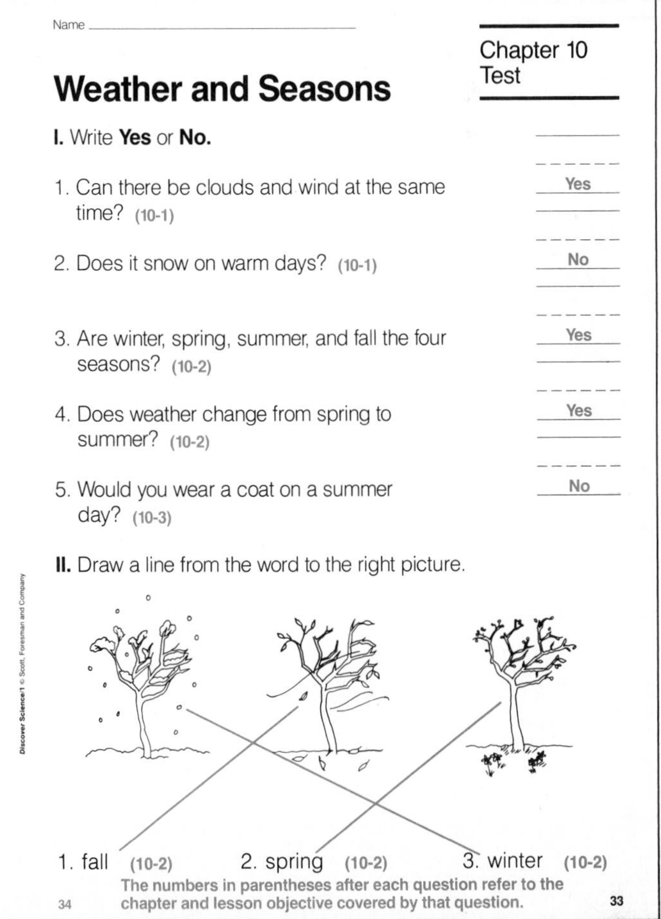

Name ____________________

Chapter 10 Test

Weather and Seasons

I. Write **Yes** or **No.**

1. Can there be clouds and wind at the same time? (10-1) Yes
2. Does it snow on warm days? (10-1) No
3. Are winter, spring, summer, and fall the four seasons? (10-2) Yes
4. Does weather change from spring to summer? (10-2) Yes
5. Would you wear a coat on a summer day? (10-3) No

II. Draw a line from the word to the right picture.

1. fall (10-2) 2. spring (10-2) 3. winter (10-2)

The numbers in parentheses after each question refer to the chapter and lesson objective covered by that question.

TEACHING PLAN

INTRODUCING CHAPTER 10

Major Concepts

Lesson 1 Different atmospheric conditions produce different kinds of weather.
Lesson 2 The weather can change in each of the four seasons.
Lesson 3 The weather affects people in a variety of ways.

Vocabulary

air temperature, fall, seasons, spring, summer, weather, winter

Chapter 10

Weather and Seasons

Suppose the sun shines on these branches.
It gets warmer outside.
What might happen to the ice?[1]

188

Teaching Options

Workbook page 55 *

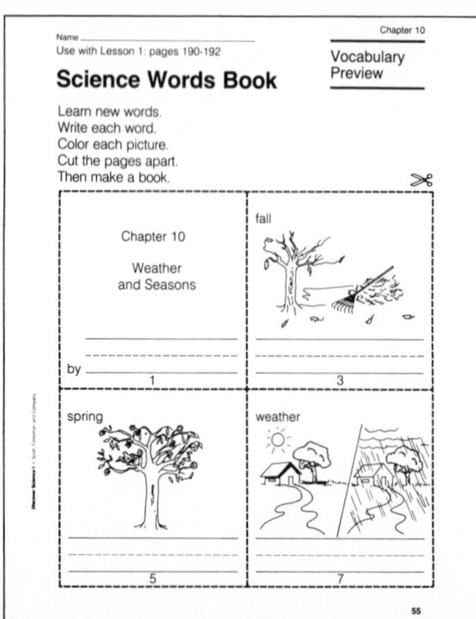

Name ___
Use with Lesson 1: pages 190-192

Chapter 10

Vocabulary Preview

Science Words Book

Learn new words.
Write each word.
Color each picture.
Cut the pages apart.
Then make a book.

Chapter 10 Weather and Seasons by ___ 1	fall 3
spring 5	weather 7

55

Workbook page 56 *

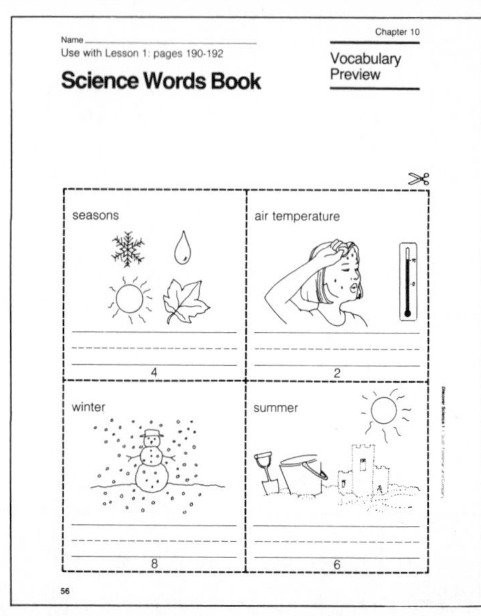

Name ___
Use with Lesson 1: pages 190-192

Chapter 10

Vocabulary Preview

Science Words Book

seasons 4	air temperature 2
winter 8	summer 6

56

♦ ***Suitable as a language development activity***

Starting the Chapter

You probably like to play outside.
You can observe when you are outside.
Do you notice if it is a warm or cold day?
Read how each day can be different.

TRY THIS

Observing the Weather

Look out the windows in your room.
Notice if the sky is clear or cloudy.
Notice if it is raining or snowing.
Draw a picture.
Show what the day is like.

189

TRY THIS

Objective ♦
This optional *Try This* activity will help students explore and build background information about the concept of weather. Later in the chapter students will be able to draw on this experience to help them assimilate the new content.

Science Process Skill
Observing

Materials
For each student: paper, crayons or colored markers, pencil

Safety Tip (See page T27.)
- Remind students not to look directly at the sun.

Teaching Tips
- Have the students think about the weather when they came to school or played outside during recess. Questions: **Was it hot? cold? warm?**
- Encourage the children to describe what kind of clothing made them feel comfortable outside. Ask them why they wore what they did.

Resource Book page 75

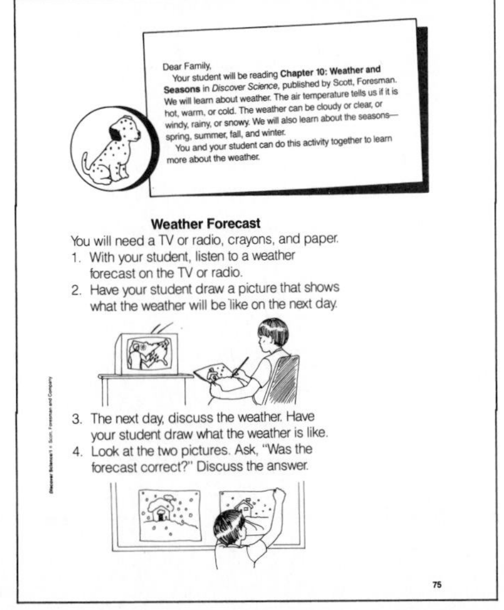

Dear Family,
Your student will be reading **Chapter 10: Weather and Seasons** in *Discover Science*, published by Scott, Foresman. We will learn about weather. The air temperature tells us if it is hot, warm, or cold. The weather can be cloudy or clear, or windy, rainy, or snowy. We will also learn about the seasons—spring, summer, fall, and winter.
You and your student can do this activity together to learn more about the weather.

Weather Forecast
You will need a TV or radio, crayons, and paper.
1. With your student, listen to a weather forecast on the TV or radio.
2. Have your student draw a picture that shows what the weather will be like on the next day.
3. The next day, discuss the weather. Have your student draw what the weather is like.
4. Look at the two pictures. Ask, "Was the forecast correct?" Discuss the answer.

75

SCIENCE BACKGROUND

Many factors influence the outside air temperature, including the directness of sunlight, nearness to water, and type of land surface.

A sunny day does not always mean a warm day. In fact, in the northern United States, some of the coldest winter days are sunny.

* *Answers to masters on pages 188E–188F*

TEACHING PLAN

LESSON 1
pages 190–192

Lesson Objectives
- *Identify* different kinds of weather.
- *Describe* characteristics of each kind of weather.

Lesson Vocabulary
air temperature, weather

1 MOTIVATE

Demonstration Activity ♦
Take the class outside to observe the weather. Have them look for as many different indicators of the weather as they can.

Discussion
Have the children tell what they *observe* about the weather. Ask them about the temperature of the air, whether it was windy or not, and to *describe* the sky.

[1] Play indoors or play outdoors in the snow.

Lesson 1 What Are Different Kinds of Weather?

Weather is what it is like outside.
Air temperature is part of weather.
The air can feel warm, hot, or cold.
It might snow on cold days.
Look at the picture.
What could you do on this day?[1]

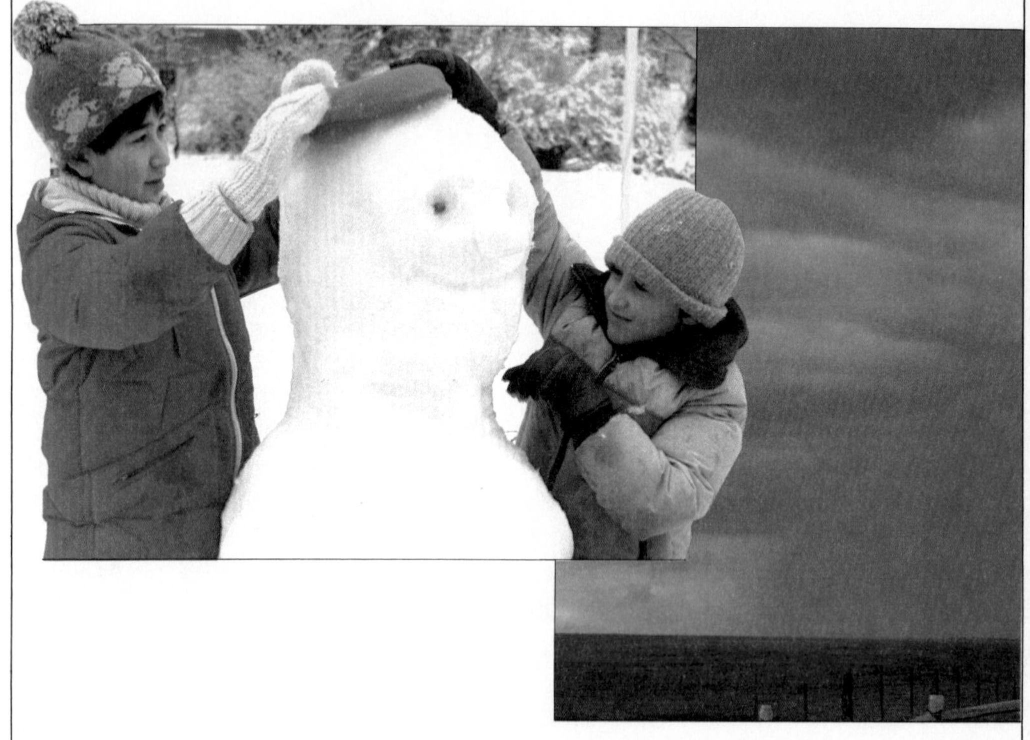

190

Teaching Options

SCIENCE BACKGROUND

Weather is the ever changing condition of outside air with respect to temperature, wind, cloud cover, precipitation, humidity, and air pressure. The sun is the source of the energy in weather. The sun heats the land, air, and water. The water vapor in air holds large amounts of energy. The sudden release of energy that occurs when water vapor changes to water in the storm cloud can produce severe thunderstorms.

A good indicator of changing weather is the barometric pressure. Changes in air pressure indicate changes in the overhead movement of air masses.

♦ ***Suitable as a language development activity***

The weather can be cloudy or clear.
Clear weather has no clouds or rain.
The weather can be windy, too.
Clouds move with the wind.
Have you ever seen clouds like these?
This kind of cloud brings rain.

2 TEACH

Teaching Tips

- Write the vocabulary words on the chalkboard. Read the words for the students and have them read the words to you.
- Call the children's attention to the illustration on page 190 and have them ***describe*** the weather condition pictured. Lead the students to infer whether the air temperature would be warm or cold on a snowy day.
- Call attention to the storm clouds in the illustration. Have the students ***compare*** the clouds in the picture to other clouds they have seen.
- **Possible Misconception:** Children might think that all clouds bring rain.

Workbook page 57 *

Name ____ Chapter 10
Use with Lesson 1: pages 190-192

How Do Clouds Move? Science Activity

Make a cloud model.
Show that wind makes clouds move.

1. Cut out three clouds.
   Glue cotton to the clouds.

GLUE

2. Get three pieces of string.
   Get three paper clips.
   Tie a string to each clip.
   Tape a string to each cloud.
3. Hang the paper clips on a hanger.
4. Blow on your clouds like the wind.
   Did your clouds move? yes no

57

*** Answers to masters on pages 182E–182F***

Special Education

Direct the children with learning disabilities to use a variety of art media to make pictures depicting different kinds of weather. Provide cotton balls for clouds.

Reinforcement

Make a weather dial with symbols for each type of weather. Choose one child each day to be the weather observer and to move the hands on the dial to the appropriate weather symbol.

TEACHING PLAN

Teaching Tip

- Encourage the students to *identify* the foggy weather in the illustration. Point out that fog is a cloud close to the ground. Discuss visibility in fog.

3 ASSESS

Lesson Review

1. Weather is what it is like outside.
2. Students can mention hot, cold, sunny, rainy, snowy, cloudy, windy, or clear weather.
Challenge! Question: **Why is the air temperature in the daytime usually warmer than the air temperature at night?** (The sun only shines during the day.) **Thinking Skill:** *Drawing conclusions*

Find Out

Students should listen to a weather forecast, and find out what weather is predicted. **Thinking Skill:** *Collecting and communicating information*

[1] foggy weather

What weather can you see and feel?
You can see all kinds of weather.
You can feel wind, snow, and rain.
What kind of weather do you see here?[1]

Lesson Review

1. What is weather?
2. What are five kinds of weather?

Find Out Listen to news about weather. What kind of weather is coming?

192

Teaching Options

SCIENCE ANECDOTE

Spacecraft have photographed violent storms in the atmosphere of Mars, Venus, and Jupiter.

Reteaching Suggestion ♦

Instruct the students to generate a list of words to *describe* the weather. The list should include such words as cold, cloudy, clear, windy, foggy, and so on. Each day have the students *observe* the weather and use the words on their list to describe it.

Game Suggestion ♦

Make a set of cards consisting of two groups—one group of weather words and the other group of matching weather symbols or pictures. Play the game using the rules of "Old Maid."

♦ ***Suitable as a language development activity***

Showing Air Temperature

Follow the Directions

1. Make three thermometer sticks.
2. Color in the sticks like this.
3. Glue the sticks to paper.
4. Mark the air temperature.
5. Write in the words.

Tell What You Learned

Tell the air temperature for each word.
Describe the weather for each temperature.

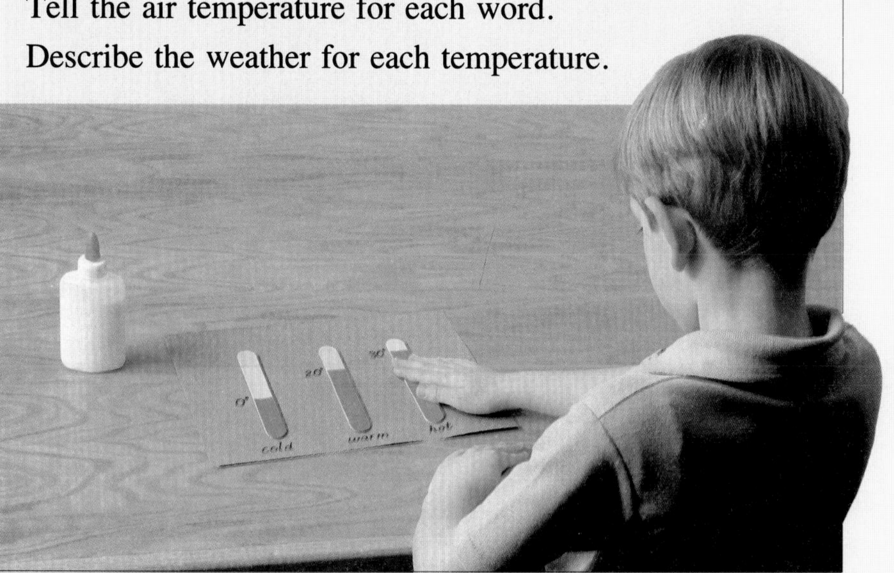

193

Enrichment Activity

Encourage the students to ***predict*** if the temperature will go up or down during the night. (The temperature usually goes down during the night.)

Activity Results

Student's thermometer models should look like the ones on the activity page.

ACTIVITY PLAN

Concept

Weather conditions are related to air temperature.

Objective/Process Skills

- *Make models* of thermometers.
- *Draw* colored portions to represent different temperatures.
- *Describe* the weather for each temperature.

Materials

For each student: 3 flat, wooden sticks; sheet of construction paper; crayons or colored markers; bottle of white glue; pencil, scissors

Time Allotment

Allow 20 minutes.

Safety Tip (See page T27.)

- Use non-toxic, water-soluble glue and markers.

Teaching Tips

- Display an alcohol thermometer. Allow small groups to come and observe it. Explain to the students that the liquid in this thermometer goes up (expands) when the temperature is high and goes down (contracts) when the temperature is low.
- Explain that the wooden sticks will be pretend thermometers. The colored portion will be the liquid in the thermometer.
- Instruct students to begin at one end of the stick and color in a bar 2 cm (about 1 in.) long. On the second stick color in a 4 cm (about 1.5 in.) bar, and on the third color in a 5 cm (about 2 in.) bar.
- Direct the students to glue the sticks vertically onto the paper. Beside the top of each colored bar, they should write the centigrade readings for each stick as follows: 0°C (2 cm bar), 20°C (4 cm bar), 30°C (5 cm bar). Then, they should write in the label below each stick: cold (0°C), warm (20°C), hot (30°C).
- ***Metric-English Equivalents*:**

0°C = 32°F
20°C = 68°F
30°C = 86°F

Answers

Tell What You Learned
cold—0°C, warm—20°C, hot—30°C

TEACHING PLAN

LESSON 2
pages 194–197

Lesson Objectives
- *Name* the four seasons.
- *Describe* weather changes from season to season.

Lesson Vocabulary
fall, seasons, spring, summer, winter

1 MOTIVATE

Demonstration Activity ♦
Tape to the chalkboard pictures depicting the four seasons.

Discussion
Have the students name the months associated with each picture. Write the names of the months under each picture. Encourage the students to *describe* the type of weather shown in each picture.

Lesson 2 How Can Weather Change in Seasons?

Many places on Earth have four **seasons.**
One season is **spring.**
How does the weather change in spring?
The air becomes warmer.
Some places have more rain.
Spring weather helps these plants grow.

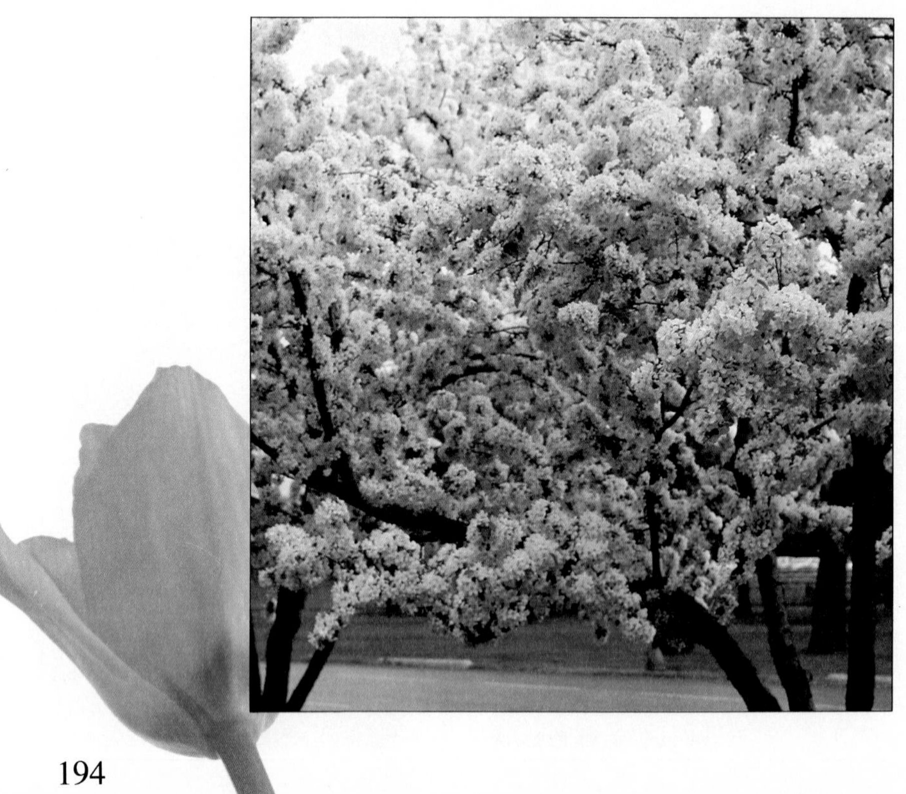

194

Teaching Options

SCIENCE BACKGROUND

The earth revolves around the sun while tilted 23.5 degrees on its axis. The four seasons with their characteristic weather conditions are related to the amount of solar energy the tilted earth receives. The tilt causes longer days in summer and shorter days in winter. In the Northern Hemisphere, summer arrives in June when the sun is directly above 23.5 degrees north latitude. This day in the Southern Hemisphere is the first day of winter. On December 20 or 21, the sun is directly above 23.5 degrees south latitude. This day is the first day of winter and the shortest day in the Northern Hemisphere, but it is first day of summer and longest day in the Southern Hemisphere.

♦ ***Suitable as a language development activity***

[1] Answers will vary

Another season is **summer.**

The weather gets much warmer in summer.

The sun shines on many summer days.

Some places have rain in summer.

This place stays very dry.

What do you like to do in summer?[1]

2 TEACH

Teaching Tips

- Write the words *spring*, *summer*, *fall*, *winter*, on the chalkboard and read them to the students. Tell the students that these are the names of the four seasons. Have the students ***define*** the word "season."
- Call the students' attention to the illustration on page 194 and have them ***describe*** the illustration. Questions: **What season do you think is pictured here? Why do you think it is spring?**
- Point out to students that the picture on page 195 shows a desert area in the United States. Discuss the amount of rain that the area receives each year. Lead students to ***conclude*** that the lack of vegetation is due to the minimal amount of rainfall.

Science and Art

Divide the class into four groups and have each group make a mural depicting a different season. Display the murals in the order in which the seasons occur, beginning with spring.

Special Education

Direct students with learning disabilities to collect or draw pictures of people participating in various sports or recreational activities. Instruct the students to group the pictures by the season in which the activities are most likely to occur.

Reinforcement

Give each child four blank cards and instruct them to write the name of a season on each. Randomly read the descriptors from pages 194–197 of the four seasons to the children. After each descriptor have them hold up the name of the season.

TEACHING PLAN

Teaching Tips

- Instruct the children to look at the illustration on page 196 and to *describe* what is happening to the leaves on the trees.
- Read the page with the students, and encourage them to discuss what will happen to the leaves next.
- Read page 197 with the students and have them discuss what the weather is like in the picture.
- Encourage the students to *compare* the winter scene in the illustration to the winter in your area.

[1] Leaves change color, die, and fall off.

The weather changes in **fall,** too.
The air gets cooler.
Some places might have less rain.
The leaves of plants can change in fall.
What happens to these leaves?[1]

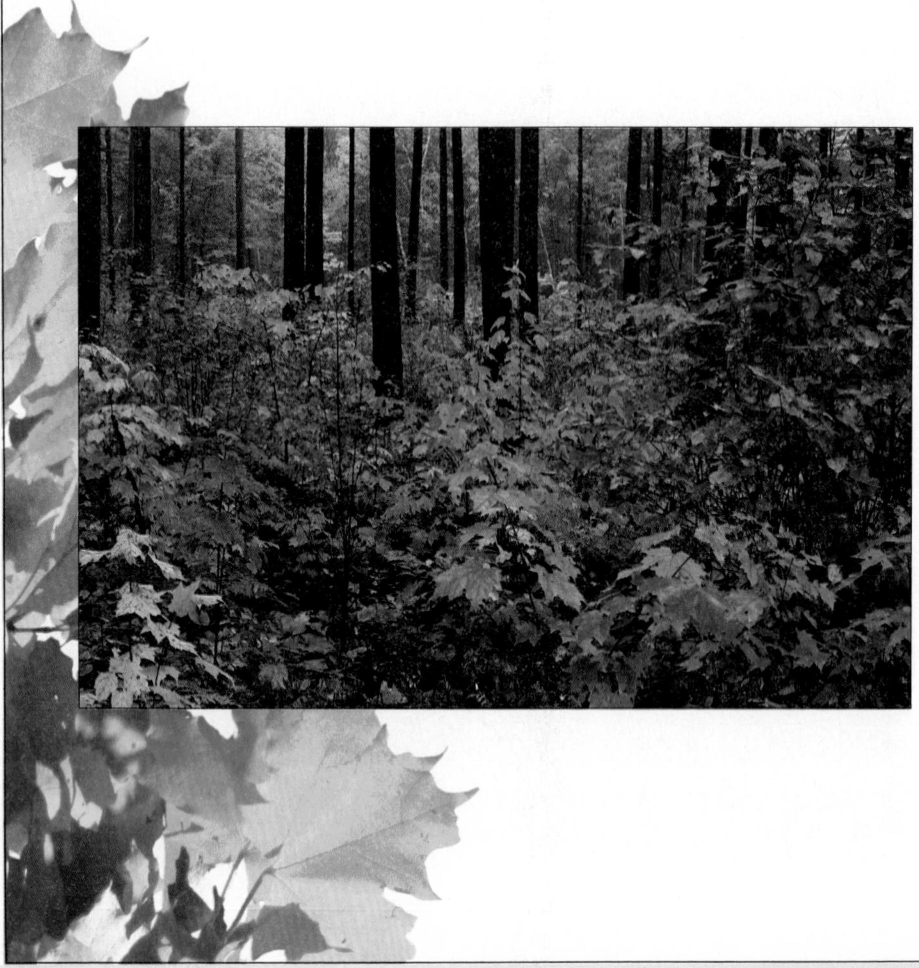

Teaching Options

SCIENCE ANECDOTE

The earth is actually closer to the sun in January than it is in July. The angle of the sun's rays determine seasonal weather.

Enrichment

Encourage interested students to *compare* the seasons in the northern and southern hemispheres. Provide an opportunity for them to report their findings to the class.

Science and Social Studies

Encourage the students to draw pictures depicting different holidays and cultural events. Let each child tell about their picture and in what season the holiday or event would occur.

♦ ***Suitable as a language development activity***

[1] cold and snowy

Winter is the coldest season.
Some places have ice and snow.
Many plants do not grow in winter.
What is this winter day like?[1]

Lesson Review

1. What are the four seasons?
2. How is weather different in seasons?

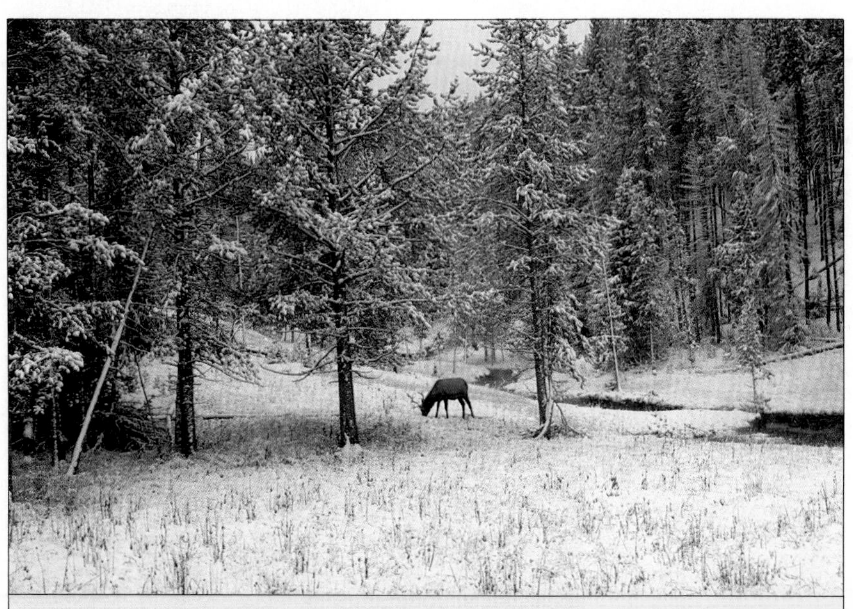

What are the seasons like in your area?
How does your weather change?

Find Out

197

Teaching Tip

• **Possible Misconception:** Children often think that all places on earth have the same weather at the same time.

3 ASSESS

Lesson Review

1. summer, winter, spring, and fall
2. summer—hot days, winter—snow and ice, spring—warmer days, some rain, fall—cooler days
Challenge! Question: **What seasons have good weather for building homes? Why?** (Summer and fall, because in most places the home builders would not get wet or cold.) **Thinking Skill:** *Applying information to new situations*

Find Out

Answers will vary. **Thinking Skill:** *Restating or explaining ideas*

Workbook page 59 *

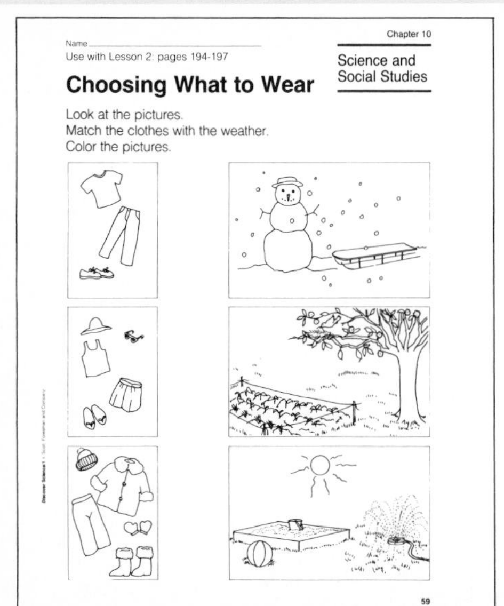

Name
Use with Lesson 2: pages 194-197
Chapter 10
Science and Social Studies

Choosing What to Wear

Look at the pictures.
Match the clothes with the weather.
Color the pictures.

59

Workbook page 58 *

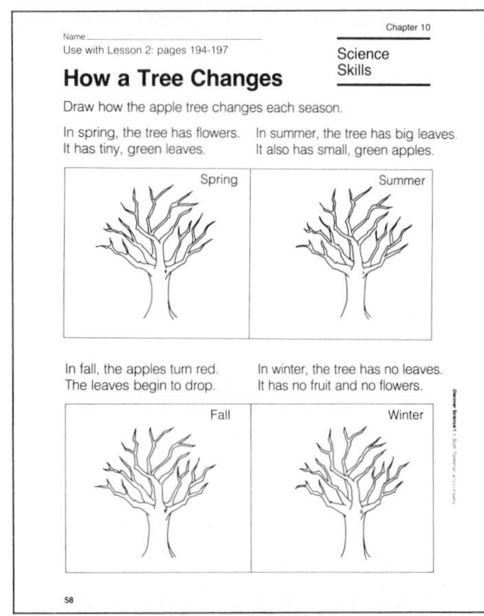

Name
Use with Lesson 2: pages 194-197
Chapter 10
Science Skills

How a Tree Changes

Draw how the apple tree changes each season.

In spring, the tree has flowers. It has tiny, green leaves.
In summer, the tree has big leaves. It also has small, green apples.

Spring
Summer

In fall, the apples turn red. The leaves begin to drop.
In winter, the tree has no leaves. It has no fruit and no flowers.

Fall
Winter

58

Reteaching Suggestion ♦

Divide the class into four groups and have each group discuss a different season. Encourage each group to make a list of words to *describe* their season. Allow time for each group to tell about the season it described.

***** *Answers to masters on pages 188E–188F*

TEACHING PLAN

LESSON 3
pages 198–199

Lesson Objective
- *Explain* that weather affects what people do and how they dress.

1 MOTIVATE

Demonstration Activity ♦
Display articles or pictures of clothing for different kinds of weather (heavy coat, raincoat, boots, bathing suit, umbrella, and so on) to the students.

Discussion
Let the students identify each of the items and tell about the weather in which they would wear the item. Discuss which items of clothing are appropriate for the current weather.

2 TEACH

Teaching Tips
- Question: **Why is weather important to people?** Encourage the students to think of ways that people are affected by weather.
- Read page 198 together. Discuss what kinds of weather could prevent pilots from flying.

[1] portable heaters

Lesson 3 How Is Weather Important to People?

Weather is important for some jobs.
Pilots cannot fly in some weather.
Farmers need sunshine and rain.
Some farmers grow oranges.
Oranges need warm weather to grow.
What protects these plants from cold?[1]

198

Teaching Options

SCIENCE BACKGROUND

Winter-weather clothing has characteristics of fur or feather body coverings. Layers of fibers trap pockets of air warmed by the body. Thus winter clothing is an insulation that holds body heat. Thin summer clothing allows for the rapid escape of body heat. Summer clothing is also often light in color to reflect radiant heat from the sun.

The houses of humans and the shelters of animals are protected from the harsh elements of weather in similar ways. Walls function as insulators and wind screens. Roofs divert rain.

♦ ***Suitable as a language development activity***

[1] Answers vary according to weather conditions.
[2] during rainy weather

Weather changes what people do.

What do people do in different weather?[1]

Weather changes what people wear.

When would you use an umbrella?[2]

Lesson Review

1. How is weather important for jobs?
2. What changes with weather?

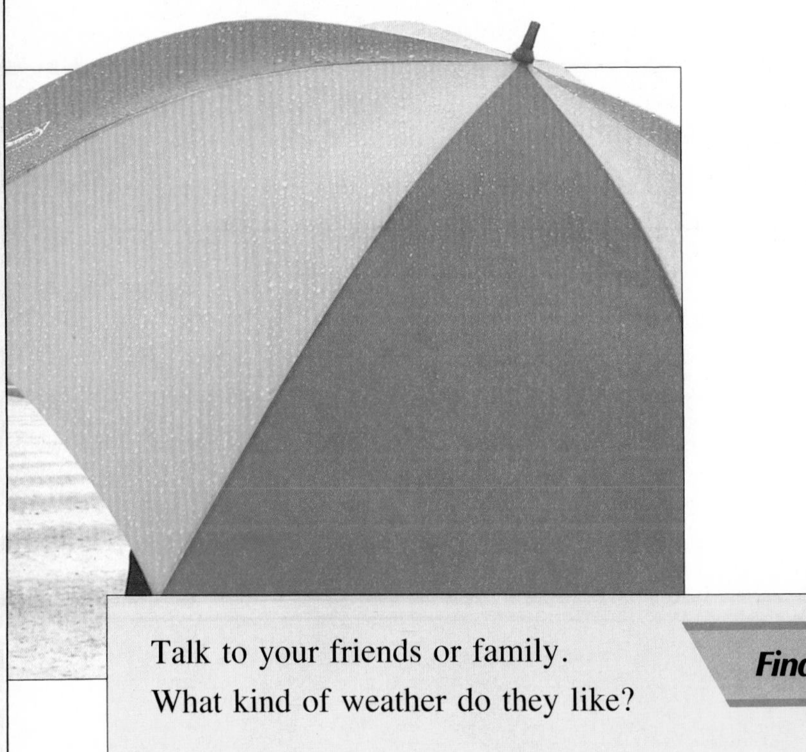

Find Out

Talk to your friends or family.
What kind of weather do they like?

Teaching Tips

- Refer students to the *TRY THIS* on page 189 in which they ***observed*** the weather. Point out that the weather helps determine what they wear and their outdoor activities.
- Call the students' attention to the illustration on page 199. Encourage the students to tell about the weather pictured.
- **Possible Misconception:** Children might think heavy clothes are warm in winter because they are a source of heat.

3 ASSESS

Lesson Review

1. Pilots need good weather to fly. Farmers need sunshine and rain. **2.** Weather determines what people do and wear.

Challenge! Question: **Why is football usually played during the fall and winter?** (Lead students to conclude that during the summer and late spring it is often too hot for players to wear their heavy pads and helmets. **Thinking Skill:** *Drawing conclusions*

Find Out

Answers will vary. **Thinking Skill:** *Restating ideas*

Workbook page 60 *

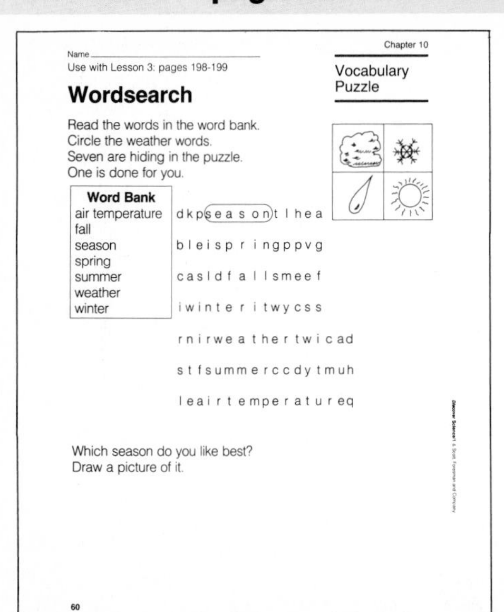

Name ____________
Use with Lesson 3: pages 198-199

Chapter 10

Vocabulary Puzzle

Wordsearch

Read the words in the word bank.
Circle the weather words.
Seven are hiding in the puzzle.
One is done for you.

Word Bank
air temperature
fall
season
spring
summer
weather
winter

d k p s e a s o n t l h e a
b l e i s p r i n g p p v g
c a s l d f a l l s m e e f
i w i n t e r i t w y c s s
r n i r w e a t h e r t w i c a d
s t f s u m m e r c c d y t m u h
l e a i r t e m p e r a t u r e q

Which season do you like best?
Draw a picture of it.

Discover Science/1 © Scott, Foresman and Company

60

*** Answers to masters on pages 188E–188F***

Special Education

Attach pictures of different kinds of weather on a bulletin board. Encourage students with learning disabilities to pin pictures or drawings of clothing that would be appropriate for each kind of weather pictured.

Reteaching Suggestion ♦

Direct the students to fold a piece of drawing paper in half. On one side have them draw a picture of a particular type of weather. On the other, have them draw a picture of appropriate clothing for that type of weather. Encourage the students to show and tell about their pictures.

Concept
Different weather conditions exist.

Objectives/Process Skills
- *Observe* weather conditions.
- *Record* observations.
- *Describe* the weather each day.

Materials
For each student: drawing paper, pencil, crayons

Time Allotment
Total time needed 45 minutes—10 minutes to begin activity, 5 minutes each day for five days, and 10 minutes for closure.

Teaching Tips
- Explain to the students that they are going to be keeping a record of the weather for five days.
- Encourage students to name different types of weather. As they name each type, write the words on the chalkboard.
- Let volunteers draw a picture symbol for each of the weather types. (a sun for sunny, rain drops for rainy, snow flakes for snowy, and so on)
- Demonstrate to the students how to make the chart.
- Each day allow the students to observe the weather and to record it with a picture weather symbol.

Answers
Tell What You Learned
The students should tell that the weather charts show what the weather was like that week. **Thinking Skill:** *Inferring*

Making a Weather Chart

Follow the Directions
1. Make a weather chart.
2. Show the weather for five days.
3. Draw one picture for each day.
4. Tell if it is cool, warm, or hot.

Tell What You Learned
Tell what your weather chart shows.

200

Activity Results
Weather charts will vary, but should accurately reflect weather conditions during a five-day period.

Enrichment Activity
Allow the students to continue to record the weather for another week. Then have them graph the results.

Taking Weather Pictures

Some spacecraft take weather pictures.
They travel far above the earth.
The pictures are sent to a computer.
People study the pictures.
They learn what weather is coming.
They let others know about the weather.

What Do You Think?

How do weather pictures help people?

TEACHING PLAN

SCIENCE IN YOUR LIFE

Discussion
Ask students if they watch the weather forecasts on television. Encourage them to describe weather broadcasts and to explain about the information given.

Teaching Tips

- If a television and a VCR are available, record a weather broadcast. Replay the program for the students and discuss the weather forecast. Question: **What kinds of information do weather broadcasts provide?**
- Explain to students that long ago before satellites people had no way of knowing what kinds of weather might be coming. Terrible storms such as hurricanes could catch people unprepared.

Answer
What Do Think?
They learn about weather changes quickly. **Thinking Skill:** *Drawing conclusions*

Teaching Options

SCIENCE BACKGROUND

The Geostationary Operational Environmental Satellites—*GOES*—orbit at the same speed as the earth turns, so they are over the same place on the earth's surface. All of the United States, the Pacific and Atlantic oceans, and parts of Western Europe can be viewed by three satellites that are each about 4,400 kilometers (about 3,000 miles) above the earth's surface. These satellites send visual black and white pictures as well as infra red pictures of the earth. In addition, laser beams sent to the earth's surface can gather such data as temperatures, humidity, air pressure, wind direction, and wind speed. Data from the satellites are fed to the supercomputers at the National Meteorlogical Center in Suitland, Maryland.

SKILLS FOR SOLVING PROBLEMS
pages 202–203

Purpose
To develop the skills of *collecting* and *organizing information* using measurement and a chart to *solve problems*

Materials
For each student: paper for charts, crayons or coloring pencils

1 MOTIVATE

Discussion
Discuss with students whether they have had their height and weight measured at the doctor's office. Question: **Why does the doctor take these measurements?** (Lead the students to *infer* that growth is a good indicator of good health and proper nutrition.) Explain to the students that measurement is important to everyone.

Skills for Solving Problems

Measuring Rain

How can you measure rain?

1. Look at the picture.
   It shows a way to measure rain.
   Notice how much it rained each day.

202

Teaching Options

SCIENCE BACKGROUND

Rainfall is best measured with a rain gauge, an instrument that measures the depth of rainfall. After a storm it may be reported that 3 cm (about one inch) of rain fell. A rain gauge was used to measure this amount. The amount of rainfall is important to farmers, firemen, environmentalists, forest rangers and so on. The amount of yearly rainfall is used for future planning such as irrigation, and flood control. The monthly measured amount is used by firemen and rangers to determine the chances of wild fires.

2. Make a chart like this one.
Show how much rain fell each day.
Find which days the most rain fell.
Find which day the least rain fell.

Monday			
Tuesday	O	G	
Wednesday	O	G	R
Thursday	O	G	R
Friday	O		

3. What does measuring rain show?

203

2 TEACH

Teaching Tips

- Explain to students after they look at the pictures that they can actually measure rainfall by putting a container outside and measuring the amount of rain it collects.
- Students should use their own paper to make up a chart indicating the amount of rainfall for each day, shown in the illustration on page 202.

3 ASSESS

Students should note that measuring rain shows how much rain has fallen.

Resource Book 79 *

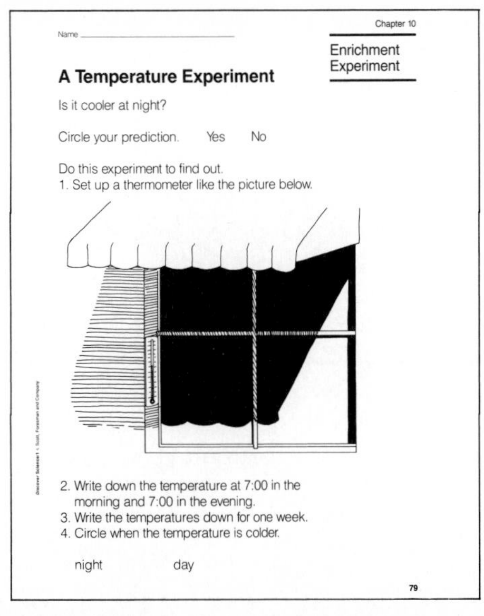
Name ____________

Chapter 10

Enrichment Experiment

A Temperature Experiment

Is it cooler at night?

Circle your prediction. Yes No

Do this experiment to find out.
1. Set up a thermometer like the picture below.

2. Write down the temperature at 7:00 in the morning and 7:00 in the evening.
3. Write the temperatures down for one week.
4. Circle when the temperature is colder.

night day

79

*** Answers to masters on pages 188E–188F***

REVIEW PLAN

CHAPTER 10 REVIEW

pages 204–205

Review Chapter Ideas

1. Students can mention any of the following kinds of weather: hot, cold, rainy, snowy, windy, cloudy, clear, sunny.
2. spring, summer, fall, winter
3. summer—hot, little rain; fall—cooler, not much rain; winter—cold, snowy, icy; spring—warmer, some rain
4. farmer—sun, sunshine, and some rain; pilot—good weather
5. Answers will vary. For example, rainy weather will cause a change in planned outdoor activities such as a baseball game.
6. Cold weather, you must wear clothes to keep warm.

For further review, use Study Guide page 236.

Chapter 10 Review

Review Chapter Ideas

1. Describe different kinds of weather.
2. Name the four seasons.
3. Tell how weather changes in seasons.
4. Look at these people.
   Tell what kind of weather they need.

a.

b.

5. Tell how weather changes what people do.
6. Tell how weather changes what people wear.

204

Teaching Options

Cooperative Learning ♦

STAD Format (See page T23.)
Assign students to work in four- to five-member teams to study Chapter 10 Review. Students should work together to make sure that they and their teammates know the material in the chapter. After students have had enough time to study together, give them a test to complete individually (Chapter 10 Test in the *Test Book*). Award Superteam certificates to teams whose average test scores exceed 90%, and Greatteam certificates to teams whose average test scores exceed 80%.

Test Book page 33 *

Name

Chapter 10 Test

Weather and Seasons

I. Write **Yes** or **No.**

1. Can there be clouds and wind at the same time?
2. Does it snow on warm days?
3. Are winter, spring, summer, and fall the four seasons?
4. Does weather change from spring to summer?
5. Would you wear a coat on a summer day?

II. Draw a line from the word to the right picture.

1. fall 2. spring 3. winter

♦ ***Suitable as a language development activity***

Review Science Words

Match the words and the pictures.

1. fall
2. spring
3. summer
4. winter

a.

b.

c.

d.

Tell what the words mean.

5. weather
6. air temperature
7. seasons

a.

b.

Use Science Ideas

Look at the pictures.

Tell what the people would wear and do.

Review Science Words

Match the words and the pictures.

1. c **2.** a **3.** d **4.** b

Tell what the words mean.

Thinking Skill: *Restating or explaining ideas*

5. Weather—what it is like outside.

6. Air temperature—a measure of how hot or cold the air is.

7. Seasons—four times of the year when the weather pattern changes for a period of time.

Use Science Ideas

Students answers will vary. Possible answers include: Snow—people would go sledding, skiing, or make a snowman. They would wear warm hats and clothing. Summer beach—people could swim or play beach games. They would wear clothing such as swimsuits or shorts. Spring—people could walk outdoors. They might wear light jackets and medium weight clothing. **Thinking Skill:** *Recognizing relevant information and data*

*** *Answers to masters on pages 188E–188F***

Teaching Plan

Chapter Components	Skills	Materials
Chapter Opener/*TRY THIS:* Looking at the Sky pp. 206-207	***TRY THIS*** p. 207 **Science Process Skills** *Observing, Communicating*	***TRY THIS*** p. 207 (individual) 30 sheets drawing paper, 30 boxes crayons, 30 pencils
Lesson 1: What Do You See in the Sky? pp. 208-209	**Thinking Skills** Challenge!: *Inferring* Find Out: *Collecting information, Recording*	**Demonstration** p. 208 no materials needed
Lesson 2: What Is the Sun Like? pp. 210-212	**Thinking Skills** Challenge!: *Drawing conclusions* Find Out: *Restating or explaining ideas*	**Demonstration** p. 210 no materials needed
Science and People: Ellison Onizuka p. 213	**Thinking Skill:** *Drawing conclusions*	
Lesson 3: What Is the Moon Like? pp. 214-216	**Thinking Skills** Challenge!: *Comparing, Making generalizations* Find Out: *Observing, Recording*	**Demonstration** p. 214 book of nursery rhymes that includes *Hey Diddle, Diddle*
Activity: Showing Day and Night p. 217	**Science Process Skills** *Making models, Observing, Inferring*	(groups of 2) 15 sticks modeling clay, 15 dowel rods, 15 flashlights, 15 sheets assorted construction paper, 15 scissors
Lesson 4: What Are the Stars Like? pp. 218-220	**Thinking Skills** Challenge!: *Making inferences* Find Out: *Collecting information*	**Demonstration** p. 218 butcher paper, scissors, staple, bulletin board
Activity: Making a Star Picture p. 221	**Science Process Skills** *Making models, Observing, Communicating*	(individual) 60 sheets black construction paper, 30 paper punches, 30 pencils
Skills for Solving Problems: Measuring Shadows pp. 222-223	**Problem Solving Skills** *Making decisions/Identifying and solving problems, Interpreting charts, maps, and graphs*	(individual) centimeter ruler, paper
Chapter Review pp. 224-225	**Thinking Skills** *Restating or explaining ideas, Predicting*	

Teaching Options

Strategies	Extensions		Resource Masters
			Family Letter: *Resource Book* p. 83 Vocabulary Preview: *Workbook* pp. 61-62
	Reinforcement p. 208 Special Education p. 209 Reteaching Suggestion p. 209		
	Special Education p. 210 Enrichment p. 211 Science and Math p. 211	Science and Art p. 211 Reteaching Suggestion p. 212	Science Skills: *Workbook* p. 63
	Reinforcement p. 214 Special Education p. 215 Enrichment p. 215	Game Suggestion p. 215 Reteaching Suggestion p. 216	Science Activity: *Workbook* p. 64
	Enrichment Activity p. 217		
	Reinforcement p. 218 Special Education p. 219	Enrichment p. 219 Reteaching Suggestion p. 220	Science and Math: *Workbook* p. 65 Vocabulary Puzzle: *Workbook* p. 66
	Enrichment Activity p. 221		
			Enrichment Activity: *Resource Book* p. 87
Cooperative Learning p. 224 (Also see p. T23)			Chapter Test: *Test Book* p. 35

Preteaching Suggestions

For Advance Preparation

Demonstration, page 214
Find a book of nursery rhymes that includes the poem *Hey Diddle, Diddle.*

Activity, page 217
Provide each group with a ball of clay, a popsickle stick, a flashlight, and a small paper cutout of a person.

Demonstration, page 218
You will need a large piece of butcher paper for this demonstration.

Activity, page 221
Each group of students will need black construction paper, a round toothpick, and a soft surface, such as a carpet square, a piece of cloth, or a plastic-foam meat tray, to press down on when punching holes.

For Vocabulary Review

Use the following sentences with your students to review the meanings of the underlined words.

1. We call the planet we live on Earth.
2. An astronaut is a person who travels in outer space.
3. A star is really a hot ball of gas.

For High-Potential Students

Ask students to make daily observations of the moon for at least four weeks. They ought to make the observations at approximately the same time and from the same place each day. Have students make drawings to show the shape of the moon and describe the location of the moon in the sky. After a couple of weeks, have students discuss the changes they noted. Besides the daily changes in the shape of the moon, they should report changes in the moon's location in the sky at a particular time of night. Encourage students to continue making observations at various times of the day until they notice the moon in the day sky as well as the night sky. Check a copy of *Science and Children* or a calendar to determine what dates the moon will be in the first quarter phase. It is best if you can begin this activity during the first quarter because the moon will be visible in the evenings when the students can make observations. (Note: The first quarter moon appears above the eastern horizon about noon and disappears over the western horizon about midnight; the full moon rises with the setting sun; the moon rises about one hour later each night.)

For Mainstreamed Students

Visually Impaired
Provide vivid visual descriptions of both the day and night sky for visually impaired students. Be sure to give clear descriptions, present them one at a time, and make very sharp distinctions between day and night. The more information visually impaired students have and the more often it is repeated, the better their understanding of the concepts will be.

Orthopedically Handicapped
If the student has significant fine motor problems, provide stickers students can put down on construction paper for the TRY THIS activity on page 207.

For Science Fair Projects

Encourage interested students to do one of the following projects:

1. Illustrate the sun's ability to provide heat by constructing a solar device to heat water.
2. Construct models of the sun, moon, and earth.
3. Construct a sundial that can be used to tell time.

Classroom Resources

Bulletin Board
Encourage students to draw pictures that show how the sky can look different in the daytime and in the nighttime.

WHAT CAN YOU SEE IN THE SKY?

Chapter 11 Poster

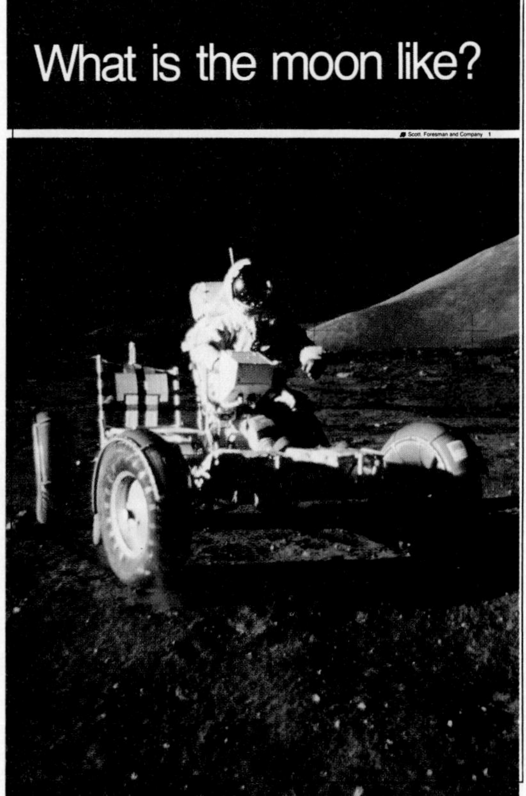

What is the moon like?

Science Discovery Center
Use pages from Chapter 11 in the *Science Discovery Center Book*. Place these worksheets in the appropriate pockets in the Science Discovery Center.

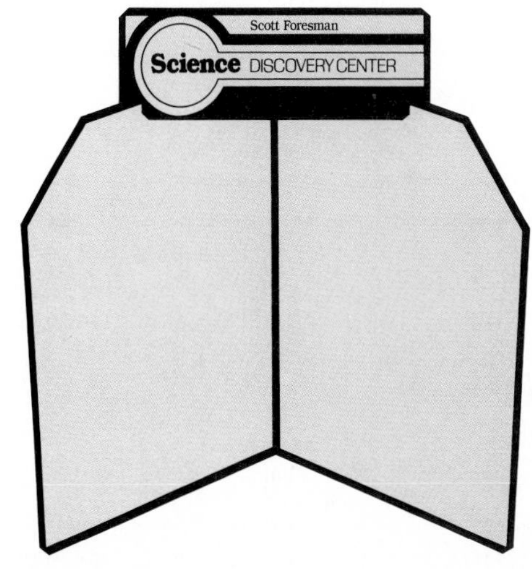

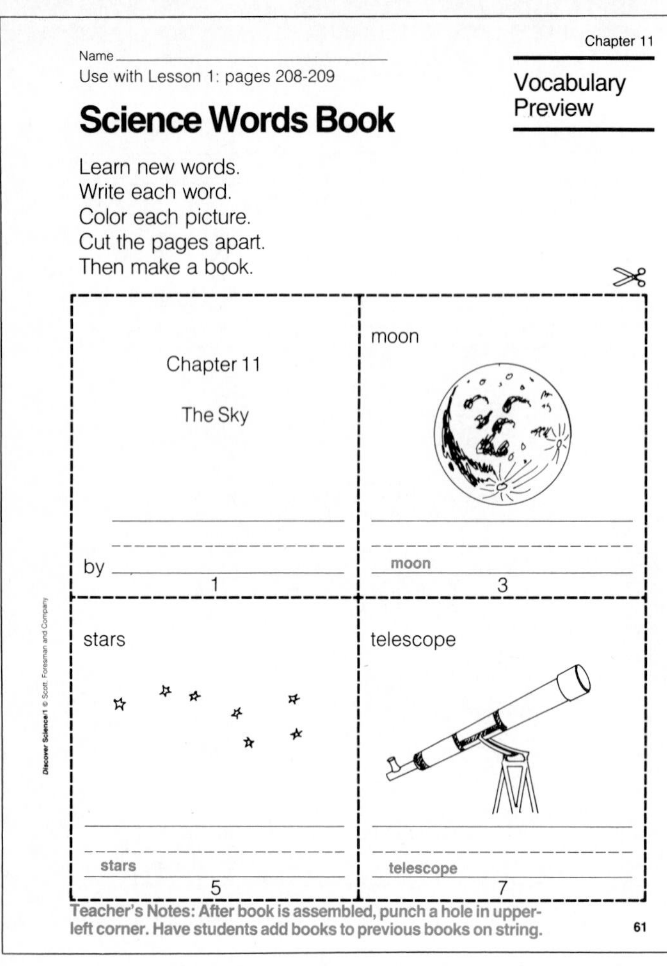

Name ____________________

Use with Lesson 1: pages 208-209

Chapter 11

Vocabulary Preview

Science Words Book

Learn new words.
Write each word.
Color each picture.
Cut the pages apart.
Then make a book.

Chapter 11

The Sky

by ____________________

1

moon

moon

3

stars

stars

5

telescope

telescope

7

Teacher's Notes: After book is assembled, punch a hole in upper-left corner. Have students add books to previous books on string.

61

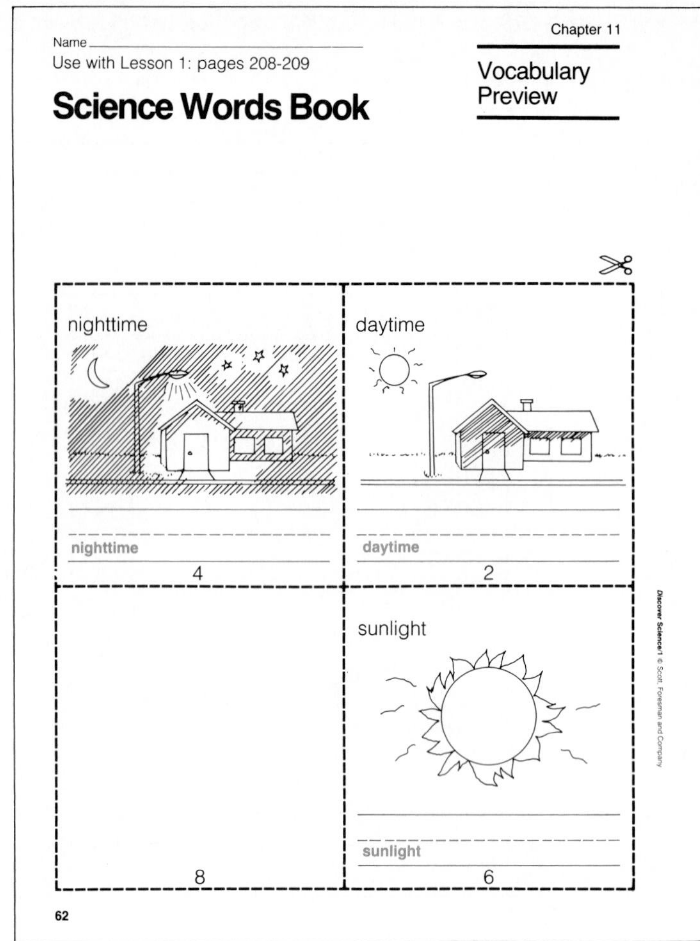

Name ____________________

Use with Lesson 1: pages 208-209

Chapter 11

Vocabulary Preview

Science Words Book

nighttime

nighttime

4

daytime

daytime

2

8

sunlight

sunlight

6

62

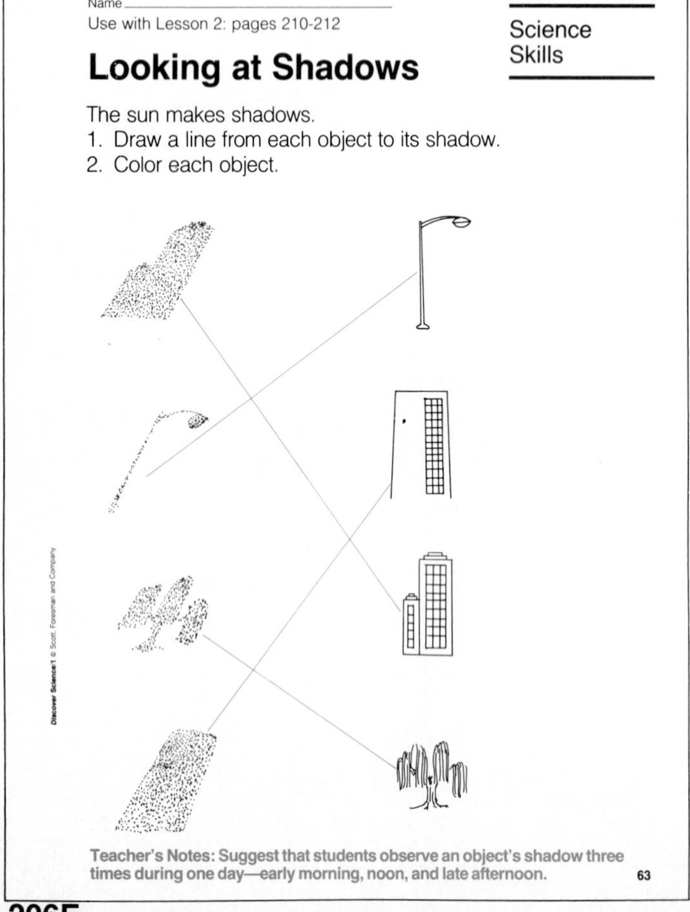

Name ____________________

Use with Lesson 2: pages 210-212

Chapter 11

Science Skills

Looking at Shadows

The sun makes shadows.

1. Draw a line from each object to its shadow.
2. Color each object.

Teacher's Notes: Suggest that students observe an object's shadow three times during one day—early morning, noon, and late afternoon.

63

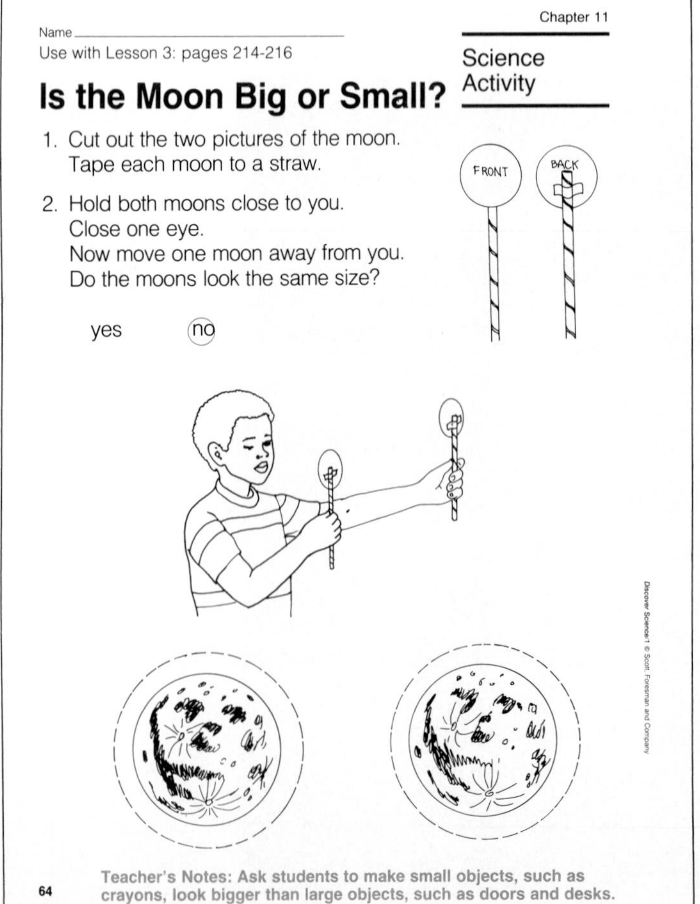

Name ____________________

Use with Lesson 3: pages 214-216

Chapter 11

Science Activity

Is the Moon Big or Small?

1. Cut out the two pictures of the moon. Tape each moon to a straw.
2. Hold both moons close to you. Close one eye. Now move one moon away from you. Do the moons look the same size?

yes no

64

Teacher's Notes: Ask students to make small objects, such as crayons, look bigger than large objects, such as doors and desks.

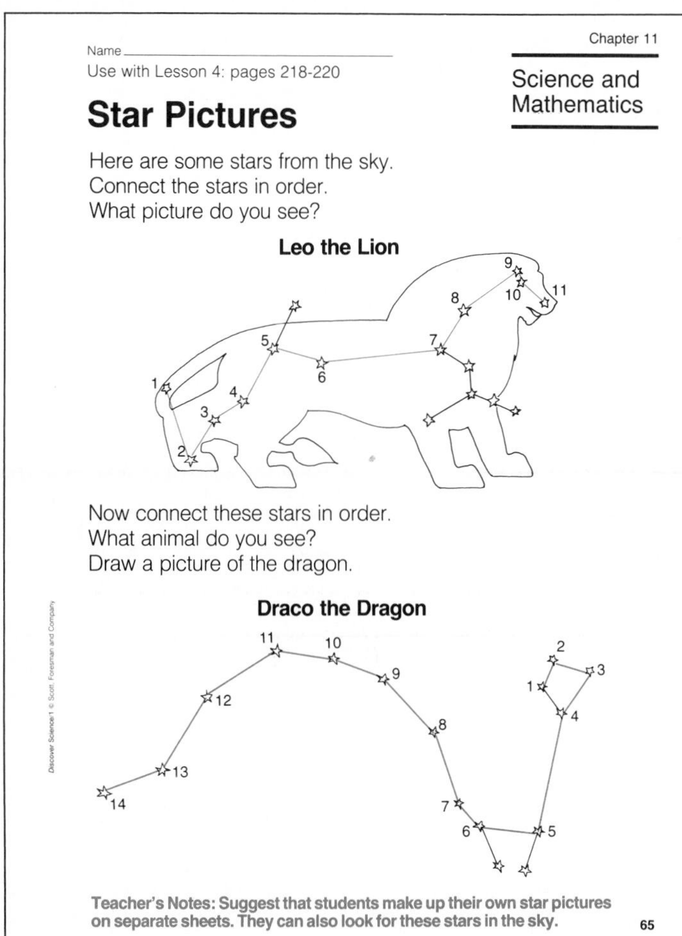
Name ______________________

Use with Lesson 4: pages 218-220

Chapter 11

Science and Mathematics

Star Pictures

Here are some stars from the sky.
Connect the stars in order.
What picture do you see?

Leo the Lion

Now connect these stars in order.
What animal do you see?
Draw a picture of the dragon.

Draco the Dragon

Teacher's Notes: Suggest that students make up their own star pictures on separate sheets. They can also look for these stars in the sky.

65

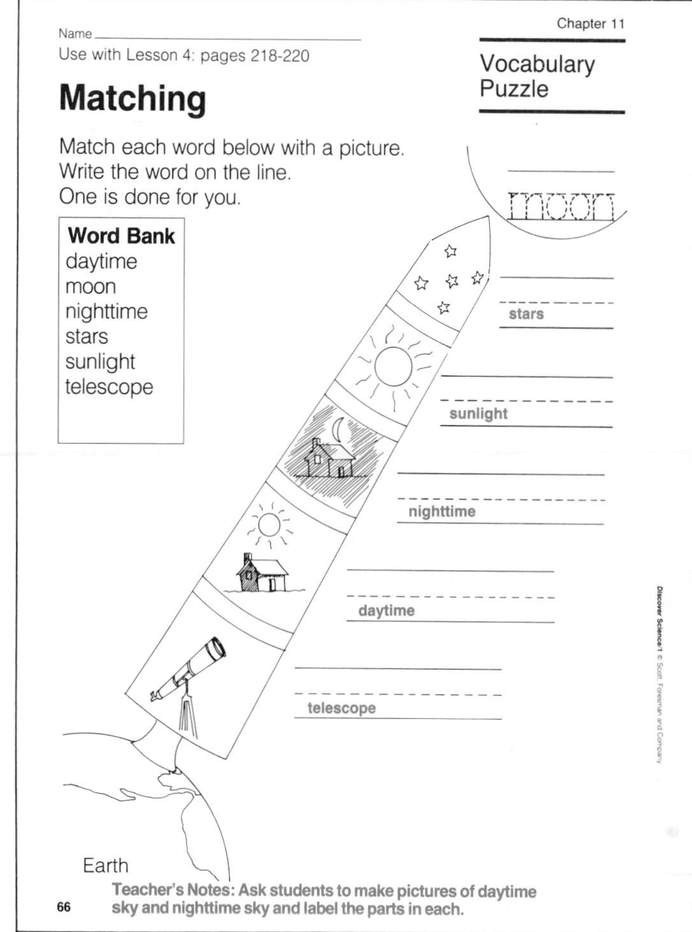
Name ______________________

Use with Lesson 4: pages 218-220

Chapter 11

Vocabulary Puzzle

Matching

Match each word below with a picture.
Write the word on the line.
One is done for you.

Word Bank
daytime
moon
nighttime
stars
sunlight
telescope

moon

stars

sunlight

nighttime

daytime

telescope

Earth

66

Teacher's Notes: Ask students to make pictures of daytime sky and nighttime sky and label the parts in each.

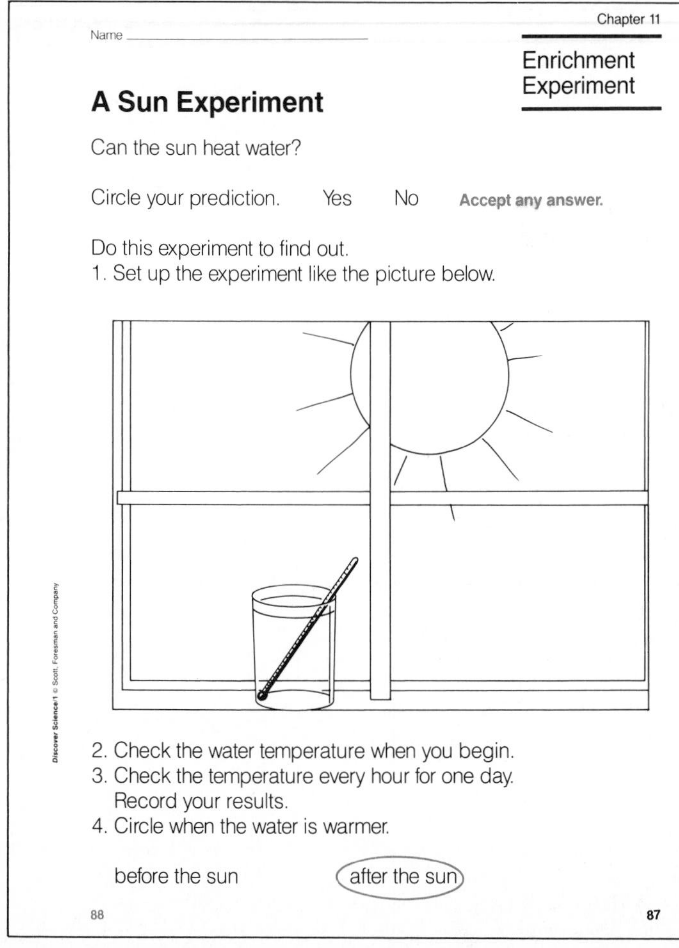
Name ______________________

Chapter 11

Enrichment Experiment

A Sun Experiment

Can the sun heat water?

Circle your prediction. Yes No **Accept any answer.**

Do this experiment to find out.

1. Set up the experiment like the picture below.

2. Check the water temperature when you begin.
3. Check the temperature every hour for one day. Record your results.
4. Circle when the water is warmer.

before the sun (after the sun)

88 87

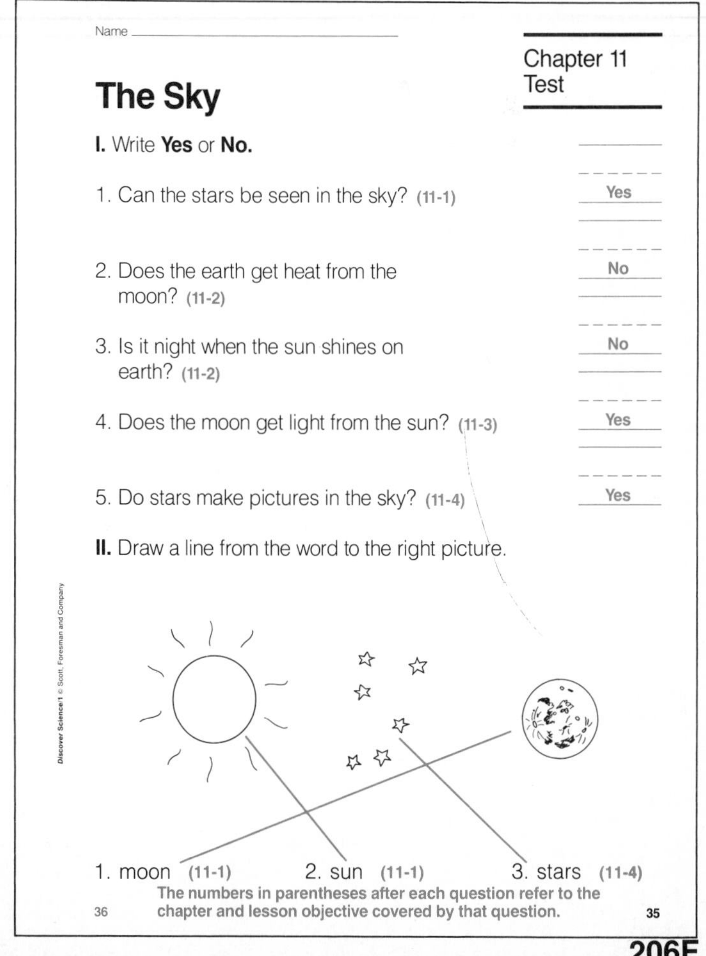
Name ______________________

Chapter 11 Test

The Sky

I. Write **Yes** or **No.**

1. Can the stars be seen in the sky? (11-1) **Yes**
2. Does the earth get heat from the moon? (11-2) **No**
3. Is it night when the sun shines on earth? (11-2) **No**
4. Does the moon get light from the sun? (11-3) **Yes**
5. Do stars make pictures in the sky? (11-4) **Yes**

II. Draw a line from the word to the right picture.

1. moon (11-1) 2. sun (11-1) 3. stars (11-4)

36 **The numbers in parentheses after each question refer to the chapter and lesson objective covered by that question.** 35

TEACHING PLAN

INTRODUCING CHAPTER 11

Major Concepts

Lesson 1 The sun, moon, stars, and the earth are visible in the sky.
Lesson 2 The sun gives off light that produces heat and causes day and night along with the movement of the earth.
Lesson 3 The moon reflects light from the sun and its phases are different shapes that appear in the sky.
Lesson 4 Stars give off their own light and make patterns in the sky.

Vocabulary

daytime, moon, nighttime, stars, sunlight, telescope

[1] at sunrise or sunset

Chapter 11

The Sky

Suppose you watch the sky.
When does the sky look like this?[1]

206

Teaching Options

Workbook page 61 *

Name
Use with Lesson 1: pages 208-209

Chapter 11
Vocabulary Preview

Science Words Book

Learn new words.
Write each word.
Color each picture.
Cut the pages apart.
Then make a book.

Chapter 11
The Sky
by
1

moon
3

stars
5

telescope
7

61

Workbook page 62 *

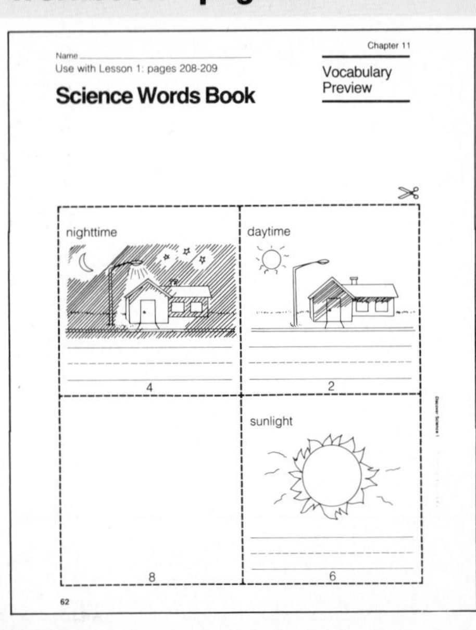
Name
Use with Lesson 1: pages 208-209

Chapter 11
Vocabulary Preview

Science Words Book

nighttime
4

daytime
2

8

sunlight
6

62

♦ ***Suitable as a language development activity***

[1] Day sky is light due to sun.
[2] Night sky is dark due to lack of sun.

Starting the Chapter

What does the day sky look like?[1]
What does the night sky look like?[2]
Think of how it looks at day and night.
Then learn more about the sky.

TRY THIS

Looking at the Sky

Fold your paper into two parts.
Write the words you see here.
Draw the objects you see each time.
Tell how the sky looks different.

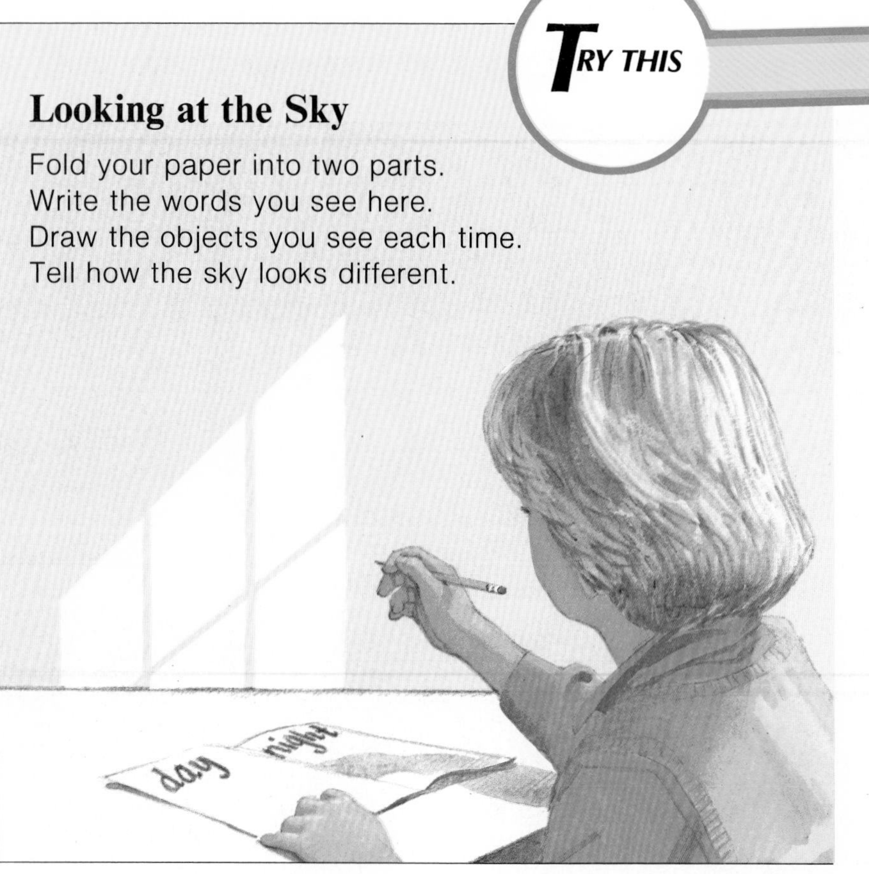

TRY THIS

Objective ♦
This optional *TRY THIS* activity will help students explore and build background information about the concept that the day and night skies look different. Later in the chapter, students will be able to draw on this experience to help them assimilate the new content.

Science Process Skills
Observing, Communicating

Materials
For each student: 1 sheet drawing paper, box of crayons, pencil

Teaching Tip
- Ask students to ***describe*** what they might see in the sky at night. (stars, moon, and so on) If possible, have them ***observe*** the day sky from the classroom. If the moon is visible, point it out. Ask students to ***list*** what they can see in the sky during the day. (sun, clouds, and so on) Question: **Why do you think that the day and night skies are so different?** (Students might respond that it is easier to see stars and the moon when it's dark. Accept reasonable responses.)

Answer
Students should ***describe*** the differences in their pictures.

Resource Book page 83

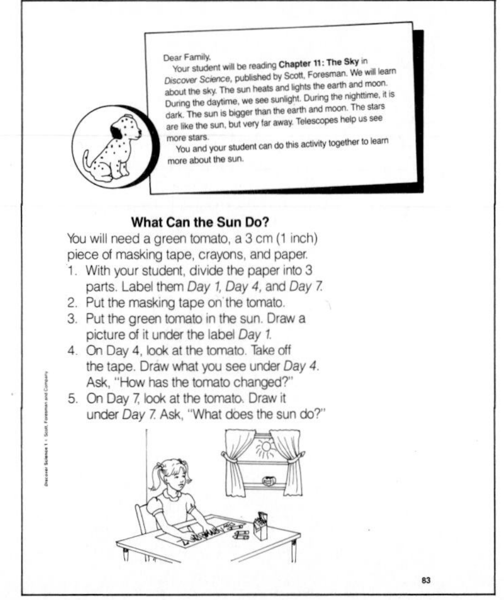

Dear Family,
Your student will be reading **Chapter 11: The Sky** in *Discover Science*, published by Scott, Foresman. We will learn about the sky. The sun heats and lights the earth and moon. During the daytime, we see sunlight. During the nighttime, it is dark. The sun is bigger than the earth and moon. The stars are like the sun, but very far away. Telescopes help us see more stars.
You and your student can do this activity together to learn more about the sun.

What Can the Sun Do?
You will need a green tomato, a 3 cm (1 inch) piece of masking tape, crayons, and paper.
1. With your student, divide the paper into 3 parts. Label them *Day 1, Day 4,* and *Day 7.*
2. Put the masking tape on the tomato.
3. Put the green tomato in the sun. Draw a picture of it under the label *Day 1.*
4. On Day 4, look at the tomato. Take off the tape. Draw what you see under *Day 4.* Ask, "How has the tomato changed?"
5. On Day 7, look at the tomato. Draw it under *Day 7.* Ask, "What does the sun do?"

SCIENCE BACKGROUND

Astronomers use television cameras and special filters to observe, photograph, and record the sun's light. Astronomers have never seen the interior of the sun, but they have calculated that the temperature of the sun's center is 15,000,000° C. The sun is so hot that it has no solid material. It is made up entirely of gases.

* Answers to masters on pages 206E-206F

TEACHING PLAN

LESSON 1
pages 208–209

Lesson Objectives
- *Name* what is visible in the sky.
- *Compare* the size of the sun, moon, and earth.

Lesson Vocabulary
moon

1 MOTIVATE

Demonstration Activity ♦
Tell students to pretend that they are on a spaceship. Describe taking off and traveling through space. Involve students in the telling of the story by having them suggest places they could go.

Discussion
Ask students what they might see in the sky before their spaceship took off from the earth. (Answers might include the moon, sun, stars, and so on.) Then, have them *describe* what they might see from space. (Accept reasonable responses.) Help students to understand that the earth appears in the sky when seen from space.

Lesson 1 What Do You See in the Sky?

You can see the sun in the sky.
You can see the **moon** and **stars.**
Pretend you could stand on the moon.
You would see the earth in the sky.
This picture shows how it might look.

Teaching Options

SCIENCE BACKGROUND

Just as the moon travels around the earth, the earth and moon travel around the sun. For thousands of years, the motions of the sun, moon, and stars have been used by people to calculate the passage of time. From these movements, we invent the time divisions: day, month, and year. In addition, everyday terms such as day, night, winter, spring, summer, and fall exist because we use them to explain changes caused by the way the earth moves around the sun.

Reinforcement

Obtain a medicine ball (or large beach ball), a softball, and a tennis ball. Show them to the students. Tell students that the balls represent the earth, moon, and sun. Have them decide which ball should represent the sun and the reason for that choice. (the medicine ball because it is largest) Continue in a similar manner with the other balls. (The softball would represent the earth and the tennis ball would represent the moon.)

♦ ***Suitable as a language development activity***

Think about the sun, the earth, and the moon.
How are their sizes different?
The sun is much larger than the earth.
The earth is larger than the moon.

Lesson Review

1. What can be seen in the sky?
2. Is the earth, moon, or sun largest?

Find Out

Go outside on a clear night.
Tell what you see in the sky.

209

2 TEACH

Teaching Tip

- **Possible Misconception:** Students might think that the sun and the full moon are the same size since both appear to be about the same size in the sky. Discuss the relative sizes of each. Help students to understand that the sun and the full moon appear to be the same size because the moon is so much closer to the earth. Remind students that objects look smaller when they are far away.

3 ASSESS

Lesson Review

1. The earth, moon, sun, and stars can be seen in the sky.
2. The sun is bigger than the earth or moon.
Challenge! Question: **How do you think the moon and earth would look from the sun?** (The moon and earth would hardly be visible from the sun.) **Thinking Skill:** *Inferring*

Find Out

Answer will depend upon what is visible for each student. **Thinking Skills:** *Collecting information, Recording*

Special Education

For students with learning disabilities, present three paper circles of different diameters—2.5 cm (1 in.), 5 cm (2 in.), and 7.5 cm (3 in.). Also present a very small circle like one cut from a paper punch. Label the little one *small*. Ask the students what the other one is called. (big or large) Put away the small circle and focus on the 5 cm and 7.5 cm circles. Identify the 2.5 cm circle as *large*, the 5 cm circle as *larger*, and the 7.5 cm circle as *largest*. Next, label the 2.5 cm circle the moon, the 5 cm circle the earth, and the 7.5 cm circle the sun. Explain that the moon is *large*, the earth is *larger*, and the sun is the *largest*.

Reteaching Suggestion ♦

Have students draw and label pictures of the sun, earth, and moon. Discuss the relative sizes of each. Check to see that students' drawings reflect knowledge that the sun is much larger than the moon.

TEACHING PLAN

LESSON 2
pages 210–212

Lesson Objectives
- *Describe* the functions of the sun.
- *Describe* what causes day and night.

Lesson Vocabulary
sunlight, daytime, nighttime

1 MOTIVATE

Demonstration Activity ♦
Take the class outside on a sunny day. Have students *observe* the difference in temperature when standing in areas with and without shade. If your classroom has windows, turn off the lights so the class can see that windows allow sunlight in the classroom.

Discussion
Ask students to *describe* their experiences outside, and guide them to *conclude* that the sun provides both light and heat. Ask them to *predict* what it would be like without the sun's light and heat. (Accept reasonable responses.)

Lesson 2 What Is the Sun Like?

The sun is a hot ball of gas.
It is very, very large.
It is hotter than anything on the earth.
The sun heats the earth and moon.
The sun lights the earth and moon, too.
This boy is playing in the **sunlight.**

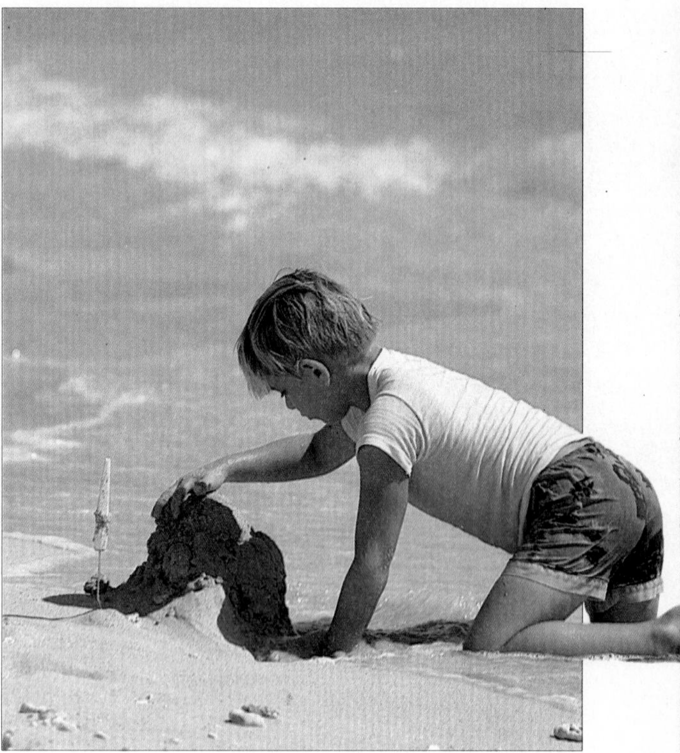

Teaching Options

SCIENCE BACKGROUND

The sun among all other stars is average in size, temperature, and brightness. Its closeness to the earth (93,000,000 miles) makes it appear tremendously large and bright. It is made mostly of hydrogen, but 60 of the natural elements found on Earth were detected in gaseous form on the sun. Most of the sun's energy comes to us as sunlight.

Special Education

Obtain a globe and a flashlight. Place a bright colored sticker dot on the area where you live. Tell students with learning disabilities that the globe represents the earth, the dot represents your city or town, and the flashlight represents the sun. Direct students to watch the dot on the globe and to avoid looking directly at the flashlight. Darken the room as much as possible. Have one student hold the "sun" while the "earth" is slowly rotated. Stop the globe. Ask students whether the dot is in daylight or night. Do this several times to reinforce the concept that the movement of the earth causes daytime and nighttime.

♦ ***Suitable as a language development activity***

The earth is always turning.
Part of the earth is turned toward the sun.
The sun lights this part.
Sunlight makes **daytime** on the earth.
It is daytime on this part of the earth.

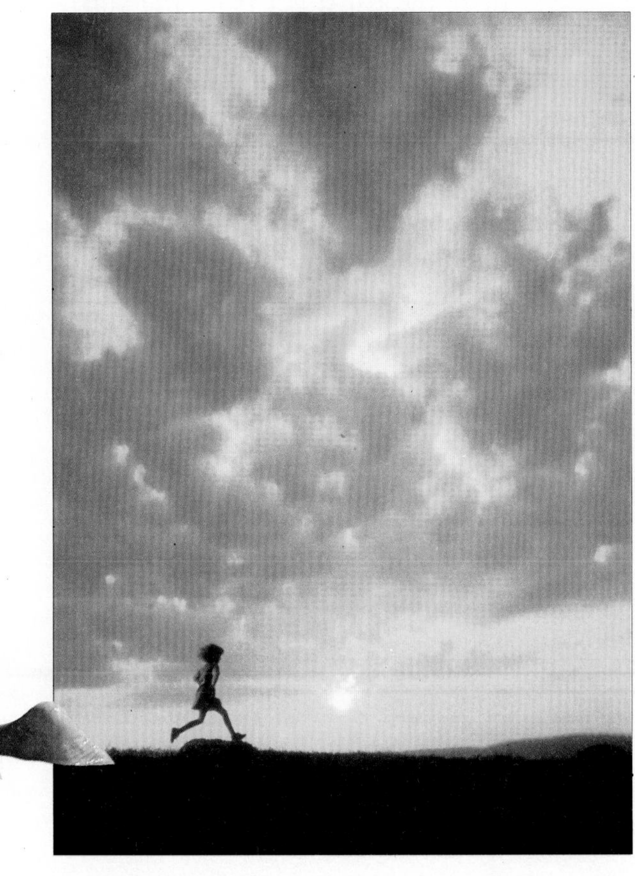

211

2 TEACH

Teaching Tips

- Call students' attention to the pictures of the children playing in the sunlight. Write the word *sunlight* on the chalkboard. Read page 210 together and discuss that both heat and light come from the sun. Lead students to ***conclude*** that the sun must be very, very hot since it can provide heat from so far away.
- Write the word *daytime* on the chalkboard and have students ***identify*** activities that occur in the daytime. (going to school, playing outside, and so on) Read page 211 together. Point out that all of the earth cannot have daytime at the same time.
- **Possible Misconception:** Since "the sun comes up" and "the sun goes down" are common phrases, students might think that the sun moves while the earth stands still. Remind them that the earth is always turning, which accounts for the *appearance* of the sun's motion.

Enrichment

Have students ***observe*** and ***compare*** the time it takes for ice cubes to melt in different conditions. Encourage students to think of ways to use heat from the sun to melt their ice quickly.

Science and Math

Have students ***measure*** and ***compare*** the temperature outside in the shade and in the sun, inside near the window and away from the window, and so on.

Science and Art

Show students pictures of sunrise and sunset. Provide water color paints and show students how to paint on wet paper. Direct them to paint pictures of sunrise and sunset, using this color-wash technique. Display the paintings in the classroom.

TEACHING PLAN

Teaching Tips

- Remind students of the *TRY THIS* on page 207, where they drew pictures of the day and night skies. Explain that the movement of the earth causes the differences that we see in the sky.
- Write the word *nighttime* on the chalkboard. Tell students that it is always nighttime somewhere on the earth. Read page 212 together, and have students ***observe*** that the part of the earth away from the sun has nighttime.

3 ASSESS

Lesson Review

1. light and heat
2. When Earth is turned toward the sun, that part has day. The part turned away from the sun has night.
Challenge! Question: **Does the sun shine all the time?** (Yes, but we can only see it part of the time because the earth turns.) **Thinking Skill:** *Drawing conclusions*

Find Out

Students should find out, with help, the time of sunrise. **Thinking Skill:** *Restating or explaining ideas*

Part of the earth is away from the sun.
The sun does not light that part.
What does this part of the earth have?
This part of the earth has **nighttime.**

Lesson Review

1. What does the earth get from the sun?
2. What makes night and day?

Find Out

Listen to a weather report.
Find out when the sun will set.

212

Teaching Options

SCIENCE ANECDOTE

Tremendous explosions on the sun shoot particles into space. When they hit the earth's atmosphere, they cause static on the radio.

Reteaching Suggestion ♦

Write *The Sun* on the chalkboard. Have students dictate sentences telling what they have learned about the sun. Write their sentences on the board. Reread Lesson 2 to the students and have them add any important points to their list of sentences.

Workbook page 63 *

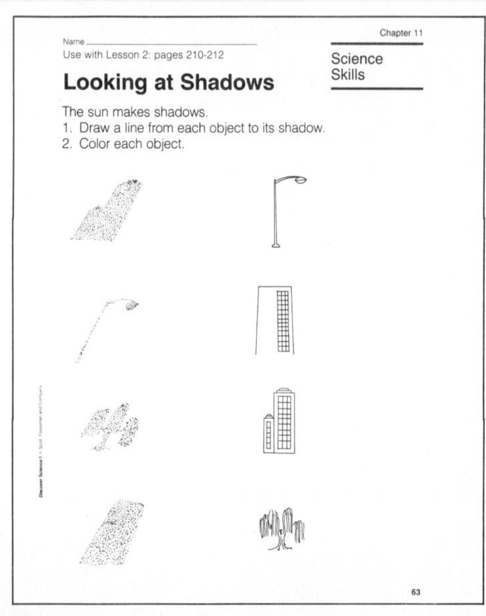

Name ____________
Use with Lesson 2: pages 210-212

Chapter 11

Science Skills

Looking at Shadows

The sun makes shadows.
1. Draw a line from each object to its shadow.
2. Color each object.

63

♦ ***Suitable as a language development activity***

Ellison Onizuka

An astronaut flies in a spacecraft.
Ellison Onizuka was an astronaut.
He always liked to study the stars.
He worked hard to be an astronaut.
He flew in one of the Space Shuttles.
It went around the earth 48 times.

What Do You Think?

How do astronauts help others?

SCIENCE AND PEOPLE

Discussion

Write the word *Astronaut* on the chalkboard and ask students to tell what they know about astronauts. Ask the class if any of them would like to be an astronaut. Point out that men and women both can be astronauts.

Teaching Tips

- Call students' attention to the picture of Ellison Onizuka. Write his name on the board and pronounce it for the students.
- Ellison Onizuka was killed in the *Challenger* disaster in 1986. You might want to discuss with students the space education project that is being developed as a result of the efforts of the families of the astronauts who died on *Challenger*.

Answer

What Do You Think?
They help people learn more about outer space. They might discover ways to live in outer space. They take living things into outer space and observe them.
Thinking Skill: *Drawing conclusions*

Books to Read

Shayler, David. *Shuttle Challenger: A Complete History of Space Shuttle Orbiter*. Prentice Hall, 1987. (for the teacher)

SCIENCE BACKGROUND

Ellison Onikuza was a Lieutenant Colonel in the United States Air Force and a NASA astronaut. Onizuka served as squadron flight test engineer and chief of the engineering support section in the training resources branch of the United States Air Force Test Pilot School. He was selected as an astronaut candidate by NASA in January 1978. He was a mission specialist on the Space Shuttle, *Discovery*, launched in 1985. *Discovery* orbited Earth 48 times in three days (January 24-27, 1985). On *Challenger*, Ellison Onizuka's special mission was to have been the filming of Halley's comet with a hand-held camera.

* *Answers to masters on pages 206E-206F*

TEACHING PLAN

LESSON 3
pages 214–216

Lesson Objectives
- *Explain* that the moon shines with light from the sun.
- *Describe* apparent changes in the shape of the moon.

1 MOTIVATE

Demonstration Activity ♦
Bring a book of nursery rhymes to class and read *Hey Diddle, Diddle* to the students, showing the illustrations.

Discussion
Question: **Is it possible for a cow to jump over the moon?** (No.) Ask students to *explain* their answers. Encourage students to ***describe*** what they already know about the moon. Write their thoughts on a piece of chart paper.

Lesson 3 What Is the Moon Like?

The moon is round like a ball.
It has rocks, soil, and mountains.
The moon has no light of its own.
What lights the moon?
Light from the sun shines on it.
Then the light bounces off the moon.

214

Teaching Options

SCIENCE BACKGROUND

Moonlight is sunlight reflected from the moon's surface. The half of the moon facing the sun is always in sunlight, but we cannot always see that half from the earth. If the moon is between the sun and the earth, we cannot see the lighted half, and the moon appears dark to us. If the earth is between the sun and the moon, and the moon is not in the earth's shadow, we see the entire lighted surface. At all other points in the moon's orbit, we can see only part of the lighted side. The moon goes through phases as it makes one trip around the earth. As viewed from Earth, the lighted part of the moon has different shapes.

Reinforcement

Have students each fold a paper in fourths and draw pictures of the moon in four different phases. Have students cut apart their pictures and place them in sequence.

♦ ***Suitable as a language development activity***

[1] full moon, crescent moon, half moon

What part of the moon do you see?
You see the part lighted by the sun.
Sometimes you see the whole moon.
Other times you see part of the moon.
What shapes of the moon do you see here?[1]

2 TEACH

Teaching Tips

• **Possible Misconception:** Students might think that the moon is only out at night since it is often only faintly visible in daytime. Remind students that the moon is always in the sky, but that it is easier to see it when the sky is dark.

• Read page 214 with students and have them ***describe*** how the moon is like the earth. (round; has rocks, soil, and mountains; has no light of its own) Discuss the illustration and ask for a volunteer to tell in his/her own words where the moon gets its light. (from the sun)

• Question: **Does the moon always look the same?** (No, it looks different at different times.) Read page 215 with students and discuss the different shapes of the moon in the illustration. Suggest that they look at the moon (or check the newspaper) to find out which picture is most like the moon at the present time.

Special Education

Obtain a film projector, and place a large ball on a table in line with the light from the projector, but several feet away. Have students with learning disabilities sit on the floor between the two, facing the ball. Explain that the light from the projector will represent the sun, the ball will represent the moon, and the students will represent the earth. Shine the light on the ball. The "moon" will appear full. Move the ball to the left, leave the light as it is, and have the students face the "moon." This will give the appearance of a half moon. Move the ball so that it is between the students and the light, and to the right of the light. This will look like a crescent moon.

Enrichment

Encourage interested students to use resource materials to explore folk wisdom and/or tales about the moon and its phases. Allow them to share their findings with the class.

Game Suggestion ♦

Play "I Am Going to the Moon." Have students sit in a circle, and designate one student to start the game by stating, "I am going to the moon, and I will take a ...," specifying an item. The second person must repeat what the first student said, adding an item. Continue around the circle, adding items to the list, until a student is unable to recall the entire list. Repeat the game if desired.

TEACHING PLAN

3 ASSESS

Lesson Review
1. Moonlight comes from the sun.
2. The moon moves around the earth and, with the earth, around the sun.
Challenge! Question: **How are the moon and the earth alike?** (They are both round in shape. Both are lighted by the sun.) **Thinking Skills:** *Comparing, Making generalizations*

Find Out
Children should draw the shape of the moon they see. **Thinking Skills:** *Observing, Recording*

How do the moon and earth move?
The moon moves around the earth.
Together, they move around the sun.
Point to the sun, moon, and earth.

Lesson Review

1. What lights the moon?
2. In what ways does the moon move?

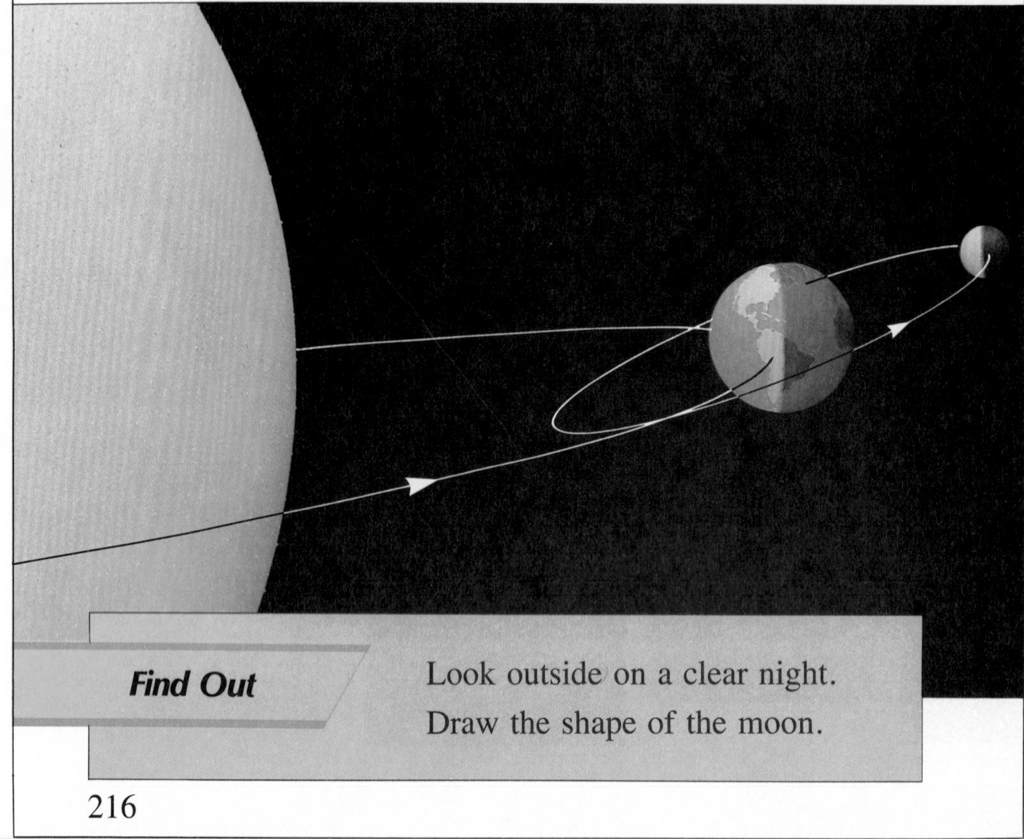

Find Out

Look outside on a clear night.
Draw the shape of the moon.

216

Teaching Options

SCIENCE ANECDOTE

The lunar month is the time interval from one new moon to the next new moon, or 29 days, 12 hours, and 44.05 minutes.

Reteaching Suggestion ◆

Refer to the sentences dictated by the students during the discussion prior to Lesson 3. Have students *compare* the information on their chart to the information about the moon on pages 214–216. Encourage them to add new information and to correct any erroneous statements.

Workbook page 64 *

Name
Use with Lesson 3: pages 214-216

Chapter 11
Science Activity

Is the Moon Big or Small?

1. Cut out the two pictures of the moon. Tape each moon to a straw.
2. Hold both moons close to you. Close one eye. Now move one moon away from you. Do the moons look the same size?

yes no

64

◆ ***Suitable as a language development activity***

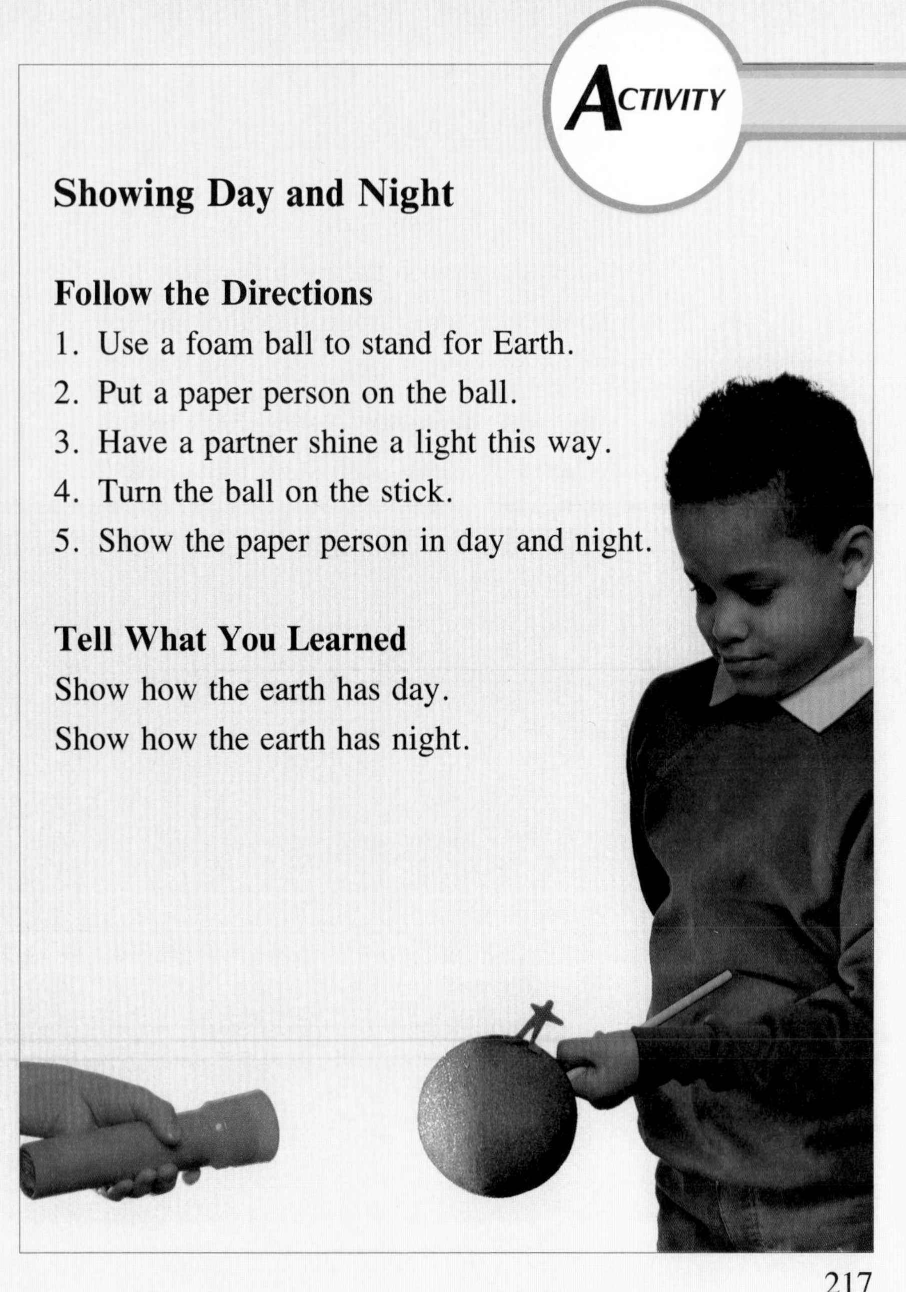

Showing Day and Night

Follow the Directions

1. Use a foam ball to stand for Earth.
2. Put a paper person on the ball.
3. Have a partner shine a light this way.
4. Turn the ball on the stick.
5. Show the paper person in day and night.

Tell What You Learned

Show how the earth has day.
Show how the earth has night.

217

Enrichment Activity

Have students use a globe and a filmstrip or slide projector to repeat this activity. Help students locate where they live on the globe, and place the paper person on that spot.

Activity Results

Students should *observe* that the paper person is in "day" when the "sun" (flashlight) shines on it. The paper person is in "night" when that side of the ball is turned away from the "sun" (flashlight).

Concept

The sun gives off light that causes day and night, along with the movement of the earth.

Objectives/Process Skills

- *Make a model* to represent the earth and sun.
- *Observe* that half the earth is lighted at a given time.
- *Infer* the cause of night and day.

Time Allotment

Allow 10 minutes.

Materials

For each pair of students: 1 plastic foam ball, 1 dowel rod, flashlight, scissors, 1 sheet construction paper

Safety Tips (See page T27.)

- Instruct students not to shine the light into other students' eyes.
- Remind students to be very careful with the dowel rod. Running or falling with the dowel rod can cause serious injury.

Teaching Tips

- Explain to students that the plastic foam ball represents the earth, and the light represents the sun.
- **Helpful Hint:** You may want to have each student make his/her own paper person. Provide necessary materials.
- Instruct students to place their ball on the dowel rod, like a lollipop.
- When students have placed their paper person on the plastic foam ball, turn out the lights in the classroom.
- Direct one student in each pair to shine the flashlight directly on the ball while the other student turns the ball to make the paper person in night and day.
- Students should discover that by turning the ball, they can make half of it appear as if it is in day and the other half appear as if it is in night.

Answers

Tell What You Learned

For the first statement, students should show their person in the light. For the second statement, students should show their person on the dark side of the plastic foam ball. **Thinking Skill:** *Applying information to new situations*

*** *Answers to masters on pages 206E–206F***

TEACHING PLAN

LESSON 4
pages 218–220

Lesson Objectives
- *Identify* stars as objects that give off their own light.
- *Identify* pictures that stars seem to form in the sky.

Lesson Vocabulary
telescope

2 TEACH

Demonstration Activity ♦
Cut a large piece of butcher paper in the shape of a five-pointed star. Staple the star on a bulletin board.

Discussion
Ask students to tell you what they know about stars. Write their responses on the paper star. Tell the class that they will learn about stars in Lesson 4, and encourage them to discuss what they would like to find out.

[1] at night or at a planetarium or observatory

Lesson 4 What Are the Stars Like?

Stars are like the sun.
They shine with their own light.
Some stars are larger than the sun.
Stars are farther away than the sun.
They are so far away they look tiny.
When have you seen stars like these?[1]

218

Teaching Options

SCIENCE BACKGROUND

A constellation is a group of stars named for an object, person, or animal. Seeing the picture pattern of the stars usually requires a lot of imagination. In fact, most of the groups bear little resemblance to the objects for which they were named. The Big Dipper is not a constellation, but is part of the constellation *Ursa Major* (Big Bear). In Orion, the sword below the belt includes the Great Nebula where new stars are being born.

Reinforcement

Have students draw a picture of an object on the chalkboard. Then, have them draw stars at strategic points on their drawings. Finally, have them erase all but their stars. Direct students to name their constellations, and help them label them.

♦ ***Suitable as a language development activity***

[1] Answers will vary.

Many people study the stars.

They imagine pictures in the sky.

Stars can seem to make pictures.

This picture is the Big Dipper.

What other star pictures can you imagine?[1]

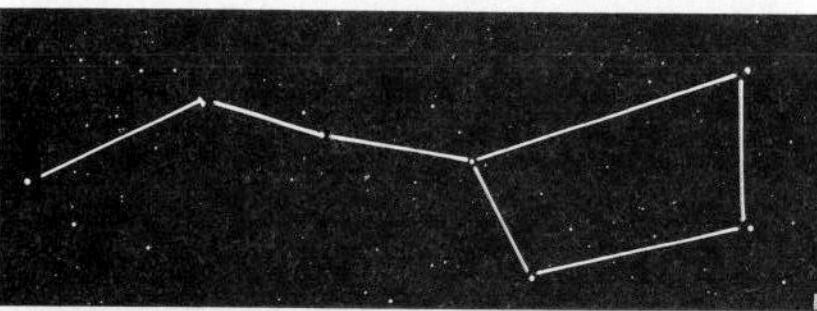

2 TEACH

Teaching Tips

- Call students' attention to the picture of the stars on page 218 and discuss how small stars appear to be. Read the page together and have students discuss how stars are like the sun.
- Point out the picture of the Big Dipper on page 219 and ask students if they ever have seen this group of stars. Tell the class that this group of stars has a special name. Read the page together and discuss why the Big Dipper is a good name for the group of stars. (It may be necessary to explain or show a dipper to the students.)

Special Education

For students with learning disabilities, write a phrase on a piece of paper. Place the paper at the end of a hallway at the students' eye level. Have students accompany you to the opposite end of the hallway and ask them what they can see that is white. Move 1/4 of the way to the paper, and again ask them what they see. Continue moving closer and discussing how the paper has "changed." Tell students that the closer we get to an object or the closer that object gets to us, the clearer it is and the easier it is to describe it correctly. Point out that a telescope makes the stars far away appear closer.

Enrichment

Encourage interested students to investigate constellations. Direct them to learn the constellations' names, and to find out how they were named. Allow students to share their findings with the rest of the class.

Workbook page 65 *

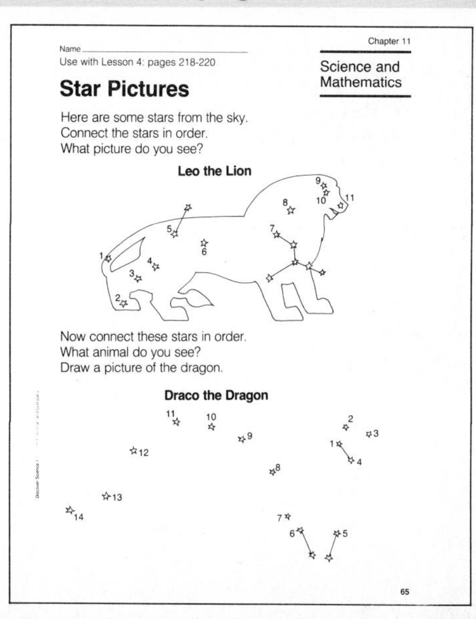

Name ______ Chapter 11

Use with Lesson 4: pages 218-220

Science and Mathematics

Star Pictures

Here are some stars from the sky.
Connect the stars in order.
What picture do you see?

Leo the Lion

Now connect these stars in order.
What animal do you see?
Draw a picture of the dragon.

Draco the Dragon

65

*** Answers to masters on pages 206E–206F**

TEACHING PLAN

Teaching Tips

- Write the word *telescope* on the board and pronounce it for the students. Have students find the telescope in the picture on page 220. Read the page together and discuss the use of a telescope.
- **Possible Misconception:** Students might think of stars as lights that turn on at night. Explain that the stars are in the sky during the day, but cannot be seen because the light from the sun is too bright.

3 ASSESS

Lesson Review

1. Stars make their own light.
2. Stars look small because they are very far away.
Challenge! Question: **Why do you think people name groups of stars?** (to help in identifying them, to help in remembering them, and to make them seem more familiar) **Thinking Skill:** *Making inferences*

Find Out

Students should find other pictures of telescopes in books about stars; the pictures will vary. **Thinking Skill:** *Collecting information*

You cannot see most of the stars.
Most stars are too far away.
How can you see more stars?
You can use a **telescope** like this.

Lesson Review

1. How is a star like the sun?
2. Why do stars look small?

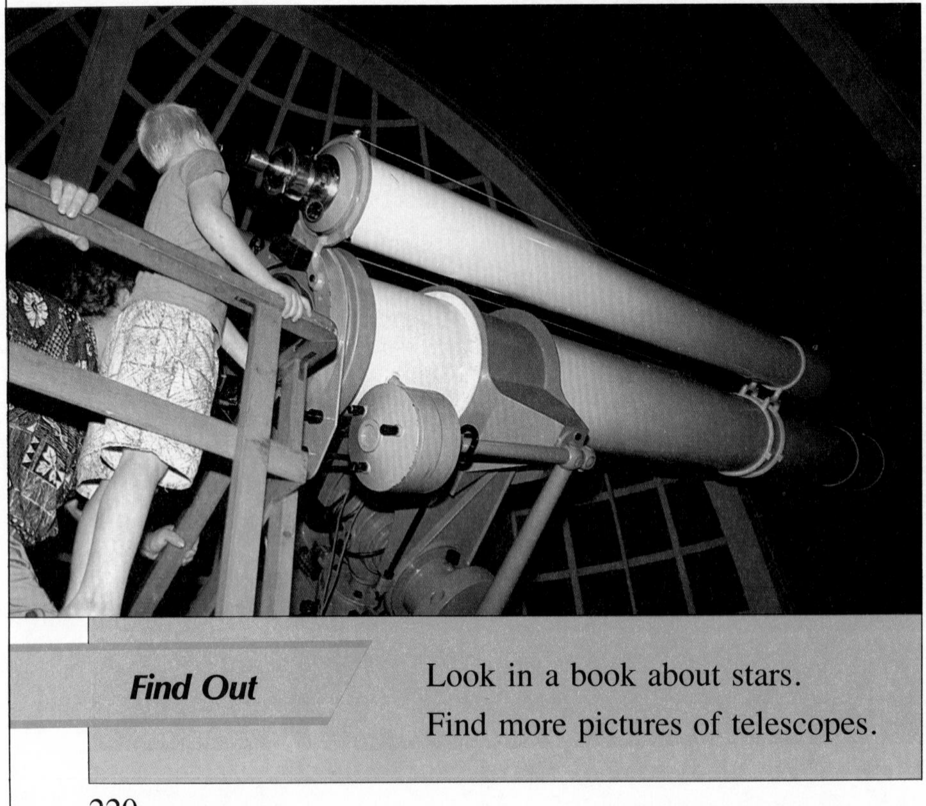

Find Out Look in a book about stars. Find more pictures of telescopes.

220

Teaching Options

SCIENCE ANECDOTE

Forty-eight of the star constellations were named in ancient times, mostly for objects or heroes of mythology.

Reteaching Suggestion ♦

Review with students what they previously knew about stars, referring to the butcher paper star. Discuss the concepts covered in Lesson 4, and have students add new information and correct any misconceptions.

Workbook page 66 *

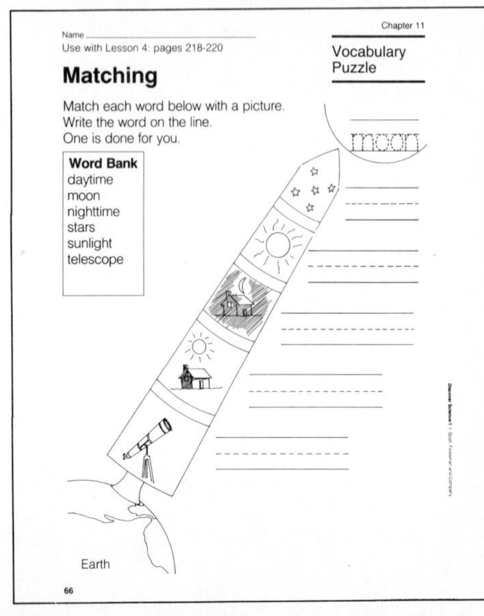

Name

Use with Lesson 4: pages 218-220

Chapter 11

Vocabulary Puzzle

Matching

Match each word below with a picture.
Write the word on the line.
One is done for you.

Word Bank
daytime
moon
nighttime
stars
sunlight
telescope

moon

Earth

66

Discover Science 1 © Scott, Foresman and Company

♦ ***Suitable as a language development activity***

Making a Star Picture

Follow the Direction

1. Look at this star picture.
2. Copy it on your own paper.
3. Make a hole for each star.
4. Hold the paper up to a light.
5. Look at your star picture.

Tell What You Learned

Tell what your star picture shows.

Make a different star picture.

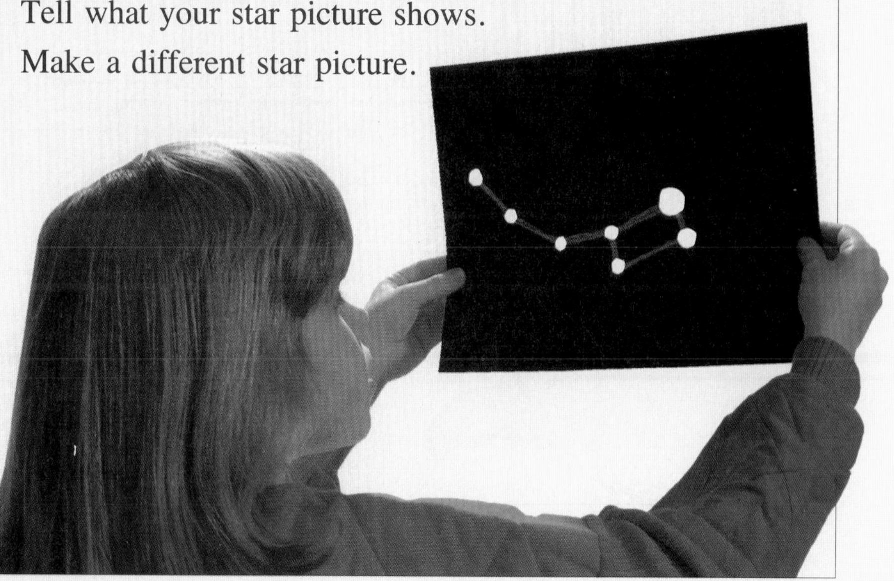

221

ACTIVITY PLAN

Concept
Stars make patterns in the sky.

Objectives/Process Skills
- *Make a model* of a star pattern.
- *Observe* the pattern.
- *Describe* the pattern.

Time Allotment
Allow 20 minutes.

Materials
For each student: 2 sheets black construction paper, paper punch, pencil

Safety Tip (See page T27.)
- Remind students to be careful when handling the hole punch.

Teaching Tips
- Instruct students to carefully punch holes in the paper to represent the star picture shown on the activity page.
- Students should be able to copy the picture of the Big Dipper and *explain* what they see.

Answers
Tell What You Learned
For the first statement, students should state that their pictures show a dipper, ladle, or big spoon, or otherwise *describe* the Big Dipper. For the second statement, students should design star patterns of their own. **Thinking Skill:** *Making physical models*

Enrichment Activity

Allow students to copy other constellations and/or design more of their own constellations.

Activity Results

Students' star pictures will vary.

* ***Answers to masters on pages 206E–206F***

TEACHING PLAN

SKILLS FOR SOLVING PROBLEMS

pages 222–223

Purpose
This feature provides students with an opportunity to measure shadows at different times of the day.

Materials
For each student: centimeter ruler, paper for chart

1 MOTIVATE

Discussion
Ask students if they have ever noticed their own shadows when outdoors on a sunny day. (Most will answer yes.) Question: **Is your shadow always the same size as you are?** (Most students will have noticed that their shadows are sometimes much taller or shorter than they are.) Explain that the length of shadows changes depending on the time of day.

Skills for Solving Problems

Measuring Shadows

How does a shadow change?

1. Look at the pictures.
   They show different times of day.
   Notice how the shadow changed.

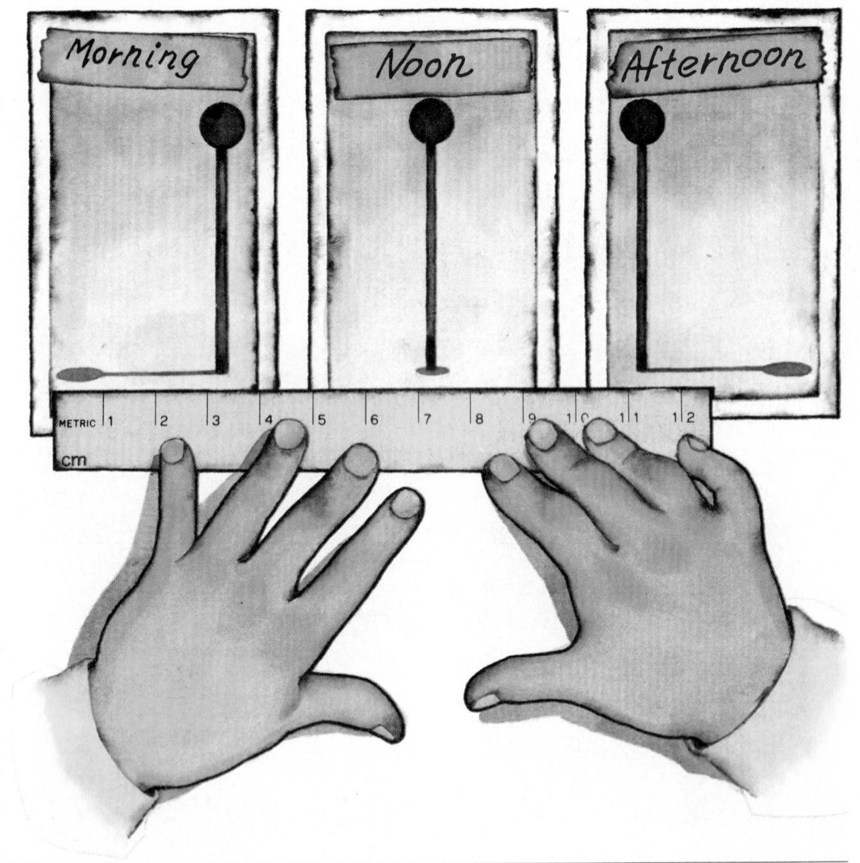

222

Teaching Options

SCIENCE BACKGROUND

Astronomers used to calculate the depth of lunar craters and the height of mountains on the moon by measuring the length of their shadows, using telescopes on Earth.

2. Measure each shadow.
   Use your own paper.
   Write how long each shadow is.
   Make a graph like this one.
   Fill in your graph.

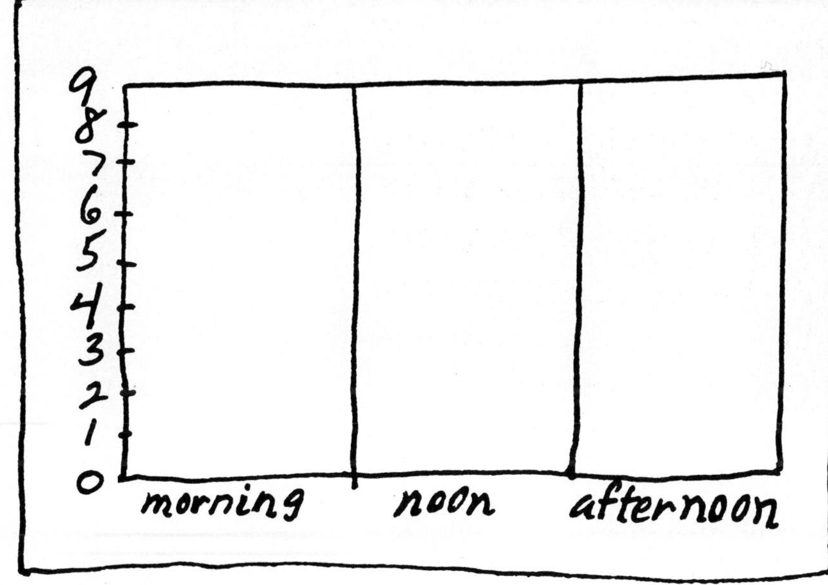

3. Look at your graph.
   How did the shadow change?

2 TEACH

Teaching Tips

- Make sure the students align the ruler with the bottom of the pictures when measuring the shadows.
- The graphs that the students draw need not be the same as the sample shown on page 223, as long as the student has recorded all the required information on the graph.

3 ASSESS

Students should note that their measurements show that the shadows get longer as the day proceeds farther into the afternoon.

Resource Book page 87 *

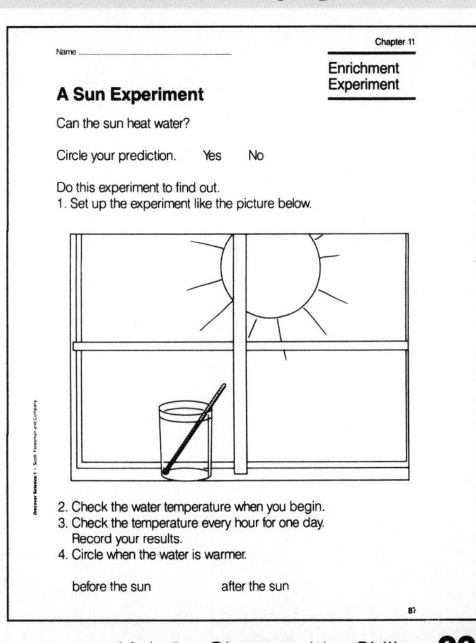
Name ______________________

Chapter 11

Enrichment Experiment

A Sun Experiment

Can the sun heat water?

Circle your prediction. Yes No

Do this experiment to find out.
1. Set up the experiment like the picture below.

2. Check the water temperature when you begin.
3. Check the temperature every hour for one day. Record your results.
4. Circle when the water is warmer.

before the sun after the sun

87

Answers to masters on pages 206E-206F

REVIEW PLAN

CHAPTER 11 REVIEW

pages 224–225

Review Chapter Ideas

1. the sun, the earth and moon, the stars
2. The sun is a ball of hot gas. It is bigger than the earth, and very far away.
3. The earth turns. The part the sun is shining on has day. The part turned away from the sun has night.
4. The moon is shaped like a ball. The sun shines on the moon. We see the lighted part.
5. The moon goes around the earth and, with earth, around the sun.
6. The stars shine with their own light, like the sun. The stars are very big, and very far away.

For further review, use Study Guide page 236.

Chapter 11 Review

Review Chapter Ideas

1. Look at the pictures of the sky. Tell what you see.

a.

b.

c.

2. Describe the sun.
3. Tell what makes night and day.
4. Describe the moon.
5. Tell how the moon moves.
6. Describe the stars.

Review Options

Cooperative Learning ♦

STAD Format (See page T23.)
Assign students to work in four- to five-member teams to study Chapter 11 Review. Students should work together to make sure that they and their teammates know the material in the chapter. After students have had enough time to study together, give them a test to complete individually (Chapter 11 Test in the *Test Book*). Award Superteam certificates to teams whose average test scores exceed 90%, and Greatteam certificates to teams whose average test scores exceed 80%.

♦ ***Suitable as a language development activity***

Review Science Words

Match the words and the pictures.

1. moon
2. sunlight
3. telescope
4. stars

a. 

b. 

c. 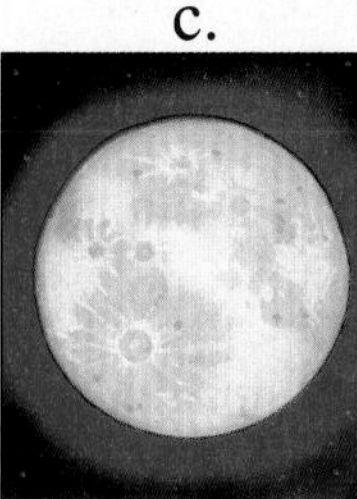

d. 

Tell what the words mean.

5. daytime
6. nighttime

Use Science Ideas

Which person will be in daytime first?

Review Science Words

Match the words and the pictures.

1. c
2. d
3. a
4. b

Tell what the words mean.

Thinking Skill: *Restating or explaining ideas*

5. daytime—the time between morning and evening

6. nighttime—the time between evening and morning

Use What You Learned

the child nearer to the sun **Thinking Skill:** *Predicting*

Test Book page 35 *

Name

Chapter 11 Test

The Sky

I. Write **Yes** or **No.**

1. Can the stars be seen in the sky?
2. Does the earth get heat from the moon?
3. Is it night when the sun shines on earth?
4. Does the moon get light from the sun?
5. Do stars make pictures in the sky?

II. Draw a line from the word to the right picture.

1. moon 2. sun 3. stars

35

* ***Answers to masters on pages 206E–206F***

TEACHING PLAN

CAREERS

Purpose
This feature familiarizes children with the specialized role of a scuba diver. Explain that it takes special training to be a scuba diver and that some people scuba dive for the fun of seeing underwater life.

Teaching Tips
• Write *scuba diver* on the chalkboard and pronounce it for students. Tell them that people who are scuba divers can stay underwater for a long time. Explain that *s c u b a* is an acronym for self contained underwater breathing apparatus.
• Call students' attention to the picture of the scuba diver. Question: **What do you see in the picture that makes it possible for this person to stay under water for a long time?** (air tank)

Careers

Scuba diver
Scuba divers can work under water.
They study living things in water.
Scuba divers take pictures under water.
Scuba divers carry tanks of air.
They breathe air from the tanks.
They can stay under water a long time.

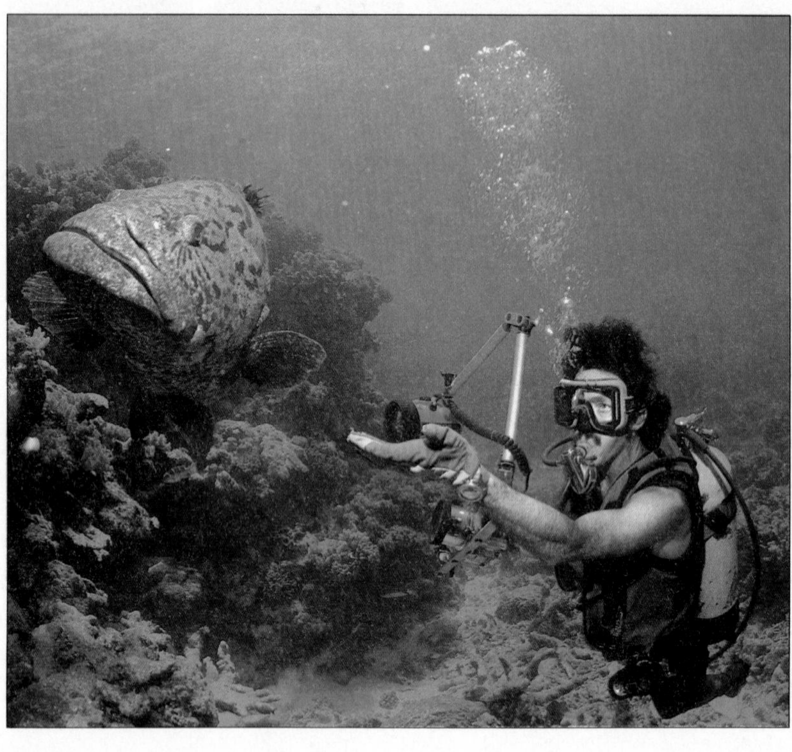

226

Teaching Options

Enrichment
Provide picture books of underwater photography. Encourage students to draw their own pictures of what they might see if they were scuba divers doing underwater research.

Where to Write
For additional information about this career contact:
National Association of SCUBA Diving Schools, ℅ John Gaffney, 641 Willow Street, Long Beach, California 90806.
U.S. National Committee for the Scientific Committee on Oceanic Research, ℅ Staff Director, Ocean Studies Boulvard, National Academy of Sciences, 2101 Constitution Avenue N.W., Washington D.C. 20418.

Lawn Sprinkler

A sprinkler can spray water.
Water flows through the hose.
It quickly pushes into the sprinkler.
The water makes the sprinkler arms turn.
The sprinkler arms have small holes.
The water sprays out of the small holes.

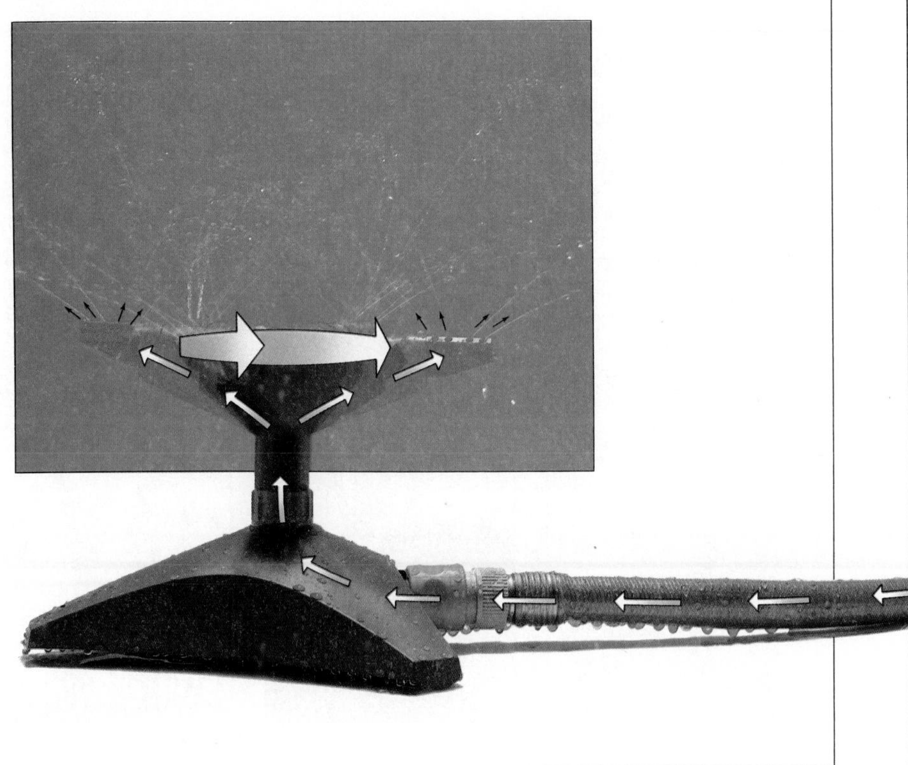

HOW IT WORKS

Teaching Tips

- Display a sprinkler. Rotate the sprinkler with your hand. Questions: **What force moved the sprinkler?** (your moving hand) **Where does the force come from to move the sprinkler in the picture?** (water) Emphasize that for any object to move a force must be applied.
- Question: **What are sprinklers used for?** (to water plants and grass) Remind the students that all organisms need water to survive.
- Have the students draw various types of sprinklers that they have seen.

SCIENCE BACKGROUND

Sir Isaac Newton, a famous British scientist, formulated three famous laws of motion. The laws explain how matter reacts when a force is applied to it. Newton's first law of motion states that a body at rest or in motion stays at rest or in motion until an outside force acts upon it. The second laws states that acceleration is directly related to the force applied. The last law explains how the water sprinkler or a rocket moves. Newton's law states that for every action there is an equal and opposite reaction. In the sprinkler, as the water is forced out of the nozzles in one direction, the sprinkler is forced to turn in the opposite direction.

REVIEW PLAN

UNIT 4 REVIEW

Answer the Questions

1. air, land, and water
2. People need air to breathe. They use air for travel, to move things, and to dry things.
3. Answers might include sunny, windy, rainy, snowy, cloudy, cold, warm, or hot. Accept reasonable responses.
4. winter—cold, snowy, icy; spring—warmer, some rain; summer—hot, rainy in some places; fall—cooler, less rain
5. The sun and stars are huge hot balls of gas. They make their own light. The stars are farther away than the sun.
6. The earth turns and also moves around the sun. The moon moves around the earth and, with the earth, around the sun.

Study the Picture

Plants grow best in spring and summer.
Thinking Skill: *Inferring*

Unit 4 Review

Answer the Questions

1. What three things does the earth have?
2. How do people use air?
3. What are four kinds of weather?
4. How does weather change in seasons?
5. What are the sun and stars like?
6. How do the earth and moon move?

Study the Pictures

Look at the pictures.

When do plants grow best?

a.

b.

c.

228

Review Options

Test Book page 37

Name ______________

Earth Science — Unit Test

I. Write **Yes** or **No.**

1. Is all of the land on earth flat? ______
2. Do people need clean water to stay alive? ______
3. Does it snow on warm days? ______
4. Does weather change from spring to summer? ______
5. Does the earth get heat from the moon? ______

II. Draw a line from the word to the right picture.

1. moon 2. sun 3. winter 4. spring 5. fall

37

What to Do

1. Draw pictures of yourself.
   Show how you enjoy air, land, and water.
2. Answer this weather riddle.
   I help plants grow.
   I make puddles.
   I can come from clouds.
   What am I?
   Now make up your own weather riddle.
3. Pretend to take a trip into space.
   Make a model spacecraft.
   Use the kinds of things you see here.

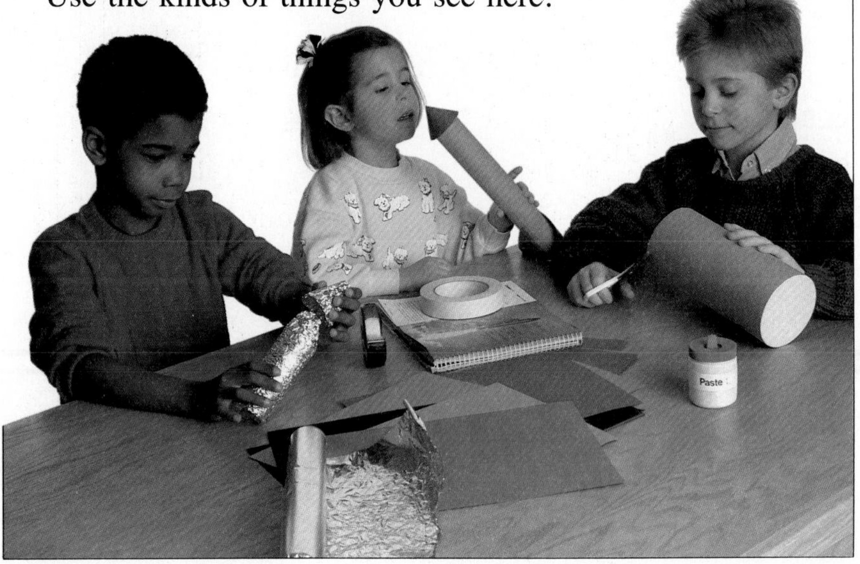

UNIT PROJECTS

Teaching Tips

1. Students could draw pictures of themselves flying kites, swimming, planting flowers, and so on.
2. The answer to the riddle is *rain*. Encourage students to write or tell their own riddles.
3. Students should make spacecraft with the items shown on the page. They might also write or tell stories describing their voyages into space.

Books in Spanish

Lewellen, John. *La luna, el sol, y las estrellas*. (moon, sun and stars) Childrens Press, 1984. (grades 1-4)
Parramon, JM. Series of four books dealing with changing of the four seasons. Barron, 1985. (grades ps-1) *La primavera. El verano. El otono. El invierno.*

Books for Students

Arvetis, Carole, Chris and Palmer. *What is the Moon?* Childrens Press, 1987. Answers questions often asked by children. (grades ps-3).
Arvetis, Carole, Chris and Palmer. *Why is the Sky Blue?* Childrens Press, 1986. Answers questions often asked by children. (grades ps-3).
Brantley, Franklyn. *Sunshine Makes the Seasons.* Crowell, 1985. Describes the motions of the earth and the sun. (grades 1-4)
Simon, Seymour. *Stars.* Morrow, 1986. Includes information on the many varieties of stars. (grades ps-3)

CHAPTER 1 STUDY GUIDE

Lesson 1
1. ears
2. tongue

Lesson 2
3. information

CHAPTER 2 STUDY GUIDE

Lesson 1
1. changes
2. taller
3. permanent

Lesson 2
4. playing

Independent Study Guide

Answer the questions for each chapter.

Chapter 1 Study Guide

Use your own paper.
Write the best word.

LESSON 1
pages 10–12

1. What helps you hear?
   eyes ears nose
2. What helps you taste food?
   eyes ears tongue

LESSON 2
pages 14–17

3. What do you get from your senses?
   friends information food

Chapter 2 Study Guide

LESSON 1
pages 26–29

1. Your body ___ as you grow.
   looks changes tells
2. You get ___ as your bones grow.
   taller smaller friends
3. You get new teeth as you grow. The new teeth are ___ teeth.
   old smaller permanent

230

LESSON 2 pages 32–34	4. What is good exercise? writing reading playing
	5. You need about ___ hours of sleep. two five ten
	6. What helps you stay well? talking washing keeping

Chapter 3 Study Guide

LESSON 1 pages 48–50	1. Which are living things? books animals chairs
	2. Many living things ___ on their own. ride sleep move
	3. Living things can be ___. rocks parents water
LESSON 2 pages 52–54	4. Living things need ___. toys plants food
	5. Ants find shelter in the ___. water ground plants
LESSON 3 pages 56–58	6. Look at the pictures Which is nonliving?

a. 

b. 

c. 

231

5. ten
6. washing

CHAPTER 3 STUDY GUIDE

Lesson 1
1. animals
2. move
3. parents

Lesson 2
4. food
5. ground

Lesson 3
6. cup

CHAPTER 4 STUDY GUIDE

Lesson 1
1. colors
2. roots

Lesson 2
3. A
4. opens

Lesson 3
5. water
6. soil

Lesson 4
7. wood

Chapter 4 Study Guide

Use your own paper.
Write the best word.

LESSON 1
pages 66–68

1. Plants have different shapes and ____.
   people colors pictures
2. Which is a part of plants?
   soil birds roots

LESSON 2
pages 70–72

3. Look at the picture.
   Which part makes seeds?

4. A seed ____ when it begins to grow.
   closes opens dies

LESSON 3
pages 74–76

5. What do plants get when it rains?
   air light water
6. What holds plants in place?
   air soil water

LESSON 4
pages 78–79

7. Paper comes from the ____ of trees.
   flowers seeds wood

232

Chapter 5 Study Guide

LESSON 1
pages 86–87

1. Coverings help ▒ animals.
   hurt protect give
2. Which is a way some animals move?
   swim feel change

LESSON 2
pages 88–90

3. Many animals ▒ when they grow.
   make use change

LESSON 3
pages 92–93

4. Which comes from animals?
   soil plants food

LESSON 4
pages 96–97

5. Which must people give their pets?
   clothing food shoes

Chapter 6 Study Guide

LESSON 1
pages 110–112

1. You can group objects by ▒.
   buttons time color

LESSON 2
pages 114–115

2. A book and water both take up ▒.
   time color space

LESSON 3
pages 116–117

3. Which has no shape of its own?
   milk book shoe

LESSON 4
pages 118–119

4. A gas can change ▒ and shape.
   objects size liquids

233

CHAPTER 5 STUDY GUIDE

Lesson 1
1. protect
2. swim

Lesson 2
3. change

Lesson 3
4. food

Lesson 4
5. food

CHAPTER 6 STUDY GUIDE

Lesson 1
1. color

Lesson 2
2. space

Lesson 3
3. milk

Lesson 4
4. size

CHAPTER 7 STUDY GUIDE

Lesson 1
1. sun
2. bounce

Lesson 2
3. sound

Lesson 3
4. heat
5. sun

CHAPTER 8 STUDY GUIDE

Lesson 1
1. near

Chapter 7 Study Guide

Use your own paper.
Write the best word.

LESSON 1
pages 128–130

1. Which makes light?
   chair window sun
2. Light can ___ off a mirror.
   block bounce stop

LESSON 2
pages 132–134

3. Which can change from loud to soft?
   light smell sound

LESSON 3
pages 136–138

4. Fires give off ___.
   heat air water
5. Which gives off heat?
   sun moon soil

Chapter 8 Study Guide

LESSON 1
pages 146–148

1. Look at the picture.
   The boy is ___ the toy.
   above below near

234

LESSON 2
pages 150–152

2. Pushing and ____ can move objects.
sitting standing pulling

3. What do magnets do?
play bounce pull

LESSON 3
pages 154–156

4. You ____ to move a heavy box.
read work sleep

5. What do people use for farming?
paper magnets machines

Chapter 9 Study Guide

LESSON 1
pages 170–172

1. The earth is shaped like a ____.
box ball pen

2. What are most mountains made of?
water sand rock

LESSON 2
pages 174–175

3. Most water on Earth is in ____.
rain oceans streams

LESSON 3
pages 176 178

4. People need air to ____.
smell taste breathe

LESSON 4
pages 180–182

5. People pump ____ from the land.
oil food air

235

Lesson 2
2. pulling
3. pull

Lesson 3
4. work
5. machines

CHAPTER 9 STUDY GUIDE

Lesson 1
1. ball
2. rock

Lesson 2
3. oceans

Lesson 3
4. breathe

Lesson 4
5. oil

CHAPTER 10 STUDY GUIDE

Lesson 1
1. clouds

Lesson 2
2. summer

Lesson 3
3. warm

CHAPTER 11 STUDY GUIDE

Lesson 1
1. sun

Lesson 2
2. daytime

Lesson 3
3. no

Lesson 4
4. telescope

Chapter 10 Study Guide

Use your own paper.

Write the best word.

LESSON 1
pages 190–192

1. Which can bring rain?
   snow sun clouds

LESSON 2
pages 194–197

2. Which season comes after spring?
   winter summer fall

LESSON 3
pages 198–199

3. Oranges need ___ weather to grow.
   warm cold winter

Chapter 11 Study Guide

LESSON 1
pages 208–209

1. The ___ is larger than the earth.
   sun moon cloud

LESSON 2
pages 210–212

2. Part of the earth faces the sun. This part of the earth has ___.
   nighttime daytime rain

LESSON 3
pages 214–216

3. The moon has ___ light of its own.
   much some no

LESSON 4
pages 218–220

4. Which can you use to see more stars?
   sunlight weather telescope

236

A

air temperature, page 190. The *air temperature* is how warm or cold air feels.

B

below, page 146. This butterfly is *below* the flower.

bones, page 26. You have many *bones* in your body.

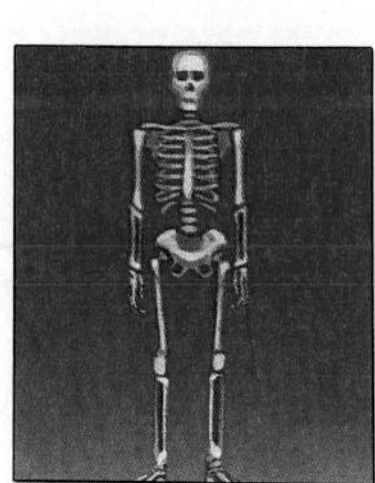

bounce, page 129. Light can *bounce* off a solid object.

C

coal, page 172. People can burn *coal* for heat.

coverings, page 86. Feathers, fur, and shells are some animal *coverings*.

D

daytime, page 211. It is *daytime* between sunrise and sunset.

direction, page 133. North, south, east, and west are each a *direction*.

distance, page 147. The space between two things is *distance*.

E

electric light, page 128. Turn on an *electric light* to see better.

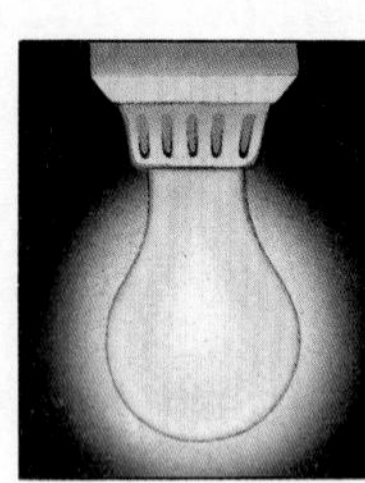

exercise, page 33. You can *exercise* to stay healthy.

F

fall, page 196. The season between summer and winter is *fall*.

G

gas, page 115. The *gases* that fill a balloon are air.

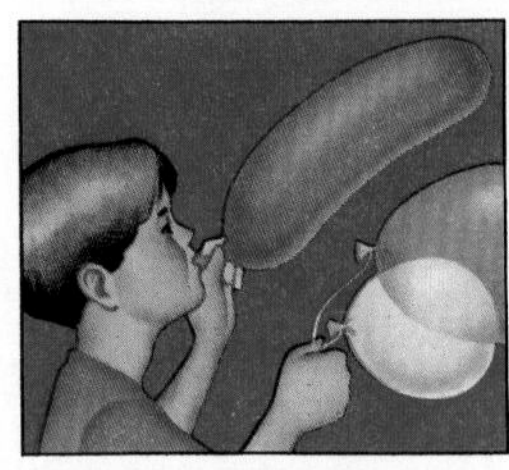

H

healthy, page 32. Eat well and exercise to stay *healthy*.

hearing, page 10. You listen with your sense of *hearing*.

heat, page 136. The sun's *heat* warms the earth.

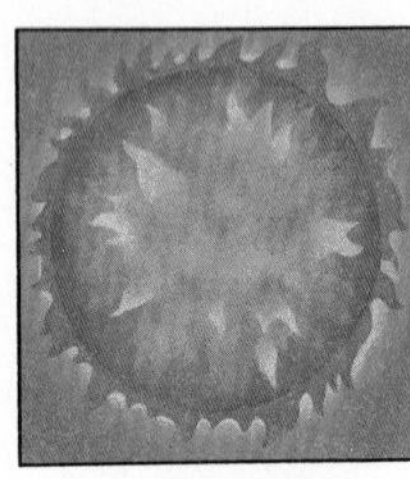

I

insect, page 90. An *insect* is a kind of very small animal.

L

leaves, page 67. Roots, stems, and *leaves* are parts of plants.

liquid, page 114. A *liquid* changes shape as it is poured from a glass to a cup.

living thing, page 48. A plant and an animal are each a *living thing*.

M

machine, page 154. A *machine* can help you work.

magnet, page 152. A *magnet* can attract some objects.

moon, page 208. The *moon* is bright in the sky at night.

mountain, page 170. A *mountain* is a very high hill.

muscles, page 26. You use your *muscles* when you move.

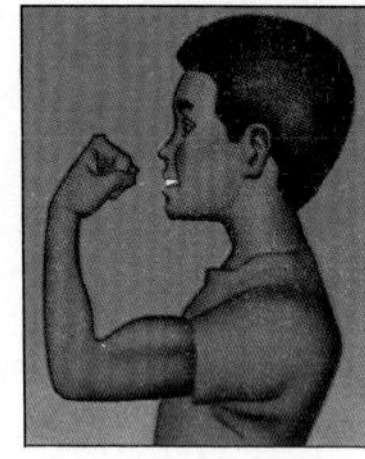

N

nighttime, page 212. The time between sunset and sunrise is *nighttime*.

nonliving thing, page 56. A rock and a book are each a *nonliving thing*.

239

O

object, page 110. An *object* is something you can see.

observe, page 14. You use your senses to *observe* things.

ocean, page 174. An *ocean* is a very large body of salt water.

oil, page 172. People pump *oil* from the earth.

P

parent, page 50. A *parent* is a mother or a father.

permanent teeth, page 27. Your *permanent teeth* take the place of your baby teeth.

pet, page 96. A *pet* is an animal you take care of.

protect, page 86. An animal's coverings help *protect* it.

R

root, page 67. A *root* is a part of a plant.

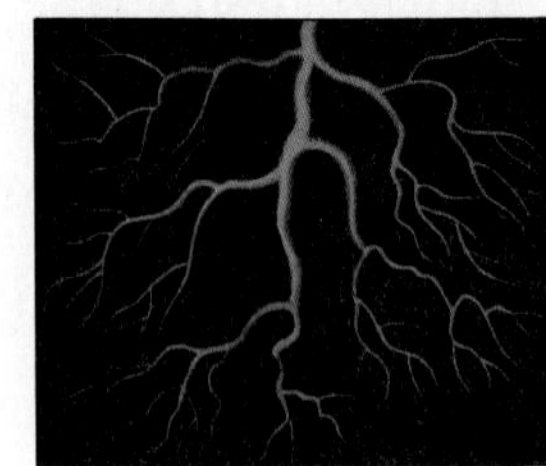

S

season, page 194. Winter, spring, summer, and fall are each a *season*.

seed, page 70. If you plant a *seed* in the ground, it might grow.

seeing, page 10. When you are looking at something, you are *seeing* it.

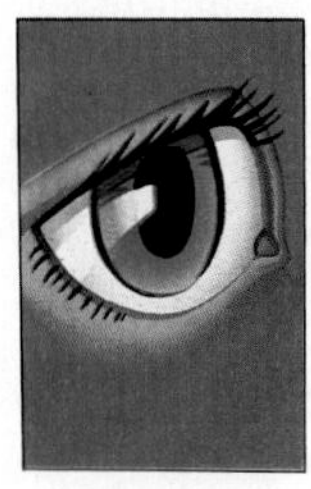

senses, page 10. Your five *senses* are seeing, hearing, feeling, tasting, and smelling.

shadow, page 130. When something blocks the light, it makes a *shadow*.

shelter, page 53. A *shelter* can be something that covers or protects.

smelling, page 10. When you breathe in an odor, you are *smelling* it.

snake, page 90. A *snake* is a long, thin animal.

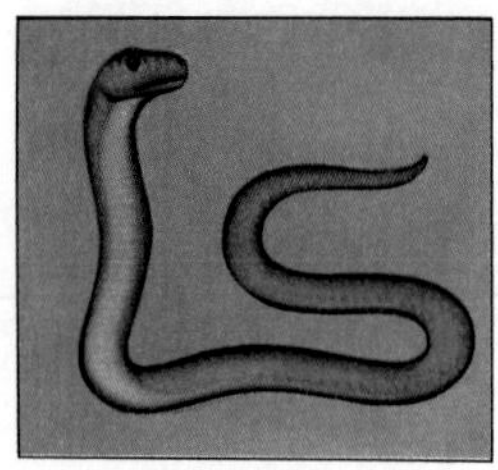

soil, page 171. Another word for dirt is *soil*.

solid, page 114. An object that is a *solid* takes up space and has its own shape.

space, page 114. The puzzle piece is the right shape to fill the *space*.

speed, page 148. How fast something moves is its *speed*.

spring, page 194. The season between winter and summer is *spring*.

star, page 208. You might see a *star* in the sky at night.

stem, page 68. A *stem* is part of a plant.

stream, page 174. A *stream* is running water.

summer, page 195. The season between spring and fall is *summer*.

sunlight, page 210. A plant can use *sunlight* to help it grow.

T

tasting, page 10. When you put something in your mouth, you are *tasting* it.

telescope, page 220. A *telescope* can help you see stars in the sky.

thermometer, page 138. A *thermometer* can tell how hot an object is.

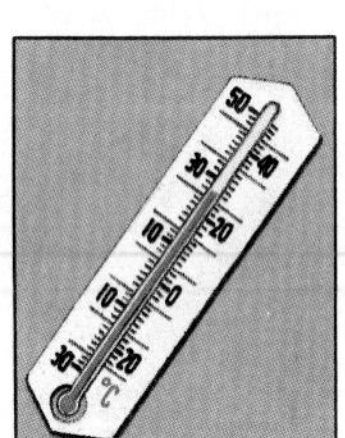

touching, page 10. When you are feeling something, you are *touching* it.

V

valley, page 170. A *valley* is a place between two mountains or hills.

W

weather, page 190. The *weather* today is sunny and cool.

winter, page 197. The season between fall and spring is *winter*.

243

Acknowledgments

Unless otherwise acknowledged, all photos are the property of Scott, Foresman and Company. If more than one photo appears on a page, abbreviations are as follows: (l) left, (r) right, (t) top, (b) bottom, (c) center, (ins) insert.

Page **iv(l):** Harald Sund **iv(r) & v(l):** REPRINTED FROM PSYCHOLOGY TODAY MAGAZINE Copyright © 1987 **vi(l):** Kjell Sandved/Sandved and Coleman Photography **vi(cr):** Michael Fairchild/Peter Arnold, Inc. **vi(r) & vii(l):** Kjell Sandved/Sandved and Coleman Photography **vii(cl):** Robert E. Lyon/Color Advantage **vii(c):** J. Serrao **vii(cr):** Kjell Sandved/Coleman & Sandved Photography **vii(r):** Frank Popper/Photographic Resources **viii(l):** FPG **viii(cl):** Water Chandoha **viii(r) & ix(l):** David R. Frazier Photolibrary **ix(c):** George Hall/Woodfin Camp & Associates **ix(cr):** Stephen Dalton/NHPA **x:** Harald Sund **x(c):** Ed Cooper **x(r):** Kim Heacox/Woodfin Camp & Associates **xi(l):** George Roth **xi(cl):** Steven Gottlieb/FPG **xi(c):** Lawrence Migdale/Science Source/Photo Researchers **xi(cr):** NASA **xi(r):** Frank Whitney/The Image Bank **xii(l):** Breck Kent/Earth Scenes **xii(r):** Simon Trevor/D.B./Bruce Coleman Inc. **2(l):** The Granger Collection, New York **2(r):** Library of Congress **3(t):** Lewis Portnoy/The Stock Market **3(bl):** Tom Raymond/Bruce Coleman Inc. **3(r):** David R. Frazier Photolibrary **4(t):** Woods Hole Oceanographic Institution **4(c):** Timothy O'Keefe/Bruce Coleman Inc. **4(b):** Al Grotell **5:** Jane Burton/Bruce Coleman Inc. **6:** © 1984 Howard Sochurek **8:** David Louis Olson **10(r):** Don and Pat Valenti **11(r):** David Phillips **12(r):** Jose Azel/Contact Press Images/Woodfin Camp & Associates **14-15:** Harald Sund **24:** REPRINTED FROM PSYCHOLOGY TODAY MAGAZINE, Copyright © 1987 **31:** Lewis Watts **44:** Kjell Sandved/Sandved and Coleman Photography **48:** Michael Fairchild/Peter Arnold, Inc. **49(l):** Walter Chandoha **49(r):** Walter Chandoha **50(l):** G. Ziesler/Peter Arnold, Inc. **50(r):** E.R. Degginger/Bruce Coleman Inc. **52-53:** Hans Reinhard/Bruce Coleman Inc. **53(ins):** Wolfgang Bayer Productions **55:** NASA **63(c):** Marty Snyderman **64:** Kjell Sandved/Coleman & Sandved Photography **66(l):** Don and Pat Valenti **66(r):** Robert E. Lyon/Color Advantage **67:** Lynn M. Stone **68(l):** J. Serrao **68(r):** Ira Cohen/New England Stock Photo **70:** Mary E. Goljenboom/Ferret **72 (tl):** Don and Pat Valenti **72(tc):** J. Serrao **72(bc):** Lynn M. Stone **72(r):** Stephenie S. Ferguson/William E. Ferguson Photography **74:** Lynn M. Stone **75:** Grant Heilman/Grant Heilman Photography **76:** J. Serrao **77:** William James/West Light **78:** Don and Pat Valenti **79(l):** R. Hamilton Smith **79(r):** Grant Heilman/Grant Heilman Photography **84:** Kjell Sandved/Coleman & Sandved Photography **86(tl):** © 1983 Carl Roessler **86(tr):** Bill Ivy **86(bl):** Sullivan & Rogers/Bruce Coleman Inc. **86-87:** MPL Fogden/ Bruce Coleman Inc. **87(ins):** Lynn M. Stone **88(all):** William E. Ferguson/William E. Ferguson Photography **89(b):** Arthus-Bertrand/Peter Arnold, Inc. **89(r):** Wayne Lankinen/DRK Photo **90(l):** D. Wilder **90(b):** E.R. Degginger/Bruce Coleman Inc. **93:** Mickey Pfleger 1987 **95:** Robert Rattner **96-97:** Frank Popper/Photographic Resources, Inc. **97 (l):** Richard W. Brown **97(r):** David Phillips **100(tl):** John Colwell/Grant Heilman Photography **100(tlc):** Grant Heilman/Grant Heilman Photography **100(tcr):** Lynn M. Stone **100(tr):** Lynn M. Stone **101(bl):** Oxford Scientific Films/ANIMALS ANIMALS **101(bc):** Oxford Scientific Films/ANIMALS ANIMALS **101(br):** Oxford Scientific Films/ANIMALS ANIMALS **102:** Brent Jones **103:** Dr. E. R. Degginger **104(cr):** Lynn M. Stone **106:** FPG **108:** Walter Chandoha **119:** David R. Frazier Photolibrary **121:** The Naval Research Laboratory **126:** David R. Frazier Photolibrary **128-129:** Norman Owen Tomalin/Bruce Coleman Inc. **132(tr):** Arthus Bertrand/Peter Arnold, Inc. **132(bl):** Herman Kokojan/Black Star **132(br):** Dwight Kuhn/DRK Photo **137(t):** Tim Bieber/The Image Bank **142(tl):** R. Hamilton Smith **144:** Geoge Hall/Woodfin Camp & Associates **146:** Stephen Dalton/NHPA **149:** Milt & Joan Mann/Cameramann International, Ltd. **155(t):** Milt & Joan Mann/Cameramann International, Ltd. **156(t):** Milt & Joan Mann/Cameramann International, Ltd. **156(b):** P. Vandermark/Stock Boston **162:** David R. Frazier Photolibrary **166:** NASA **168:** Harald Sund **170-171:** Tom Algire **171(r):** Harald Sund **172 (t):** Larry Lee/West Light **172(b):** Larry Lee/West Light **174-175:** Harald Sund **174(l):** Lawrence Hudetz **177(r):** Peter Menzel **180-181:** Ed Cooper **181(t):** Milt & Joan Mann/Cameramann International, Ltd. **183:** Erich Hartmann/Magnum Photos **186(tl):** FPG **186(tc):** J. Cigano/FPG **186(tr):** David R. Frazier Photolibrary **186(bl):** J. Divine/FPG **186(br):** Joy Spurr/Bruce Coleman Inc. **188:** Kim Heacox/Woodfin Camp & Associates **190(l):** Dan McCoy/Rainbow **190-191:** Lawrence Hudetz **192:** Lawrence Hudetz **194:** George Roth **195:** David Muench **196(l):** George Roth **196(r):** R. Hamilton Smith **197:** Lynn M. Stone **198:** Randy Taylor/Black Star **199:** Steven Gottlieb/FPG **201:** Lawrence Migdale/Science Source/Photo Researchers **204(t):** D.P. Hershkowitz/Bruce Coleman Inc. **204(b):** Andy Burridge/Bruce Coleman Inc. **206:** E. Nagele/FPG **208:** NASA **209:** NASA **210:** 1986 John Apolinski **211:** Frank Whitney/The Image Bank **212:** NASA **213:** NASA **214:** NASA **215(bl):** Jeff Adams/The Stock Market **215(tl):** Luis Villota/The Stock Market **215(tr):** Jules Bucher/Science Source/Photo Researchers **215(br):** Dennis Milon **218-219:** John Bova/Photo Researchers **219(t):** John Bova/Photo Researchers **220:** David R. Frazier Photolibrary **224(b):** Jerry Schad/Science Source/Photo Researchers **224(tl):** Warren Faubel/Bruce Coleman Inc. **224(tr):** Lenn Short/Bruce Coleman Inc. **226:** Marty Snyderman **231(r):** Don and Pat Valenti

244

KINDERGARTEN SCOPE AND SEQUENCE

Life Science

Plants

Chapter 4 Seeds and Plants
Lesson 1 Kinds of seeds
Lesson 2 Growth from seeds to plants
Lesson 3 Kinds of plants
Lesson 4 Plant parts
Lesson 5 Needs of plants
Lesson 6 Uses of plants

Animals

Chapter 5 Animals
Lesson 1 Kinds of animals
Lesson 2 Animal growth from baby to adult
Lesson 3 Animal movements
Lesson 4 Needs of animals
Lesson 5 Animal habitats
Lesson 6 Uses of animals

Ecology

Chapter 3 Living and Nonliving
Lesson 1 Living things
Lesson 2 Nonliving things
Lesson 3 Using living and nonliving things

Physical Science

Matter

Chapter 6 Comparing and Grouping Matter
Lesson 1 Color
Lesson 2 Shape
Lesson 3 Mass
Lesson 4 Number
Lesson 5 Position

Energy

Chapter 7 Heat and Cold
Lesson 1 Sources of heat
Lesson 2 Uses of heat
Lesson 3 Heat and cold change things

Chapter 8 Sound
Lesson 1 Loud sounds
Lesson 2 Soft sounds

Chapter 9 Movement
Lesson 1 How things move
Lesson 2 Magnets
Lesson 3 Sinking and floating

Earth Science

Earth

Chapter 12 Seasons
Lesson 1 Winter
Lesson 2 Spring
Lesson 3 Summer
Lesson 4 Fall

Chapter 13 Helping Our World
Lesson 1 Protecting resources
Lesson 2 Saving electricity
Lesson 3 Saving water
Lesson 4 Saving paper
Lesson 5 Picking up litter

Weather

Chapter 11 Weather
Lesson 1 Kinds of weather
Lesson 2 Air and wind
Lesson 3 Temperature
Lesson 4 Effects of weather changes

Space

Chapter 10 Earth and Sky
Lesson 1 Land and water
Lesson 2 Day and night
Lesson 3 Sun and moon

Human Body

Chapter 1 Your Senses
Lesson 1 Seeing
Lesson 2 Hearing
Lesson 3 Smelling
Lesson 4 Touching
Lesson 5 Tasting

Chapter 2 Growing and Changing
Lesson 1 Body parts
Lesson 2 Growth from baby to adult
Lesson 3 Getting new teeth
Lesson 4 Eating and exercising

Life Science

Plants

Chapter 4 Learning About Plants
Lesson 1 How plants are alike and different
Lesson 2 How plants grow
Lesson 3 What plants need to grow
Lesson 4 Why people need plants

Animals

Chapter 5 Learning About Animals
Lesson 1 Ways animals are different
Lesson 2 How animals grow
Lesson 3 Why people need animals
Lesson 4 How to care for a pet

Ecology

Chapter 3 Living and Nonliving
Lesson 1 What a living thing is
Lesson 2 What living things need
Lesson 3 What nonliving things are like

Physical Science

Matter

Chapter 6 Grouping Things
Lesson 1 Ways to group things
Lesson 2 Matter takes up space
Lesson 3 What solids and liquids are like
Lesson 4 What gases are like

Energy

Chapter 7 Light, Sound, and Heat
Lesson 1 How light can change
Lesson 2 How sound can change
Lesson 3 What can be learned about heat

Chapter 8 Moving and Working
Lesson 1 Ways objects move
Lesson 2 What can move objects (magnets)
Lesson 3 Work machines can do

Earth Science

Earth

Chapter 9 The Earth
Lesson 1 Mountains, valleys, soil, rocks, and resources
Lesson 2 Location of water on earth
Lesson 3 How air is useful
Lesson 4 How people use land and water

Weather

Chapter 10 Weather
Lesson 1 Different kinds of weather
Lesson 2 How weather can change in seasons
Lesson 3 How weather is important to people

Space

Chapter 11 The Sky
Lesson 1 What is seen in the sky
Lesson 2 What the sun is like
Lesson 3 What the moon is like
Lesson 4 What the stars are like

Human Body

Chapter 1 Your Senses
Lesson 1 Learning
Lesson 2 Using the senses

Chapter 2 Growing and Changing
Lesson 1 How people change
Lesson 2 What helps people grow

GRADE 2 SCOPE AND SEQUENCE

Life Science

Plants

Chapter 1 How Plants Are Different

Lesson 1 How plant parts can differ
Lesson 2 What plants use to make food
Lesson 3 Different ways plants grow
Lesson 4 Where plants grow

Animals

Chapter 2 How Animals are Different

Lesson 1 Some groups of animals
Lesson 2 Where animals live
Lesson 3 What animals need to stay alive
Lesson 4 How animals change as they grow

Ecology

Chapter 3 Life on Earth Long Ago

Lesson 1 Evidence of life long ago
Lesson 2 What dinosaurs were like
Lesson 3 Other animals that lived long ago
Lesson 4 What can change plants and animals
Lesson 5 Coal, oil, and gas made from plants and animals that lived long ago

Physical Science

Matter

Chapter 4 Matter Around You

Lesson 1 What matter is
Lesson 2 How matter can be grouped
Lesson 3 How matter can change

Energy

Chapter 5 Heat, Light, and Sound

Lesson 1 What heat is
Lesson 2 What light is
Lesson 3 How heat and light can be used safely
Lesson 4 What sound is
Lesson 5 How sound is helpful

Chapter 6 Machines and Electricity

Lesson 1 What machines can do
Lesson 2 What magnets can do
Lesson 3 What electricity can do
Lesson 4 How machines and electricity can be used safely

Earth Science

Earth

Chapter 7 Water and Air

Lesson 1 Where to find fresh water
Lesson 2 What oceans are like
Lesson 3 Why clean water is important
Lesson 4 What air is like
Lesson 5 Why clean air is important

Weather

Chapter 8 Changes in Weather

Lesson 1 How weather can change
Lesson 2 What makes clouds, rain, and snow
Lesson 3 What weather is like around the world

Space

Chapter 9 The Sun and Other Stars

Lesson 1 What the sun is
Lesson 2 Planets move around the sun
Lesson 3 Why most stars look small

Human Body

Chapter 10 How Your Body Works

Lesson 1 How bones and muscles work
Lesson 2 What the brain can do
Lesson 3 How the heart and lungs work
Lesson 4 What happens to food that is eaten

Chapter 11 Keeping Healthy

Lesson 1 What is needed for good health
Lesson 2 Protection from sickness
Lesson 3 How to stay safe

GRADE 3 SCOPE AND SEQUENCE

Life Science

Plants

Chapter 1 Plant Growth
Lesson 1 Importance of Roots, stems, and leaves
Lesson 2 Importance of flowers and cones
Lesson 3 How plants grow from seeds

Animals

Chapter 2 How Animals Grow
Lesson 1 How animals can be grouped
Lesson 2 How some animals with backbones grow and change
Lesson 3 How some animals without backbones grow and change

Ecology

Chapter 3 Living Things Need Each Other
Lesson 1 The five groups of living things
Lesson 2 How organisms live together
Lesson 3 How organisms get food

Chapter 4 How People Affect Plants and Animals
Lesson 1 How people change the lives of plants and animals
Lesson 2 How people protect plants and animals
Lesson 3 How people use plants and animals

Physical Science

Matter

Chapter 5 Properties of Matter
Lesson 1 What matter is
Lesson 2 The make-up of matter
Lesson 3 How matter can change

Energy

Chapter 6 Work and Machines
Lesson 1 What work is
Lesson 2 What simple machines are
Lesson 3 What compound machines are

Chapter 7 Forms of Energy
Lesson 1 Some kinds of energy
Lesson 2 What electricity is
Lesson 3 How matter is heated
Lesson 4 How light travels

Chapter 8 Sound
Lesson 1 What sound is
Lesson 2 How sound travels
Lesson 3 How people make sound

Earth Science

Earth

Chapter 9 Rocks and Soil
Lesson 1 How rocks are formed
Lesson 2 What soil is made of
Lesson 3 How people use rocks and soil

Chapter 10 Changes in the Earth
Lesson 1 What the inside of the earth is like
Lesson 2 How water and wind change the earth's crust
Lesson 3 How earthquakes and volcanoes change the earth's crust
Lesson 4 How living things change the earth's crust

Weather

Chapter 11 Clouds and Storms
Lesson 1 How clouds form
Lesson 2 Water in clouds
Lesson 3 Causes of storms

Space

Chapter 12 The Sun, Moon, and Planets
Lesson 1 How the earth and the moon move
Lesson 2 What the sun and the planets are like
Lesson 3 What scientists learn from space travel

Human Body

Chapter 13 The Body's Support
Lesson 1 The make-up of the body
Lesson 2 The importance of bones
Lesson 3 The importance of muscles

Chapter 14 Your Body's Health Needs
Lesson 1 How to stay healthy
Lesson 2 Causes of disease
Lesson 3 How alcohol, tobacco, and drugs affect the body

GRADE 4 SCOPE AND SEQUENCE

Life Science

Plants

Chapter 1 Flowering Plants
Lesson 1 How plants are classified
Lesson 2 What the parts of a flower do
Lesson 3 How seeds and fruits develop
Lesson 4 How seeds scatter and grow

Animals

Chapter 2 Animal Behavior
Lesson 1 How animals live in groups
Lesson 2 How animals care for their young
Lesson 3 How animals behave

Ecology

Chapter 3 Food Chains and Food Webs
Lesson 1 Where green plants get energy
Lesson 2 Where animals get food
Lesson 3 What a food chain is
Lesson 4 What a food web is

Chapter 4 Animal and Plant Adaptations
Lesson 1 How adaptations help animals and plants survive
Lesson 2 How animals are adapted to their environment
Lesson 3 How plants are adapted to their environment

Physical Science

Matter

Chapter 5 Measuring Matter
Lesson 1 What matter is
Lesson 2 The composition of matter
Lesson 3 How length and volume are measured
Lesson 4 How mass and density are measured

Energy

Chapter 6 Work and Energy
Lesson 1 What makes things move
Lesson 2 How work and energy are related
Lesson 3 How machines use energy to do work

Chapter 7 Electricity and Magnetism
Lesson 1 What electricity is
Lesson 2 What magnetism is
Lesson 3 How electricity and magnetism are related

Chapter 8 Light and Sound
Lesson 1 What light is
Lesson 2 How light travels
Lesson 3 How light and sound are similar and different

Earth Science

Earth

Chapter 10 Changes in Landforms
Lesson 1 The composition of the earth
Lesson 2 How volcanoes and earthquakes change landforms
Lesson 3 How weathering changes landforms
Lesson 4 How rocks are made

Chapter 11 Oceans
Lesson 1 What oceans are and how they are important
Lesson 2 How ocean water moves
Lesson 3 The ocean bottom

Weather

Chapter 9 Measuring Weather Conditions
Lesson 1 Causes of different air temperatures
Lesson 2 How temperature affects air pressure and wind
Lesson 3 Low temperature causes clouds and precipitation
Lesson 4 How weather is predicted

Space

Chapter 12 Movement in the Solar System
Lesson 1 How the earth moves
Lesson 2 Phases of the moon
Lesson 3 How planets move
Lesson 4 Other objects in the solar system that move

Human Body

Chapter 13 Digestion and Circulation
Lesson 1 How the digestive system works
Lesson 2 How the circulatory system works
Lesson 3 How to keep body systems healthy

Chapter 14 Your Brain and Your Sense Organs
Lesson 1 How the brain gets information
Lesson 2 How the eyes work
Lesson 3 How the ears work
Lesson 4 How the tongue and nose work
Lesson 5 How the skin gathers information

GRADE 5 SCOPE AND SEQUENCE

Life Science

Plants

Chapter 2 Plant Processes

Lesson 1 Plant cells
Lesson 2 How plants take in materials
Lesson 3 How plants make and use food
Lesson 4 How plants produce seeds
Lesson 5 How plants reproduce without seeds

Animals

Chapter 3 Invertebrates and Vertebrates

Lesson 1 Organisms in the animal kingdom
Lesson 2 How invertebrates are classified
Lesson 3 How arthropods are classified
Lesson 4 How vertebrates are classified

Ecology

Chapter 1 Classifying Living Things

Lesson 1 Ways all living things are alike
Lesson 2 Classifying living things into kingdoms
Lesson 3 Dividing kingdoms into smaller groups

Chapter 4 Populations and Communities

Lesson 1 What populations and communities are
Lesson 2 How populations share environments
Lesson 3 How populations affect each other
Lesson 4 How populations change
Lesson 5 How communities change naturally

Physical Science

Matter

Chapter 5 Investigating Matter

Lesson 1 Properties of matter
Lesson 2 What atoms are
Lesson 3 What elements are
Lesson 4 Combining atoms
Lesson 5 Solutions and suspensions

Energy

Chapter 6 Heat and Matter

Lesson 1 Heat and temperature
Lesson 2 How matter is heated
Lesson 3 How heat affects matter
Lesson 4 How temperature is measured

Chapter 7 Changing Forms of Energy

Lesson 1 How energy changes form
Lesson 2 How electric energy is produced
Lesson 3 How electric energy is changed and used
Lesson 4 Measuring work and force

Chapter 8 Energy Resources

Lesson 1 Fossil fuels as sources of energy
Lesson 2 Atoms as a source of energy
Lesson 3 Moving water as a source of energy
Lesson 4 How people use sunlight and wind
Lesson 5 Using heat inside the earth as a source of energy

Earth Science

Earth

Chapter 9 Earth's Changing Crust

Lesson 1 How weathering changes the earth's crust
Lesson 2 How moving water causes erosion
Lesson 3 How glaciers and wind cause erosion
Lesson 4 How rocks change
Lesson 5 How fossils form

Chapter 10 Protecting the Environment

Lesson 1 Protecting water
Lesson 2 Protecting air
Lesson 3 Protecting the land
Lesson 4 Solving local pollution problems

Weather

Chapter 11 Climate

Lesson 1 What climate is
Lesson 2 How sunlight affects climate
Lesson 3 How land and water affect climate
Lesson 4 How the shape of the land affects climate
Lesson 5 Factors that cause climates to change

Space

Chapter 12 Mapping the Stars

Lesson 1 How scientists learn about the universe
Lesson 2 Measuring distance in space
Lesson 3 How people map the stars
Lesson 4 Brightness of the stars

Human Body

Chapter 13 Body Support, Movement, and Growth

Lesson 1 How the bones help the body
Lesson 2 How muscles help the body work
Lesson 3 How to keep bones and muscles healthy
Lesson 4 How the body grows

Chapter 14 Respiration and Excretion

Lesson 1 How the body takes oxygen from the air
Lesson 2 How the body uses oxygen
Lesson 3 How the body gets rid of cell wastes
Lesson 4 How to care for the respiratory and excretory systems

GRADE 6 SCOPE AND SEQUENCE

Life Science

Plants

Chapter 4 Plant Response
Lesson 1 How plants respond to environments
Lesson 2 Stimuli
Lesson 3 Plants flower at different times
Lesson 4 Light and temperature affect leaves

Animals

Chapter 1 Cells and Heredity
Lesson 1 How living things are organized
Lesson 2 Cell reproduction
Lesson 3 How many-celled organisms reproduce
Lesson 4 How traits are inherited
Lesson 5 Dominant and recessive genes

Ecology

Chapter 2 The Fossil Record
Lesson 1 What scientists learn from fossils
Lesson 2 Patterns in the fossil record
Lesson 3 Divisions of geologic time
Lesson 4 Inferring about dinosaurs

Chapter 3 Change Through Time
Lesson 1 Adaptations
Lesson 2 How species change
Lesson 3 How species become extinct

Chapter 5 Ecosystems and Biomes
Lesson 1 Energy flow in a community
Lesson 2 How materials cycle through ecosystems
Lesson 3 Land biomes
Lesson 4 Water biomes

Physical Science

Matter

Chapter 6 Structure of Matter
Lesson 1 Describing matter
Lesson 2 The building blocks of matter
Lesson 3 Classifying matter

Chapter 7 Changes in Matter
Lesson 1 Compounds
Lesson 2 Chemical reactions
Lesson 3 Acids and bases

Energy

Chapter 8 Electrical Energy
Lesson 1 What electricity is
Lesson 2 How electro-magnets work
Lesson 3 How electricity is made and used
Lesson 4 How electronic devices work

Chapter 9 Investigating Light and Sound
Lesson 1 What light is
Lesson 2 How light behaves
Lesson 3 How color is seen
Lesson 4 What sound is
Lesson 5 How people communicate using light and sound

Earth Science

Earth

Chapter 11 Earth's Moving Plates
Lesson 1 How continents have changed positions
Lesson 2 How plate tectonics explains movement of continents
Lesson 3 How plate tectonics explains earthquakes and volcanoes

Chapter 12 Resources and Conservation
Lesson 1 How replacement rates of earth's resources vary
Lesson 2 Resources provided by air and land
Lesson 3 Resources provided by water
Lesson 4 How people affect the earth's resources

Weather

Chapter 10 Forecasting Weather
Lesson 1 How forecasts benefit people
Lesson 2 Data needed to make a forecast
Lesson 3 How data are used to forecast weather
Lesson 4 How severe weather is predicted

Space

Chapter 13 Exploring Space
Lesson 1 How the sun and moon affect the earth
Lesson 2 About the sun
Lesson 3 Composition of the universe
Lesson 4 How the universe formed
Lesson 5 Exploring space

Human Body

Chapter 14 The Body's Control Systems
Lesson 1 How the body controls life processes
Lesson 2 How the endocrine system is involved in control
Lesson 3 How messages travel through the body
Lesson 4 How the body responds to the environment

Chapter 15 Growing Up Healthy
Lesson 1 Stages in the human life cycle
Lesson 2 Causes of disease
Lesson 3 Protections from disease
Lesson 4 How drug abuse can affect health

Audio-Visual Sources

AIMS Media
6901 Woodley Avenue
Van Nuys, CA 91406

Benchmark Films, Inc.
145 Scarborough Road
Briarcliff Manor, NY 10510

BFA Educational Media
Phoenix/BFA Film and Video, Inc.
468 Park Avenue South
New York, NY 10016

Bullfrog Films, Inc.
Oley, PA 19547

Churchill Films
662 N. Robertson Boulevard
Los Angeles, CA 90069

Coronet Films and Video
108 Wilmot Road
Deerfield, IL 60015

Encyclopaedia Britannica Education Corporation
425 North Michigan Avenue
Chicago, IL 60611

General Educational Media,Inc.
701 Beaver Valley Road
Wilmington, DE 19803

Great Plains Films
P. O. Box 80669
Lincoln, NE 68501

Higgins Productions, Inc.
9100 Sunset Blvd.
Los Angeles, CA 90069

Hubbard Scientific
1946 Raymond
Northbrook, IL 60062

International Film Bureau, Inc.
332 S. Michigan Avenue
Chicago, IL 60604

Jam Handy
School Service, Inc.
2781 E. Grand Boulevard
Detroit, MI 48211

Knowledge Unlimited
P. O. Box 52
Madison, WI 53701

Macmillan
34 MacQuesten Parkway, South
Mt. Vernon, NY 10550

Marshfilm, Inc.
P.O. Box 8082
Shawnee Mission, KS 66208

McGraw-Hill Training Systems
Box 641
674 Via De Lavalle
Delmar, CA 92014

Media, Inc.
P.O. Box 496
Media, PA 19063

NASA Film Library
National Aeronautics and Space Administration
National Audiovisual Center
General Services Administration
Washington, DC 20409

National Educational Media, Inc.
21601 Devonshire
Chatsworth CA 91311

National Geographic Society
17th and M Streets NW
Washington, D.C. 20036

National Oceanic and Atmospheric Administration
Motion Picture Service
12231 Wilkins Avenue
Rockville, MD 20852

Palisades Wildlife Film Library
1205 S. Ogden Drive
Los Angeles, CA 90019

Roller Skating Rink Operators Association
P.O. Box 81846
Lincoln, NE 68501

Sigma Electronics, Inc.
1184 Enterprise Road
East Petersburg, PA 17520

Stanton Films
2417 Artesia Boulevard
Redondo Beach, CA 90278

Sterling Educational Films
241 East 34th Street
New York, NY 10016

United States Department of Agriculture
Soil Conservation Service
Room 0054-S
P.O. Box 2890
Washington, D.C. 20013

Visual Instruction Productions
112 Brentwood Drive
Stamford, CT 06903

Walt Disney Educational Media Co.
500 S. Buena Vista Street
Burbank, CA 91521

Computer Software Sources

Aquarius People Materials
P. O. Box 128
Indian Rocks Beach, FL 33535

Astronomical Society of the Pacific
1290 24th Avenue
San Francisco, CA 94122

Bohle Company
1901 Avenue of the Stars
Los Angeles, CA 90067

Brain Bank, Inc.
200 Fifth Avenue
New York, NY 10001

CBS Interactive Learning
One Fawcett Place
Greenwich, CT 06836

CC Publications
P. O. Box 23699
Tigard, OR 97005

COMPress
P.O. Box 102
Wentworth, NH 03282

Concept Educational Software
P. O. Box 6184
Allentown, PA 18001

Diversified Educational Enterprises, Inc.
725 Main Street
Lafayette, IN 47901

Educational Activities, Inc.
P. O. Box 392
Freeport, NY 11520

Educational Computing Systems, Inc.
136 Fairbanks Road
Oak Ridge, TN 27830

Educational Materials and Equipment Co.
P. O. Box 2805
Danbury, CT 06813

Focus Media, Inc.
839 Stewart Avenue
Garden City, NY 11530

D. C. Heath
125 Spring Street
Lexington, MA 02173

Holt, Rinehart, & Winston
383 Madison Avenue
New York, NY 10017

HRM
175 Tompkins Avenue
Pleasantville, NY 10570

Ideatech, Inc.
P. O. Box 62451
Sunnyvale, CA 94088

J & S Software
140 Reid Avenue
Port Washington, NY 11050

Micrograms, Inc.
P. O. Box 2146
Loves Park, IL 61130

Mindscape Inc.
3444 Dundee Road
Northbrook, Illinois 60062

Minnesota Educational Computing Consortium
2520 Broadway Drive
St. Paul, MN 55113-5199

Orange Cherry Media
7 Delano Drive
Bedford, NY 10507

Queue
5 Chapel Hill Drive
Fairfield, CT 06432

Right-On Programs
P. O. Box 977
Huntington, NY 11743

Scholastic Software
730 Broadway
New York, NY 10003

Science Research Associates
155 Wacker Drive
Chicago, IL 60606

Scott, Foresman and Co.
1900 East Lake Avenue
Glenview, Illinois 60025

Society for Visual Education
1345 Diversey Parkway
Chicago, IL 60614

Spectrum Software
75 Todd Pond Road
Lincoln, MA 01773

Sunburst Communications, Inc.
39 Washington Avenue
Pleasantville, NY 10570